METHODS in MICROBIOLOGY

METHODS in MICROBIOLOGY

Edited by

J. R. NORRIS
Borden Microbiological Laboratory,
Shell Research Limited,
Sittingbourne, Kent, England

D. W. RIBBONS
Department of Biochemistry,
University of Miami School of Medicine,
and Howard Hughes Medical Institute,
Miami, Florida, U.S.A.

Volume 7A

 1972

ACADEMIC PRESS
London and New York

ACADEMIC PRESS INC. (LONDON) LTD
24–28 Oval Road
London NW1

U.S. Edition published by
ACADEMIC PRESS INC.
111 Fifth Avenue
New York, New York 10003

Library of Congress Catalog Card Number: 68–57745
ISBN: 0–12–521507-X

PRINTED IN GREAT BRITAIN BY
ADLARD AND SON LIMITED
DORKING, SURREY

LIST OF CONTRIBUTORS

R. C. W. BERKELEY, *Department of Bacteriology, The Medical School, University of Bristol, Bristol, England*

C. B. C. BOYCE, *Shell Research Limited, Woodstock Agricultural Research Centre, Sittingbourne, Kent, England*

H. F. DAMMERS, *Shell Research Limited, Sittingbourne Laboratories, Sittingbourne, Kent, England*

A. J. HEDGES, *Department of Bacteriology, The Medical School, University of Bristol Bristol, England*

D. KAY, *Sir William Dunn School of Pathology, University of Oxford, South Parks Road, Oxford, England*

W. R. MAXTED, *Central Public Health Laboratory, London, England*

ANNA MAYR-HARTING, *Department of Bacteriology, The Medical School, University of Bristol, Bristol, England*

M. ROBERTS, *Shell Research Limited, Woodstock Agricultural Research Centre, Sittingbourne, Kent, England*

P. H. A. SNEATH, *Medical Research Council Microbial Systematics Unit, University of Leicester, Leicester, England*

G. C. WARE, *Department of Microbiology, University of Bristol, Bristol, England*

v

ACKNOWLEDGMENTS

For permission to reproduce, in whole or in part, certain figures and diagrams we are grateful to the following—

Analytical Chemistry, Washington, D.C., U.S.A.; *Bacteriological Reviews*, Baltimore, U.S.A.; *Experimental Agriculture*, London, England; *Journal of Bacteriology*, Baltimore, U.S.A.

Detailed acknowledgments are given in the legends to figures.

PREFACE

It was inevitable with a Series as large and wide ranging as "Methods in Microbiology" that some topics would fall outside the themes on which the majority of the Volumes were based, and that some contributions intended for inclusion in earlier Volumes would be unavailable at the time they were required. To a certain extent therefore, Volume 7 is a miscellany of disconnected topics.

As with other Volumes, the material has been divided into two parts; a step necessitated primarily by the amount of material presented, but which enabled us to group together related contributions. Thus, Volume 7A contains Chapters dealing with the use of computers in microbiology and a treatment of the mathematical bases of assay methods. Two Chapters concern bacteriophage and one bacteriocins. The rest of the material comprises topics which are of considerable interest and importance but whose themes are unrelated to one another.

Volume 7 completes the initial Series of "Methods in Microbiology" and this preface affords us a welcome opportunity to express our thanks and appreciation to our many contributors whose ready help, co-operation and patience has done so much to make our task of editing an enjoyable one. We are also grateful to numerous of our colleagues who, although not themselves contributing to the series, have provided valuable advice and comment concerning the subject matter. Our thanks are due to Shell Research Limited, The University of Miami and The Howard Hughes Medical Institute, without whose material assistance in many ways the production of the Series would have been far more difficult, if not impossible. Finally, we would like to acknowledge the assistance of the publishers and that faithful army of typists, secretaries, technicians, research students and sympathetic wives and husbands whose painstaking work and attention to detail earns them little recognition but provides the essential basis for a work of this kind. We would particularly like to mention our appreciation of the co-operation of Dr. C. Booth who edited Volume 4 and enabled the Series to cover techniques in Mycology; an area which was outside our own experience.

The question of continuing the Series comes to the fore at this time. Several contributions have been offered for a further Volume and we have decided to produce one more, a single Volume 8 which should appear early in 1973 following a manuscript date of May 1972. After that we have no plans but we will reconsider the situation from time to time as and when advances in techniques and methodology suggest that the production of a further Volume will be useful. Of course, not all possible topics have been covered and needless to say we would welcome comments and suggestions for future articles from our colleagues in the field of microbiology.

J. R. NORRIS

D. W. RIBBONS

March, 1972

CONTENTS

CONTENTS OF PUBLISHED VOLUMES

xi

CHAPTER I

Computer Use in Microbiology

G. C. WARE

Department of Microbiology, University of Bristol, England

I. COMPUTER FUNDAMENTALS

There are two main classes of computers, analogue and digital. Consider first the characteristics of each type.

A. Analogue computers

Analogue computers deal in quantities whose numerical value need not be expressed nor, indeed, need the quantity have any exact numerical value. An analogue computer may handle quantities such as spatial positions, pressures, rates of flow, without these quantities being first expressed in numerical form. Similarly, the answer may not be in numerical form and need not have an exact value. Two simple examples of analogue computers are the slide rule, where the spatial arrangement of two rods can convey information resulting from their relative positions even if the operator is unable to count. If the slide rule is calibrated and the operator numerate an approximate numerical value may be derived from it. Similarly, quantities of fluid in a measuring cylinder may represent an addition sum, where again an approximate numerical answer may be derived with appropriate equipment.

A more sophisticated analogue computer is shown in Fig. 1. The object of this machine is to calculate the time required for any given journey according to the equation

$$\text{time} = \frac{\text{distance}}{\text{speed}}.$$

A potentiometer with a scale calibrated in miles, VR1, is set to the required distance and supplies a proportional voltage to the rest of the circuit. The speed is set on the variable resistance, VR2, whereupon the time for the journey is indicated by the calibrated meter, M. The calculation depends upon Ohm's Law, $I = E/R$, where I is the current in the circuit, E the applied voltage and R the resistance, and these three parameters correspond to T, the time, D the distance and S, the speed ($T = D/S$).

Our three examples serve well to illustrate the fundamental characteristics of analogue computers. First, analogue computers tend to be purpose-designed, that is, they are not easily adaptable from one calculation to another. Secondly, analogue computers can produce an "instantaneous" answer—in an ideal circuit there would be no measurable delay in the establishment of a particular current corresponding to the settings VR1 and VR2 in Fig. 1. Analogue computers are therefore particularly applicable to *real time* calculation where the answer is required concurrently with the input data. Their main disadvantage is their comparative unadaptability. Thirdly, the input and output data need not be numerical. Modern design techniques and production methods have led to the production of

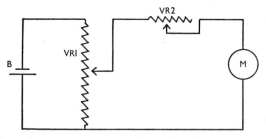

Fig. 1. Simple analogue computer circuit to solve the equation time = distance/speed by application of Ohm's Law.

To obtain accurate results the potentiometer VR1 and the meter M should be of low impedance and VR2 of comparatively high impedance.

exceedingly powerful analogue machines and, provided that the problem can be stated in the form of a mathematical equation, simulations can be carried out. For example, Hammond *et al.* (1967) successfully simulated the growth of *Escherichia coli* after treatment with streptomycin on a PACE TR 48 Analogue Computer.

Their patching diagram for solution of the equations:

(1) $dP_1/dt = 0.693\ G_s\ P_1$ where
$$G_s = G_s\,(0) + [G_s\,(\infty) - G_s\,(0)]\,(1 - \exp K_s\,(T - t)).$$

(2) $dP_2/dt = 0.693\ G_n\ P_2$ where
$$G_n = G_n\,(0) + [G_n\,(\infty) - G_n\,(0)]\,(1 - \exp K_n\,(T - t)),$$

where:

P = Total population (in population units)
P_s = Survivor population (in population units)
P_n = Non-survivor population (in population units)
S = Survivor fraction (dimensionless)
G = Growth rate of total population (doublings/h)
G_s = Growth rate of survivors (doublings/h)
G_n = Growth rate of non-survivors (doublings/h)
K_s = Rate constant at which survivor growth rate changes (per min)
K_n = Rate constant at which non-survivor growth rate changes, per min

representing growth of ultimate survivors and non-survivors after strepto-mycin treatment, is shown in Fig. 2.

Hammond's treatment of the situation was, of necessity, simplified and we shall see later how it might be possible to simulate a system whose complexity defies mathematical representation, by reiterative digital techniques.

B. Digital computers

Conversely, digital computers deal in discrete numerical values and the input data must be converted into numerical form before it can be handled by the computer, which works according to the simple rules of arithmetic by addition and sometimes also by subtraction. Time is required for the computer to go through the motions of addition and subtraction, even though this time may be short. Simple forms of digital computers are sets of counters, the abacus and the desk calculating machine, to use any of which some counting ability on the part of the operator is essential. The digital computer's chief advantage lies in the readiness with which it may be modified to carry out a wide variety of calculations where speed is of secondary importance

This versatility has led to the almost universal adoption of digital

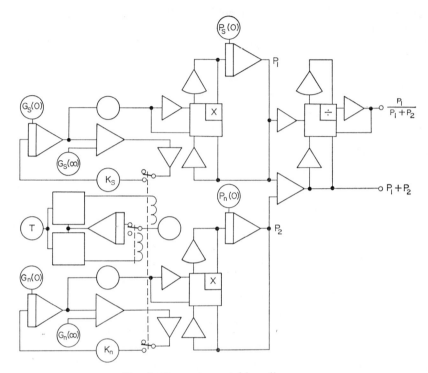

FIG. 2. Computer patching diagram.

The above interconnections of computer components generates curves for the theoretical populations P_1 and P_2 according to the equations given in the text. Outputs corresponding to (P_1+P_2) and $P_1/(P_1+P_2)$ are also provided for comparison with experimental data. The constants of the equation appear as settings of the computer potentiometers as annotated.

In the diagram each symbol represents a complete electronic circuit, usually an amplifier. The exact function of each amplifier is indicated by its shape. For example:

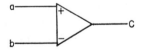

indicates a differential amplifier producing at terminal c a current proportional to the difference between a and b. Analogue computers consist of many such amplifiers giving outputs which may represent almost any mathematical function of the input signal.

Programming may take the form of building the amplifier blocks into a circuit. It may be accomplished by cross connecting existing amplifiers by wires or linking pins on a "patchboard" or in the most sophisticated devices by establishing the required circuitry by punched cards.

machines for general computation and we may therefore largely confine our attention to this type of computer.

C. Communication with the computer

Before any calculation may be performed by any computer the user must instruct the computer on the calculations to be performed and on the nature of the data with which it is to be provided. These instructions must be written in a language comprehensible to the computer and must be detailed to include every minute step needed to evaluate the mathematical or logical expressions involved remembering that the digital computer may well only be able to add, albeit rapidly.

In analogue computers the language of communication is often one of cross connections of wires contrasting with the written instructions given to digital machines. Unfortunately, manufacturers have not agreed† on a common language or method of working for their various computers and almost every individual model relies upon a different language or machine code. Indeed, this is a necessary result of the continual evolution of more sophisticated circuitry or **hardware.**

Computers work most efficiently when communication with them is in their own machine code and it would therefore be ideal for each person using a computer to learn the language of the particular machine. Most machine codes are, however, difficult languages and some are almost unfathomable.

D. Composition of digital computers

The hardware of a computer consists of various peripheral devices for reading and printing tapes, typescripts and graphs, and one or more stores comprising a large number of storage locations in which numbers may be held. These locations are usually numbered from zero and each of them may be addressed by its own reference number. Also part of the hardware will be an arithmetic unit capable, by means of built-in circuitry, of interpreting simple instructions such as add, divide, subtract, and implementing them by an appropriate sequence of additions. The more sophisticated the computer the wider will be the choice of pre-programmed operations, the larger and faster its stores and the more numerous and the more efficient its peripheral devices; as a serious consequence the more complex its instruction code becomes.

E. Digital machine languages

Consider first a hypothetical machine instruction code for a small computer of, say, 8000 store locations in which 44 is the code for "add"

† Some agreement has now been reached but there remain strong business reasons for manufacturers not wishing to share a common machine code.

and 43 for "subtract", and each order to the computer is in five parts. First the operation code, that is, whether the operation will be addition, subtraction or multiplication, etc. Secondly, an address, that is the number of the store location in which the first operand is stored. Thirdly, the address of the second operand, fourthly, the address in which the answer is to be stored, and finally, the address where the next instruction to be obeyed is stored.

Consider next a series of machine instructions written in this code to evaluate the expression $(a+b)-(c+d)$ and assume that the value of a is held in computer location 5, b in 6, c in 7, and d in 8; and the programme itself held in locations 1–2–3. The instructions will therefore read:

$$
\begin{array}{lccccc}
(1) & 44 & 5 & 6 & 5 & 2 \\
(2) & 44 & 7 & 8 & 7 & 3 \\
(3) & 43 & 5 & 7 & 5 & 4 \\
(4) & 00 & 0 & 0 & 0 & 4 \\
\end{array}
$$

When obeyed the answer will be in location 5 and the computer's next instructions in location 4 in this case, go back to 4 again or "wait".

Machines having an instruction code similar to this are usually referred to as multiple address machines, since each instruction word contains the address of more than one location.

Alternative hardware designs include single address machines, where the instruction word contains only one address and the computer normally works serially through the instructions. Consider single address instructions to evaluate the same expression, with a, b, c, d stored as above and the same meaning for 43 and 44. Additionally, however, 30 means fetch number from store to arithmetic unit, 20 write from arithmetic unit to store, and 70 jump to instruction n.

$$
\begin{array}{lcc}
(1) & 30 & 7 \\
(2) & 44 & 8 \\
(3) & 20 & 8 \\
(4) & 30 & 5 \\
(5) & 44 & 6 \\
(6) & 43 & 8 \\
(7) & 20 & 5 \\
(8) & 70 & 8 \\
\end{array}
$$

Again, the answer will be in location 5 and the computer waits at location 8. A series of such machine instructions is referred to as a computer programme. Programming in machine language, though easy for calculations such as we have just described, would become tedious for increasingly involved calculations since the writer of the programme must continuously remember in which location of the store the various values are stored. Moreover, if after writing the programme he wishes to vary the sequence or add a single additional instruction he may have to change the whole series of instructions to accommodate the alteration.

F. Standard computer languages

To sidestep the difficulties of learning and writing any of the multitude and variety of machine codes in existence, several standard *high level languages* have been evolved, resembling normal English as far as possible, and it is nowadays incumbent upon a computer manufacturer to provide his client with programmes (*software*) capable of translating these high level languages into the machine code of his particular machine. Translation software provided by manufacturers are known as *compilers* since they take the programmer's high level language and compile suitable machine instructions from his programme with an efficiency which is an important determinant of the value of the compiler.

Thus, in theory, a programme can now be written in a standard high level language and run subsequently on any computer.

Ideal as this system sounds, there are several important functions of a computer which, because of machine and system differences, it is not practical to cover in the standard languages. These omissions are important, since a user will, as a result, almost always have to modify a programme written for one particular machine before it can be run on another, even though the machines are identical and a standard language has been used. The situation is incomplete in other respects also; computer manufacturers orient their software and sales talk toward one or other of the main standard languages and compilers may not be available for a particular language on a particular machine. For example, in scientific work the two languages **Algol** and **Fortran** are most common, whilst for business purposes **Cobol** is considered more useful. Machines devised principally for business work may therefore have only Cobol compilers available from stock and smaller scientific machines only Fortran.

Of the two scientific languages Fortran and Algol each has its advantages and disadvantages. Fortran arrived first and became widely established in the U.S.A. It is the easier of the two languages to learn and more completely defined than Algol, that is in theory it is selfcontained and applicable to any computer with a Fortran compiler.

Large libraries of Fortran programmes, mostly originating in the U.S.A. exist and help to perpetuate Fortran in the face of the generally acknowledged more powerful Algol. Algol's greater power is achieved at the expense of a slightly more complex syntax requiring in turn longer, more complicated and therefore more expensive compilers. Because of its later arrival on the computer scene, from Europe, and because of the entrenched position of Fortran, it remains to be seen which language will finally emerge superior or whether both will be superseded by new and ever more powerful languages such as Programming Language PL.1.

In the meantime, for the serious scientific programmer who does not wish to rely too heavily on the works of others, Algol is the language of choice.

G. The language ALGOL (Backus *et al.* (1962))

Before we can proceed to consider the *technique* of computer use in microbiology, it is essential to acquire at least a rudimentary knowledge of at least one computer language. Like other languages, computer languages, and Algol in particular, are made up of a range of characters, which with rules of grammar and syntax can be used to form a vocabulary of words and enable the language to convey meaning. Since the computer is immune to the intentions and intimidations of the user, and carries out only the precise instructions contained in the programme, clarity and precision are essentials of the language and errors of punctuation, syntax or spelling will be immediately rejected by the compiler as introducing possible ambiguity.

The characters used in Algol comprise the upper and lower case letters of the alphabet, the numerals 0 to 9, together with various signs of arithmetic and logic, brackets, punctuation marks, and a few other symbols. These are used according to the syntax of the language to form sentences or *statements*, one or more of which may constitute a programme. Because the decimal point and the full stop could be confused, in Algol the decimal point has its arithmetic meaning only and the full stop is replaced by the semi-colon which is used to terminate a statement in the same way as a full stop terminates a sentence in English. There are also a few *basic words* in the language; these are written in lower case underlined and have special meanings. Examples are: *begin, end, and* and *go to.*

The most important feature of the Algol language is that it is not necessary for the programmer to concern himself in any way with the Machine Language of the computer nor to consider how the computer will in fact execute his orders nor even, in general, where the information will be stored within the computer though with big programmes the compiler of many second and third generation computers will undoubtedly appreciate guidance on such matters as where to store certain classes of information.

All the detailed instructions necessary are worked out by the compiler at the time of translation of the programme into machine code. It is, however, necessary for the programmer to obey strictly certain rules of programme writing. He must, for instance, declare the variables he proposes to use by listing them at the beginning of the programme so that the compiler may allocate storage space and addresses for each. In the original example (evaluation of $(a+b)-(c+d)$) the programmer would need to make certain declarations at the beginning of the programme, specifying his intention to use the "words" a, b, c and d in a calculation. The compiler would automatically assign these words to locations in the store known only to itself and thereafter the programmer would be free to use the words a, b, c and d in his programme.

The programmer is not limited to single letters to identify the variables of a programme. For example, he could use "total", "mean", "x1", "x2", and "answer" as five different variables in a programme and then write an expression such as

$$\text{answer} := (\text{total} - \text{x2}) + (\text{mean} + \text{x1} + \text{x2}/123);$$

He must, of course, be careful not to use the same name for two different things, nor to use a mis-spelt or undeclared variable, since the compiler would not then know to what he was referring and would, as for any error in grammar or syntax, reject the programme.

H. Assignment statements

The only character in Algol whose meaning is not immediately clear is the assignment sign $:=$. This has the meaning "becomes equal to", or "takes the value of".

To the computer this means that after execution of the expression the location named on the left hand side must be numerically equal to the value of the evaluated expression on the right hand side of the sign $:=$.

We may similarly write more complex statements; for example,

$$\text{total} := (\text{sum } 1 + \text{sum } 2 + \text{sum } 3)/\text{average} \times 2;$$

or

$$\text{living organisms} := \text{original number} + \text{number added} - \text{organisms killed};$$

provided that we have previously declared all the words used in the statement. The Algol language does not limit us to multiplication, division, addition and subtraction, but values may be raised to any power, logarithms, sines, cosines, and many other functions readily determined; nor are we limited to positive integers but may use decimals and negative numbers as required.

For example,

$$\text{remaining} := 1/\text{sqrt} (\ln(r - s/t) + 0 \cdot 5);$$

evaluates the expression $\dfrac{1}{\sqrt{\log_e (r - s/t) + 0 \cdot 5}}$

and places the answer in "remaining".

Though Algol makes no allowance for the fact, every computer has a limit to the size of the largest number it may hold and care must be taken not to exceed this number. For many applications integers of the order of $\pm 10^{12}$ are large enough and are about the limit of many second generation computers, but in microbiology these numbers are frequently realized and may therefore represent real limitations to the microbiologist using a computer. Working thus, with integers, computers are completely accurate. Using real numbers (decimals) the representation of the number in the computer is as exponent and mantissa. This enables it to handle larger numbers but accuracy is no longer absolute since the number of digits available to represent, for example, a recurring decimal is limited. If such limits are exceeded, or if the computer is asked to carry out functions which are mathematically impossible such as evaluating the logarithm of a negative number, the compiler will intercept the operation and report accordingly.

I. Conditional clauses

Another basic facility of Algol which we must consider is the ability of the computer to make a decision as a result of a logical statement. Statements in Algol may be prefaced by a condition, for example

$$if \; a = 0 \; then \; b := c+d;$$

In this case the computer will only obey the statement $b := c + d$ if on looking into the location it called a it finds the value there to be zero, otherwise it will skip this statement and proceed to the next in the programme. The condition may be made as complicated as required in the form

$$if \; a = 145 \; then \; b := c+d \; else \; if \; b = c \; then \; b := x+y \; else \; \text{etc., etc.;}$$

In this case, before proceeding to the next statement the computer will obey the first appropriate instruction. Another form of condition stipulates that a number of conditions be fulfilled before a particular operation is carried out, for example

$$if \; a > b \; and \; x = 0 \; and \; p \leqslant q \; and \; (not \; c \; or \; d) \; then \; a := b \times 2;$$

In this way the computer can be instructed to take or not to take certain actions in response to certain existing and changing conditions.

J. Programmed jumps

We need only consider two further aspects of Algol. First, the facility whereby the sequence of execution of statements in a programme may be altered. Normally the computer works through a programme executing the statements in the order in which they appear, but by the use of a "go to" statement and an appropriate "label" we may cause the computer to jump to any section of the programme.

For example

incubation temp   := 37;

incubation time   := 24;

inoculum   := 10000;

if substrate > 1000 *then go to* grow *else if*

substrate < 10 *then go to* die *else go to*
static;

................;

................;

die: ....;

static: ....;

grow: ....;

...................;

...................;

Clearly two places in the programme must not have the same label.

During the programme the computer will examine the value of the variable "substrate" and jump to the appropriate part of the programme as a result.

Finally, we may wish to execute certain calculations several times in different places in a programme. We might, for example, require to calculate the total cell wall weight of strains in a mixed culture at different places in a programme. We could write a section of the programme in the usual way, calculating cell wall weight, and make a jump to it with a "go to" statement each time we wished to use it. Though quite possible this becomes clumsy because we have also to arrange for selection of the appropriate strain and a return jump to the appropriate part of the programme.

K. Algol procedures

In Algol such selections and the return jump can be looked after automatically if the calculation is written in the form of an Algol "*procedure*". This is done by declaring and naming the relevant section of programme, for instance, "cell wall". Thereafter should we wish to jump to that section all we need to write in the programme is

cell wall;

this is known as *calling* the procedure.

It is perfectly legitimate and quite common to write whole programmes as series of procedures. In this way a programme written by one person may be incorporated in another programme as a procedure of the new programme merely by declaring it as a procedure within the new programme. Over the years large numbers of programmes which could be used in this way have been written and published, though only a few are related to bacteriology.

L. Programme sources

Specific programmes are sometimes available from computer manufacturers ready modified for their own computers, but this is usually only the case for well-established methods. Copies of other published programmes may usually be obtained from authors but will invariably need modification for the new user's computer and unless the listings of such programmes contain copious explanatory notes they will be difficult to understand and the new user might well find it easier and quicker to write a completely new programme from scratch. It is therefore important always to write into programmes whilst they are being composed profuse explanatory notes to help, at a later date, the writer or other readers understand the programme. Algol makes special provision for the compiler to ignore all such explanations to readers provided they are written after the introductory basic word *"comment"* and terminated as usual with a semi-colon.

For example

Mu: = MuMax × (Substrate/(Substrate + Ks));
comment growth equation derived from Herbert Elsworth and Telling (1956);

Best of all, the prospective user's computer centre may have its own library of procedures and programmes available for the asking or may offer facilities for adapting existing programmes to its own machines, though in the fields of biological simulation and indeed simulation generally it is rare that any ready-made programme will be suitable for a new user.

II. DIGITAL COMPUTERS AND SIMULATION

Clearly, as in other fields of science, computers may be used to process all the data derived from experimental microbiology using standard statistical and other methods producing the results as drawn graphs, histograms or tables. This use of computers as advanced and high-speed calculating and printing machines should not concern us here as it can hardly be considered a microbiological technique (see Boyce and Roberts, this Vol. page 153 for a general account). *Simulation* and *list processing* have, however, both been used successfully in microbiology, list processing in association with Adansonian classification, where comparisons must be made between a hundred or more characteristics of an organism and of all other known strains. List processing is dealt with elsewhere in this Volume in greater detail (Sneath, this Vol. p. 29).

A. Simulation

The simulation of a system can best be described as the production of a working model. Theoretical mathematical models have been used for some time in the exploration of theories in many fields of science, for example Perrett (1960). In non-biological fields the relatively simple and well-understood mechanics underlying most reactions are amenable to mathematical representation as equations. In biology less is known of the underlying parameters and controlling laws, and the formation of equations to delineate biological processes is not often possible. It is in these circumstances that stepwise simulations can sometimes provide useful information.

B. Simulations based on a complex equation

Simulations are basically of two kinds. Having derived a mathematical statement of a biological phenomenon, or at least a first approximation to one, it is possible to use the computer to evaluate the equation for many different conditions and determine how closely the results follow the expected, thereby verifying the accuracy of the original hypothetical equation. For example, Knowles *et al.* (1965) simultaneously determined the growth rate, "Michaelis" constant, and population densities of nitrifying bacteria in the River Thames. Assuming the conversion of ammonia to nitrite only by *Nitrosomonas* and thence to nitrate only by *Nitrobacter*, differential equations were derived and then solved on a digital computer for various arbitrary values of the growth parameters of both organisms. By comparing the curves obtained by computation and experiment for several observed phenomena such as nitrification suitable values were obtained for the growth constants of the organisms. The values obtained fell well within the expected range and may be assumed closely to approach the real values. In this work Knowles incorporated in his programme published procedures for integration of the equations and briefly discussed the source of these procedures.

C. Stepwise simulations

Before considering the application of reiterative simulation in problems where complete equations as used by Knowles are not available, consider the processes of reiterative simulation as a whole and their value. It is often stated that such simulation techniques are unable themselves to show more than is already known and cannot therefore contribute to our knowledge.

Consider first a simple household budget equation concerning the weekly consumption of milk, given by the simple balance equation,

$$stock = deliveries - use$$

Milk consumption is not constant, however, and the equation does not reveal all the facts. A more complete equation would be given by equation

$$\text{current stock} = \text{old stock} + \text{deliveries} - \text{spoilt} - \text{use}$$

If we know any four values we may calculate the fifth and the housewife would usually want to know how much milk to order—that is "deliveries". If the values were constant a computer could calculate the consumption, stock or demand during any period of time and advise the housewife on her daily need. In a normal household, however, these factors are not constant, nor do they vary in any manner easily transcribable to mathematical notation. For example, let us assume the case of an exceptionally regularly behaved family where the mother uses milk for her tea and takes a cup of cocoa before bed with a daily requirement of one pint. She uses fresh if there is enough but does not mind it old. Father drinks only half a pint a day in his tea but insists it must be fresh that day, but requires no milk on Tuesdays as he is away all day. The daughter is at school as a weekly boarder and requires no milk in term-time except on Saturdays and Sundays, when she drinks $1\frac{1}{2}$ pints per day, mostly in milk shakes but including $\frac{1}{2}$ pint neat which must be fresh. The son is only home on Mondays, Wednesdays and Fridays, on which day he requires 1 pint. Moreover, the family go away for their annual holiday during the month of August and the mother has found by experience that casual demands by visitors in summer may be 3 pints per day but in winter do not exceed 1 pint per day. To allow for this casual demand she likes to keep an appropriate additional stock in her refrigerator. As is normal practice in some areas, the milkman delivers on weekdays only and only in 1-pint bottles. Cooking demand is only for milk puddings at week-ends (2 pints per week). Milk left over for 3 days is considered unusable.

An equation to represent this state of affairs would be complex but a simulation could easily be written. We would need some additional information, for example, the frequency of the random visits in summer and winter, and suitable definitions for summer, winter and term-time. Clearly, even this simulation is not complete and could be further elaborated to include, for example, consideration of the effect on consumption of the price of milk at various times of the year and the demands of the cat and its occasional families of kittens.

D. Value of a simulation

Though it is true in the strictest sense that a simulation cannot provide new information on this family as could experiments, it can bring to light features of the system which are not immediately obvious, for example, the frequency of unexpected coincidental demand from all sources and the maximum storage capacity likely to be required of a refrigerator to be purchased by the family, as well as providing the correct order each day for the milkman. Subsequently, used as a procedure in a larger programme it could help consider interactions of a system too complex to be otherwise appreciated as a whole or in conditions which for one reason or another could never be implemented experimentally.

The writing of simulation programmes of the reiterative type relies so much on the use of procedures it will be advantageous to take a deeper look at this aspect of Algol.

E. More about Algol procedures

Procedures, or sub-routines, are, as we have seen, sections of programme written in a form in which they may be re-used or *called* as often as required without having to be re-written each time. Referring again to our simple simulation of a household milk budget, consider a section of programme which adjusts the stock of milk in the refrigerator. We could write simply.

total milk: = total milk + in now − out now;

where, of course, "total milk" represents the stock in the larder and "in now" and "out now" quantities either used or added as a result of some particular operation.

We could, of course, write this one line of programme each time we wish to adjust the milk stock and in this particular case it would be relatively simple so to do; more difficult though to calculate bacterial growth occurring in unit time. It is possible, however, to write the adjustment in the form of a procedure as follows

procedure adjust stock;

total milk: = total milk + in now − out now;

all we have now to write is the simplest statement "adjust stock" and the compiler will provide for adjustment of the value of "total milk" according to the current values of "in now" and "out now".

Suppose further that the housewife kept a supply of two kinds of milk in her larder—silver top and gold top. We could use procedures as we have just used for each material. For example

procedure adjust gold;

gold top: = gold top + in now − out now;

and similarly for silver top, and call whichever is appropriate at relevant parts of the programme. Suppose, however, on occasions a particular call was for silver top and on other occasions gold top, dependent on some other condition in the programme, for instance the day of the week. We could modify our procedure as written above to account for this by writing in brackets after the name of the procedure what are known as *formal parameters* of the procedure and making all our calculations within the procedure relate not to gold top nor silver top but to the formal parameter only, for example:

procedure adjust stock (type);

type: = type + in now − out now;

On calling the procedure we would have to state whether the adjustment was to be made to gold top or silver top and could call, for instance,

adjust stock (silver top);

whereupon substitutions would be made by the computer so that the values then present in locations "in now" and "out now" would be used in adjusting the value in silver top stock.

We are not limited to one formal parameter of procedure but may have any number we require. The above procedure could be elaborated to include description of the quantities which are to be added or subtracted, for example

procedure adjust stock (type, source, sink);

type: = type + source − sink;

A call of this procedure might then take the form,

adjust stock (gold top, bought, drunk);

or

adjust stock (pooled, otherwise waste, cat);

This latter call might adjust the stock of pooled milk as recorded in the location pooled by reducing the otherwise wasted total by the appropriate consumption for the cat. In a call of a procedure the values substituted for the formal parameters are known as *actual parameters*.

F. An example of a simulation flow chart

Examine now the flow diagram, Fig. 3, for a programme indicating the call of certain procedures to simulate the household budget elaborated earlier in order to predict the daily milk demand for a period of one year and the size of the required refrigerator.

All simulators require one or more setting procedures which initiate the programme. In the example shown there are two, "set calendar" which sets the day of the week appropriately and the date to January 1st and by application of the usual rules determines whether or not the year is a leap year. The second setting procedure sets all stocks to zero. The operation

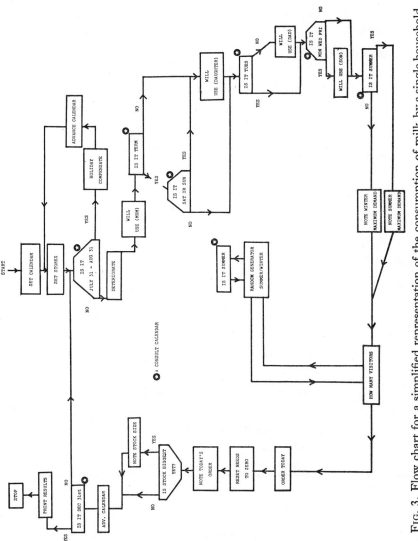

Fig. 3. Flow chart for a simplified representation of the consumption of milk by a single household.

of most of the other procedures should be clear from their names, but we will consider two in greater detail, namely, procedure "will use" and procedure "deteriorate". It will be noticed that whereas procedure "deteriorate" is self-contained, procedure "will use" has a formal parameter, "Who".

procedure deteriorate;
begin

total wasted := total wasted + waste now;
waste now := day 3 stock;
day 3 stock := day 2 stock;
day 2 stock := fresh;
fresh := order;
ordinary
pool = fresh + day 2 stock

end procedure deteriorate;
procedure will use (Who);
value Who; *integer* Who;
begin

if Who = dad *then*
need fresh := need fresh + 0·5
else if Who = son *then*
need fresh := need fresh + 1
else if Who = mum *then*
need ordinary := need ordinary + 1
else
begin comment Who must be daughter;
need fresh := need fresh + 0·5;
need ordinary := need ordinary + 1
end;

end procedure will use;

G. Specialized simulation languages

As well as the two basic languages—Algol and Fortran—which we have already discussed, there exist today a number of simulation languages, most of which are purpose-orientated, for example, in the playing of war games **Como 1 and 2** are specially suitable for the simulation of air battles, **Militran** for land ones. **Monte code**, on the other hand, is primarily concerned with simulations employing those mathematical methods known as Monte Carlo techniques and dependent upon chance phenomena.

1. *Algol simulation languages*

These special languages require, of course, special compilers for their translation into machine code, but there are more general simulation languages or rather simulation procedures, written in Algol and amenable to compilation by standard compilers. Examples are the Elliott Simulator Package (E.S.P.), (Williams *et al.*), being a collection of Algol procedures useful in simulation work, *Simon* (Hills, 1964) and *Simula* (Dahl and Nygaard, 1965). The procedures of these languages in general make it possible to call the user's procedures in specified sequence at pre-determined times after the co-existence of one or more conditions. The procedures themselves may then, of course, call themselves or other procedures at given intervals after their own call. It is the principal function of the simulator programme to keep account of the chain of procedure calls so generated and simulated time.

Whether it is worth a prospective investigator learning one of these languages for his own simulation is questionable. In some cases they may save the experimenter time but in others the simulator will require so many additions and modifications that the experimenter would be well advised to write his simulator from scratch and by so doing probably produce yet another purpose-oriented set of Algol simulation procedures of limited application.

2. *Feasibility and cost*

It is unfortunate that simulation programmes of any validity in biology tend to be long and elaborate requiring considerable store space and computer time to run on digital machines. This is particularly true if written in a relatively inefficient Algol simulation language. Computer time, even today, may cost between £50–£100 per hour and though the speed of computation is high, reiterative techniques which repeatedly circulate slightly modified loops for small increments in time or other parameters may be lengthy to run. In one particular growth simulator written by the author the running time would have equalled the real time required for a similar real world experiment and had to be abandoned.

For this reason some authors have preferred to write in machine code or simplified symbolic languages, thereby obtaining greatly increased speed.

It is not essential, of course, that all simulators must run faster than the real world equivalent experiment, indeed many simulators are slower than the real thing but this is generally acceptable only where the real thing is even more costly than the simulation!

H. Simulation of bacterial growth

We can now examine the proposed working of a simple bacterial culture simulator. Consider the simulator shown in Fig. 4. The programme has three setting procedures; the first, "read parameters", consults the input data to ascertain the nature of the organisms, the medium and any antibiotic substances which may be added to the culture, the length of the incubation period, the frequency with which counts are to be made, and the form in which the results are to be plotted or tabulated. This represents the briefing of a technician. The second procedure, "initial calculations", is concerned with calculating constants such as the maximum permissible growth rates and yield constants for the various organisms in the medium specified and represents calculations normally done by the organisms. The third and last setting procedure, "set clock", returns the simulation clock to zero.

1. *Growth*

The simulation then proceeds to select a first strain, from those introduced to the culture in read parameters, to be considered in this iteration of the growth loop. The currently existing numbers and masses of the selected strain are extracted from the store. Consideration is given to the prevailing conditions of growth and current time and a determination made of whether the organism is in the lag phase. The next part of the programme extracts the appropriate maximum growth rate for the selected strain determined earlier and calculates the growth rate, modified for any lag or other restraint expected, applicable for this increment of growth in accordance with the usual equations involving substrate concentration and Michaelis constant for the selected strain. The amount of growth taking place in the increment of time is then calculated and a note made of the substrate thereby consumed. The sections of programme so far have considered only the growth of the biophase.

2. *Division and mutation*

The biological implications of this growth must now be simulated and the question asked; has the increase in biophase mass of this organism been sufficient to allow cell division? If it has, then a doubling of numbers can be said to have occurred and the probability of mutation must be considered with due regard to mutation rates specified for the strain. If mutation is found not to have occurred at this division, the simulator proceeds to consider the effects of the change in population density with

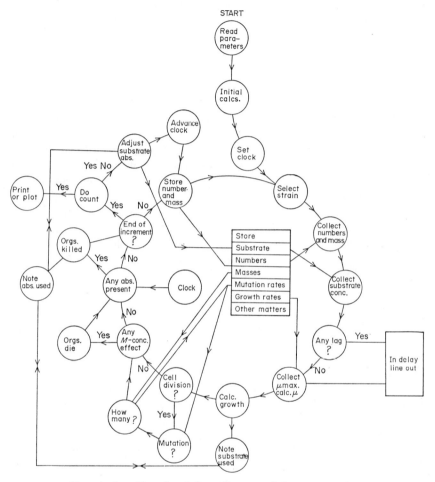

FIG. 4. An abbreviated flow diagram of the programme.

Abbreviations:

        abs —antibacterial substance

        μ —growth rate

        calc —calculations

        orgs —organisms

        conc —concentration

The sections "Any lag?", "Delay line" and "Calculate" are reproduced in full in "real procedure actual rate (which)" as illustrative of the programme technique. Appendix I.

"procedure M-concentration". If the population density is high, the effect of M-concentration (Bail, 1929) may be either to reduce the growth rate slightly by introducing a rate modifying constant to the next growth rate estimation or it may cause the culture to die off more rapidly than it would at lower cell densities, or both.

If, however, mutation was found to have occurred, then consideration must be given to the range of mutant types specified as able to arise from this parent strain and the number of each type produced at this cell division. The numbers of the parent strain are accordingly reduced and the populations in mutant strains increased as appropriate. After consideration of the M-concentration effect as above the effect of any antibiotic substance present is considered. Reference to the current simulator clock will ascertain whether such an addition has been made as prescribed by the initial parameters. If an active substance is present an appropriate number of organisms is killed and a note is made of any antibiotic substance so used up. The simulator returns the new numbers and masses of the currently considered strain to store and ascertains whether it has yet considered all the strains present in the culture; if not, it selects the next strain present and proceeds likewise to calculate the changes during this increment until each strain has been adjusted. When all the strains existing in the culture have been caused to grow for this time interval the simulator adjusts the substrate concentration for all the growth which occurred during the course of time increment just passed and similarly modifies the antibiotic concentration, if any.

If the initial parameters called for a viable count at this time then procedure "do count" enumerates the culture at this time and may print or plot suitable output statements as required. The clock is then advanced by one increment and the entire procedure repeated. This routine is continued until either the prescribed incubation period is over, the culture dies, or some other terminating condition is reached.

It would be impracticable, indeed meaningless without a complete exposition of the Algol language†, to reproduce here in detail all the procedures used in this simulation (Ware, 1967) but we may consider some of the difficulties with which the procedures must deal.

3. Simulation errors

First, to approach reality the time increment for each reiteration should approach the generation time for the smallest existing unit of the cell— perhaps a molecule. In this case the programme would be impossibly slow and costly to run. On the other hand, simulated time increments of 1 minute

† For further reading: (Elementary) Ware (1967a, b); (Advanced) Collins and Almond (1967).

dividing a cell division into perhaps only 20 steps, though rapid to run, might depart too far from reality to give a reasonable simulation and some compromise must be sought.

As it is impossible for want of computer space and time in most second generation computers to consider the fate of each individual organism separately, all the individuals of any particular strain existing in a culture were by Ware (1967a) considered to grow and divide synchronously. With third generation systems using large megabit high speed drum stores an individual cell treatment would undoubtedly be possible.

Consider also the mode of death in procedure "M-concentration" and elsewhere. Whereas growth occurs as a continuous process, death is an all or nothing effect mandate upon individual organisms and cannot there-fore be considered as merely the reverse of growth. The questions must be asked whether death rate is proportional to biophase mass or numbers and whether half a dead organism is dead or alive or half dead. The answer might well be ascertained by fitting simulated curves of both possibilities to experi-mental results. Difficulty also arises in this particular simulation as a result of mutation. Organisms within any individual strain are dividing synchron-ously but they are not necessarily in synchrony with organisms of any other strain whose generation time may be different. If any new organisms of these latter strains are formed by mutation from the parent strain their age and size will correspond to the age and size of the parent strain cells and not to the mutant strain to which they now belong and an appropriate

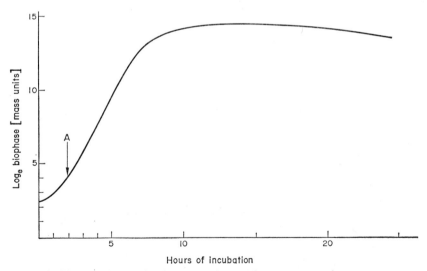

Fig. 5. Simulated growth of an organism with parameters chosen to represent *Escherichia coli* in nutrient broth.

calculation adjusting the ages and masses of the mutant organisms is necessary, with a corresponding compensation in the amount of substrate previously thought to have been used, as though the new organisms had reached their new size as a result of normal growth.

4. *Results of a simulation of bacterial growth*

Fig. 5 shows the growth in pure culture of a theoretical organism similar to *Escherichia coli*. The simulator included provision for determining the moment of the end of the lag phase and it ended after 1 h and 49 min incubation. This point (A Fig. 5) also marks the moment of maximum

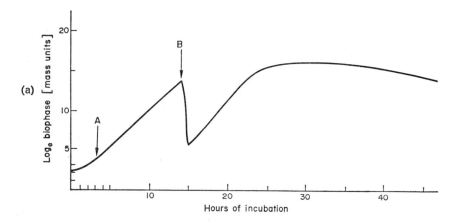

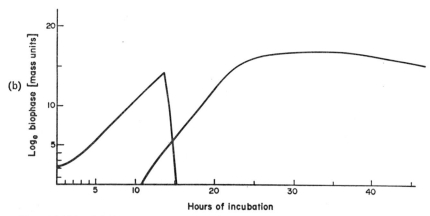

Fig. 6 (a) Total living organisms in a culture to which an anti-bacterial substance rapidly lethal for the wild type is added at "B".

(b) Strain counts of the same culture showing the rise of the mutant population and its success after addition of the anti-bacterial substance.

specific growth rate since previously the growth rate was reduced through considerations of the lag phase and subsequently it will be reduced by a fall in substrate concentration. Subsequent sections of the curve agree with those normally expected from such an organism growing in nutrient broth.

Fig. 6(a) shows the growth of a culture inoculated with ten organisms of a strain with a doubling time of 40 min and a high sensitivity to a certain theoretical anti-bacterial substance. The strain had a mutation rate of 10^{-5} to a mutant which differed from the parent strain by full resistance to the anti-bacterial substance and by having a doubling time of 30 min and a back-mutation rate of 10^{-10} to the original strain. As the simulator was able to keep a full record of the formation of mutants it is known that

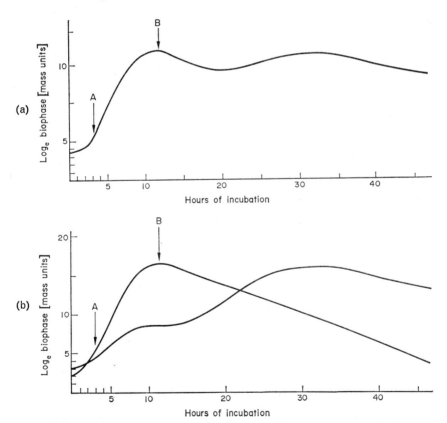

FIG. 7. (a) The total viable population in a culture of two strains of differing doubling time and sensitivity to an anti-bacterial substance added at B, arrowed, that is, in the stationary phase.

(b) An analysis of the curve in (a) showing the behaviour of each strain.

the first mutant arose 11 h 11 min after inoculation. Sufficient anti-bacterial substance to kill all sensitive organisms present was added after 14 h incubation and subsequent behaviour of the individual strains was plotted directly by the computer and is shown in Fig. 6(b).

In a further experiment a culture was simulated by inoculation of medium with 30 organisms of a resistant strain having a doubling time of 45 min and 10 organisms of a sensitive strain with a doubling time of 20 min. Fig. 7 (a and b) shows the total viable count and individual counts of the two strains. A substance slowly bacteriocidal for the sensitive strain was added at 12 h.

After the end of the lag phase (3 h 20 min) both strains grew for a total of 8 h but the M-concentration (let us suppose a result of de-oxygenation of the medium) then began to exert an influence on both populations, the effect being most marked on the slower growing organism.

After addition of the anti-bacterial substance the population of sensitive organisms declined steadily and about 2 h later, when numbers of the sensitive strain had fallen sufficiently, growth of the resistant strain recommenced reaching a maximum population after 32 h 30 min incubation. Growth and death of the resistant organism continued and the sensitive strain died out after 32 h 57 min.

Although neither sufficiently precise simulators nor adequate information about the controlling parameters exists at the moment to enable a full replacement of experimental bacteriology by simulation, it is clearly already possible for pilot fermentations, assessment of drug activity and phenomena of microbial resistance to be probed rapidly by computer rather than laboriously, experimentally determined.

REFERENCES

Backus, J. W., Bauer, F. L., Green, J., Katz, C., McCarthy, J., Naur, P., Perlos, A. J., Rutishauser, H., Samelson, K., Vanquois, B., Wegstein, J. H., van Wungaarden, A., and Woodger, M. (1962). "Revised Report on the Algorithmic Language ALGOL 60". Association for Computing Machines, New York; Springer-Verlag, Berlin; Regnecentralen, Copenhagen. Also *Comput. J.*, 5, 349.

Bail, O. (1929). *Z. Immun Forsch. exp. Ther.*, **60**, 1.

Collins, J. S., and Almond, M. (1967). "The Principles of Algol 60 Programming". George Hamp Ltd., London.

Dahl, O., and Nygaard, K. (1965). SIMULA, a Language for Programming and Description of Discrete Event Systems. Norwegian Computing Centre, Oslo.

Fredrickson, A. G., Megee, R. D. and Tsuchiya, H. M. (1970). "Advances in Applied Microbiology", 13, 419.

Hammond, B. J., Kogut, Magot, and Lightbown, J. W. (1967). *J. gen. Microbiol.*, **48**, 189–203.

Hills, P. R. (1964). "SIMON. A Computer Simulation Language in Algol." Bristol College of Science and Technology, Rept. No. MDM 1401.

Knowles, G., Downing, A. L., and Barrett, M. J. (1965). *J. gen. Microbiol.*, **38**, 263.

Perrett, C. J. (1960). *J. gen. Microbiol.*, **22**, 589.
Ware, G. C. (1967a). *J. theor. Biol.*, **17**, 91–107.
Ware, G. C. (1967b). *Lab. Pract.*, **16**, 980.
Williams *et al.* "Elliott Simulator Package". Elliott Bros. Ltd., Boreham Wood, Herts.

Appendix—An Abbreviated Flow Diagram of the Programme and Details of a Typical Procedure

The function designator "actual rate" deals with the calculation of growth rate and includes the statements considering lag delay shown in Fig. 4.

```
real procedure actual rate (which);
value which; integer which;
begin
    integer h, reduction, delay;
    real theoretical rate, mod 1, normal rate;
    own real rateratio, mod 2;
    if substrate > 0·0 then
    begin
        mod 1: = if time ≥ adntime and sensitivity
            {which} > 1 and anticonc > 1 then 1/1 n
        (anticone)–1/1n (sensitivity{which}) else 1;
        if which = 1 then mod 2: = if tmassnow >
        mconc then mconc/tmassnow else 1;
        theoretical rate: = maxrate{which}*substrate/
        (halfmax{which} + substrate);
        if which = 1 and theoretical rate > predicted
        rate then
        begin
            delay: = maxdelay*(theoretical rate-
            predicted rate)/theoretical rate;
            if delay ≥ 1 then
        begin
            normal rate: = 0·0;
            reduction: = old delay – delay;
            for h: = 1 step 1 until delay – 1 do
            hysteresis{h}: = hysteresis {h +
            reduction + 1};
            hysteresis{delay}: = (hysteresis{1}
            *2 + theoretical rate)/3;
            for h: = 1 step 1 until delay do
            normal rate: = normal rate + hysteresis
            {h}/delay
            rateratio: = normal rate/theoretical
            rate
        end else
        begin
            rateratio: = 1;
            normal rate: = theoretical rate
        end;
```

```
   predicted rate: = normal rate;
   if old delay ≠ 0 and delay = 0 and
   marka = −2 then
   begin
      marka: = time;
      if time div reading ≠ time/reading
      then do count (2)
   end;
      old delay: = delay
   end else
      normal rate: = theoretical rate*rateratio
end else
   normal rate: = 0·0;
   actual rate: = normal rate*mod 1*mod 2
end;
```

CHAPTER II

Computer Taxonomy

P. H. A. SNEATH

Medical Research Council Microbial Systematics Unit,
University of Leicester, Leicester

I. INTRODUCTION

There are many differences between taxonomic practices in the major groups of micro-organisms. Algae and fungi are traditionally studied by techniques used in botany, and protozoa by zoological methods, and in all of these there is heavy reliance on morphological criteria. The scanty morphological detail in bacteria has led to the development of chemical, physiological, biochemical and serological methods, and in this Chapter it is primarily bacterial taxonomy that will be discussed. Those interested in the systematics of other micro-organisms should, however, find this article of interest for these groups, because many of the newer techniques, and in particular numerical taxonomy, are being increasingly applied to organisms other than bacteria. The taxonomy of viruses is still in the exploratory phase, and no attempt will be made to cover this field. A survey of classification methods in the major groups of micro-organisms will be found in Ainsworth and Sneath (1962). Other general references, to bacteria in particular, include publications by Sneath (1964), Skerman (1967), Cowan (1968) and Lockhart and Liston (1970) and Colwell (1971).

The Sections are arranged so as to reflect the logical steps required in classification. Section I covers briefly the theory of classification. Section II describes the kinds of primary data required, while Section III takes up the computer processing of this data to yield the generalizations to be embodied in a formal classification. Sections IV and V deal respectively with interpretation of the findings and with nomenclature, while in Section VI some ancillary information is provided for the practical worker.

A. Purposes of taxonomic work

There are many different purposes of taxonomic work. These include the assessment of relationships between bacteria, the construction of taxonomic groups and naming them, identification, and also the use of taxonomic evidence to explain phenomena in fields like ecology, genetics, biochemistry and infectious diseases. The primary objects of most taxonomic studies are the first three—relationship, grouping, and identification. Broad discussions of these purposes may be found in works such as Davis and Heywood (1963), Sokal and Sneath (1963) and Simpson (1961).

Whenever a biologist wishes to make generalizations about the organisms he studies he needs to arrange them into groups of some sort, about which he can make suitable generalizations, and the kind of generalization will determine the sort of groups he requires. In taxonomy one usually needs groups that are loosely termed "natural", and the nature of these is discussed below. First, however, different sorts of relationship will be considered, for it is on these that groups are based.

1. *Taxonomic relationship*

Taxonomic relationship can be of several kinds. In higher organisms much attention is paid to phylogeny, but with most micro-organisms, and bacteria in particular, very little is known about their ancestry. The relationships that are studied are therefore *phenetic*, that is they are based on the observed characters of the organisms without regard to ancestry.

Phenetic relationships, however, can also be of several kinds. The overall similarity (i.e. considering all the characters together) is the usual sort of phenetic relationship employed in taxonomic work. Genetic relationship is also of interest, though it has several common meanings. It may be used as a synonym of phylogenetic relationship, but more often it means relationship demonstrated by genetic experiments. The degree to which two bacteria can hybridize or exchange genes is most usually meant, and in bacteria this can be broadened to include such phenomena as cross-reactions with bacteriophage. Such phenomena usually imply high phenetic similarity because the internal constituents of cross-reacting bacteria are presumably very similar. This is therefore a partial estimate of phenetic relationship based on largely unknown details of their organization. The relationship shown by nucleic acid pairing (often ambiguously termed nucleic acid homology or hybridization) is also a form of phenetic relationship, because this is due to close similarity in the genetic messages in the genomes (genomic relationship) and thus the pairing reflects closely the degree of overall resemblance in genotype and phenotype. The % GC of DNA is a special case, while serological relationship is an involved concept, and both of these are discussed in Section II.B. For reviews of this field see Jones and Sneath (1970) and Stanier (1971).

Phenetic resemblance can be estimated in a number of ways. It should be noted that in practice we always make an estimate from a sample of the attributes of the organisms. We can only use characters that are accessible to our current techniques, whether these are explicit (as when assaying for a chemical substance) or hidden (as when phage cross-reactions are studied). These characters constitute only a part of the total genetic information of the organism, although this proportion may be high with nucleic acid pairing (which provides a theoretical justification for the value of this technique). Most types of taxonomic work will cover only a small part of the genome, and any resemblance measure will thus be subject to sampling error. This is the reason why phenetic relationships should be based on large numbers of characters. For example, it is clear that if we took only two qualitative characters, the resemblances could only be 0% 50% or 100%, and one could not place much reliance on any single value, while with 100 characters we would expect that a resemblance of say 65%, was reasonably reliable. Despite certain theoretical difficulties, phenetic estimates have proved quite trustworthy in practice, and statistical aspects (and also the agreement between results based on different sets of characters which provides empirical justification), are taken up at greater length in later Sections.

2. Natural groups

There are numerous ways in which organisms can be grouped together, but only a few are considered as taxonomic classifications. These are often described as natural classifications, though this term is open to ambiguity. Phylogenetic groups, for example, may be termed natural. The view is now widely held that "natural" groups are of the kind proposed by Gilmour (1951), and this is the sense employed here. Gilmour pointed out that a classification depends on the purpose for which it is constructed, and he distinguished two main kinds, which are however simply the extremes of a continuous series. At one end are special purpose classifications, like an alphabetic catalogue, useful for a narrow purpose. At the other are general purpose classifications, in which the groups are so constructed that one can make the maximum number of generalizations about their included members. These are "natural" groups, and they allow the greatest number of predictions about what properties will be found in an individual organism. The group "mammals" is of this kind, and allows one to predict with high probability a large number of attributes of any member. In contrast, the special purpose group "white animals" only allows the prediction that its members are white.

Natural groups are thus groups of high information content, and are those composed of organisms that have in common the greatest number of characters. Such groups are termed *polythetic*, because this criterion does not necessarily require that any character should be constant within a group; this makes provision for individuals that are exceptional in some respects. In contrast are *monothetic* groups, which are defined uniquely upon certain given characters, which are therefore invariant within the groups, and permit of no exceptions. Taxonomic groups (taxa) are polythetic, though in practice they are usually partly monothetic.

In constructing polythetic groups it is usual to give equal weight to every feature, for several reasons. The most fundamental is that each piece of information is of equal interest for a general purpose classification, but in addition it is extremely difficult to find any logical basis for differential weighting *a priori* (that is before the groups are known). Since the early French botanist Adanson was a pioneer of these ideas, numerical taxonomic groups are often called Adansonian. Two points, however, should be noted: complex characters are broken down into unit characters which each receive unit weight; and different weights may be properly employed for identification, where the groups are already known and appropriate weights can be given *a posteriori*.

A formal taxonomy is based on a hierarchy of taxa, so that the groups are non-overlapping. While hierarchies may not apply to bacteria as well as they do to other organisms (see below) they are useful in that they provide economical summaries of the relationships. Overlapping groups have not proved very useful in practice.

3. *Identification*

Identification should be clearly distinguished from the process of constructing taxonomic groups. As noted above, one can weight more heavily the characters that are most useful for identifying an unknown once the groups are known. These diagnostic characters are then used predictively, for they imply that the unknown should possess the other attributes characteristic of the taxon with which it is identified. Identification is an important purpose of taxonomic work, because it relates the organism to the literature and hence to the other known characters of the taxon to which it belongs. It also includes the production of keys and diagnostic tables, together with methods for discriminating between forms that are easily confused. It should be clear that satisfactory schemes of identification can only be based on good taxonomies.

4. *Other purposes of taxonomic work*

Taxonomic work is often undertaken to explain natural phenomena of very varied kinds, and provides basic knowledge for a deeper understanding of such phenomena. The study of infectious disease is an obvious example, and taxonomic studies may explain problems such as the source of infection (e.g. Talbot and Sneath, 1960; Ibrahim and Threlfall, 1966). Similarly it can contribute to problems in biochemistry, genetics, and industry, and indeed to any sphere of microbiology.

5. *The species concept in bacteria*

The species concept has played a prominent part in the taxonomy of higher organisms, but it is now recognized that there are many different meanings of the term species. This is well discussed by Davis and Heywood (1963) and Ravin (1963) As far as bacteria are concerned, Ravin's terms are the most applicable, which are as follows:

taxospecies: a group of bacteria of high mutual similarity, and thus a polythetic phenetic group approximating to a natural taxon;
genospecies: a group of bacteria whose members are capable of exchanging genes;

nomenspecies: a group bearing one binomial name, but not necessarily natural in a phenetic or genetic sense.

These terms are not defined in an absolute way, since they will depend on different methods of study or opinions on nomenclature. The word species in bacteria usually means a taxospecies.

Most argument centres on what taxospecies there are among bacteria, or more generally what is the pattern of variation in bacteria. Opinions vary from the view that all bacteria fall into discrete phenetic clusters to

3

the view that they form a merging spectrum of forms with so many intermediates that one cannot find any natural boundaries between clusters
(see Cowan, 1962). Perhaps the commonest opinion is that there are dense
clusters representing traditional species which occasionally touch, or which
are sometimes connected by a few intermediate forms (e.g. Lysenko and
Sneath, 1959; Liston *et al.*, 1963; Jessen, 1965). There is evidence, however, that the variation pattern may be much more complex (Colobert and
Blondeau, 1962; Hill *et al.*, 1965; Rovira and Brisbane, 1967; Quadling
and Hopkins, 1967; Goodfellow 1969). It may be that scattered strains
occupy large parts of phenetic space fairly evenly, while embedded in this
diffuse pattern there are local concentrations of points which represent the
conventional species (Fig. 1). This has consequences for formal taxonomy
(see Section IV.C).

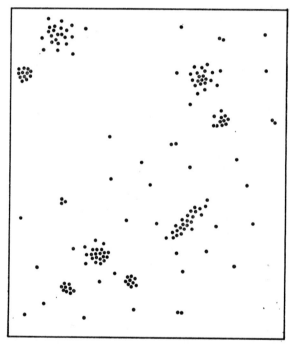

Fig. 1. A possible pattern of phenetic variation in bacteria simplified to two dimensions. The dense clusters represent conventional species with scattered atypical
strains between them.

B. Logical outline of the process of classification

The steps in classification can be divided into four main ones, and after
the first they can be handled by computer methods.

1. A wide range of characters (morphology, physiology, chemistry, etc.) is examined and the characters of the strains are recorded. A large number of such characters is essential to obtain a representative sample of the properties of the organisms.
2. The strains are compared with one another to obtain the resemblances between every pair of strains. These resemblances will ordinarily be estimates of phenetic similarity, but they may be estimates of taxonomic relationship in the wider sense, because measures other than phenetic ones can be used.
3. The strains are now grouped together to give groups (clusters) whose members are very similar to one another. By successive steps the clusters are built up into higher clusters so as to yield a taxonomic hierarchy.
4. The groups of organisms are now examined to obtain useful generalizations about them. The commonest is the construction of keys or tables for identification of unknown isolates. At this stage (but not normally at stage 2) the characters are weighted according to their importance in distinguishing between the groups that were found in stage 3.

It should be clear that these four steps form a logical sequence whose order cannot be altered. Thus one cannot estimate relationships before observing the characters, relationships must be estimated before clusters of similar organisms can be found, and one cannot know which characters serve best to distinguish the groups until the groups are obtained.

II. SOURCES OF DATA FOR TAXONOMY

The sources of data for taxonomy fall under two headings, cultures and characters.

A. Sources of cultures

Taxonomic studies are commonly of two kinds, the study of apparently new forms, and the taxonomic revision of known forms. Many studies include both of these, and the worker will usually need to obtain some strains from other collections for comparative purposes. Lists of culture collections can be found in Appendix II in Ainsworth and Sneath (1962) and a selection of these is given in Section VI.A below. Specialists in the various groups are also usually willing to provide strains. Those who intend to maintain their own collections are referred to the articles of Lapage *et al.* and of Bridson and Brecker in this Series, Vol. 3A. It may be noted that continued subculture may encourage atypical variants, and if strains are not kept frozen or freeze-dried it is best to use a practice advocated originally by Sir John Ledingham (Cowan, personal communication). In this the growth for transfer is taken as a sweep through a number of colonies (which must of course contain no obvious contaminants). This greatly reduces the chance of perpetuating variant forms. It must also be emphasized that the cultures must be pure, and this should invariably be checked on a non-selective medium at intervals throughout the work. Neglect of this simple precaution has been a potent source of confusion. Particular care should be taken with obligate anaerobes. Streptomycetes and their allies also require care, since if heterokaryons occur in nature (see Hopwood, 1967) these might segregate during the course of a study.

Whatever kind of study is attempted, it is important to have reference strains suitable to the task. These are of two sorts, nomenclatural types (type strains) and *ad hoc* reference cultures such as typical or authentic strains, or reference strains of serotypes, phage types, etc. Nomenclatural types (discussed further in Section V.C) are, in essence, reference strains for named species and subspecies, though they are not necessarily typical strains. It is essential to use these type strains wherever possible, though they may be supplemented by other authentic strains. One should aim at using type strains of all the taxa thought to be present in the survey, together with those for nearby taxa. If type strains are not used the worker is at the mercy of any misidentifications in his alleged authentic cultures, and much unnecessary confusion has arisen from this source. The strains of related taxa help to orientate the study, and to show if some of the collection belong to these other taxa, and not to those to which they were first thought to belong.

If possible some recently isolated strains should also be included, because old type strains may not be entirely typical of the groups in nature. They also serve as an internal check, because if three or four strains of each taxon are found to cluster tightly together this will give added confidence to the conclusions. Most available computer methods can only handle about 200 strains; for large data sets, see Ross (1969).

Sources of type strains are listed in Section V.C. A thorough search for relevant ones should always be made early in the investigation.

B. Types of characters

The sort of data available to the taxonomist are very varied. At one extreme are characters that consist of simple all-or-none statements, e.g. motile or non-motile. At the other extreme are data which are virtually measures of resemblance, such as the degree of DNA pairing. In between are character complexes which are not readily expressed as either of these (e.g. electrophoretic patterns), but which provide a good deal of potential information. Any characters, provided they can be recorded accurately, are of value in taxonomy if they reflect intrinsic properties of the strains. Some may be too unreliable to include or (like geographical origin) be of dubious significance. The taxonomist should attempt to obtain a wide and representative cross-section of the properties of the organisms. A useful list of tests is given in Lockhart and Liston (1970).

It is important to obtain data under standardized conditions. In some taxa carefully standardized methods are widely used, and these should generally be followed, to allow the conclusions to be related to other studies. The worker will otherwise have to do his own standardization. It is more important to provide standardized methods than to aim at an absolute criterion that is unattainable. For example, an enzyme cannot be said unequivocably to be absent because very low levels will be undetectable. In practice one must score it as present or absent under certain conditions. It is therefore better to think of tests as test methods (e.g. Kovacs positive rather than oxidase positive).

Another general problem is to devise a suitable basal medium, together with standard growth conditions, for the strains, and this is sometimes intractable. Where a bacterium cannot be cultivated (e.g. the leprosy bacillus) the taxonomy has to be based on special or indirect methods such as serology. With groups like lactobacilli it may be difficult to find a simple medium, and results may vary according to the brand of peptone, etc. Some tests (e.g. nitrate reduction) are very susceptible to unknown factors in the medium. For these reasons the brand of peptone, agar, and so on, should be specified, or widely accepted formulations should be followed.

Standard conditions for growth are usually fairly easy to specify. Although there is little published evidence for this, there is a general impression that the most reliable results are obtained when growth occurs under near optimal conditions, so these should be preferred. However, temperatures below the optimum may not greatly affect the results, with some exceptions, e.g. motility, though tests take longer to become positive (in which case some statistical correction may be considered, see Sneath 1968a). If some strains have different optima than others (e.g. some grow at low temperatures and others at high temperatures) it is usually most satisfactory to choose a condition that allows reasonably good growth with all strains.

More difficult are cases where strains have different obligate requirements. Sometimes these are not completely exclusive. Thus one could add 10% NaCl to media for any obligate halophiles, or perhaps better, add it to the media for all strains if it was not too inhibitory for any of the strains (on the assumption that the salt does not greatly affect the results). It should be noted that we have very little experience in such cases, though the work of Melville (1965) with facultative anaerobes suggests that the phenetic resemblances are not very different if they are grown aerobically or anaerobically. But obligate aerobes and obligate anaerobes can only be compared indirectly, and this is a problem still unstudied.

1. *Morphological data*

Methods for morphological studies are described in this Series by: Quesnel, Vol. 1 and Vol. 5A; Norris and Swain, Vol. 5A and Dring, Vol. 4. Relevant information is also presented under specific microbial groups in Vol. 3B, 4 and 6.

Microscopic characters generally used include size, shape (including curvature) presence of spores (and their size, shape and position) presence of capsules and whether the ends of the organisms are rounded or pointed. The arrangement of the organisms, whether singly, in chains, or in palisade arrangement, may also be noted. Marked pleomorphism may also be a useful character. It is best to express size and shape together as length and breadth in microns; an eyepiece micrometer should be used because of the difficulty in judging these by eye (Quesnel, this Series, Vol. 5A). Flagella should be scored for number and arrangement (polar or peritrichous, or sometimes polar and lateral flagella are distinguishable morphologically and should be scored separately). With polar flagella the average number per pole (Lautrop and Jessen, 1964) can be scored. The flagella can also be measured for length, wavelength and amplitude, as advocated by Leifson (1960) (Norris and Swain, this Series, Vol. 5A). Staining reactions include Gram stain, acid fastness, bipolar staining and the presence of meta-chromatic granules, and these can sometimes be divided into several grades.

With all these characters the growth conditions and time of incubation should be standardized. If there are large changes during growth it may be permissible to score the results at two incubation times separately, although the sets of characters will not be entirely independent. It is best to base the scoring on averages of a number of organisms, and occasionally the degree of variation may also be usefully scored.

Similar principles apply to electron microscopy. A general review is that of Murray (1962). The details visible may include flagellation, features in the cell wall, fine details of spores (e.g. Bradley and Franklin, 1958; Ettlinger *et al.*, 1958) disposition of DNA, ribonucleoprotein particles and mesosomes (e.g. Weibe and Chapman, 1968).

The morphology of growth in liquid culture provides relatively little information, though the presence of pellicle, ring and deposit, and the form of liquefaction in a gelatin stab, may be useful. Colonial morphology is of more value; shape of colony, and nature of the edge and surface can be recorded, but it should be noted that colonial diameter is largely an expression of growth rate, which the taxonomist may wish to discount (see Sneath, 1968a). Pigment may be scored here, or under physiological or chemical data.

2. Chemical constituents

Numerous technical methods for chemical constituents are described in this work, e.g. Herbert, Phipps and Strange, this Series, Vol. 5B and relevant information is presented by other authors in the same Volume.

Some constituents do not vary much between bacteria, and will therefore not be suitable as taxonomic characters. Electrophoresis or chromatography of cell constituents can however provide much useful information, especially the constituents of cell walls. Cummins and Harris (1956) showed that some cell wall constituents were characteristic of certain Gram-positive groups, although the method has less value for Gram-negative bacteria. In the latter the carbohydrate components of cell wall antigens may be distinctive (see Cummins, 1962; Martin, 1966) though the analyses are laborious.

Infrared absorption spectroscopy and gas chromatography give complex patterns whose value in taxonomy is somewhat uncertain (Norris, 1959; Ifkovits and Ragheb, 1968). The electrophoretic patterns of proteins, on the other hand, have proved of great interest (Norris, 1964; Lund, 1965; Baillie and Walker, 1968; Morichi et al., 1968). Certain protein bands are often characteristic of some species of bacteria, although there may sometimes be a good deal of strain variation. DNA analyses are discussed under II.B, 6 below.

Chemical constituents are easily coded for numerical analysis if individual compounds can be recognized, either as presence or absence or as quantitative characters. With complex patterns, such as electrophoretic bands it is at present usual to compare these patterns by eye when judging how similar they are to one another, and no wholly satisfactory method of coding them for numerical analyses has yet been developed. One approach is to consider that two bands are homologous if they have almost the same position (Whitney et al., 1968), but there are some theoretical and practical objections to this; the bands may perhaps be produced by different enzymes, and the same enzymes in different organisms may have different mobility. Recent studies of this problem are those of Shipton and Fleischmann (1969), Rouatt et al. (1970) and Johnson and Thien (1970).

3. Physiological tests

The upper and lower temperatures for growth should be studied on fairly rich media, and since results are sometimes found to be erratic on solids it may be better to use liquid media, despite the greater difficulty of reading. It should be noted that above about 35°C incubation in a water bath is needed for accurate results; also that at low temperatures a long period (1–2 weeks) should be allowed before discarding cultures as negative. Steps of 5°C will usually be suitable.

The effects of oxygen tension are usually studied only on solid media, under fully aerobic or anaerobic conditions. Estimating different degrees of microaerophily may not be easy, for although the zone of densest growth in agar tube cultures can be recorded, the effects of CO_2 tension may interfere with interpretation. Similarly, pH limits are rather trouble-some. At high pH values the media may become less alkaline due to absorption of CO_2. At both high and low pH levels the growth of organ-isms usually shifts the pH quickly towards neutrality, so that media must be well buffered, and an internal pH indicator is therefore useful as a check on this. It should be noted that some bacteria are particularly resis-tant to certain acidic ions rather than simply to low pH; lactobacilli are tolerant of lactic acid and acetobacters of acetic acid, and they may not be so tolerant of other acids at the same pH.

Salt tolerance is readily determined by adding graded amounts of NaCl to liquid media. Except for obligate halophiles it is seldom possible to find a lower limit of salt that is needed for growth. A few marine bacteria appear to require unknown constituents, or the exact ionic balance, of sea water.

In the tests mentioned above it is wise to keep the other conditions close to the optimum in order to avoid synergistic effects.

Resistance to lethal agents (e.g. heat or phenol) can be conveniently tested by plating out loopfuls at successive times. This is probably adequate for most cases, although decimal reduction times are more logical measures of resistance. Antibiotic sensitivities are widely performed by measuring the zones of inhibition around antibiotic discs, and this is usually satisfactory.

For testing the utilization of compounds as sole sources of carbon or nitrogen one must have a suitable basal medium, which must generally contain potassium, phosphate and magnesium ions as well as a utilizable source of carbon or nitrogen. Glucose, succinate or lactate as carbon sources, and ammonium ions as nitrogen source, are widely useful. Since organisms will fail to grow if they have accessory growth factor requirements it may be necessary to add these, and organisms with complex growth require-ments may be difficult to handle. One way which sometimes works is to add a very small amount of yeast extract that gives only a trace of growth in the controls (Sneath, 1960). Solid media may give difficulty, because some bacteria seem to be able to utilize unknown trace materials in agar, and it may be hard to find an agar that is pure enough. Glass distilled water should be used, because deionized water can contain traces of utilizable compounds. A very wide range of compounds can be tested for utilization (carbohydrates, amino-acids, organic acids, amides, aromatic compounds, etc.).

4. Biochemical tests

The distinction between physiological and biochemical tests is not sharp. The latter comprise tests for specific enzymes, and it is usual to include carbohydrate fermentations and other tests whose biochemical bases are fairly clear. Common ones are tests for indole and H_2S production, nitrate reduction, oxidase, catalase, the Methyl red and Voges Proskauer tests and hydrolysis of substrates like casein, gelatin and starch. With most of these careful standardization is important. (See Holding and Collee, this Series, Vol. 6.)

Carbohydrate fermentations are widely used, and generally give sharp results. It should be noted that an organism that does not metabolize glucose generally will not attack other carbohydrates, because these are usually first converted into compounds closely related biochemically to glucose. For this reason there may be a case for ignoring negative results when considering matching coefficients (see Section IIIB.2). The term "fermentation" should be used with care. What is usually observed is the production of acidity from carbohydrates. It is now common to use fermentation to mean the production of acidity under anaerobic conditions, while acidity under aerobic conditions alone is commonly called "oxidation". This distinction is the basis of the widely used method of Hugh and Leifson (1953). Carbohydrate tests depend greatly on the sensitivity of the pH indicator, the buffering capacity of the medium and the degree of oxygenation, and the Hugh and Leifson technique, in which these are better controlled, is generally superior to the traditional peptone water sugars.

Many enzyme reactions (common ones are urease, catalase, phenylalanine deaminase, phosphatase and various amino-acid decarboxylases) can be performed with internal indicators for the reactions, and if a suitable spectrophotometer is available many more can be detected by characteristic changes in u.v. absorption spectra. Many enzymes are adaptive, and are only produced during growth in the presence of the substrate, so that inconsistent results may sometimes occur with micromethods using dense cell suspensions where little or no growth occurs. Care is sometimes needed to distinguish different biochemical mechanisms of attack; thus clearing in casein plates may be due to enzymatic hydrolysis or to the production of alkali.

5. *Serology*

Serological characters, like genetic ones (discussed below), may be quite different from most taxonomic characters. The degree of serological cross-reaction is not an attribute of a single organism, but is rather an estimate of similarity between two organisms based on the chemical fine structure and resemblance of the antigens. The difficulty here is that we have no easy way of deciding what weight should be given to a serological resemblance compared to one based on other characters, so it is difficult to combine the two estimates. If the antigens are widely occurring carbo-hydrates then cross-reactions may occur between quite unrelated bacteria, and these can be misleading. If the antigens are proteins, e.g. flagella, the reactions are highly specific, though usually they only occur between strains of the same species. Most systems of antigens lie between these extremes.

Early serological methods used mainly surface antigens that are readily masked by others, or are subject to smooth-rough variation, though some (e.g. streptococcal group antigens) are reliable for taxonomic work. Newer methods like gel diffusion allow the precipitin lines to be distinguished, and this allows individual antigens to be scored as ordinary properties, as can also be done with individual antigens in schemes such as the Kauffmann-White scheme for *Salmonella* (an example is given by Lockhart and Holt, 1964). Other methods have been proposed by Moore and Goodman (1968) and by Lee (1968). While serology is most valuable at low taxonomic levels, new techniques may allow it to be applied at higher ones (e.g. Barbu *et al.*, 1961). (See Oakley, Walker *et al.* and Batty, this Series, Vol. 5A.)

6. *Genetic data*

Many genetic methods are described in this Series by De Ley, Duggan and Skidmore, Hopwood, Billing, Kay and others. They fall into three main groups as far as taxonomy is concerned.

(a) *Gene exchange.* The ability of two bacteria to exchange genes (by recombination, transduction, transformation or episome transfer) implies that they have very similar biochemical pathways and internal properties. This in turn implies close phenetic relationship. Meynell (1964) has pointed out that integration of a gene into the recipient's chromosome implies closer relationship than simply transmission and temporary gene expression. Still less significance can be attached to interference with metabolism by the by-products of gene action (e.g. phage adsorption or bacteriocin action). Thus with bacteriophages, lysogenization indicates closer relationship than phage lysis, while phage adsorption and killing is of much less significance. When quantitative estimates can be obtained (e.g. the frequency of transformation) these are partial estimates of phenetic similarity, like serological similarity, but like the latter, it may be possible to code some properties as characters (such as sensitivity to given phages). It should be noted, however, that negative evidence is of very little value, because even in subcultures of the same strain there may be factors that prevent gene exchange. General reviews of gene exchange in taxonomy may be found in Sneath (1968b) and Jones and Sneath (1970).

(b) *Nucleic acid pairing.* (De Ley, this Series, Vol. 5a.) The degree of base pairing between different single-strand nucleic acids is a technique that in effect estimates phenetic resemblance by physicochemical methods. In principle this is based on the resemblance between the whole genomes, and is thus of great theoretical, as well as practical, importance. It is an excellent indication of phenetic similarity, for it is highly congruent with the latter (Fig. 2). The relationship is not linear (Fig. 2a) however, since there is very little pairing at phenetic similarities below about 50%, but can be made approximately linear by suitable transformation (Fig. 2b).

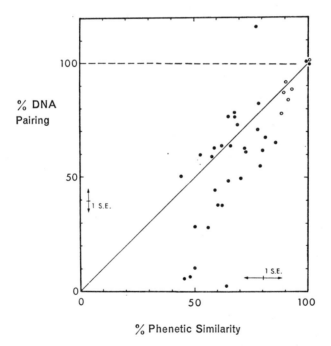

FIG. 2(a). Congruence between DNA pairing and phenetic similarity. The circles show the % DNA pairing and % phenetic similarity of individual pairs of strains of the genera *Pseudomonas* and *Xanthomonas*, from data cited in Sneath (1968b). The arrows show the standard errors attributable to experimental or statistical error. It is seen that most points lie in a band only a few standard errors wide.

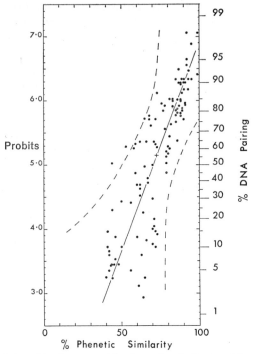

Fig. 2(b). Relationship between % phenetic similarity (S_{SM}) and % DNA pairing as probits.

The data are from Jones and Sneath (1970) and Sneath (1971) with the addition of new data points from Colwell (1970). The dashed lines show the expected approximate 95% confidence limits.

The best fitting principal axis (solid line) is that obtained if the two axes are first standardized to zero mean and unit variance, from the values: variance (% S) = 261·948, variance (probit % DNA) = 1·117, covariance = 14·267, r = 0·834. The centroid (72·705; 5·151 is shown by the cross).

The equation of the line is:

$$\text{probit}\,(\%\ \text{DNA}) = 0 \cdot 4029 + 0 \cdot 0653\,(\%\ S).$$

Nucleic acid resemblances should be processed further by cluster analysis. One drawback is the labour of comparing all pairs of strains, and and unfortunately we do not yet have much information on how valid and reliable are clusters that are based on only a few of the possible inter-strain comparisons. Another point is that for most taxonomic purposes, including identification, the worker will still require to know phenotypic characters, so that nucleic acid pairing does not do away with the need for more ordinary studies.

(c) *Percent GC.* (Duggan and Skidmore, this Series, Vol. 5a.) The molar percentage of guanine plus cytosine in DNA is now widely used in bacterial taxonomy (reviewed by Hill, 1966). If two strains have very different GC values they cannot have very similar nucleotide sequences, as De Ley (1969) has shown mathematically. The significance of GC differences, from De Ley's paper, can be summarized as follows. Differences of less than about 2% are probably not significant with present assay methods, for there is always some heterogeneity in the GC composition of DNA fragments. Differences of 5% or less are usual among strains of well defined species (Colwell and Mandel, 1964, showed that phenetic groups corresponding to common bacterial species had GC values within about this range; gene exchange between bacteria with about this degree of GC difference has also been recorded, Catlin and Cunningham, 1964). If however two strains differ by 20–30% they are distantly related taxonomically, and one would be reluctant to place them in the same genus, or even in the same family. However, some genera and families are poorly studied, so this last point should not at present be interpreted too rigidly.

It should be noted that it is only *differences* in GC values that are significant; two bacteria may be quite different but may have the same %GC (e.g. *Streptococcus* and *Haemophilus*). Shaded diagrams of the difference in %CG (Sébald and Véron, 1963) should be interpreted with this in mind, because close GC values do not necessarily imply close relationship. It is in any case not possible to express complex taxonomic relationships on a single scale. The diagrams of GC ratios against phenetic difference or DNA pairing (De Ley and Park, 1966) are much more useful.

7. *Protein sequences*

Protein sequences are only just beginning to be applied to bacterial taxonomy (Ambler, 1968), but as new analytic methods become available they will assume increased importance. Similarities between sequences of the same protein (e.g. cytochrome *c*) in different higher organisms have been shown to parallel closely the taxonomic relationships. Dayhoff (1969) reviews the present knowledge. Variation among bacterial proteins seems rather large, but they should allow quantitative comparisons between very diverse bacteria. Thus ferredoxins from *Micrococcus* and *Clostridium* have a resemblance of about 69%. Of course one is here assuming that the fine structural differences in one cistron do parallel the differences between the whole genomes.

Methods of determining homologies within proteins and calculating resemblances are discussed by Fitch (1966, 1970), Cantor (1968) and Sackin (1969). This field may prove of particular value for reconstructing phylogenies (Fitch and Margoliash, 1967).

C. Evaluation of data

A taxonomic study will usually be based on the worker's own data, and he will need to consider it critically before proceeding further. It is certainly possible to use data from monographs and the like, but this is often unsatisfactory, because results on individual strains may not be given, the internal variation of taxa may not be recorded, and the techniques may not have been adequately standardized. Sophisticated computing cannot correct for these: "rubbish in, rubbish out".

1. *Considerations of practicality and automation*

In no other branch of biology is the cost of obtaining information so high as it is in bacteriology (unless it be virology). The information from morphology is very limited. In testing a bacterium to obtain a single piece of information, such as the indole reaction, one must spend a good deal of time and effort. There is therefore considerable pressure to use quick and simple methods for performing large numbers of tests. It is worth noting, however, that much saving of effort can be made by careful planning of the work. The need for complete tables of data for computer analysis will itself help the worker to marshal his material in an orderly fashion. He should try to list his strains and tests at the start and in particular he should obtain all the cultures early on, to avoid having to repeat various tests on late arrivals. Although all characters are of equal value *a priori*, considerations of reliability will enter into their choice and this is discussed in II.C, 2 below. The need for a representative selection of different sorts of characters has already been stressed.

Many rapid testing methods are now being developed. Replica plating, multiple inoculation methods, and other semi-automated techniques offer considerable savings in cost, time and effort. (See Meyrath and Suchanek, this Series, Vol. 7B.) Divided Petri dishes are very cheap and convenient (Sneath and Stevens, 1967; Lovelace and Colwell, 1968) while Hartman (1968) and Bussière and Nardon (1968) describe a variety of micromethods. Microtests (Cowan and Steel, 1965) are quick, and allow many tests to be made from one slant culture, though it was noted earlier that adaptive enzymes may not always be detected. Automation will no doubt rapidly enter the field of microbiology once problems of sterility can be overcome.

2. *Considerations of reliability*

Abundance of information is not sufficient; the information must also be of good quality. Tests should be repeatable and readily standardized. Some tests which are poor in these respects, and are used largely for historic reasons, would be best replaced by newer ones. However it is not possible to generalize from the experience in one group to their performance in another; many tests are reliable in some taxa but not in others.

Much useful information on standardizing tests is contained in Conn (1957) and Skerman (1967). The statistical technique known as Analysis of Variance (described in standard texts such as Snedecor, 1956, and Sokal and Rohlf, 1969) can be valuable in tracking down unsuspected sources of variability (report by the *Pseudomonas* Working Party of the Society for General Microbiology). Variation (apart from that between strains) includes that between different media, between laboratories, between times of reading, and (most important) between replicates done under identical conditions. The magnitude of these sorts of variation can be very helpful in choosing the best techniques. The variation between replicates is the most critical. If this is too high the test should either be improved or abandoned. A rough rule would be to exclude tests where replicates differed in more than 10–15% of the strains. The reliability of many well-known tests is poor, and it is perhaps surprising that such good numerical taxonomies have often been constructed from such unpromising material! However, as will be shown later, statistical methods are fairly robust to such errors.

Although inconstant characters are best avoided, a constant tendency to mutate in a specific way would seem quite acceptable as a character (e.g. mutations that constantly give late lactose fermentation with some enterobacteria). The importance of standardized inocula for growth (though these are desirable) is not yet very clear, and requires closer study; this is likely to be more critical for short incubation times than longer ones.

III. PROCESSING OF DATA

After a worker has obtained enough data on his strains he must still process this further if he wishes to obtain a taxonomy or a diagnostic key. He may of course do much of this in his head as he goes along, but it is particularly difficult to do this effectively with bacteria, and computer methods are now to be preferred. This Section therefore takes up the following points in turn: the need for proper processing, the way computers can be used to do this, and mathematical details of computer methods.

A. The importance of proper data processing

The importance of proper methods of analysing data on bacteria is now widely appreciated. It is difficult to make sense of large tables of strain data by eye. The worker cannot readily see what groups are present, what are the relationships between individual strains or between groups, or what characters are most useful for identification of the different groups. He may be tempted to make arbitrary and unnatural groupings by relying on a few characters to which he gives great importance, without being able to justify these characters as against other ones. It is important, too, that the best use should be made of information that he has obtained after considerable time and effort. The further effort to understand the taxonomic conclusions of this data can be greatly reduced by computation at very moderate cost.

Besides these points, numerical taxonomy offers objective techniques together with the increase in power that attends the introduction of quantitative methods in any field. It also requires the user to give attention to the quality of his data. It forces him to evaluate critically his views on the logic of classification and on character weighting, and to consider carefully the precise aims of his work. It may be noted that the computer steps follow closely the way a taxonomist works intuitively, obtaining successively the mutual resemblances between strains, the sorting of strains into homogeneous groups, and finally obtaining information about the groups for purposes of diagnosis, or for testing explanatory hypotheses of natural phenomena.

B. Computer methods

There is now a wide variety of computer methods for taxonomy. Those described here are those most suited for bacteriology, and for other applications reference should be made to Sokal and Sneath (1963). The selected methods are illustrated by small examples. Programming details are not included, but the sources of some suitable computer programmes are given in Section III.C. Useful information on specific details may be found in Sneath (1957a, b, 1962), Sokal and Sneath (1963), Skerman (1967) and Lockhart and Liston (1970).

Before proceeding to the description of the mathematics involved the reader may find helpful an outline of how the computer is used. The four steps mentioned in the Introduction (I.B) are dealt with in turn.

1. The primary data which have been collected are first coded to make them suitable for numerical treatment. For example positive values may be coded as 1 and negatives as 0. Tables of strains versus characters are prepared in coded form from the laboratory records. The entities to be classified, called Operational Taxonomic Units or OTUs, will usually be individual strains, and the number of these is denoted by t. The number of characters is n. The table of n characters and t OTUs is punched on cards or paper tape and fed into the computer with the programme. Details of this step are given in III.B, 1 below.

2. The next step (details in III.B, 2) is the calculation of relationship between the OTUs. There are several ways this can be expressed. One can calculate the overall similarity as the number of agreements in the characters of two strains, and express this as a Similarity Value. Or it may be more convenient to count differences between strains (Dissimilarity) which is the complement of Similarity. The term Resemblance is convenient to include both of these, so collectively the measures of relationship are called Coefficients of Resemblance. These coefficients are commonly scaled to a percentage, so that for example a high similarity of 97% would correspond to a low dissimilarity of 3%. Dissimilarities are useful because they can represent the *taxonomic distance* between strains, where the distance is 0 for complete identity (equivalent to 100% similarity).

The result of these computations is to give a chequer-board table of each strain compared with every other. It is therefore of dimensions $t \times t$, with the cells representing comparisons of strains with themselves lying along the principal diagonal. These of course will contain the resemblance value for identity, i.e. 100% similarity or 0% dissimilarity (or distance). It is only necessary to calculate one half of the table, so that, a triangular *S-matrix* (or *D-matrix*) is formed in the machine.

3. The strains must now be grouped together to bring like next to like (III.B, 3 below). This is done, in essence, by sorting through the *S*-matrix and looking for values indicating high similarity between strains. These pairs of highly similar strains form the nuclei of the groups, and as other strains are found that are similar to one group or another they are added to the previous groups.

It is usual to programme the computer to construct a taxonomic hierarchy, by combining similar groups, and groups of groups, until all the OTUs have joined. This hierarchy is commonly presented as a *dendrogram* or tree-like diagram, familar enough in the guise of a taxonomic tree. It is sometimes called a *phenogram*, (to distinguish it from trees based on phylogeny, etc.) because it is based on phenetic relationship. The user can then choose levels of similarity (which appear on one axis of the dendrogram, and denote the similarity level at which the groups formed) to define natural groupings, or *phenons*. These phenons can be chosen at any level, from the small homogeneous groups at high similarity levels to the less homogeneous groups formed of less similar strains. There are also ways of displaying the groups other than by dendrograms, and these are described in Section III.B, 3.

4. This last step (see III.B, 4) comprises all those procedures that draw generalizations about the phenons found in step 3, but the most important is the constructing of schemes for identification. Once the groups are defined their most constant characters can be found and tabulated. These

characters are the most useful for diagnostic keys and tables. In addition computer programmes are now being developed for identification itself; in these an unknown strain, u, is compared with the characters of a set of q taxa, to see if it agrees acceptably with one of these taxa.

1. *Assembling and coding of data*

The laboratory records of the strain results should be first arranged as a table of n characters versus t OTUs. This will nearly always need some alterations, and these are of two types (a) those due to coding the results on taxonomic grounds and (b) those due to the punching requirements of the computer to be used. Unnecessary copying of data tables can waste much time, so it is well first to look over the computer requirements. The programme specification should give the symbols permitted (including the "No Comparison" symbol, see (e) below) and whether characters must be the rows or the columns of the input table.

(a) *Preliminary examination.* All the OTUs and characters should be first inspected, and any ambiguities in the records checked. It is important to try to obtain a complete $n \times t$ table, with as few missing entries as possible. It is wise to omit OTUs for which few characters are recorded, and also to omit characters that are not scored for many of the OTUs. Although we do not yet have much experience of the effects of gaps in the data, it would seem very unwise to retain OTUs or characters where more than half of the entries are blank. This figure is probably too lax, and 80% completeness would seem desirable. At this stage, too, the tests that are technically unsatisfactory should be omitted, and any imbalance in the numbers of characters of different classes can be reviewed. It is convenient for later steps to arrange the characters into major classes (morphology, physiology, etc.), though neither the order of the characters nor of the OTUs makes any appreciable difference to the results of computer processing.

(b) *Number of OTUs.* There is no essential reason for setting a minimum number of OTUs (unlike the position with characters; see below), but clearly one should try to represent adequately any taxa that are thought to be present, and this has been discussed in Section II.A. Computers are however limited by the maximum number of OTUs they can handle. For most current machines this limit will lie between 200 and 400 OTUs. If there are too many OTUs they may be divided into two or more sections, which can be run independently. The identities between phenons observed in each run can be found in a final run (e.g. by using just a few representative strains from each phenon of each earlier run).

(c) *Number of characters.* The confidence limits of a resemblance coefficient depend critically upon the number of characters (see III.B, 2). A minimum of about 60 characters should ordinarily be employed, and if possible there should be 100–200. Above 200 the law of diminishing returns begins to operate as far as confidence limits are concerned, so unless there is some special reason one would not obtain more characters. Computers are much less limited by the number of characters, but if there are too many, one can run the data in sections and average the corresponding similarity values from each run.

(d) *Variation within OTUs*. In microbiology the OTUs will normally be individual strains whose internal variation will be negligible in most respects. Occasionally one may wish to use species descriptions and the like as OTUs, and one then must take into account variation within the OTUs. Reliable methods for this have yet to be developed, so that it is best at present to avoid this problem by taking a number of strains of the species as separate OTUs, but if this cannot be done great care should be taken to ensure that the description does represent a homogeneous group with little internal diversity. Where this can be assured, the commonest, or the average, result for each character may be scored, as long as it is realized, in interpreting the results, that the OTU now only represents the centre of a cluster possessing a definite if small diameter in character hyperspace (see III.B, 3). If the original groups were heterogeneous, the computer cannot dissociate them into their components; it cannot untie the bundles, as it were. An assessment of internal heterogeneity can be made by counting the variable characters in the species description, and if this is large, the species should be replaced by a number of strains as OTUs. It should be noted that some computer programmes cannot accommodate fractional characters, e.g. 40% of positives may have to be scored as 0 if only 1, 0 scoring is allowed. Very occasionally a measure of character variability will be warranted, though rarely in microbiology (for this see Sokal and Sneath, 1963, and Crovello, 1968).

(e) *Scaling and coding of characters*. Computers require to be presented with data in the form of defined symbols or numbers. The taxonomist must therefore transform laboratory records such as "weak", or "pale yellow", into suitable symbols. In microbiology it is a common convention to record a positive as + and a negative as −, but they may also be scored as 1 and 0, and this is preferable in being rather more generally applicable. Thus, in some numerical taxonomic methods the character values can be given as other numbers, e.g. wing length 3·1 mm. These latter methods are not much used in bacteriology and will only be briefly mentioned. There is also need for a symbol indicating "no comparison". This is to be used where a definite 1 or 0 cannot be employed, either because the datum is missing or because there is some logical reason why it cannot be scored.

An example of the latter is when a pale yellow pigment is masked by a dark blue one; a strain that is blue cannot be scored for the character "yellow pigment present" (unless of course a chemical separation of pigments has been performed).

At this stage, therefore the characters should be examined systematically, noting the range of each, and writing out the name of the character and the scoring system to be used. Thus the original data might show five alternatives, "negative", "trace", "plus-minus", "definite" and "strong positive", and these might be reduced perhaps to four—"negative", "weak" (trace or plus-minus), "moderate" and "strong". The aim of character state coding is to divide the values into a small number of states such that the following main principles are achieved:

(a) The divisions should be meaningful. If too coarse, information is lost, if too fine, the divisions are without significance. It is rarely justifiable with bacteria to have more than five divisions.

(b) The scoring reflects the proper order for characters that have magnitude.

(c) The states express all the relevant information.

These points can be tested by empirical questions:

(1) Could one be fairly sure of distinguishing state x from state $x+1$ from an unknown OTU? If not, the character is too finely divided.

(2) Is there more resemblance between "large" and "medium" values than between "large" and "small" values? If so, the order is acceptable.

(3) Does each state reflect a substantially new and significant fact that cannot be deduced from the other states, and are all significant facts expressed by the states? If so, the coding is satisfactory.

(4) Do the scores reflect small numbers that are fairly evenly spaced (e.g. 0, 1, 2, 3)? If not, a suitable transformation should be used. For example the concentrations of antibiotic inhibiting growth might range from 1 μg/ml to 1000 μg/ml. One would not be justified in scoring these as 1 and 1000, because for resistant OTUs this one character would swamp all the others. It would be better to divide the concentrations into powers of ten (e.g. 0–1 μg/ml, 1–10 μg/ml, etc.) and in this instance a logarithmic scale would be particularly appropriate, because drug effects are commonly proportional to the logarithm of concentration. The effect of this rule is to restrict the maximum weight that any character can have due to its being subdivided; the exact number of steps is not important, for the practical effect of using say three instead of five divisions is usually negligible when many characters are employed.

Discussions of coding methods may be found in Sneath (1962), Sokal and Sneath (1963), Lockhart (1964), Carmichael *et al.* (1965) and Lockhart and Liston (1970). A few reliable ones for microbiology are given below. We may illustrate these with our example as follows.

(f) *Two-state coding.* Many characters are best treated as simply positive or negative. If we do this with our example we might score it as 1 or 0 in a column which has a temporary reference number, e.g.

Character state	Reference number
	17
Negative (− or trace)	0
Positive (±, definite or strong positive)	1

One only needs to decide the diversion between negative and positive, and for most applications it is immaterial which state is scored as 1 (exceptions are discussed in Section III.B, 2 below).

(g) *Multistate additive coding.* When more than two grades of reaction are distinguished it is best in general to use additive coding, because this preserves information about the magnitude of the character. We can convert the three states we originally chose in our example into three binary (i.e. two-state) characters as follows:

Character state	Character state numbers		
	36	37	38
Negative	0	0	0
Weak positive	1	0	0
Moderate positive	1	1	0
Strong positive	1	1	1

In this way computer programmes that only handle 1, 0 data can accommodate quantitative characters. If the machine is not so restricted one can code the states by the scheme described in the next paragraph.

(h) *Multistate numerical coding.* Here the coding can be as follows:

Character state	Character number
	29
Negative	0
Weak positive	1
Moderate positive	2
Strong positive	3

(i) *Non-additive coding*. The taxonomist may wish to discount the effect of magnitude of character, although it now seems that this has few advantages over additive coding. As it was used in early work (Sneath, 1957b, 1962), however, it may be mentioned for completeness. Non-additive coding scores only one difference between character states whatever the magnitude of the difference:

Character state	Character state numbers			
	31	32	33	34
Negative	0	NC	NC	NC
Weak positive	1	1	0	0
Moderate positive	1	NC	1	0
Strong positive	1	NC	NC	1

The symbol NC ("no comparison") indicates that this entry is not used in calculating resemblances.

(j) *Mutually exclusive non-ordered states*. The states sometimes cannot be arranged in order of magnitude, like the symbols *+§, where no two are more alike than any other two. An example would be colours like red, green, blue. These can be coded as follows:

Character state	Character state numbers		
	42	43	44
Red	1	0	0
Green	0	1	0
Blue	0	0	1

This in effect breaks the complex character into independent ones. It has the effect of giving more weight to the complex character, for this is proportional to the number of states. To avoid this some programmes have a facility for treating them as letters (e.g. A, B, C) where any disagreement scores as only one difference, but this cannot readily be achieved by 1, 0 coding (Lockhart and Hartman, 1963; Lockhart, 1964). It may be argued that the additional weight is appropriate for a complex character, but it seems best to try to break down such characters into logical parts. Thus "spores spiny", "spores ridged" can be appropriately treated as "spines present" and "ridges present", because spores both with ridges and spines are possible. Also there may be some states that conceal others, such as "red" concealing "pale yellow", so that logical scoring may be difficult. For these reasons it is to be hoped that characters with non-ordered states can be kept to a minimum.

(k) *Missing characters: primary and secondary characters*. If a structure is absent in some OTUs then one cannot score properties of the structure in these OTUs. If spores are absent, for example, one cannot score "spore oval" and "spore round". Here the presence or absence of spores is referred to as a primary character, while spore shape is a secondary character. Spore position would be another secondary character. These might be coded as follows:

	Character numbers		
	51	52 (spore shape; 0 = round, 1 = oval)	53 (spore position; 0 = central, 1 = terminal)
Character states	(spores present)		
Spores present			
Spore round			
Spore central	1	0	0
Spore terminal	1	0	1
Spore oval			
Spore central	1	1	0
Spore terminal	1	1	1
Spores absent	0	NC	NC

Lockhart (1964) has discussed several alternative ways of coding such cases, which avoid making more comparisons between OTUs possessing primary characters than between those that lack them. These however bring certain attendant disadvantages (an organism without spores scores several differences with an organism possessing them) and for most work it is likely that the scheme given above will be adequate. Little experience with the alternative scoring systems is yet available; the study of Lockhart and Koenig (1965) suggests that they give very similar results when many characters are used, but that omitting secondary characters altogether gives less satisfactory results because the total information is reduced (see also Lockhart and Liston, 1970).

(1) *Preparing clean copy for punching.* In making up the coded $n \times t$ matrix one should now exclude any column that consists exclusively of 1's or 0's, because these are constant character states and do not contribute to differences between the OTUs (though they may be valuable in distinguishing the group under study from other taxa not in the survey). A character that is uniform in all but one OTU is however best retained, for this OTU may show unique character states for other characters too, and to omit these characters may hide the fact that this OTU is aberrant. A checklist of OTUs and characters can now be made, and a clean copy of the coded $n \times t$ table prepared. The data for punching are conveniently written in pencil on square paper ($\frac{1}{4}$ in. squares are satisfactory). This helps to

reduce punching errors, which may be serious. Most programmes for instance, only know which character is which by their order, so that accidental omission of one of them will mislabel all succeeding characters. It is therefore useful to mark off the columns into regular groups (e.g. every 20 columns) with coloured pencil, or to leave a gap of one column between the groups. The punch-operator can then leave a gap between groups, and can see if symbols are missed or reduplicated by looking down the regular blocks of symbols. It is also useful to write only on alternate rows of the paper to make punching easier. Coloured pencil to indicate gaps between every fourth or fifth OTU may also be helpful.

Most programmes require the OTUs to be numbered sequentially from 1 to t, and may require the characters to be similarly numbered from 1 to n. This should be done at the final revision, so space should be left for a final numbering of rows and columns.

(m) *Revision and final check.* This consists of checking over the characters and OTUs for reduplications, etc., cutting and pasting as required, and adding the final numbering as mentioned above. The computer staff may need some indication of the number of levels of sorting for the cluster analysis. If a few adjacent OTUs are examined at random, one can quickly get an idea of whether the similarities cover a large or a small range, and thus decide whether clustering should be done at, say, the 10% (or the 5% or 2%) levels. The expected Standard Error is also relevant here; there is no point in sorting at less than one SE. This is considered in Section III.B, 2 below. The check lists of OTUs and characters can then be amended, and the data is ready for punching.

(n) *Example of coded $n \times t$ matrix.* An example of a matrix is given below, which is here only partly filled in.

	Reference numbers of OTUs							
	1	2	3	4	.	.	.	t
Reference numbers of characters								
1	1	0	0	1	.	.	.	x_{1t}
2	0	1	NC	0	.	.	.	x_{2t}
3	1	1	1	0	.	.	.	x_{3t}
4	0	0	1	0	.	.	.	x_{4t}
5	1	0	0	1	.	.	.	x_{5t}
.	.	.	.	.	.	.	.	.
.	.	.	.	.	.	.	.	.
n	x_{n1}	x_{n2}	x_{n3}	x_{n4}	.	.	.	x_{nt}

The general symbol for the value of the ith character of OTU j is x_{ij}.

2. *The estimation of resemblance*

Many measures of phenetic resemblance have been proposed in numerical taxonomy. Some of these are concerned with separating general factors of the morphology of higher organisms, such as shape and size, and as these have less importance in microbiology they will not be considered here in detail. Likewise the statistical step of standardization of the character state values has little application in microbiology. A few resemblance coefficients therefore are given here which have been found reasonably reliable for microbiological studies, with the formulae for some others.

The two columns of character states (which are here taken as consisting only of 1, 0 or NC) for any given pair of OTUs can be compared over all the characters, and arranged in a 2×2 table. For OTUs 1 and 2 in the $n \times t$ matrix given above there is one character where both are 1, one where both are 0 and two and one that are 1, 0 and 0, 1 respectively. The 2×2 table is then:

	OTU 1	
	State 1 (+)	State 0 (−)
State 1 (+)	1	1
OTU 2		
State 0 (−)	2	1

These four cells in the table are conveniently labelled a, b, c and d, and we may include also the marginal totals:

$$a \quad b \quad a+b$$
$$c \quad d \quad c+d$$
$$a+c \quad b+d \quad a+b+c+d = n$$

(a) *Matching coefficients.* In the example above the agreements over the five characters are 2, being $a+d$, and expressed as a percentage of the total, n, this is 40%. This coefficient $(a+d)/n$ is the Simple Matching Coefficient S_{SM}. It may be given as the fraction 0·4, or as a percentage as above.

If we turn to the comparison of OTUs 1 and 3 we see that there is an NC entry in one character of OTU 3. This only allows four characters to be compared, so that $(a+d)/n$ is $(1+0)/4$, = 25%. In this way the similarities between all possible pairs of OTUs are calculated, giving the similarity or resemblance matrix of size $t \times t$ (here $t = 4$). This chequer board matrix is:

Per cent S_{SM}
OTUs

		1	2	3	4
	1	100			
OTUs	2	40	100		
	3	25	75	100	
	4	80	20	0	100

These values range from the most similar pair 1 and 4, with $S_{SM} = 80\%$, to the least similar, 3 and 4 which in this example have no characters that agree. Any OTU compared with itself gives of course 100% similarity. The upper right hand part of this table need not be filled in because it is a mirror image of the other part. This is because the similarity between OTUs 3 and 1, for example, is the same as that between 1 and 3.

Several other formulae have been used. One of these is S_J, which is $a/(a+b+c)$. In this no account is taken of negative matches (d), so that mutual absence of a character is not taken as a similarity. Although S_J usually gives in practice very similar results to S_{SM} it seems better in general to use S_{SM} (Sneath, 1962; Sokal and Sneath, 1963). We may be uncertain for example, whether to score drug resistance or sensitivity as positive. The main difficulty arises with characters that may either be negative or simply inapplicable. Thus a bacterium that does not ferment glucose may be unable to ferment any carbohydrate, so that the other fermentation reactions, though negative, should properly be scored NC; we may sometimes be in doubt about the correct course, and S_J minimizes differences due to this factor. Nevertheless, S_{SM} is to be preferred in general. It may be noted that several coefficients used in higher organisms reduce to S_{SM} when all characters are scored 1, 0 (Colless, 1967; Carmichael et al., 1965; Gower in Sheals, 1963).

(b) *Vigour and pattern.* Recent work has shown the need for separating the analogues of "size" and "shape" for micro-organisms, and proposals have been made for this (Sneath, 1968a). Though little experience has yet been gained, the coefficients D_V and D_P are worth further exploration. With these, the total dissimilarity D_T, which equals $1 - S_{SM}$, is broken into two components.

$$D_V = |c-b|/(a+b+c+d)$$
$$D_P = 2\sqrt{bc}/(a+b+c+d)$$

The squares of these two add up to the square of D_T. The former, D_V, is a measure of the relative "vigour" of the strains as shown by the number of positive reactions, while D_P is dissimilarity due to a different pattern of reaction. The reason for suggesting these coefficients is that a pair of strains may show dissimilarity solely because one grows more slowly (or is read at an earlier time). This is shown by the D_V value equalling D_T. If, however, their difference is not accounted for by this factor it is shown by a high D_P value. Of course, for this method it is necessary to use only those characters that can be unambiguously scored as positive and negative (rather than simply as two alternatives of which one is arbitrarily taken as the positive state). A minor correction, that takes the growth rate difference into account to an appropriate degree is to divide the Vigour range in the OTUs into x states, and when a given pair differ in y of these to calculate $(nD_P+y)/(n+x)$, but when many characters are used this correction will be so small as to be immaterial. D_P measures dissimilarity, and its complement $S_P = 1-D_P$ can be used for similarity. Recent experience in this laboratory has shown the value of S_P both for correcting for the effects of growth rates and helping to insure against spurious similarity between metabolically inactive bacteria due to a high proportion of negative test results.

(c) *Other coefficients.* A coefficient with some properties of D_P has been used by Brisbane and Rovira (1961). It is $S_Y = (ad-bc)/(ad+bc)$. The phi coefficient is $S_\phi = (ad-bc)/\sqrt{(a+b)(a+c)(b+d)(c+d)}$; this is useful for some statistical problems as it is related to chi-square and can be used in factor analysis (Section III.B.3 and see Lance and Williams, 1965; Gower, 1966). The coefficient of Rogers and Tanimoto (1960) for 1, 0 data is $S_{RT} = (a+d)/(n+b+c)$.

In organisms with complex morphology and hence with numerous quantitative characters, two coefficients are much used. The correlation coefficient r is:

$$r = \frac{\sum[(x_{ij}-\bar{x}_j)(x_{ik}-\bar{x}_k)]}{\sqrt{[\sum(x_{ij}-\bar{x}_j)^2][\sum(x_{ik}-\bar{x}_k)^2]}}$$

where x_{ij} and x_{ik} are the values of the ith character for OTUs j and k, and $\bar{x}$ signifies the average of the values for OTU j or k. The 1, 0 analogue of r is S_ϕ.

Taxonomic distance, d, is

$$d = \sqrt{\frac{1}{n}\sum(x_{ij}-x_{ik})^2}$$

and corresponds to the Euclidean distance in a multidimensional space (a hyperspace with one dimension for each character). Euclidean distance is the familiar distance in ordinary three-dimensional space; it is the shortest line in a space with straight axes at right angles to one another. It is common to use standardized character values for d and r and for this, and problems associated with size and shape see Sokal and Sneath (1963) and Sneath (1967).

The Peculiarity Index of Hall (1965) is related to the allied concept of atypicality, as is the Deviant Index of Goodall (1966b); these might find application in microbiology. It may be noted that atypicality can be viewed geometrically as the distance of an OTU from the centre of gravity of the whole OTU set in a character hyperspace (see below); atypical organisms are far from the centre. The angle of separation of two OTUs as viewed from this point is a measure of the related concept of distinctiveness (Sneath, 1967). Some other recently developed coefficients related to information statistics should also be further studied in microbiology (e.g. Goodall, 1964, 1966a; Williams *et. al.* 1966; Hall, 1967a, b, 1969; Estabrook, 1967; Orloci, 1969).

(d) *Taxonomic distances.* For some applications it is useful to represent the OTUs as points in a hyperspace of n dimensions. The Euclidean distances between them are related to S_{SM} as follows:

$$d = \sqrt{1 - S_{SM}}$$

where d is the 1, 0 analogue of taxonomic distance mentioned above. The quantity $1 - S_{SM}$ is also used as dissimilarity (D) and equals D_T. This is the "city block" distance, i.e. the distance travelled in traversing the sides of a unit hypercube, but is not the Euclidean (diagonal) distance, d. For the special case of 1, 0 characters D is equal to the mean character difference,

$$\frac{1}{n} \sum |x_{ij} - x_{ik}|$$

used with quantitative characters (Cain and Harrison, 1958).

(e) *Confidence limits of resemblance coefficients.* The confidence limits of a coefficient of resemblance are closely related to the number of characters employed. If we start with only a few characters and successively add additional ones the similarity values at first fluctuate widely, and then, when the characters become numerous, we expect them to settle down near some percentage (Fig. 3). This is only strictly true if our characters are random samples from a very large set, but practical experience shows that this holds sufficiently well for most situations. Goodall (1968) has discussed the statistical details, but he shows that the Standard Error of the binomial distribution is a reasonable indication of the confidence limits of a given S_{SM} value. This is

$$\text{SE} = \sqrt{(S_{SM})\,(1 - S_{SM})/n}$$

Thus for a value of 0·6 (i.e. 60% S_{SM}) based on 100 characters we have

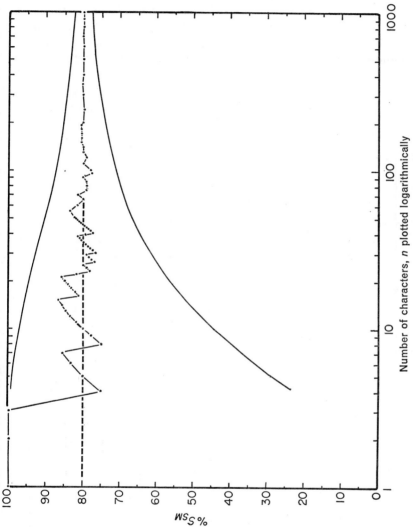

Number of characters, n plotted logarithmically

FIG. 3. Typical behaviour of S_{SM} values on increasing the number of binary characters randomly chosen from a population containing 80% of positives. The curved lines show the 95% confidence limits of the binomial distribution.

$\sqrt{(0\cdot6\times0\cdot4)/100} = 0\cdot049$, which is 4·9%. This represents one standard deviation, so if we take (from tables of the normal distribution) 1·96 SD as the 95% confidence limits, we can say that about 95% of the time our similarity values will lie within $1\cdot96\times4\cdot9\%$ of the true value, i.e. between 50·4% and 69·6%. The confidence limits for S_J can be calculated by the same formula. The standard error is an approximate method; more accurate limits can be obtained from transforming to 2 arcsin $\sqrt{S_{SM}}$ whose standard error is $1/\sqrt{n}$ (see Owen, 1962 p. 293). A graph of the binomial 95% confidence limits is given in Fig. 4. The standard error is quite reliable except at very high or very low S_{SM} values.

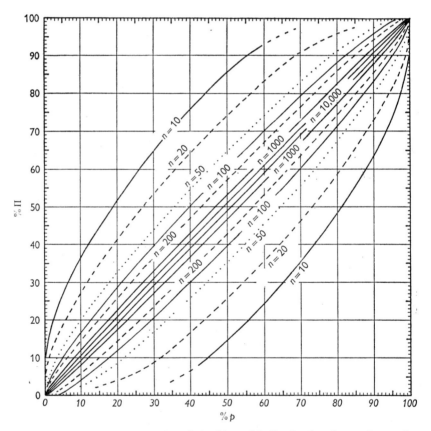

FIG. 4. 95% confidence limits of the binomial distribution for various values of n. For example, if the proportion, Π, of positive values in a large population is 70% and one takes repeated samples of size $n = 20$, then in 95% of cases the observed proportion of positives, p, will lie between *45·7* and *88·1*% (from Sneath, 1962, with permission of the Society for General Microbiology).

Recent study (Sneath, 1971) has shown the effect of experimental error in performing tests, as applied to S_{SM}. If the average proportion of errors (on repeated testing with the same strains, taking the majority result as the true one) over a set of tests is p, then the similarity value will be displaced from S to a new value, S', nearer 0·5. The errors will also introduce scatter, so that S' will not always be the same on every occasion. The following approximations were derived:

Expected $S' = S(2p-1)^2 + 2p(1-p)$

Variance of $S' = f \times 2p\,(1-p)/n$, where f is a factor equal to $|2S-1| + S(1-S)$.

The variance due to experimental error should be added to that due to sampling error (assuming that the sources of error are uncorrelated, as is likely to be true) to give a combined variance, whose square root is a more realistic expression of the standard error to be found in practice.

It can be shown that if p is below 0·1 these effects will be fairly small, and in most bacteriological work it appears that p is about 0·05 (from data in Liston et al., 1963, and Lapage et al., 1970). This explains the stability of numerical taxonomies to minor experimental errors. It was also noted that if tests are taken in order of reliability (starting with a few tests and low p, and adding the less reliable tests, so that n and p increase), the total error at first falls because of the increase in n, and only rises when the most unreliable tests are added (which sharply increase p). There is therefore good reason for using as many tests as possible unless they are very unreliable. Nevertheless, error rates of over 0·1 must be a cause for concern, and warrant improvements in techniques.

The confidence limits for D_T are the same as for S_{SM}, while the standard error of D_P is very approximately equal to $\sqrt{[D_P\,(1-D_P)/n]}$. The standard error of 2 arcsin d ($d = \sqrt{1-S_{SM}}$) is about $1/\sqrt{n}$. A very rough guide for S_{SM} near 0·5 is that SE(d) is about $\sqrt{2} \times$ SE(S_{SM}). Confidence levels of other resemblance coefficients may be found in Sokal and Sneath (1963) and Sneath (1968a).

3. Cluster analysis and other ways of revealing taxonomic structure

The matrix of resemblances between strains records the taxonomic relationships between individual OTUs. It is necessary to carry this further, and construct taxonomic groups of OTUs which can be described as higher units and given appropriate names. There are two basic ways of revealing the taxonomic structure of a table of resemblances. The first is cluster analysis, which produces discrete clusters of similar OTUs. The other is ordination, by which OTUs are arranged into some order but are not split into distinct groups. The two methods are complementary, but for most taxonomic studies cluster analysis is the more useful.

(a) *Cluster analysis.* There are numerous methods of cluster analysis but few have received a thorough trial in microbial taxonomy. Some are described in the papers on coefficients related to information statistics mentioned in III.B, 2. Others are discussed by Sokal and Sneath (1963), Ball (1965) and Wishart (1969). We shall consider two which have been generally satisfactory, but before describing them a comment is required on

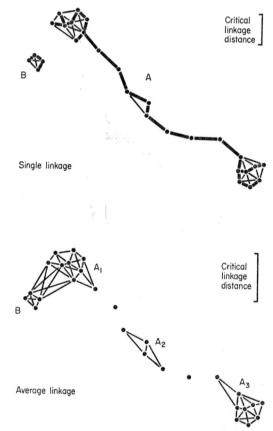

FIG. 5. Different clusters obtained by differing methods of cluster analysis. The upper part shows one elongated cluster, A, and a small compact one, B, formed by the single linkage method at the critical distance shown. The lower part shows that B joins A_1 before A_1, A_2 and A_3 form to give A if average linkage is used.

The links responsible for fusion with single linkage are shown as heavy lines (these critical links cannot be shown for average linkage). Some links have been omitted for clarity.

clusters in general. The concept is complex, and there are various basic ideas involved (Sneath, 1969a). Two important classes are compact "round" clusters and elongated "straggly" ones (Fig. 5). If the clusters are separated by wide gaps different cluster methods will give almost the same results. In microbiology, however, one expects some intermediates between the denser clusters, and there may be significant differences according to which sort of cluster is extracted by the clustering method. At this stage of knowledge it is difficult to give definite recommendations, but the techniques for finding compact clusters seem rather better in general. Both sorts are of taxonomic interest, and ideally one would use both methods and compare the findings.

Single Linkage Analysis finds straggly clusters. This is performed as follows. We write out the similarity values between OTUs in order of magnitude, and our earlier example yields the list below

$\%S$	OTU pairs
80	1 : 4
75	2 : 3
40	1 : 2
25	1 : 3
20	2 : 4
0	3 : 4

The steps in clustering are illustrated as follows.

Step	Clusters
1. The highest value, 80%, links OTUs 1 and 4, so this pair is formed first.	1, 4
2. The next highest value forms the pair 2, 3 at 75%	1, 4 2, 3
3. The next link is 1 : 2 at 40%, and this joins up the clusters 1, 4 and 2, 3.	1, 4, 2, 3

This completes the analysis for this example, since all OTUs have joined into one cluster. The rule for cluster formation is that any one link (the highest) between members of two clusters (or an OTU and a cluster) allows the groups to form. Thus the highest link between 1, 4 and 2, 3 joins them (in this case 1 : 2) and the other links (like 1 : 3, 4 : 2) are ignored.

Average Linkage Analysis uses a different criterion for linkage. Admission of an OTU to a cluster or joining two clusters occurs at the level of the average of S values between them, illustrated below.

Step	Clusters
1. The highest value again links 1 and 4 at 80%	1, 4
2. The next highest value again links 2 and 3 at 75%	1, 4 2, 3

4

3. The next value, 40% attempts to link 1 and 2, but the computer now tests the average of the four values for 1 : 2, 1 : 3, 2 : 4 and 3 : 4. This is the average of $40 + 25 + 20 + 0$, $= 21 \cdot 25$, and this is below the current level of 40, so fusion is postponed.

                    1, 4   2, 3

4. The similarity level is reduced until it reaches $21 \cdot 25\%$ when 1, 4 and 2, 3 join.

                    1, 4, 2, 3

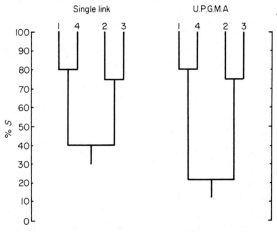

FIG. 6. The dendrograms obtained from the example in the text, using single link cluster analysis and the unweighted pair group method with arithmetic averages.

In this example the results are the same as the single link analysis, except for a different level of fusion (Fig. 6) but in larger studies the order of joining may be different, giving different trees. If the computer searches every S value in descending order then it will only join OTUs to a cluster one at a time. This means that the stems fuse only in pairs, and is called pair group analysis. In this example, too, each stem is effectively given the weight of the number of OTUs it contains, so this is unweighted for OTU number. In addition arithmetic averages are used, so this illustration shows the Unweighted Pair Group Method with Arithmetic Averages (UPGMA). There are other variants where the stems are differentially weighted, etc. (see Sokal and Sneath, 1963) but UPGMA is generally satisfactory.

If the computer sorts through at given levels of S (either fixed, e.g. in 5% steps, or using some given drop from the last level) then the analysis may join more than two stems at each level. This gives one of the Variable

Group Methods (VGM). The results of these are usually similar to pair group methods where spaced lines are drawn across the tree and all stems within the lines are brought together at the lower of the two levels. The user should set the successive S levels in VGM programmes so they are sufficiently fine to show the significant structure. If the levels are spaced at one standard error of S (see III.B, 2) then branching that occurs at adjacent levels will be barely significant. If 2 SE is used then the branching will be much more significant. Somewhere between 1 and 2 SE is therefore recommended. Thus for 100 characters one should use levels that descend between 5% and 10% each time.

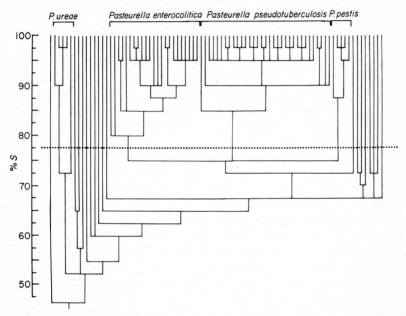

Fig. 7. A dendrogram from a study of strains of *Pasteurella*. Four of the more distinct phenons (clusters) are labelled. The other strains are of related organisms, many of them single reference strains of various species. From data of Stevens (1969, UVGMA).

The dotted line shows that three of the clusters form phenons at the 77·5% level, while *P. ureae* is a phenon at a somewhat lower level.

(b) *Dendrograms*. A common way of displaying the results of clustering is as a tree-like diagram or dendrogram, which is a formalized version of the linkages shown above, and Fig. 6 illustrates this. This is more properly a *phenogram* as it is based on phenetic data. The dendrogram is readily drawn by following the steps below.

1. The order of OTUs as given in the final cluster is written across the top of the paper.
2. A line is dropped from each OTU until it reaches the S level at which it joins something else. A crossbar is drawn between the lines at this level.
3. Once a pair or cluster is formed a single line is continued down from it, which in due course reaches a level where another fusion occurs and another crossbar is drawn.
4. Finally all OTUs are joined into one cluster, and a final single line can be drawn down from this if desired.

The dendrogram is thus a taxonomic hierarchy, with the OTUs at the tips. The stems of the dendrogram indicate phenetic groups (*phenons*) and these are then taken as equivalent to natural taxa. Fig. 7 shows a more complex dendrogram. The phenons at a given similarity level are shown by drawing a dotted line across the figure. The numerical values do not themselves tell what is the rank category of the phenons. Thus a level of 60% S does not necessarily indicate a genus or a family, and this is considered further under Section IV. Bar diagrams (skyline diagrams) (Sneath, 1957b; Lockhart and Liston, 1970) are related to dendrograms but are less useful than the latter.

Dendrograms have certain drawbacks. They cannot represent all the relationships between the OTUs because this is multidimensional, and those shown with the least fidelity are those at the base, i.e. between the major clusters. These clusters may be quite diffuse, and their relationships are consequently not easily represented by a single "distance" between them. Various methods for avoiding this have been described, and that of Carmichael *et al.* (1968) has proved useful in microbiology (Carmichael and Sneath, 1969). Nevertheless dendrograms are convenient summaries which take up little space, and the branches can be labelled with names in a taxonomic hierarchy.

(c) *Shaded diagrams.* Dendograms may be supplemented with shaded similarity matrices after the OTUs have been arranged in the order given by the cluster analysis (this rearrangement can be made by hand by trial and error, but is difficult to do satisfactorily). Shaded matrices show some extra detail (Fig. 8). Phenons are shown by dark triangles that indicate high mutual similarities, but the hierarchic structure is less easily seen than in dendrograms, particularly if one omits shading for the lower similarity levels.

(d) *Cophenetic analysis.* We may wish to know how faithfully the dendrogram represents the similarity matrix from which it was derived. The cophenetic correlation technique of Sokal and Rohlf (1962) is very useful

for this. This is illustrated with our example of single linkage clustering.
The similarity matrix is written out as a single long column of S values,
by arranging the columns one under the other in turn, with the OTU
pairs in the margin. Call these values X. The values of S required to pass

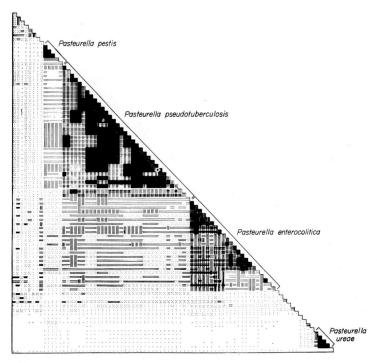

FIG. 8. A shaded similarity matrix, with several phenons labelled. From the
same study as Fig. 7. Such diagrams show rather more detail than dendrograms;
for example the paler area of the rectangle of comparisons of *Pasteurella pestis*
and *P. enterocolitica* indicates that these two species are less similar than either is
to *P. pseudotuberculosis* (not so clear from Fig. 7).

Shading: black = 90–100; cross-hatched = 80–89; vertical lines = 70–79;
horizontal lines = 60–69; five, two and one dot = 50–59, 40–49 and 30–39% S
respectively.

from the tip representing one of the pair to that representing the other of
the pair (by descending the tree, crossing and ascending again) are written
in a second column. These values are called Y. The order of OTU pairs
must be the same for the two columns.

Thus we have:

OTU pairs	%$S=X$	% S level in dendrogram = Y
1 : 2	40	40
1 : 3	25	40
1 : 4	80	80
2 : 3	75	75
2 : 4	20	40
3 : 4	0	40

The correlation coefficient between X and Y is now calculated using the formula for r given previously. This is now a measure of agreement not between a pair of OTUs but between the similarity matrix and the dendrogram. For this example $r = 0.9150$, which is good, as r ranges from $+1$ for perfect agreement to -1 for a perfect inverse relationship, and if $r = 0$ the relationship is entirely haphazard. For our example the correlation between the S matrix and the UPGMA dendrogram is only very slightly better at 0.9154. This method can be used to compare two dendrograms or two S matrices based, for example, on different sets of characters (e.g. Rohlf, 1965) and is a valuable check on how concordant are the classifications from different character sets. Significance tests for r can be found in standard texts (e.g. Snedecor, 1956); it is probably safest to use only $t-1$ degrees of freedom, as the $\frac{1}{2}t(t-1)$ similarity values are not all independent.

(e) *Ordination.* These techniques attempt to show the salient trends in the variation by diagrams or models, and are thus analogous to maps. The dimensions in the character hyperspace which show least variation are then presented as scatter diagrams of the positions of the OTUs in a reduced form of the hyperspace. The analogy of a map is here appropriate: one suppresses the vertical detail (altitude) and retains that in the North–South and East–West dimensions. Yet further simplification is attained by showing only one dimension, as in a diagram of a railway line showing the stations approximately spaced according to their map distances. This, however, clearly represents the original topography with even less fidelity. It is usual to retain only the first two or three dimensions thus allowing scatter diagrams or three-dimensional models (or 3-D stereoscopic diagrams) to be made.

One trouble with ordination methods is that the significant variation may not lie in any of the original character dimensions. A railway line may for example run NW to SE, rather than N–S or E–W, and a projection on to the usual N–S or E–W axes may not be satisfactory. To find the significant axes of variation (which are usually at an angle to the character axes) is involved mathematically, and is the realm of factor analysis.

Interesting work has been done in bacteriology, in particular by Gyllenberg and his colleagues (Gyllenberg, 1965a; Gyllenberg and Eklund, 1967; Gyllenberg, 1967). Principal Component Analysis is the usual technique, which calls for correlation coefficients (or their analogue in 2×2 tables, and this is the coefficient $S\phi$). Another promising method is Principal Coordinate Analysis (Gower, 1966, 1967) which gives a more direct representation of the positions in hyperspace, and can employ $d = \sqrt{1 - S_{SM}}$ (Fig. 9). It may come as a surprise that relations between OTUs that are all at the vertices of a hypercube (when binary characters are used) can yield results that appear to be in a familiar two or three dimensional

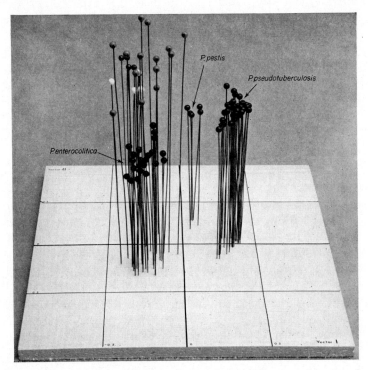

FIG. 9. Three-dimensional model of the phenetic distances between bacteria of the genus *Pasteurella* and related organisms.

Based on principal coordinate analysis of taxonomic distances ($d = \sqrt{(1 - S_{SM})}$) from the same study as Figs. 7 and 8. Vector I points to the right, Vector II away from the viewer, while Vector III is vertical. The cluster at bottom left (dark beads) is *Pasteurella enterocolitica*, that at the extreme right is *P. pseudotuberculosis*, while the five beads just to its left represents *P. pestis*. The *P. ureae* cluster is largely hidden in this view.

space, but this is a consequence of the high dimensionality of the hyper-space due to using many characters.

Finally, it should be noted that in factor analysis plots or models one usually has got to do some clustering, but by eye. This is how the groups are recognized. Since the clusters are based on the reduced space they do not take account of all the variation, and it would seem better on theoretical grounds to cluster on the unchanged space (as is done in ordinary cluster analysis). No critical examination of how far this matters has been made but the results of Skyring and Quadling (1969) who used a rather similar method suggest caution here. Factor analyses have two strengths; (1) they allow explanatory hypotheses to be tested (for example, do the more pathogenic strains occur higher on the II axis?) and (2) they give visual representations of considerable value for teaching or for getting to know the general orientation of the taxonomic structure. These mathematical methods have superseded the trial-and-error attempts of some earlier studies (e.g. Lysenko and Sneath, 1959). Other ordination methods for displaying taxonomic structure have been described by Hill *et al.* (1965) and Quadling and Hopkins (1967), while the techniques of Quadling and Colwell (1964) and De Ley and Park (1966), though not factor analytic, give diagrams that are formally ordinations. The construction of stereo-grams is described by Rohlf (1968).

4. *Identification*

The construction of schemes for identification, once taxa have been defined by cluster analysis, is an important practical step. Much of this can undoubtedly be performed by computer, but the computer programmes are only slowly being written, so that the following discussion will deal more with the logical ideas than with details. It has been noted that differential weighting of characters is desirable at this stage.

(a) *Character weighting for identification.* The major criterion for differential weighting of characters is their constancy within the taxa that are to be considered. It is clear that those with the greatest constancy (either positive or negative) are the best. A second criterion (but one which has not attracted much study to date) is experimental; those tests that are both easy to perform and give highly repeatable results are to be preferred.

A simple index of constancy is the G index of Sneath (1962) which is the difference between the frequency of a character state in one taxon and in another. Those characters with high absolute values of G (i.e. either near $+1$ or -1) are preferred. This measures the constancy for a given pair of taxa. It should be noted that G can vary with the pair of taxa considered, because what is constantly positive in a certain group may have a frequency of 50% in other groups, and it would be useful for distinguishing members of the first group but not members of the others. Another approach is to use the average constancy over all the taxa in the study, and despite the fact that its value for different taxa can vary widely, this is very useful. Gyllenberg (1963) described a separation index S (not to be confused with similarity). This is the number of taxa in which a test is predominantly positive multiplied by the number in which it is predominantly negative, choosing some levels for these. Thus one might require a test to have a frequency in a taxon of 90% or more to count as predominantly positive, and 15% or less to count as predominantly negative. An example of the use of S to evaluate a new test is given by Lapage and Bascomb (1968). Gyllenberg also uses an index R, which is S multiplied by the sum of C over all taxa, where C is the proportion of $+$ or $-$ results in a taxon, whichever is the higher. Tests with highest R are the best for discrimination of groups. Rypka *et al.* (1967) have extended Gyllenberg's S to several tests considered simultaneously. For most purposes G or S should be adequate, but the others mentioned may be convenient for sophisticated computer programmes like that of Rypka *et al.* Other methods are described by Niemelä *et al.* (1968).

(b) *Formal arrangement of data for identification.* The discussion will be aided by using the previous small example laid out in a formal scheme. The cluster analysis showed two groups of OTUs 1, 4 and 2, 3, which will be taken as taxon 1 and taxon 2 respectively. A new table, the K matrix, is prepared, together with an unknown strain u which is to be identified.

	Taxon 1		Taxon 2		Unknown
OTUs	1	4	2	3	u
Characters					
1	1	1	0	0	1
2	0	0	1	NC	0
3	1	0	1	1	0
4	0	0	0	1	1
5	1	1	0	0	1

The entries are the original coded character states with the OTUs grouped into the q taxa (each taxon with t_1, t_2, etc., OTUs). Then G for taxon 1 versus taxon 2 with character 3 for example is $(0\cdot5 - 1\cdot0) = -0\cdot5$. S for character 3 is $(0 \times 1) = 0$ if we choose 90% as the cut off level, while for character 5 it is $(1 \times 1) = 1$. If some characters are discarded as being useless for identification then the number of characters is reduced from n to m.

The problem of identification is thus to allocate u to the appropriate taxon. In this simple example it can be seen that u is most similar to OTU 4, and after that to OTU 1, so we would feel it most likely belonged to taxon 1. There are however several ways we could reach a decision, and they illustrate the three main strategies of identification. These are the *sequential*, the *simultaneous* and the *mixed*. If in addition we can attach a figure that expresses the probability that the identification is correct then the strategy is also *probabilistic*.

A sequential strategy would be to choose a character that was invariant within taxon 1 and taxon 2 (though different in the two groups), such as character 1. Then since u is 1 in taxon 1 we would allocate it to that group, and if we had had subdivisions of taxon 1 we would choose another suitable character to allocate u to subtaxa. This is effectively a simple key, with character 1 used for the first division, and other characters if we were to carry it further. Note that we here argue that character 1 being invariant is important for identification, so that at the first division we give it infinite weight by ignoring all the others. Similarly in succeeding steps we would have given other characters infinite weight. The division is thus monothetic.

A simultaneous strategy would be to consider several characters together, and this we might do by matching u in turn with every OTU, and choosing the best match. In this case it would be with OTU 4, and what is effectively a similarity value would be obtained, which for u: 4 is 80% (using S_{SM}). No character has infinite weight, so the division is polythetic. The question of weighting is further discussed later.

A mixed strategy is useful for large matrices, and we might then take the unknown to one of the taxa using a simultaneous strategy with one subset of characters, and follow this up by allocating it to subtaxa, again using a simultaneous strategy on some other subset of characters.

The two most useful methods are sequential keys and simultaneous tables, and these will be described in greater detail.

(c) *Keys*. Existing keys are of course numerous, and in bacteriology the generic key of Skerman (1967) is deservedly prized. It may be quite difficult to make a good key, and there is little in the literature on this, though the following publications are of value: Stearn (1956), Metcalf (1954) and Davis and Heywood (1963). A key should be dichotomous and the couplets must contrast, that is they must be distinctive and mutually exclusive (it is surprising how often this simple requirement is not met). It should be of reasonable length and should work in reverse to allow false leads to be retraced. It should deal with all the taxa and limitations or omissions should be noted. The characters should show high constancy in the taxa that are separated at the several steps. They should be easy to determine, not readily lost on cultivation and not unduly sensitive to small differences in technique. Where possible well known tests should be used, and methods or references to them should be given.

There are two main kinds of key, the indented and the bracket, and the latter is the most useful. An example of a bracket key is shown below.

Key to species of *Proteus*

1.	Gelatin hydrolysed . . .	2
	Gelatin not hydrolysed . . .	3
2(1)	Indole positive . . .	*Proteus vulgaris*
	Indole negative . . .	*Proteus mirabilis*
3(1)	Acid from mannitol . . .	*Proteus rettgeri*
	No acid from mannitol . . .	*Proteus morganii*

A key that splits off one taxon in turn upon a unique character is apt to be long and unwieldy compared with one that divides the taxa successively into about equal numbers. If it is not possible to find completely constant characters (and one can readily run out of contrasting leads, especially with bacteria) a small number of exceptions can be handled by keying out the same taxon at several places. A key is purely arbitrary, and need not follow the taxonomic hierarchy: it must not attempt this if this would make it less workable. Any key should be thoroughly tested, both against organisms used in the study and if possible also with new isolates and any atypical forms that are likely to occur (e.g. unpigmented or non-motile variants).

A device for automatic keying out has been described by Olds (1966), which transilluminates punched cards. Véron (1966) has described a similar apparatus. It may be impossible to make a satisfactory key at low taxonomic ranks because sufficiently constant characters cannot be found. It is then

TABLE I

Diagnostic table for species of *Proteus*

	Proteus vulgaris	*Proteus mirabilis*	*Proteus morganii*	*Proteus rettgeri*
Gas from glucose	+	+	+	−
Gelatin hydrolysis	+	+	−	−
Citrate utilization	variable	variable	−	+
Acid from sucrose	+	+	−	variable
Acid from mannitol	−	−	−	+
Indole	+	−	+	+
Ornithine decarboxylase	−	+	+	−
H$_2$S production	+	+	−	−

+ = over 80% of strains positive.
− = less than 20% of strains positive.
variable = 20–80% of strains positive.

better to make diagnostic tables which can accommodate exceptional strains. Keys are seldom probabilistic, though Möller (1962) has described one. Computer programmes for producing keys automatically from sets of data are now being developed (e.g. Pankhurst, 1970).

(d) *Diagnostic tables*. The outstanding examples of diagnostic tables are those for medical bacteriology developed by Cowan and Steel (1961, 1965). These require the user in effect to match the unknown against the columns (a simple aid to this is that of Cowan and Steel, 1960). For such tables m of the more constant characters of the taxa are chosen, e.g. those with frequencies in the taxa of less than 10% or over 90%. The choice of appropriate cutoff points requires some experience. An example is given in Table I. The formal difference from the K matrix is that we now have replaced the individual OTUs by a column that expresses in some way the average behaviour of the members of each taxon, so that we no longer match the unknown against actual OTUs but against some formalized description of the taxa as new entities. This leads to methods in which the importance of the characters is differentially weighted (apart from simply omitting some characters as unhelpful).

(e) *Weighted matching methods*. We can now generate from the K matrix a new table, where each taxon has only one character state (normally the commonest) and a weight based on constancy. In the example below we shall take these weights as 0 (for very variable characters), 1 or 2 (arbitrarily allocating these to illustrate the principle involved).

Characters	Taxon 1 State	Taxon 1 Weight	Taxon 2 State	Taxon 2 Weight	u
1	1	1	0	2	1
2	0	1		0	0
3		0	1	1	0
4	0	1		0	1
5	1	2	0	1	1

The variable characters (number 3 for taxon 1 and numbers 2 and 4 for taxon 2) need not be scored, as will appear from the method of use. We then calculate (for each taxon compared to u) the sum of the products of the agreements and the weights. An agreement (either 1 with 1 or 0 with 0) counts as 1, which is multiplied by the corresponding weight. Thus for taxon 1 we have a score of $(1 \times 1) + (1 \times 1) + (0 \times 1) + (1 \times 2) = 4$. Compared with taxon 2 the score is $(0 \times 2) + (0 \times 1) + (0 \times 1) = 0$. We choose as the identification the taxon with the highest score. Such schemes can be worked either by hand or on a computer. To avoid interference by vigour factors the use of S_P might be considered in this method. If it is to be made probabilistic the use of chi-square tests should be explored.

(f) *Conditional probability models.* Several computer programmes have been developed (e.g. Rypka *et al.*, 1967; Dybowski and Franklin, 1968) that work out the probability that u belongs to each taxon, employing a form of diagnostic table. The second is the simplest to explain, and is now receiving extended trial with bacteria isolated from clinical laboratories, so an outline of it is given below. A fuller discussion of this, and of experience at the National Collection of Type Cultures, is given by Lapage *et al.* (1970) (see also Sneath, 1969b). The method of Dybowski and Franklin uses a table of the frequencies of positive results in each taxon and this is stored in the computer. Because there is a chance that an atypical result may be obtained with the unknown, or that a mistake has been made in testing, the entries for constant characters are never 0 or 1·0, but are set to figures such as 0·05 or 0·95. This prevents a mismatch on one test from completely excluding a group in the process described below.

The argument is then as follows. If a taxon has 0·2 of positives on the first test, then the chance that an unknown which scores + really belongs to that group is taken as only 0·2. If u scores −, then the chance is taken as 0·8. Now suppose in a second test the proportion of positives is 0·65. Then an unknown scoring + + on the two tests is taken as $0·2 \times 0·65 = 0·13$. In this manner the individual test probabilities are multiplied together for as many tests as are available.

As the number of tests is increased the joint likelihood becomes increasingly small for a misidentification. For a correct identification it falls more slowly. Some expression is needed to take this into account. A useful one is to calculate the joint likelihood for an unknown that possesses the commonest state for every character. In the example above this would be one scoring − and +, for which we have $0·8 \times 0·65 = 0·52$. The value for the unknown (scoring + +) is compared to this as 0·13/0·52, and this gives the Model Likelihood Fraction or MLF, which is 0·25. This approaches 1 for the best possible identifications, and when it approaches a value say of 0·95 we can say that this indicates roughly a 95% probability that the identification is correct.

At some chosen level of MLF the computer can print the presumptive identification, together with the next best candidate and its probability. Furthermore it can also print the next tests that will be most efficient in distinguishing between the candidates, or in raising the probability to an acceptable level. One can then perform these in the hope of clinching the matter. The original scheme of Dybowski and Franklin ran into some difficulties, but recent experience (Lapage *et al.*, 1970) shows that a modified method is very promising. The National Collection of Type Cultures uses a set of 50 tests covering 60 groups of Gram-negative rods of medical interest. They obtain around 80% of correct identifications (at the stringent 99·9% level) with field strains when a free choice of 35 out of the 50 tests is used. The remaining 20% are not necessarily badly misidentified, for they are usually allocated to the correct general area. Better taxon descriptions and tables would undoubtedly reduce the number, but it should be noted that with culture collection strains over 92% are correctly identified, so this suggests that there may be around 5–10% of field strains that are not members of recognized groups and are either intermediate forms or aberrant strains. These may represent the scattered strains around dense clusters in Fig. 1. The method also promises considerable savings in the number of tests required. Thus in most diagnostic tables the number of tests required for satisfactory identification is rather more than the number of taxa, so that m/q is about 1·2; with the computer method it may be as low as 0·6.

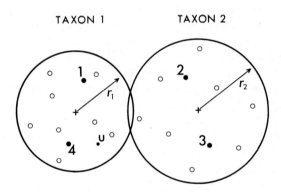

FIG. 10. Identification using a distance model (see text). The unknown u falls within the radius r_1 of taxon 1. The radii have been chosen arbitrarily to show a small degree of overlap.

(g) *Distance models*. Distance models use a simultaneous strategy, but treat the scores as distances in some kind of character space. The taxa are now represented as a rule by a centre and an envelope (commonly defined by a radius around the centre). Gyllenberg (1965b) has described such a method, which should be consulted for details, but the principles are easy to illustrate. One can readily work in the original n dimensions (or in m selected ones) but for illustration we will consider our small example of a K matrix in two dimensions obtained by factor analysis

(Fig. 10). In this figure in addition to the four OTUs some additional points have been given as open circles, to show how one can draw boundaries round the taxa if one has a number of strains in each. The taxon radius can be calculated by methods given in III.B, 5 below.

The unknown *u* is now introduced, and its distance measured from each taxon centre. If it lies within the critical radius of only one taxon it is identified with that group. If it lies in the overlap between two taxa it is an intermediate, while if it lies outside any taxon it is an aberrant strain or belongs to a group not represented in the system. It may be noted that a powerful form of distance model, in which character correlations are taken into account, is used in multivariate statistics (Mahalanobis D^2 and canonical vectors, which are allied to Fisher's discriminant function, see Seal, 1964). The centres of taxa using binary characters may be quite artificial in the sense that they may not represent actual strains, but are related rather to centroids or hypothetical median organisms (see III.B, 5). Matching identification schemes can be thought of as distance models in which either Euclidean or "city block" distances are used, depending on the type of resemblance coefficient employed. Distance models can be probabilistic if the taxon envelopes represent confidence limits.

(g) *Mixed strategies.* If a key contains more than one character at any division then it is a combination of simultaneous and sequential strategies. Each division employs in effect a summarized diagnostic table. It is implicit, though rarely stated explicitly, that unless otherwise mentioned the choice should depend on the majority decision on the several characters, because the unknown will not always agree upon all of them. Provided that this is kept in mind such keys are satisfactory, and gain strength from the simultaneous strategy.

In practice diagnostic tables, unless very small, also follow this mixed strategy. Thus Cowan and Steel (1965) give a first-stage diagnostic table for Gram-positive bacteria, and after identifying the main group the user proceeds to a second-stage table, e.g. to *Mycobacterium* and *Nocardia* and thence to a third-stage table for species of *Nocardia*.

5. *Cluster parameters*

Both for construction of phenons and for identification certain parameters of clusters are useful, and for convenience they are discussed together here. They include measures of the centre and dimensions of a cluster, and its degree of stragglyness. There are three commonly used measures of the centre of a cluster.

(a) *The average organism or centroid.* This is an abstraction and does not represent an actual strain. It is the point in phenetic space given by the mean value for each character, and for 1, 0 data this is the observed frequency of the characters among the members of the cluster. It thus represents a point within the phenetic hypercube, while all actual strains lie at corners. It is nevertheless convenient mathematically, and is widely used in distance models, particularly for identification (e.g. Gyllenberg, 1965a, b). It also represents the centre of gravity of the cluster, or centroid.

(b) *The hypothetical median organism.* This was introduced by Liston *et al.* (1963), and is again not an actual strain (except by chance). It is the hypothetical strain that possesses the commonest state for each character, and is primarily used with 1, 0 data. It thus has all its characters 1 or 0 and lies at a corner of the phenetic hypercube—that corner that is closest to the centroid (a) above.

(c) *The centrotype.* This is due to Silvestri *et al.* (1962). It is (when generalized from their specific method) the strain that has the highest mean S when compared with all other strains of the cluster. It is the OTU nearest to the centroid for Euclidean distance models (not necessarily for others) and unlike (a) and (b) it is an actual strain.

The usefulness of these three concepts will be evident from their definitions: the average organism is convenient for many mathematical purposes; the hypothetical median organism is the nearest to the ideal typical organism, and to the centroid, that can be given in 1, 0 terms; while the centrotype is the most typical actual strain in the study, and would, for example, be suitable as a type or reference strain.

(d) *The dimensions of a cluster.* The commonest measure used in bacterial taxonomy is a taxon radius. This is satisfactory as long as the clusters are not too elongated, but it may be noted that the standard deviations of an individual cluster on factor axes (obtainable from many ordination methods) are often an approximation to the effective dimensions of the oval (more strictly hyperellipsoidal) shape of the cluster. These standard deviations, however, should be checked using only the one cluster in the factor analysis. Without some factor analysis (and not always then) one cannot be certain that a cluster is sufficiently hyperspherical to allow the use of a taxon radius, but with bacteria this assumption seems reasonably safe in practice, and some check is provided by the technique in (e) below.

Two methods are suggested for calculating a taxon radius. The first is to use $r = 2\sqrt{(\sum d_{jc}^2/t)}$, where the d_{jc} are the distances of the t cluster members from the centroid, as suggested by Gyllenberg (1965a, b). This is twice the intracluster standard deviation.

The second and preferable method is to draw a histogram of the distances (or their equivalent) of cluster members from the centroid, and obtain a radius empirically (Fig. 11). The histogram will probably approximate a normal curve (this can be tested by standard methods, e.g. Snedecor, 1956), and its mean, $\bar{d}_{jc}$, and standard deviation, σ, can be used by setting

$$r = \bar{d}_{jc} + k\sigma$$

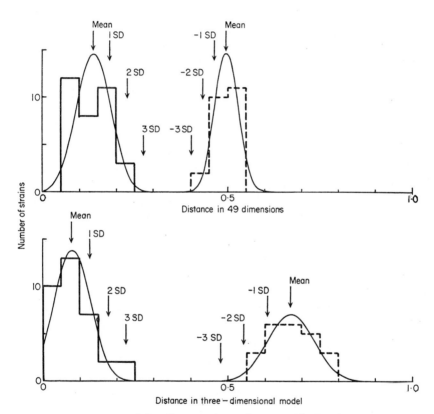

FIG. 11. Histograms of the distances from the centroid of a chosen taxon. The lower part shows the distances from the centroid of the *Pasteurella pseudotuber-culosis* cluster of Fig. 9 of strains of *P. pseudotuberculosis* (solid lines) and of *P. entero-colitica* (dashed lines). The upper part shows the distances ($d = \sqrt{(1 - S_{SM})}$) in the original 49 dimensions. The two sets of distances differ in the main by a scaling factor used in calculations for the model.

Normal curves have been superimposed, and above these are marked the means, and 1, 2 and 3 standard deviations away from them. It can be seen that the two species do not overlap at the 3 SD level. The *P. pseudotuberculosis* histogram from the model is not very close to a normal distribution, and this is a consequence of the fact that it is based on only three dimensions.

5

One can choose k according to the desired one-tailed value for the normal distribution. Thus with $k = 2.33$ one would expect all but 1% of strains to lie within r. This formula is available both for the original hyperspace and for models of reduced dimensionality like Fig. 9, but r will not be the same in each case. Other central measures besides the centroid will usually be suitable.

(e) *Criterion of stragglyness or chaining.* A simple and effective one is to examine the histogram described in (d) above. If it shows a peak well away from the origin it suggests that the cluster is reasonably compact, while a straggly cluster will give a flattened histogram falling off from the origin. More exact statistical techniques await development.

(f) *Tests of distinctiveness between clusters.* This area has not yet received much detailed attention. The simplest method is to look at the depth of the cleft between two clusters in a dendrogram, and if this is several times the standard error of the similarity coefficient it is fairly safe to consider the clusters are distinct. This (and with ordination methods inspection by eye) will commonly be sufficient. Hutchinson *et al.* (1965) suggest plotting the S values (one could equally use distances) of all strains of two clusters A and B from the centre of cluster A, and examining the resulting histogram (Fig. 11; the histogram of members of A is effectively the same as that mentioned in (d) and (e) above). They used as the central strain that with the lowest standard deviation of S values when compared with all other members of A, but other central measures would seem quite suitable. However the significance of the distinctness cannot be determined by a t test (e.g. Snedecor, 1956) as suggested by Tsukamura (1967). It can be shown that an arbitrary division of an oval cluster may give a significant t value for the two halves. Instead one can calculate the mean and standard deviation of each histogram. If one then chooses a 95% confidence limit, for example, a mark that is 1.96 SD of A above the mean of A should lie below the mark that is 1.96 SD of B below the mean of B (Fig. 11). This will be a fairly safe indication that the clusters do not have more than 5% of overlap.

C. Availability of computer programmes

Computer programmes for numerical taxonomy are often difficult to find, and are often not easily transferred from one machine to another. Most of them are now written in high-level computer languages such as FORTRAN or ALGOL (see Ware, this Volume, p. 1) but even so the different dialects of these languages cause difficulty. There are no convenient published listings of programmes (which in any event rapidly become out of date). It is best therefore to write to a known user, and obtain the programmes direct.

The following unpublished newsletters are of help in tracing programmes: Taxometrics (issued by the National Collection of Type Cultures, Colindale, London), the Classification Programmes Newsletter (issued by the M.R.C. Microbial Systematics Research Unit, University of Leicester). The series of Computer Contributions of the Kansas Geological Survey, University of Kansas, Lawrence, Kansas, contains a number of programmes that can be adapted for numerical taxonomy. It is often most practical to arrange for data to be run on a computer at another institution rather than to obtain and adapt an existing programme.

IV. INTERPRETATION

All taxonomic results need some interpretation. They have to be evaluated against the background of existing knowledge, including evidence from sources such as genetics. It is also evident that experimental error and differences in techniques of testing or of numerical analysis may affect the findings, so that some guide is needed to the significance of such effects. The points fall under three main headings; phenetic evidence, genetic evidence and question of taxonomic rank, which are taken up successively below.

A. Phenetic evidence

Fortunately most numerical taxonomic studies have proved fairly easy to interpret. The phenons have usually been satisfactory taxonomic groups (although their taxonomic rank does at present raise subjective considerations which are discussed in IV.C); if the number of characters has been large, and representative of a wide range of properties, considerable reliance can be placed on this. The sampling error of the resemblance coefficient should be used to evaluate the significance of the finest divisions (see III.B, 2, III.B, 3 and IV.C below). Some published work has drawn distinctions that are based on slender grounds.

Disagreements with background knowledge may concern certain individual OTUs, or the analysis as a whole. In the former case these may be due to some error in the technique used for testing, or the use of atypical or misnamed strains. They may also be due to an inappropriate numerical technique. Thus if there are pronounced differences in growth rate of the strains the question of vigour should be looked into. Again, with single link clustering, some clusters may depend on fortuitously high resemblance between certain OTUs, and average link analysis or ordination may explain this. It may be noted that stems of a dendrogram may be rotated at will, and this is often useful to show the mutual resemblances better by bringing nearer the most similar strains of different phenons.

Where there is disagreement in the analysis as a whole the cophenetic technique may be used with advantage to test how faithfully the cluster method has reflected the resemblances, while most ordinations provide similar criteria in the form of the amount of variation that is accounted for by the reduced dimensions. The cophenetic method too can indicate discrepancies in individual OTUs, because for these the absolute values of the difference between pairs of entries will be high. It may also be employed for comparisons between different studies, provided account is taken of the fact that different strains and tests are usually involved, so that close correspondence cannot always be expected. Discordance with other numerical studies is of more concern than discordance with traditional taxonomies that are often frankly arbitrary. There has been little deliberate comparative work with different sets of characters on the same strains, but a re-examination of data on *Chromobacterium* (Sneath, 1957b) shows that the correlation between S_J values based on 29 morphological and 76 physiological plus biochemical characters was 0·612, which is not much less than that found between random sets of 29 and 76 characters ($r = 0·753$, which must be close to the error due to sampling). Whatever is the source of trouble the best course is to appeal to new evidence in the form of new strains or new tests if the discrepancies are serious ones. It should be noted that such discrepancies may indicate unsuspected sources of biological variation that may be worth attention in their own right as phenomena of interest in other fields. Thus disagreement involving drug resistance might illuminate the mechanisms by which different bacteria become resistant. There is a tendency for some sources of discrepancy to assume undue importance in the eyes of the worker; it may be hard to believe that a certain metabolic pathway or a certain form of flagellation is not of the greatest consequence when viewed against the whole phenotype— until an obvious exception is encountered.

B. Genetic evidence

As was pointed out earlier, little account should be taken of the lack of gene exchange between phenetically similar bacteria, and similar considerations apply to lack of serological cross reactions. More serious are cases where apparently unrelated bacteria can exchange genes. If this is not due to technical errors (either in the genetic or the phenetic methods) it raises problems of special difficulty, for it would strike at the assumption that gene exchange can only take place between rather similar bacteria. Such cases appear rare and none has yet been carefully investigated, but they need very careful study using techniques such as %GC and DNA pairing.

Severe discordance between %GC or DNA pairing and phenetic resemblance should likewise be investigated further. As to GC ratios the theoretical bases are not as yet very firmly established, and it would be unwise to be too dogmatic that a moderate difference in %GC necessitated separation into several taxa. One would be more cautious in dismissing a serious discrepancy with DNA pairing, both because of its stronger theoretical basis and because its concordance with other taxonomic evidence appears to be very good. Such a case would of course be of the greatest interest as a new biological phenomenon. If anything like a complete table of resemblances can be constructed from genetic evidence it will be invaluable to compare this with the phenetic similarity matrix from more usual characters, and the cophenetic method should then be used.

C. Bacterial species and taxonomic rank

1. *The species concept in bacteria*

The distinction between taxospecies, genospecies and nomenspecies was made in the Introduction. Nomenspecies may be anything we choose to give a binomial name, but the other two can be at least partly defined experimentally. A taxospecies is effectively a cluster or phenon, but may not coincide with a genospecies. Thus restriction of gene exchange to a few strains of a cluster would imply a taxospecies containing several genospecies, while gene exchange between well defined clusters (like genera of enterobacteria) implies several taxospecies within a genospecies. Our main concern is then what groups to regard as species in a formal taxonomy. Genospecies are not suitable for this, both because they may change drastically with improved methods of bacterial hybridization and because they may be far too large or too small for convenience and of vastly different internal variability, from single strains to whole families.

There is much to recommend the common practice of regarding each well defined and well separated cluster as a species in a formal taxonomy. This implies that intermediates are poorly adapted to survival, or they would be more frequent, although it is possible that they represent biotypes that are common in certain special habitats. Nevertheless there are difficulties. A cluster may be very homogeneous or more spread out, so the internal variability may not be the same in all species. Some clusters may overlap a good deal, as is probably true with the *Pseudomonas fluorescens* group (Rhodes, 1961; Jessen, 1965). Aberrant strains may pose problems; it would be impracticable to name each as separate species, but if they were all united into one the species might be inconveniently large, and would contain denser clusters within it. It would seem best to treat distinct clusters as species if their variability was about the same as that of other clusters in the same area of bacteria. Just occasionally a cluster of clusters might be treated as a species where there were numerous distinct but exceedingly homogeneous biotypes forming a larger cluster (as may be the case with some pathogens; e.g. *Xanthomonas* might be considered a single species with numerous biotypes in different host plants). It is wise to require that there should be at least three characters that separate the majority of strains of two species, and that overlap of clusters should be quite small (involving perhaps less than 5% of the strains). Aberrant strains could then be either united with the nearest clusters, or referred to as intermediates between species, or (Hill, 1959) simply placed in the "*X*-branch" where *X* is a species cluster. At the lowest taxonomic levels the experimental variation should be considered; Liston *et al.* (1963) noted that subcultures of strains of *Pseudomonas aeruginosa* could not be clustered according to parental origin, because small variations in test results led to similarity between subcultures of about 95% *S* (the same as that between many strains). Heterokaryosis (as perhaps in streptomycetes) will similarly limit the smallest phenons that can be recognized.

2. *Higher ranks*

There is an increasing opinion that rank categories above species and genus are of little meaning in bacteria, except as convenient ways of making manageable groups of genera. Genera should be established as groups of closely related species with an appreciable gap from nearby genera, but preserving well known names where this can be done without doing violence to the facts. Above the genus the taxonomic hierarchy in bacteria is probably very indistinct, and some artificiality may be hard to avoid.

Since we lack absolute criteria of rank, at least at present, the levels of the dendrogram (or other diagram) used to define ranks should be chosen so as to give where possible the same sort of taxa that are widely recognized. The lines should not however wander up and down across the dendrogram at the whim of the investigator. Attempts have been made to define a certain similarity level for a rank. Skerman (1967) notes that traditional species and genera are often well defined by 75% and 65% *S* respectively, but it is not possible to follow Liston *et al.* (1963) in trying to insist on rigid figures, because if one repeats an analysis on one phenon the similarity levels will fall since the invariant characters of that phenon will be discarded. It is best to establish a reasonably small number of taxa with scientific names in a formal taxonomy. More detail can be given with numbered phenons or in dendrograms, or else the phenon nomenclature of Sokal and Sneath (1963) can be used, where, for example, an 80% phenon refers to a group formed at or above 80% *S*.

V. NOMENCLATURE AND REQUIREMENTS FOR PUBLICATION

A. International codes of nomenclature

There are four international codes, which apply respectively to the following organisms:

Botanical code; algae, fungi and higher plants
Zoological code; animals including protozoa.
Bacteriological code; bacteria.
Horticultural code; cultivated plants.

The code for viruses has not yet appeared.

Many microbiologists find difficulty in following the rules of nomenclature. These rules are phrased in legalistic language which can scarcely be avoided if they are to be unambiguous. Guides to the codes may be found in Savory (1962), Ainsworth and Sneath (1962), and Ainsworth (1968). A brief description of the main concepts of the Bacteriological Code is given here, with certain rules noted in parentheses. It should be noted however that there are proposals to make very considerable changes in the existing Bacteriological Code within the next few years (Lessel, 1971).

The code contains:

principles: the intentions embodied in the code;
rules: regulations that are obligatory;
recommendations: not obligatory, but guides to good practice;
notes: which give illustrative examples;
annotations: which compare other codes and give further examples;
provisions: which allow for exceptions or changes of rules.

The code aims at three main purposes, although they overlap:

names should be stable;
names should be unambiguous;
names should be necessary.

1. *Stability*

Names of taxa must be correctly proposed and made available to bacteriologists by publication if they are to be considered. The code sets a starting date for publication (rule 10, an unrealistically early one in the opinion of many). *Effective publication* (rule 11) is making a name available in an accessible publication, because bacteriologists cannot be expected to consider names that are not reasonably accessible in the literature (publication of names in theses is undesirable though technically acceptable).

Valid publication (rules 12–14) means that a name is both effectively published and also that it is made clear what it refers to; a description or reference to a previous description is thus essential to valid publication, and the author must make a serious taxonomic proposal.

2. *Unambiguity*

Scientific names of taxa are recognizable by their latinized form. Nomenclature deals with two classes of names, names of categories (e.g. family, genus) and names of taxa themselves (e.g. Pseudomonadaceae, *Bacillus subtilis*). The categories form a hierarchy; the major ones are Class, Order, Family, Genus and Species in descending rank. Uniform suffixes to names above genus are desirable: thus—aceae indicates a family (rules 3 and 4). A bacterium should not bear the same name as another micro-organism (but it can bear the same name as a higher animal or plant, for this would take excessive labour to avoid). The names of genera are latinized nouns in the singular with an initial capital letter (rule 5). Names of species must consist of two separate latinized words, the genus name and the *specific epithet* which agrees grammatically; no two species may have the same name (rule 6; rule 7 deals similarly with the ternary names of subspecies).

A name is intended simply as a reference symbol, and not a description (which experience has shown to be impracticable). The highest categories may have descriptive names, but the others are regulated by the *nomenclatural type method*. This is seldom clearly described and is often misunderstood. It is a device to make clear what is meant by a taxon name and no better method has been found. It has never been practicable to define a name by some attribute of the organisms. Instead a reference point is recognized as the *nomenclatural type* (rule 9). This always presupposes a given or implied taxonomy. For example, the family Bacillaceae comprises those genera that are, in the opinion of the user, in the same family as the type genus *Bacillus*. The species of *Bacillus* are those in the same genus as the *type species* of this genus, *Bacillus subtilis*. This species has a *type strain*, the Marburg strain. Ultimately (at least in theory) each taxon is referred, by successive types, to a type strain, which can be examined if there is any doubt about what a name refers to. Types can thus be either lower taxa, or actual strains (in default of strains, descriptions may sometimes serve as types). Where no type strains exist there are alternative provisions, or procedures for establishing a type strain. If a type strain has to be later chosen for a published name it is called a *neotype* (see Section V.C). It is important to note that a type is simply an agreed reference point which *need not be typical*. The similarity in the words does not imply this; it is easy to see that the first described strain can be the type but obviously cannot be guaranteed to be typical. A type is a constituent element of a taxon that is permanently attached to a name; if the type is excluded the name must be changed.

Several authors may inadvertently use the same name for different organisms, and it must be traceable, so the citation in the literature is attached to the name: it is not a credit to the author (rule 15). Rules 25 and 27 cover other sources of confusion.

3. *Necessity for names*

A taxon can have only one correct name, the earliest in accordance with the rules, to prevent unnecessary names (rule 26). This is determined by the *principle of priority* because this has been found the best criterion in practice (though certain exceptions are allowed). The correct name depends on the taxonomy accepted by the user: if one worker believes two bacteria belong to the same species he must use a single species name for them, but another worker is fully entitled to consider them as different species and to use two names. Nomenclature does not dictate taxonomy. It simply regulates names in a given or implied taxonomy.

There are two kinds of synonym. If two taxa have the same type they are *nomenclatural synonyms*. Thus *Bacillus coli* Migula is the same bacillus as *Escherichia coli* (Migula) Castellani and Chalmers. No question of opinion is involved, and only the correct name (in the taxonomy used) is retained. If two taxa are considered to be the same taxonomically they are *taxonomic synonyms*. *Pseudomonas aeruginosa* (Schroeter) Migula is generally held to be of the same species as *Bacillus pyocyaneus* Gessard, but this is a matter of opinion.

A consequence of the type concept is that widening or narrowing the scope of a taxon does not of itself warrant a change of name. This is to prevent proliferation of names for sets of organisms that are almost the same (rule 17). Again, to avoid unnecessary new names, a species ordinarily retains its species epithet if it is transferred to a new genus (rule 18), and if two taxa are united only the oldest name is retained. Certain other rules are also aimed at avoiding creating unnecessary new names (rules 20–24) and at fostering uniformity of spelling (Rules 27–28).

The provisions of the codes are concerned with the mechanism for amending the rules and making exceptions to them. The most important is the *conservation* of commonly used names, which are thus established by international agreement (instead of having to be changed because they contravene some technicality). The International Committee on Systematic Bacteriology is the body responsible for the Bacteriological Code, and its Judicial Commission considers requests for opinions and changes and exceptions to the rules.

B. Basic requirements of the codes

The basic requirements of the codes are all similar and are quite few. A new taxon requires a latinized name in proper form that has not been used previously (i.e. it is not a homonym of an earlier name). The standard check list of bacterial names is Buchanan *et al.* (1966), and if a name is not listed there, or in Hatt and Zvirbulis (1967), it is extremely unlikely that it has been used earlier. A new taxon also requires a description and a nomenclatural type. The description may be a brief one, to distinguish the taxon from its neighbours (a diagnosis) but it is important with new species and subspecies to give a detailed description. A single type strain (if cultivable) should be designated and deposited in one of the recognized culture collections and the collection number listed in the publication. A single type strain does not of course give any information about the variation within the species, so that it can with advantage be supplemented with further numbered strains. It may not be practical to deposit all of these, but they should be noted in the publication. New higher taxa should have a designated type taxon and a list of the subordinate taxa included in it.

If a taxon is reclassified its name may need changing. The new name is then the earliest available under the code, modified as appropriate to the taxonomic change, or occasionally an entirely new name is required. If a taxon is divided into two, the old name is retained for the part containing the type of the old taxon. If a species is moved to another genus the specific epithet is retained if it is still available under the rules, thus creating a *new combination* of genus name and specific epithet. If a taxon is merged with another the older available name is retained. These cover most of the usual cases. There are some additional provisions for imperfect stages of fungi in the Botanical Code.

C. Type strains

Type strains are not available for many bacterial species, or may be hard to trace. The following are useful here; the list of Sneath and Skerman (1966) with addenda by Hendrie *et al.* (1966) and Lapage *et al.* (1967) and the catalogues of the American Type Culture Collection.

There are several kinds of type strain. The single designated type strain is the *holotype*, and this automatically fixes a name. Any strain from the describing author's collection is a *cotype* (or syntype). A *neotype* is a strain chosen by international agreement to replace a lost type. Neotypes for bacteria must be formally proposed in the International Journal of Systematic Bacteriology, though the Judicial Commission may set aside inappropriate neotypes (rule 9d). The holotype takes precedence, except over a neotype (which by convention takes precedence over all others).

In choosing type or neotype strains the most typical strains should be preferred (despite the fact that a type need not be typical). The centrotype (see III.B, 5) would generally be suitable, or the strain closest to the Hypothetical Median Organism. Type strains should be carefully preserved. J. W. Carmichael (personal communication) suggests that washed lyophilized cells, even if non-viable, might be preserved as type material for study by serological and other methods.

D. Publication of taxonomic work

The requirements for publication can be summarized as follows. The work should be based on enough pure cultures (which adequately represent the group under study), examined for a sufficient number of reliable tests (covering a wide range of properties of the organisms). The data should be adequately processed to give taxonomic groups, and these taxa should be well described and correctly named. Type strains should be designated for all new species and preserved.

It may not be possible to publish extensive data tables, and these may be deposited in suitable archives. The strains and characters should be listed, with references to published testing methods. The salient points of the taxa should be summarized as short diagnostic tables of characters useful for discrimination. Fuller descriptions of the taxa should note any variable characters, preferably by giving the per cent of strains with each character state. Graphic representations of the taxonomy may be included, and if so at least a dendrogram should be given, supplemented by shaded similarity tables or other diagrams as required. Indispensable texts are *Bergey's Manual* (Breed *et al.*, 1957), *Index Bergeyana* (Buchanan *et al.*, 1966) and the *International Journal of Systematic Bacteriology*.

VI. ANCILLARY INFORMATION

A. Reference laboratories and culture collections

Reference laboratories exist for certain groups of micro-organisms, usually those of medical or agricultural importance. These are commonly under the auspices of various national public health services (e.g. see Anonymous, 1961), but many of the culture collections can provide information on their whereabouts, and some culture collections are themselves able to undertake examination of unknown micro-organisms. Culture collections play an indispensable role by maintaining a wide range of living organisms for comparative studies. Some of these collections are listed below, while the International Centre for Information on Type Cultures, 19 Avenue Cesar Roux, Lausanne, Switzerland, provides an information service on culture collections. (See also Lapage *et al.*, this Series, Vol. 3A.)

Algae and protozoa.	Culture Collection of Algae and Protozoa, Botany School, Downing Street, Cambridge.
Fungi.	Mycological Reference Laboratory, London School of Hygiene and Tropical Medicine, Keppel Street, London W.C.1 (fungi pathogenic to man and animals).

National Collection of Yeast Cultures, Brewing Industry Research Foundation, Nutfield, Redhill, Surrey (yeasts).

Commonwealth Mycological Institute Collection of Fungus Cultures, Ferry Lane, Kew, Surrey (other fungi).

Centraalbureau voor Schimmelcultures, Oosterstraat 1, Baarn, Netherlands (general; yeasts at Yeast Division, Centraalbureau voor Schimmelcultures, Delft, Netherlands).

American Type Culture Collection, 12301 Parklawn Drive, Rockville, Maryland 28052, U.S.A. (general).

Bacteria.　National Collection of Type Cultures, Central Public Health Laboratory, Colindale Avenue, London N.W.9 (human and animal pathogens).

National Collection of Industrial Bacteria and National Collection of Marine Bacteria, Torry Research Station, Aberdeen, Scotland (general and marine).

National Collection of Dairy Organisms, National Institute for Research in Dairying, Shinfield, Reading, Berks. (dairy organisms).

National Collection of Plant Pathogenic Bacteria, Plant Pathology Laboratory, Hatching Green, Harpenden, Herts. (plant pathogens).

American Type Culture Collection, 12301 Parklawn Drive, Rockville, Maryland 28052, U.S.A. (general).

Institut Pasteur, 25 Rue du Docteur Roux, Paris 15e, France.

Centraalbureau voor Schimmelcultures, Oosterstraat 1, Baarn, Netherlands (actinomycetales).

Japanese Type Culture Collection, Nagao Institute, Kitashinagawa, Tokyo, Japan.

Institute for Fermentation, Osaka, Japan.

Czechoslovak Collection of Micro-organisms, Purkyne University, Brno, Czechoslovakia.

B. Textbooks, monographs and keys

The lists of references given in Ainsworth and Sneath (1962) and Kerrich *et al.* (1967) are the most useful and cover all groups of micro-organisms.

A few selected titles are given below. The dictionary of Cowan (1968) is also very useful.

Protozoa.   Doflein and Reichenow (1949–1953) is the established leading textbook, while Grassé (1952, 1953) covers most of the area.

Algae.   The indispensable Fritsch Collection of Illustrations of Freshwater Algae is kept at the Freshwater Biological Association, Far Sawry, Ambleside, Westmorland. Schussnig (1953, 1960), Fritsch (1935, 1945) and Fott (1959) are also important.

Fungi.   The standard comprehensive work is Saccardo (1882–1931), while Ainsworth (1961) is a handy reference book including a key to families. The Commonwealth Mycological Institute at Kew issues two valuable serials, the *Index of Fungi* and the *Bibliography of Systematic Mycology*.

Viruses.   Useful works are Burnet and Stanley (1959–1960), Andrewes and Pereira (1967) and Smith (1957).

Bacteria.   The standard work is Bergey's Manual, at present in the 7th edition (Breed *et al.*, 1957). The 6th edition (Breed *et al.*, 1948) is still one of the most useful books on the more obscure bacteria. Buchanan *et al.* (1966) give a check list of bacterial names, while Skerman (1967) provides a key to bacterial genera, with generic descriptions and taxonomic methods. Skerman (1969) gives technical details of numerous test methods. Cowan and Steel (1965) give diagnostic tables for bacteria of medical interest. A useful series on identification methods is being issued by the Society of Applied Bacteriology (Gibbs and Skinner, 1966; Gibbs and Shapton, 1968). The reports of international subcommittees are extremely valuable, and are found in various issues of the *Journal of Systematic Bacteriology*.

C. Planning a taxonomic study

In this concluding Section a resumé is given of a suggested plan for undertaking a taxonomic study. This should be viewed as a flexible one, but in broad outline it will be of general application. The Sections where fuller details are given are shown in parentheses.

The first step should be to collect a representative set of strains and to read the relevant literature. Type cultures and recently isolated strains should be obtained (Sections II.A, V.C and VI).

The next step should be to draw up a list of characters and tests, and to find or develop suitable basal media and experimental methods. Careful consideration should be given to the purposes of the study, to standardized conditions of testing and to the reliability of the techniques (Sections I.A and II).

The worker can now obtain the test results and fill in a table of strains versus characters (Section III.B). Usually some results must be checked (Section II.C).

The data now require processing; a suitable coding scheme can be drawn up and a computer programme chosen (Section III.B).

The computer results should be evaluated against the available background knowledge (Section IV) and a formal taxonomy drafted, with keys or diagnostic tables (Sections III.B, 4 and IV.C).

The nomenclature of the formal taxonomy should be attended to before preparation for publication (Section V).

REFERENCES

Ainsworth, G. C. (1961). "Ainsworth and Bisby's Dictionary of the Fungi". Commonwealth Mycological Institute, Kew.

Ainsworth, G. C. (1968). *Rev. med. vet. Mycol.*, **6**, 379–385.

Ainsworth, G. C., and Sneath, P. H. A., Eds. (1962). *Symp. Soc. gen. Microbiol.*, **12**, 456–476.

Ambler, R. P. (1968). *In* "Chemotaxonomy and Serotaxonomy" (Ed. J. G. Hawkes), pp. 57–64. Academic Press, London.

Andrewes, Sir C. H., and Pereira, H. G. (1967). "Viruses of Vertebrates", 2nd ed. Baillière, Tindall and Cox, London.

Anonymous (1961). *Mon. Bull. Minist. Hlth*, **20**, 202–210.

Baillie, A., and Walker, P. D. (1968). *J. appl. Bact.*, **31**, 114–119.

Ball, G. H. (1965). *Proc. Fall Jt. comput. Conf.*, 1965, 533–559.

Barbu, E., Panijel, J., and Quash, G. (1961). *Annls Inst. Pasteur, Paris*, **103**, 989–1004.

Bradley, D. E., and Franklin, J. G. (1958). *J. Bact.*, **76**, 618–630.

Breed, R. S., Murray, E. G. D., and Hitchens, A. P. (1948). "Bergey's Manual of Determinative Bacteriology", 6th ed. Williams and Wilkins, Baltimore.

Breed, R. S., Murray, E. G. D., and Smith, N. R. (1957). "Bergey's Manual of Determinative Bacteriology", 7th ed. Williams and Wilkins, Baltimore.

Brisbane, P. G., and Rovira, A. D. (1961). *J. gen. Microbiol.*, **26**, 379–392.

Buchanan, R. E., Holt, J. G., and Lessel, E. F., Jr. (1966). "Index Bergeyana". Williams and Wilkins, Baltimore.

Burnet, F. M., and Stanley, W. M., Eds. (1959–1960). "The Viruses, Biochemical, Biological and Biophysical Properties", 3 vols. Academic Press, New York.

Bussière, J., and Nardon, P. (1968). *Annls Inst. Pasteur, Paris*, **115**, 218–231.

Cain, A. J., and Harrison, G. A. (1958). *Proc. zool. Soc. Lond.*, **131**, 85–98.

Cantor, C. R. (1968). *Biochem. biophys. Res. Commun.*, **31**, 410–416.

Carmichael, J. W., George, J. A., and Julius, R. S. (1968). *Syst. Zool.*, **17**, 144–150.

Carmichael, J. W., Julius, R. S., and Martin, P. M. D. (1965). *Nature, Lond.*, **208**, 544–547.

Carmichael, J. W., and Sneath, P. H. A. (1969). *Syst. Zool.*, **18**, 402–415.

Catlin, B. W., and Cunningham, L. S. (1964). *J. gen. Microbiol.*, **37**, 341–352.

Colless, D. H. (1967). *Syst. Zool.*, **16**, 6–27.

Colobert, L., and Blondeau, H. (1962). *Annls Inst. Pasteur, Paris*, **103**, 345–362.

Colwell, R. R. (1970). *J. Bact.*, **104**, 410–433.
Colwell, R. R. (1971). *In* "Recent Progress in Microbiology", X (in press).
Colwell, R. R., and Mandel, M. (1964). *J. Bact.*, **87**, 1412–1422.
Conn, H. J., Ed. (1957). "Manual of Microbiological Methods". McGraw-Hill, New York.
Cowan, S. T. (1962). *Symp. Soc. gen. Microbiol.*, **12**, 433–455.
Cowan, S. T. (1968). "A Dictionary of Microbial Taxonomic Usage". Oliver and Boyd, Edinburgh.
Cowan, S. T., and Steel, K. J. (1960). *Lancet*, i, 1172–1173.
Cowan, S. T., and Steel, K. J. (1961). *J. Hyg., Camb.*, **59**, 357–372.
Cowan, S. T., and Steel, K. J. (1965). "Manual for the Identification of Medical Bacteria". Cambridge University Press, London.
Crovello, T. J. (1968). *Univ. Calif. Publs. Bot.*, **44**, 1–61.
Cummins, C. S. (1962). *Symp. Soc. gen. Microbiol.*, **12**, 212–241.
Cummins, C. S., and Harris, H. (1956). *J. gen. Microbiol.*, **14**, 583–600.
Davis, P. H., and Heywood, V. H. (1963). "Principles of Angiosperm Taxonomy". Oliver and Boyd, Edinburgh.
Dayhoff, M. O. (1969). "Atlas of Protein Sequence and Structure 1969". National Biomedical Research Foundation, Silver Spring, Maryland.
De Ley, J. (1969). *J. theor. Biol.*, **22**, 89–116.
De Ley, J., and Park, I. W. (1966). *Antonie van Leeuwenhoek*, **32**, 6–16.
Doflein, F., and Reichenow, E. (1949–1953). "Lehrbuch der Protozoenkunde", 6th ed. G. Fischer, Jena.
Dybowski, W., and Franklin, D. A. (1968). *J. gen. Microbiol.*, **54**, 215–229.
Estabrook, G. F. (1967). *Taxon*, **16**, 86–97.
Ettlinger, L., Corbaz, R., and Hütter, R. (1958). *Arch. Mikrobiol.*, **31**, 326–358.
Fitch, W. M. (1966). *J. molec. Biol.*, **16**, 9–16.
Fitch, W. M. (1970). *J. molec. Biol.*, **49**, 1–14.
Fitch, W. M., and Margoliash, E. (1967). *Science*, **155**, 279–284.
Fott, B. (1959). "Algenkunde". G. Fischer. Jena.
Fritsch, F. E. (1935, 1945). "The Structure and Reproduction of the Algae", 2 vols. Cambridge University Press, London.
Gibbs, B. M., and Shapton, D. A., Eds. (1968). "Identification Methods for Microbiologists, Part B". Academic Press, London.
Gibbs, B. M., and Skinner, F. A., Eds. (1966). "Identification Methods for Microbiologists, Part A". Academic Press, London.
Gilmour, J. S. L. (1951). *Nature, Lond.*, **168**, 400–402.
Goodall, D. W. (1964). *Nature, Lond.*, **203**, 1098.
Goodall, D. W. (1966a). *J. gen. Microbiol.*, **42**, 25–37.
Goodall, D. W. (1966b). *Nature, Lond.*, **210**, 216.
Goodall, D. W. (1968). *Biometrics*, **23**, 647–656.
Goodfellow, M. (1969). *Publs Syst. Ass.*, **8**, 83–104.
Gower, J. C. (1966). *Biometrika*, **53**, 325–338.
Gower, J. C. (1967). *Statistician*, **17**, 13–28.
Grassé, P. P., Ed. (1952. 1953). "Traité de zoologie", Vol. 1. Masson, Paris.
Gyllenberg, H. G. (1963). *Ann. Acad. Sci. fenn.*, Ser. A IV Biol., No. 69, 23 pp.
Gyllenberg, H. G. (1965a). *Annls Med. exp. Biol. Fenn.*, **43**, 82–90.
Gyllenberg, H. G. (1965b). *J. gen. Microbiol.*, **39**, 401–405.
Gyllenberg, H. G. (1967). *In* "The Ecology of Soil Bacteria" (Eds. T. R. G. Gray and D. Parkinson), pp. 351–359. Liverpool University Press, Liverpool.

Gyllenberg, H. G., and Eklund, E. (1967). *Ann. Acad. Sci. fenn.*, Ser. A IV Biol., No. 113, 19 pp.

Hall, A. V. (1965). *Nature, Lond.*, **206**, 952.

Hall, A. V. (1967a). *Nature, Lond.*, **214**, 830–831.

Hall, A. V. (1967b). *J. S. Afr. Bot.*, **33**, 185–196.

Hall, A. V. (1969). *In* "Numerical Taxonomy" (Ed. A. J. Cole), pp. 53–68. Academic Press, London.

Hartman, P. A. (1968). "Miniaturized Microbiological Methods". Academic Press, New York.

Hatt, H. D., and Zvirbulis, E. (1967). *Int. J. syst. Bact.*, **17**, 171–225.

Hendrie, M. S., Horsley, R. W., Mackenzie, A. R., Mitchell, T. G., Perry, L. B., and Shewan, J. M. (1966). *Int. J. Syst. Bact.*, **16**, 435–457.

Hill, L. R. (1959). *J. gen. Microbiol.*, **20**, 277–283.

Hill, L. R. (1966). *J. gen. Microbiol.*, **44**, 419–437.

Hill, L. R., Silvestri, L. G., Ihm, P., Farchi, G., and Lanciani, P. (1965). *J. Bact.*, **89**, 1393–1401.

Hopwood, D. A. (1967). *Bact. Rev.*, **31**, 373–403.

Hugh, R., and Leifson, E. (1953). *J. Bact.*, **66**, 24–26.

Hutchinson, M., Johnstone, K. I., and White, D. (1965). *J. gen. Microbiol.*, **41**, 357–366.

Ibrahim, F. M., and Threlfall, R. J. (1966). *Proc. R. Soc. B.*, **165**, 362–388.

Ifkovits, R. W., and Ragheb, H. S. (1968). *Appl. Microbiol.*, **16**, 1406–1413.

International Code of Botanical Nomenclature. (1961). International Bureau for Plant Taxonomy and Nomenclature, Utrecht.

International Code of Nomenclature of Bacteria. (1966). *Int. J. syst. Bact.*, **16**, 459–490 (the earlier annotated edition is published by Iowa State University Press, Ames, Iowa).

International Code of Nomenclature for Cultivated Plants. (1958). "Regum Vegetabile", Vol. 10.

International Code of Zoological Nomenclature. (1964). International Trust for Zoological Nomenclature, London.

Jessen, O. (1965). "*Pseudomonas aeruginosa* and Other Fluorescent Pseudomonads: A Taxonomic Study". Munksgaard, Copenhagen.

Johnson, B. L., and Thien, M. M. (1970). *Am. J. Bot.*, **57**, 1081–1092.

Jones, D., and Sneath, P. H. A. (1970). *Bact. Rev.*, **34**, 40–81.

Kerrich, G. J., Meikle, R. D., and Tebble, N., Eds. (1967). "Bibliography of Key Works for the Identification of the British Fauna and Flora", 3rd ed. Systematics Association, London.

Lance, G. N., and Williams, W. T. (1965). *Computer J.*, **8**, 246–249.

Lapage, S. P., and Bascomb, S. (1968). *J. appl. Bact.*, **31**, 568–580.

Lapage, S. P., Hill, L. R., Midgley, J., and Shelton, J. E. (1967). *Int. J. syst. Bact.*, **17**, 93–103.

Lapage, S. P., Bascomb, S., Willcox, W. R., and Curtis, M. A. (1970). *In* "Automation, Mechanization and Data Handling in Microbiology" (Eds. A. Baillie and R. J. Gilbert), pp. 1–22. Academic Press, London.

Lautrop, H., and Jessen, O. (1964). *Acta path. microbiol. scand.*, **60**, 588–598.

Lee, A. M. (1968). *Nature, Lond.*, **217**, 620–622.

Leifson, E. (1960). "Atlas of Bacterial Flagellation". Academic Press, New York.

Lessel, E. F., Jr. (1971). Minutes of the Judicial Commission, Mexico City. *Int. J. syst. Bact.*, **21** (in press).

Liston, J., Weibe, W., and Colwell, R. R. (1963). *J. Bact.*, **85**, 1061–1070.
Lockhart, W. R. (1964). *Devls ind. Microbiol.*, **5**, 162–168.
Lockhart, W. R., and Hartman, P. A. (1963). *J. Bact.*, **85**, 68–77.
Lockhart, W. R., and Holt, J. G. (1964). *J. gen. Microbiol.*, **35**, 115–124.
Lockhart, W. R., and Koenig, K. (1965). *J. Bact.*, **90**, 1638–1644
Lockhart, W. R., and Liston, J., Eds. (1970). "Methods for Numerical Taxonomy". American Society for Microbiology, Bethesda, Maryland.
Lovelace, T. E., and Colwell, R. R. (1968). *Appl. Microbiol.*, **16**, 944–945.
Lund, B. M. (1965). *J. gen. Microbiol.*, **40**, 413–419.
Lysenko, O., and Sneath, P. H. A. (1959). *J. gen. Microbiol.*, **20**, 284–290.
Martin, H. H. (1966). *A. Rev. Biochem.*, **35**, 457–484.
Melville, T. H. (1965). *J. gen. Microbiol.*, **40**, 309–315.
Metcalf, Z. P. (1954). *Syst. Zool.*, **3**, 38–45.
Meynell, E. (1964). *J. gen. Microbiol.*, **36**, 461–469.
Möller, F. (1962). *Giorn. Microbiol.*, **10**, 29–47.
Moore, G. W., and Goodman, M. (1968). *Bull. math. Biophys.*, **30**, 279–289.
Morichi, T., Sharpe, M. E., and Reiter, B. (1968). *J. gen. Microbiol.*, **54**, 405–414.
Murray, R. G. E. (1962). *Symp. Soc. gen. Microbiol.*, **12**, 119–144.
Niemelä, S. I., Hopkins, J. W., and Quadling, C. (1968). *Can. J. Microbiol.*, **14**, 271–279.
Norris, J. R. (1964). *J. appl. Bact.*, **27**, 439–447.
Norris, K. P. (1959). *J. Hyg., Camb.*, **57**, 326–345.
Olds, R. J. (1966). *In* "Identification Methods for Microbiologists, Part A" (Eds. B. M. Gibbs and F. A. Skinner), pp. 131–136. Academic Press, New York.
Orloci, L. (1969). *In* "Numerical Taxonomy" (Ed. A. J. Cole), pp. 148–164. Academic Press, London.
Owen, D. B. (1962). "Handbook of Statistical Tables". Pergamon Press, London.
Pankhurst, R. J. (1970). *Computer J.*, **13**, 145–151.
Quadling, C., and Colwell, R. R. (1964). *Devls ind. Microbiol.*, **5**, 151–161.
Quadling, C., and Hopkins, J. W. (1967). *Can. J. Microbiol.*, **13**, 1379–1400.
Ravin, A. W. (1963). *Am. Nat.*, **97**, 301–318.
Report of the Pseudomonas Working Party. *J. gen. Microbiol.* (in press).
Rhodes, M. (1961). *J. gen. Microbiol.*, **25**, 331–345.
Rogers, D. J., and Tanimoto, T. T. (1960). *Science*, **132**, 1115–1118.
Rohlf, F. J. (1965). *Taxon*, **14**, 262–267.
Rohlf, F. J. (1968). *Syst. Zool.*, **17**, 246–255.
Ross, G. J. S. (1969). *In* "Numerical Taxonomy" (Ed. A. J. Cole), pp. 224–233. Academic Press, London.
Rouatt, J. W., Skyring, G. W., Purkayastha, V., and Quadling, C. (1970). *Can. J. Microbiol.*, **16**, 202–205.
Rovira, A. D., and Brisbane, P. G. (1967). *In* "The Ecology of Soil Bacteria" (Eds. T. R. G. Gray and D. Parkinson), pp. 337–350. Liverpool University Press, Liverpool.
Rypka, E. W., Clapper, W. E., Bowen, I. G., and Babb, R. (1967). *J. gen. Microbiol.*, **46**, 407–424.
Saccardo, P. A. (1882–1931). "*Sylloge fungorum*", 25 vols. Pavia.
Sackin, M. J. (1969). *In* "Numerical Taxonomy" (Ed. A. J. Cole), pp. 241–256. Academic Press, London.
Savory, T. (1962). "Naming the Living World". English Universities Press, London.

Schussnig, B. (1953, 1960). "Handbuch der Protophytenkunde", 2 vols. G. Fischer, Jena.

Seal, H. L. (1964). "Multivariate Statistical Analysis for Biologists". Methuen, London.

Sébald, M., and Véron, M. (1963). *Annls Inst. Pasteur, Paris*, **105**, 897–910.

Sheals, J. G. (1963). *Proc. Linn. Soc. Lond.*, **176**, 11–21.

Shipton, W. A., and Fleischmann, G. (1969). *Can. J. Bot.*, **47**, 1351–1358.

Silvestri, L., Turri, M., Hill, L. R., and Gilardi, E. (1962). *Symp. Soc. gen. Microbiol.*, **12**, 333–360.

Simpson, G. G. (1961). "Principles of Animal Taxonomy". Columbia University Press, New York.

Skerman, V. B. D. (1967). "A Guide to the Identification of the Genera of Bacteria", 2nd ed. Williams and Wilkins, Baltimore.

Skerman, V. B. D. (1969). "Abstracts of Microbiological Methods". John Wiley, New York.

Skyring, G. W., and Quadling, C. (1969). *Can. J. Microbiol.*, **15**, 141–158.

Smith, K. M. (1957). "A Textbook of Plant Virus Diseases", 2nd ed. Churchill, London.

Sneath, P. H. A. (1957a). *J. gen. Microbiol.*, **17**, 184–200.

Sneath, P. H. A. (1957b). *J. gen. Microbiol.*, **17**, 201–226.

Sneath, P. H. A. (1960). *Iowa St. J. Sci.*, **34**, 243–500.

Sneath, P. H. A. (1962). *Symp. Soc. gen. Microbiol.*, **12**, 289–332.

Sneath, P. H. A. (1964). *A. Rev. Microbiol.*, **18**, 335–346.

Sneath, P. H. A. (1967). *J. Zool. Lond.*, **151**, 65–122.

Sneath, P. H. A. (1968a). *J. gen. Microbiol.*, **54**, 1–11.

Sneath, P. H. A. (1968b). *Classification Soc. Bull.*, **1** (No. 4), 28–45.

Sneath, P. H. A. (1969a). *In* "Numerical Taxonomy" (Ed. A. J. Cole), pp. 257–271. Academic Press, London.

Sneath, P. H. A. (1969b). *J. clin. Path.*, **22**, Suppl (Coll. Path.) 3, 87–92.

Sneath, P. H. A. (1971). *In* "Recent Progress in Microbiology", X (in press).

Sneath, P. H. A., and Skerman, V. B. D. (1966). *Int. J. Syst. Bact.*, **16**, 1–133.

Sneath, P. H. A., and Stevens, M. (1967). *J. appl. Bact.*, **30**, 495–497.

Snedecor, G. W. (1956). "Statistical Methods Applied to Experiments in Agriculture and Biology". Iowa State University Press, Ames, Iowa.

Sokal, R. R., and Rohlf, F. J. (1962). *Taxon*, **11**, 33–40.

Sokal, R. R., and Rohlf, F. J. (1969). "Biometry". W. H. Freeman. San Francisco.

Sokal, R. R., and Sneath, P. H. A. (1963). "Principles of Numerical Taxonomy". W. H. Freeman, San Francisco.

Stanier, R. Y. (1971). *In* "Recent Progress in Microbiology", X (in press).

Stearn, W. T. (1956). *In* "Supplement to the Dictionary of Gardening" (Ed. P. M. Synge), pp. 251–253. Clarendon Press, Oxford.

Stevens, M. (1969). *J. med. Lab. Technol.*, **26**, 253–263.

Talbot, J. M., and Sneath, P. H. A. (1960). *J. gen. Microbiol.*, **22**, 303–311.

Tsukamura, M. (1967). *Jap. J. Microbiol.*, **11**, 213–220.

Véron, M. (1966). *Annls Inst. Pasteur, Paris*, **111**, 314–333.

Weibe, W. J., and Chapman, G. B. (1968). *J. Bact.*, **95**, 1862–1873.

Whitney, P. J., Vaughan, J. G., and Heale, J. B. (1968). *J. exp. Bot.*, **19**, 415–426.

Wishart, D. (1969). *In* "Numerical Taxonomy" (Ed. A. J. Cole), pp. 282–311. Academic Press, London.

Williams, W. T., Lambert, J. M., and Lance, G. N. (1966). *J. Ecol.*, **54**, 427–445.

CHAPTER III

Data Handling and Information Retrieval by Computer

H. F. Dammers

Shell Research Limited, Sittingbourne Laboratories, Sittingbourne, Kent, England

I. INTRODUCTION

The volume of information, be it research data or published literature, which is being produced and has to be assimilated and evaluated by the research worker, is steadily increasing. At the same time, the methods of data analysis employed by him are becoming much more sophisticated. Developments such as these have already established the need to use computer processing in many areas of research. In addition, avenues of enquiry have been or are now being opened which were virtually blocked before the arrival of the computer; as examples one might mention X-ray analysis of large molecules, simulation studies of complex kinetic networks, the quantitative study of structure/activity relationships, etc. Application of computers in the latter cases may be taken for granted as it is in large areas of mathematical and statistical research work.

Yet there are substantial areas of data handling and analysis where the computer has hardly begun to make its impact. Such activities may account for say 20% or more of the research workers' time, hence reduction of this effort via computer use could lead to a worthwhile increase in productivity.

As yet computer facilities are still relatively scarce and expensive. However, computer capacity is increasing extremely quickly, the results obtained in a cost/performance analysis of computers over the past 25 years (Knight, 1965, 1966, 1968) suggest that it has been nearly doubling each year, i.e. increasing around 1000-fold in 10 years. Perhaps the rate of expansion is now slowing down and may well be nearer doubling every 2 years; even so one may expect to see during the next 5 to 10 years a profound change in the impact of mechanical information processing facilities (Joseph, 1968; Dammers, 1968). They should cease to be scarce and are likely to affect drastically most aspects of human activity. We should also see the use of computers predominantly for non-numeric rather than arithmetic work.

The improvement in computer facilities over the past few years has already been impressive not only as regards the capabilities provided by large systems but also with regard to the availability of cheap and fast small computers.

The various options now open to a user might be roughly outlined as follows:

(a) Batch processing on either a local or remote computer. In the former case, the computer is available in the institute or university concerned, in the latter an arrangement is made as between various U.K. universities and the Atlas Computing Laboratory, Chilton, for example. This is the conventional type of use, still quite prevalent today. Job turn-around time may be of the order of a day to several days.

(b) Direct access to a central computer, available either on site or at a remote location. Communication with the computer takes place through a suitable terminal positioned at the user location and connected with the central computer via a telephone line. Terminal facilities can vary considerably in their capabilities, ranging from simple teletypewriters to terminals which have processing facilities of their own (Univac 9300, IBM 1130, Cope 45, etc.).

The central processor can deal with jobs received from the remote terminals either in batch processing mode, as is done in UCC's (University Computing Company) Univac 1108 system or in a time-sharing mode as is the case, for example, at the University of Cambridge where the Atlas computer is accessed by teleprinters in various laboratories.

Large scale sophisticated time-sharing systems have been struggling with serious problems during recent years, problems which arise from the enormous complexity of the operational systems involved. Less ambitious time-sharing systems are, however, now in operation in many organizations and are also increasingly being offered on a commercial basis.

(c) Alternatively, one can obtain a small computer for one's own purpose, e.g. systems such as the IBM 1130 which may cost £20,000– £30,000 or even very small ones like the PDP 8, which may cost less than £4000 for a machine with 4 K (4000 positions) memory.

Looking over the development of the past few years, the improvement in cost/performance has been quite significant and this is making it worthwhile considering computer processing for a much wider area of data handling than has hitherto been considered economically feasible. A stage may well have been reached whereby the expansion of computer use is likely to depend predominantly on the ability to deal effectively with the systems and programming aspects involved.

Computer use tends to increase roughly in direct proportion to the systems design and programming effort available to initiate, sustain and further develop it. (Sackman, 1967a; Weinwurm, 1965). A large system such as the Univac 1108 may require as much as one man-month programming and systems support for every hour of productive use of the central processor. The main reason for this is not only that new programmes are continually being written but also that existing ones are rarely run for very prolonged periods without modifications.

The supply of skilled computer programmers needed for the steadily widening range of computer applications is not increasing at the same rate as computer capacity. Hence it would appear that, only when users themselves are in a position to take an active part in the systems and programming work concerned, can one hope to achieve on the one hand the speed of implementation required, and on the other, an efficient adaptation to specific user requirements. This may well lead to a less efficient use of the computer as such but the rapidly decreasing processor cost should more than compensate for this.

Substantial libraries of programmes are now available (see Appendix II); hence it is often feasible to obtain programmes that have been operational elsewhere and use them for one's own purpose with only a modest programming effort being required to adapt them to specific user requirements and to the computer facilities available. Having said that it should be stressed again that computer programmes tend to have a rather short life. Very few systems remain in operation for a prolonged period, say several years, without modification. The more common experience, in particular in the research environment, is one of regular change in order to adapt programmes to changing user needs as well as changing computer facilities. This again emphasizes the need for user participation.

The rapid development in the computer field also means that it is not very profitable to devote much space to the description of specific systems. They tend to be out of date in a relatively short time. Instead, it is proposed to discuss rather more general operational approaches and illustrate these with some specific examples.

II. DATA HANDLING

The volume of data produced by the research worker has tended to increase substantially due mainly to improved instrumentation. In many cases, the need to aid in the interpretation of these results has induced instrument manufacturers to develop equipment that provides an output format more readily amenable to interpretation. In some cases, it is leading to the addition of small special purpose computers dedicated to the instrument concerned as is done, for instance, with some spectrometric applications. As yet, however, only a limited number of research applications, except where there is an association with production control, appear to warrant dedicated use of computers.

The move towards computer use can have some additional benefits. In the first place, it induces the research worker to be more aware of the precision of his data and of the format in which they are presented. In the second place, by producing the data in machine-readable form the way is opened to machine storage and retrieval of those data which warrant further investigation at some future date.

As regards the means of converting data into a digital form compatible with computer use, a variety of options are available.

A. Alphanumeric data

If the data to be processed are available in alphanumeric form, i.e. as letters, numbers or special characters, for instance, after recording in a laboratory notebook or on record sheets, the conversion is a manual operation which is commonly carried out by the various means indicated in Fig. 1.

The three routes indicated all provide a machine-readable record, i.e. a punched (IBM) card, a punched papertape or a digital magnetic tape record. The American computer industry has been mainly orientated towards the use of punched cards, whereas British machines have tended to make more use of papertape input. Both forms have their pros and cons. Punched cards permit easier re-arrangement of or addition to the

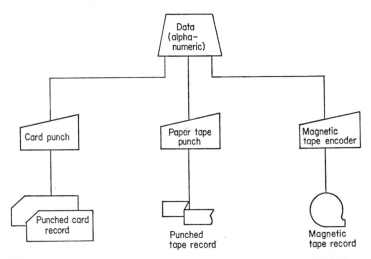

FIG. 1. Conversion of alphanumeric data into machine-readable form.

data file or programme deck before input into the computer; on the other hand, papertape has advantages over punched cards when a long sequence of data has to be entered; it is likely to be quicker and possible disturbance of the sequence is avoided. Also the papertape keyboard punch with verifying and reproducing functions is likely to be cheaper than the corresponding punched card equipment. Similarly, papertape readers are likely to be less costly than punched card readers for a given speed.

A still cheaper means of conversion, but, of course, a very slow one, is the use of a simple hand punch or of pre-scored punched cards. An application of the latter approach and also of mark sensing in field experimentation is described by Berry et al. (1966).

Speed of the keyboard operated punches is equivalent to that of typewriting, i.e. four to five characters/sec; speed of input into the computer varies from 30 to 1000 characters/sec for various types of papertape readers and is in the range 300–1000 characters/sec for card readers.

More recently the third method shown in Fig. 1 has come to the fore, i.e. direct keyboarding on to computer compatible tape (Price, 1967). The advantage of this approach is that input into the computer can now occur at the speed with which magnetic tape is read (30,000–100,000 characters/sec); in addition, it appears that keyboard operators, when dealing with large sets of similar data, can achieve a higher rate of throughput than with the more conventional encoders. This type of equipment is relatively expensive, starting with a cost of perhaps £3000 for the basic keyboard encoder, but its use is gaining ground and a range of additional facilities is available which will allow transmission from the tape via telephone lines, production of typewritten hard copies, interfacing with fast printers, etc. The rate of developments in this field suggests that costs will fall appreciably.

Other methods of conversion which should be mentioned are mark sensing and optical character recognition (OCR). In the case of the former, one needs special record forms on which marks can be read (either magnetically or optically) by special mark sensing devices; in the latter case, one needs as a rule documents typed with a particular type fount, that can then be read via OCR readers. As yet such equipment is quite expensive hence only economically justified when dealing with rather large volumes of input.

B. Direct conversion

With regard to direct conversion of data from instruments, usually represented by continuous voltage variations, Fig. 2 gives a schematic outline of some of the possible procedures that can be employed. For a more general discussion of instrument data processing systems see, for example, Barlow (1967).

Assuming the output from an instrument is available in the form of electrical signals, either direct or via suitable transducers, it will be necessary to convert the analogue signal obtained into a digital one suitable for computer input. This might be achieved for example by means of a digital voltmeter or more generally an analogue/digital converter. The simplest next step is then often output via a papertape punch.

Alternatively, one might interface the digital output direct with the computer or store it as a digital magnetic tape record. In the latter case, however, in order for the magnetic tape record to be acceptable for processing via the magnetic tape unit of the computer, one might require blocking of the continuous record. This is likely to call for some processing facility which, at the same time, might be used for data reduction. In view of the rather high cost which may be involved in this there is a tendency to favour the use of a small computer for this purpose, at least when the data rate is high. Such a small computer could in some cases also deal with further processing of the digital tape file.

A further variant is to add an analogue recorder and play-back equipment in between the data source and the analogue/digital converter. This is worthwhile when there are a number of data sources making use of one centrally installed analogue/digital conversion unit which might be interfaced with the computer direct or via magnetic tape. For examples of this type of arrangement see Alexander and Wortzman (1968); Gillard and Lamb (1967). It is not the intention here to discuss the technical aspects of

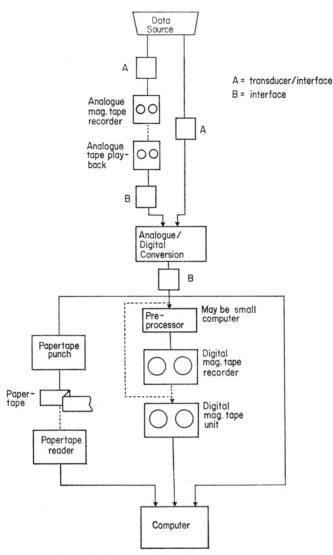

FIG. 2. Data acquisition from instruments.

analogue/digital conversion in any detail; this has been dealt with in various survey articles, e.g. Macey (1965).

With data acquisition systems the interfacing, i.e. the interconnection of the various system components, tends to present problems which can be costly in time and money to resolve. Each specific combination of system components (see Fig. 2) tends to require a special interface which all too often is not readily available from the manufacturers or is expensive. The initiative of the National Physical Laboratory, Teddington, in producing a standard interface for use in the collection and analysis of data from scientific experiments would therefore appear to be very welcome (Barber, 1967). It is to be hoped that it can be made compatible with a much wider range of computers and peripherals.

It will be obvious from the above brief outline that a wide selection of input procedures is available, ranging from procedures which may be relatively cheap in equipment, though perhaps rather expensive in labour, to comprehensive on-line data acquisition systems which may well reach a cost of say £100,000. The higher the data rate and the greater the speed of response one has to cater for the more expensive the system is likely to be.

As a rough approximation data rate (a few hundred/day to 20,000/sec) and response time (several days to milliseconds) cover ranges of the order of $1 : 10^6$. The cost of equipment required ranges from £100 to £100,000 ($1 : 10^3$).

As usual costs tend to soar when one wants to provide a system that is intended to deal with all possible requirements at all times.

C. Real time operation

As indicated by Sackman (1967b), there is every likelihood that we will need to move more and more towards real time information processing, i.e. a form of information processing which allows continual sensing of and response to selected changes in the experimental environment, thus allowing regulation and control of specified events in the system whilst they are in progress within the bounds of given acceptable levels of performance. This is already obvious in process control but is also apparent in biomedical research, in various analytical chemistry techniques, in geophysics (e.g. weather forecasting) (Aron, 1967; Fraser, 1968). It is likely to mean development towards the more expensive type of data acquisition systems mentioned. Apart from the not inconsiderable hardware expenditure involved, this will also demand substantial effort on the software aspects, the techniques and data organization. This may well begin to affect a significant proportion of research workers in a wide variety of fields during the next 5–10 years.

For the time being, however, we are likely in most areas of research to get more operational value out of the computer by turning it to the more mundane tasks of eliminating some of the more laborious and stereotype calculations and tabulations.

D. Data evaluation/tabulation

As an example of such an application we will describe in some detail the processing of amino-acid analyser results; it will, at the same time, provide

Steps in calculation

(0·5 μmol of norleucine is used as standard)

1. Calculate integral factor (IF) of Norleucine $= H_{\text{Norleucine}} \times W_{\text{Norleucine}}$

2. Calculate $Z = \dfrac{0·5}{\text{IF}_{\text{Norleucine}}}$

3. For each amino-acid in turn:
   (a) calculate integral factor (IF) $= H \times W$

   (b) calculate μmoles amino-acid present $= \dfrac{\text{IF} \times Z}{\text{NLE}}$

   (c) calculate corrected μmoles $= \dfrac{\mu\text{moles}}{\text{correction factor (CF)}}$

   (d) calculate μg $N = $ corrected μmoles $\times A$
   (e) calculate μg AA (amino-acid) $= $ corrected μmoles $\times B$

4. Total μg N for all amino-acids $= \Sigma\mu$g N

5. Total μg amino-acids $= \Sigma\mu$g AA

6. Calculate % recovery $N = \dfrac{\Sigma\mu\text{g } N}{C \times D} \times 10^4$

7. Calculate % bound amino-acids $= \dfrac{\Sigma\mu\text{g } AA_1}{C} \times 100$

8. Calculate for each amino-acid moles/10^5 g sample $= \dfrac{\text{corrected } \mu\text{moles}}{C} \times 10^5$

9. Calculate for each amino-acid grams of free amino-acid per 100 g sample $=$

   $\dfrac{\Sigma\mu\text{g } AA_2}{C} \times 100$

$\quad\quad H = $ Peak height
$\quad\quad W = $ Peak width
$\quad\quad A = 14$ except for lysine (28), histidine (42), arginine (56)
$\quad\quad B_1 = $ mol wt of amino-acid
$\quad\quad B_2 = $ anhydro–mol wt of amino-acid
$\quad\quad C = $ ashless dry weight of sample in μg
$\quad\quad D = $ % nitrogen in ashless dry sample
$\quad$NLE $= $ Norleucine equivalent for each amino-acid $= \dfrac{\text{IF}_{AA}}{\text{IF}_{\text{Norleucine}}}$; determined

$\quad\quad\quad\quad$ in standard run in which each amino-acid is present in 0·5 μmol
$\quad\quad\quad\quad$ concentration

$\Sigma\mu$g $AA_1 = $ total μg amino-acids calculated using B_1

$\Sigma\mu$g $AA_2 = $ total μg amino-acids calculated using B_2.

FIG. 3. Outline of automatic amino-acid analysis calculation.

an illustration of the type of data organization and preparation required as well as the gradual move towards a more highly automated form of processing.

Protein analysis by means of the automatic amino-acid analyser (Schmidt, 1966) provides output via a pen-on-paper recorder of a series of about 20 peaks, corresponding to the amino-acids present. The peaks are measured using two parameters, i.e. height and width, and by comparison with a standard (norleucine). The amino-acid composition is calculated as well as nitrogen recovery, etc. The complete calculation (see Fig. 3) though simple can be time-consuming and error-prone, hence it seems an obvious step to carry it out via the computer. In order to facilitate this a special record sheet was devised (Fig. 4) which indicates the layout needed for the punched cards.

By means of a programme, written in FORTRAN, the calculations were carried out on a Univac 1108, accessed via a Univac 1004 terminal and an output as shown in Fig. 5 produced (in triplicate). The time taken to run this on the Univac 1108 was around 10 sec, of which, however, only a small fraction was accounted for by the actual calculation; most of the computer time used was absorbed by relocation and other system overheads. Even so, the cost of executing the calculation via the Univac 1108 compares favourably with doing it manually (Fig. 6).

In addition, of course, much greater speed and accuracy is achieved. The procedure outlined might be acceptable if the analysis is only carried out relatively infrequently. If, however, a substantial number of analyses were to be carried out per day, it may be worthwhile carrying the automation one step further and provide output from the automatic amino-acid analyser (AAA) via a digital voltmeter and papertape punch in addition to the graph recorder. Output from the AAA would then no longer need an intermediate conversion by a human operator but could be read into the computer—as indicated in the middle part of Fig. 7. A system of this nature, using an IBM 1130 computer, has been described by Cavins and Friedman (1968).

To put the AAA on-line to the computer, as indicated in the right-hand part of Fig. 7, would seem hardly worthwhile in view of the rather low rate of data output from the AAA and the limited requirements for feedback control.

Another case that might be worth mentioning here is the processing of data from an assimilation chamber. The aim in this case is to follow the rate of respiration and photo-synthesis of plants in a closely controlled environment. To this end humidity (wet and dry bulb temperatures) and CO_2 content in the chamber are continuously monitored (van Oorschot and Belskma, 1961).

cc 80 = 6

Run Identification 1 ... 10 ... 20 ... 30

Date 37 ... 40

Card Type 2

cc 80 = 3

Wt. of Dry Ash Free Sample (μg) 1 ... 10 % N in Dry Ash Free Sample 11 ... 20

Card Type 3

cc 80 = 1

Name	Anhydrous Mol. Wt. (20 21–26)	N	Correction Factor (28–32)	N.L.E. (33–38)	Δ (39–45)	mls (46–53)	H (54–59)	W (60–66)
NORLEUCINE	113.2	1	1.0					
CYSTEIC ACID								
ASPARTIC ACID	115.1	1	1.0					
THREONINE	101.1	1	0.947					
SERINE	87.1	1	0.895					
GLUTAMIC ACID	129.1	1	1.0					
PROLINE	97.1	1	1.0					
GLYCINE	57.1	1	1.0					
ALANINE	71.1	1	1.0					
VALINE	99.2	1	1.0					
D.A.P.	172.2	2	1.0					
METHIONINE	131.2	1	1.0					
ISOLEUCINE	113.2	1	1.0					
LEUCINE	113.2	1	1.0					
TYROSINE	163.2	1	0.950					
PHENYLALANINE	147.2	1	1.0					
LYSINE	128.2	2	1.0					
HISTIDINE	137.2	3	1.0					
AMMONIA	16.0	1	1.0					
ARGININE	156.2	4	1.0					

FIG. 4. Automatic amino-acid analyser standard record sheet.

GALLAGHER,P.J. AMINO-ACID ANALYSER.DATA   DATE 030768 PAGE 10

ANALYSIS OF DATA FROM AMINO-ACID ANALYSER - MAY 1968

RUN MUSCA AUTUMNALIS   RUN NO A1   2

ASHLESS DRY WEIGHT OF SAMPLE ANALYSED = 923.800 MICROGRAMS

NITROGEN IN ASHLESS DRY SAMPLE = 9.20 PERCENT

AMINO-ACID	DELTA	MLS. ELUATE	H	W	INTEGRAL FACTOR (IF)	MOLES AA	CORRECTION FACTOR (CF)	CORRECTED MICRO-MOLES AA	N	BOUND AA	MOLES AA/ 100,000GMS SAMPLE	PERCENT AA	GMS FREE AA/100GM SAMPLE
NORLEUCINE	26.50	154.50	.031	53.00	1.64								
ASPARTIC ACID	10.00	181.00	.084	44.60	3.75	1.290	1.000	1.290	18.06	148.45	139.61	16.069	18.582
THREONINE	32.50	191.00	.046	48.00	2.21	.742	.947	.784	10.98	79.27	84.68	8.580	10.108
SERINE	19.00	223.50	.042	48.50	2.04	.656	.895	.733	10.27	63.84	79.34	6.910	8.339
GLUTAMIC ACID	56.50	242.50	.069	61.00	4.21	1.464	1.000	1.464	20.50	188.99	158.47	20.457	23.310
PROLINE	16.00	299.00	.010	58.00	.58	.735	1.000	.735	10.30	71.42	79.62	7.730	9.163
GLYCINE	40.50	317.00	.051	70.00	3.58	1.208	1.000	1.208	16.92	69.01	130.82	7.470	9.824
ALANINE	18.50	357.50	.036	79.80	2.88	1.010	1.000	1.010	14.14	71.78	109.29	7.770	9.737
VALINE			.088	30.20	2.66	.883	1.000	.883	12.37	87.59	95.58	9.481	11.202
D.A.P.			.000		.00	.000	1.000	.000	.00	.00	.00	.000	.000
METHIONINE	17.00	376.00	.008	36.00	.29	.092	1.000	.092	1.29	12.02	9.92	1.301	1.479
ISOLEUCINE	13.00	393.00	.030	47.50	1.43	.452	1.000	.452	6.33	51.14	48.90	5.535	6.416
LEUCINE	14.00	406.00	.025	50.50	1.27	.395	1.000	.395	5.54	44.75	42.79	4.844	5.614
TYROSINE	20.00	474.00	.020	84.00	1.68	.529	.950	.557	7.80	90.93	60.31	9.842	10.928
PHENYLALANINE	40.50	494.00	.009	72.00	.65	.203	1.000	.203	2.85	29.90	21.99	3.236	3.632
LYSINE	16.00	67.00	.040	37.90	1.52	.481	1.000	.481	13.46	61.61	52.03	6.669	7.606
HISTIDINE	20.00	83.00	.032	46.00	1.48	.542	1.000	.542	22.78	74.41	58.71	8.054	9.111
AMMONIA	53.00	103.00	.389	69.00	26.85	2.760	1.000	2.760	38.64	44.16	298.72	4.779	10.156
ARGININE	.00	156.00	.015	77.00	1.16	.431	1.000	.431	24.16	67.37	46.69	7.292	8.133
GLUCOSAMINE	22.00	45.00	.784	33.50	26.27	7.937	1.000	7.937	111.12	1422.34	859.19	153.966	169.431

TOTALS   347.42   2678.90

RECOVERIES(PERCENT)   408.78   289.99

FIG. 5. *AA* analysis output tabulation.

Input: various experimental conditions + peak parameters.
Effort/cost involved in processing of data from one to three analyses at a time.

Computer processing

Keypunching	6–15 min	(at 75 p/h)
Computer time	10–13 sec	(Univac 1108 time)
Cost	ca. 80p–110p	(for one to three sets processed at a time; Univac 1108 time charged at £250/h)
Cost	ca. 200p–275p	(Univac 1108 time charged at £725/h, i.e. incl. all equipment charges + support staff)
Labour effort	15–30 min	

Manual processing

Calculation	1½–4 h	(at £2–£2½/h, i.e. cost of direct research staff)
Typing	20–40 min	(at 75p/h)
Cost	ca. 350p–650p	
Labour effort	2–5 h	

Hence computer processing shows marked cost advantage in particular when processing three sets of data at a time; in addition there is a reduction in labour effort and error-rate.

Fig. 6. Automatic amino-acid analyser calculation: cost/performance assessment.

In this case manual recording of the data and subsequent keypunching is clearly unhelpful and instead one has to aim at least at recording the data on punched papertape, which can then be processed and tabulated and plotted via the computer once every 24 h, or more frequently if desired. It might perhaps prove of advantage to move eventually to on-line operation and provide periodic tabulations, graph plots and perhaps also feedback control.

It is as yet difficult to pin-point an area in microbiological research where on-line computer use is considered essential at the present time. Perhaps the most likely research activity to make use of this method of information processing is the study of fermentation processes where already the development is towards close control of the many variables that affect the growth and metabolism of micro-organisms. This type of application is already evident in the fermentation industry for production control purposes, e.g. at Dista Products, Liverpool (Maskell, 1968). The literature as yet does not appear to provide information on actual on-line systems in operation for this purpose in research, but it is not unrealistic to expect that this situation will change appreciably in the next few years.

On-line processing in a number of other fields of research (e.g. medicine, analytical chemistry, mass spectrometry, etc.) is already becoming more and more accepted. Examples of such systems are given in Fig. 8, depicting

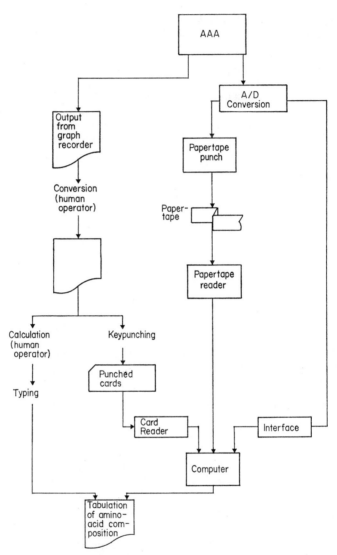

Fig. 7. Alternative methods of processing automatic amino-acid analyser output.

schematically an on-line NMR spectrometry system, and Fig. 9, showing
schematically the simplified processing flow scheme in the case of large-
scale automatic blood analysis (Fraser, 1968). Other analytical chemistry
applications are discussed by Kienitz and Kaiser (1968) and medically-
oriented ones in the A.M.A. Computer Symposium, 1966. The computers
used in such cases are often relatively small, dedicated machines; however,

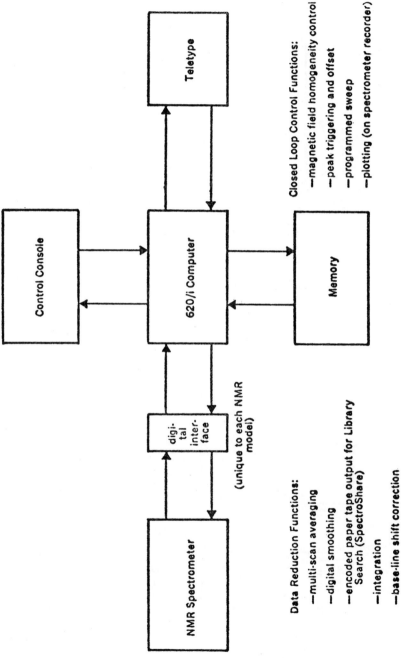

FIG. 8. Diagram of on-line NMR spectrometry system (according to Fraser, 1968).

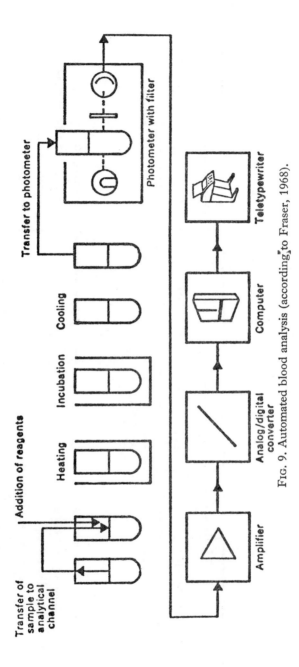

Fig. 9. Automated blood analysis (according to Fraser, 1968).

a similar approach is also being realized in time-sharing environments using larger computer systems (Lockerman and Knutsen, 1967; Lindberg, 1965; Estrin, 1968). Such facilities will allow a much greater degree of sophistication in experimental control and data analysis than hitherto feasible. In fact Tukey and Wilk (1966) have pointed out the close analogy between experimentation and data analysis. Interaction, feed-back, trial and error play an essential part in both. On-line computer systems represent tools which are basically well suited to deal with these types of processes (Lockerman and Knutsen, 1967). One may therefore expect them to gain rapidly in acceptance in the near future.

E. Data storage and retrieval

As indicated earlier, computer processing has the additional advantage of providing data in machine-readable form amenable to computer storage and retrieval. I will now illustrate some instances of this type of application.

Figure 10 gives examples of data cards, i.e. punch cards on to which experimental results have been entered in a standardized format using fixed field representation.

In Fig. 10(a) this is done in a very simple fashion; it gives in columns 2–10 the compound code (code number of the chemical compound which has been subjected to various tests).

In columns 11–13   card codes (in column 11 field of testing, column 12 type of data card for that field, column 13 sequence number of cards of the type indicated in 12).

In columns 14–19   test code (a numeric code representing the type of test(s) carried out and the corresponding data expression).

In columns 20–30   the results for tests carried out on 11 different organisms, each result being expressed by a single digit number in a given column.

This data card illustrates the highly standardized type of data expression and recording; representation in fixed fields, whereby a given type of result is always recorded in a specific column, enables the card file to be searched and sorted by a punched card sorter, as well as by computer.

Fig 10(b) shows the use of a specially pre-printed punched card. In this form the cards are more useful for visual perusal in addition to their use for mechanical punched card sorting and computer use. Data are entered on to the above-mentioned cards by keypunching, e.g. using an IBM 026 or 029 keypunch. Fig. 10(c), however, shows the use of a pre-scored

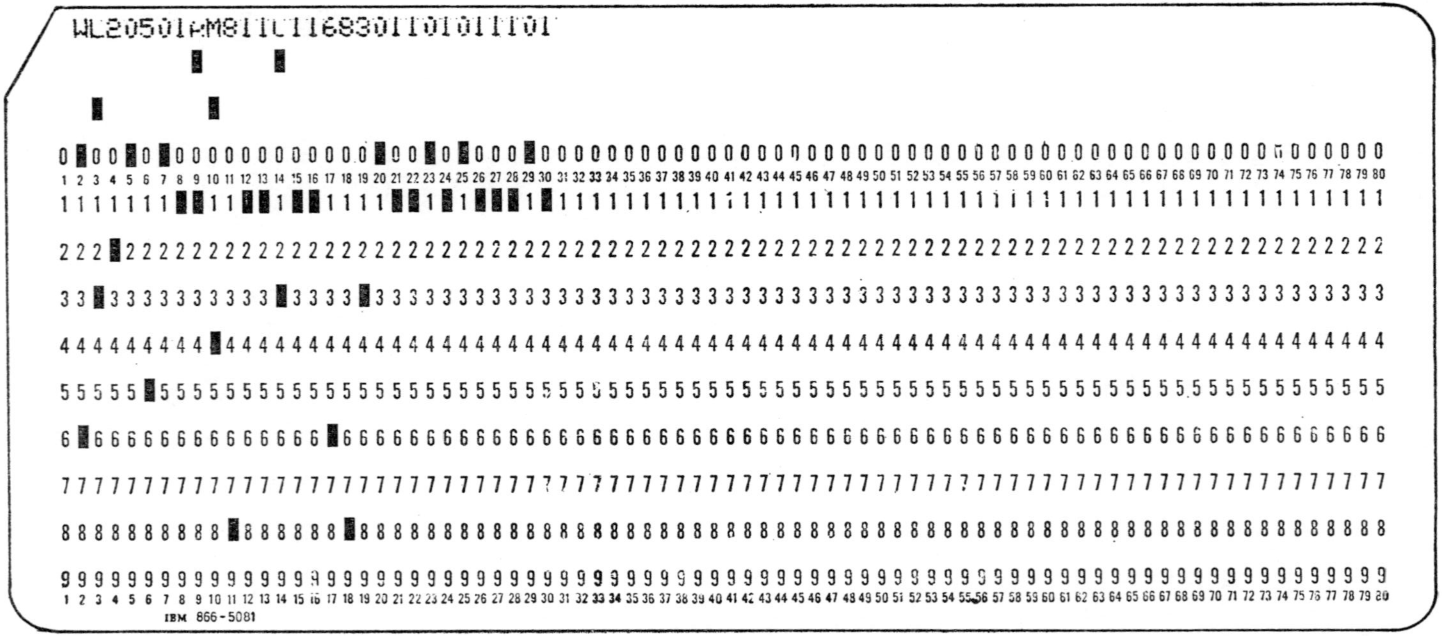

FIG. 10(a). Microbiocide screening data card.

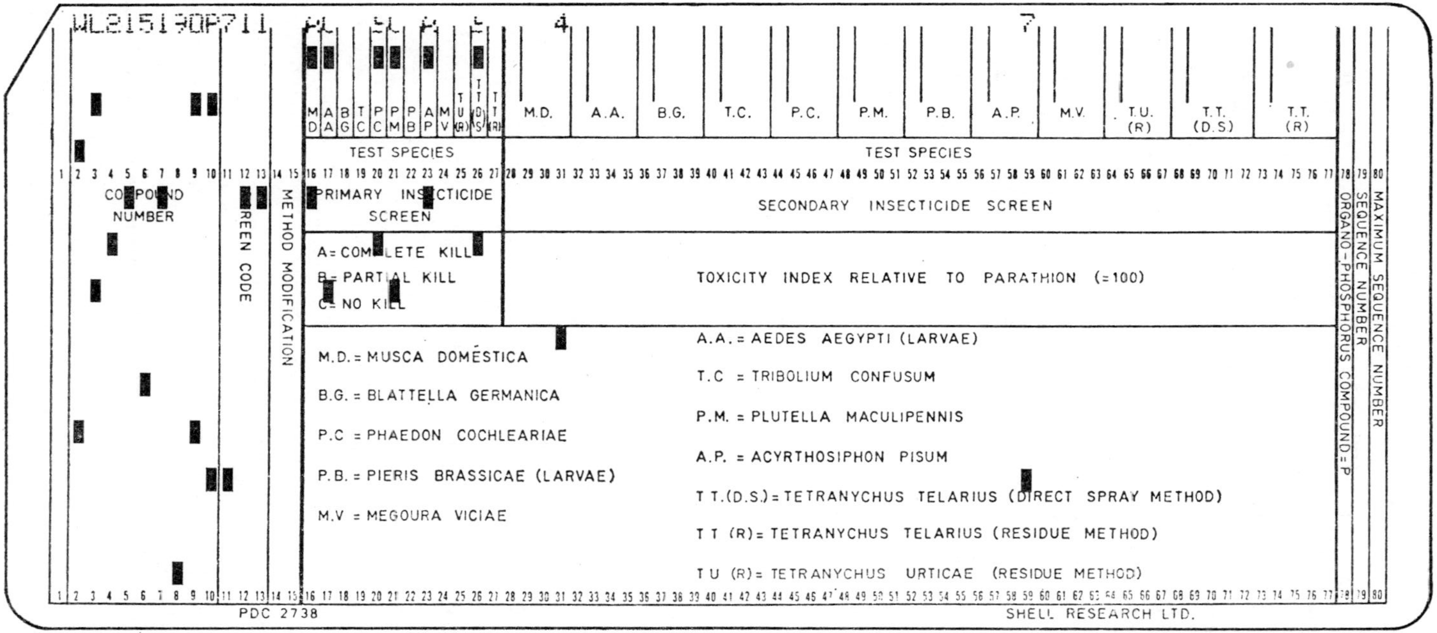

FIG. 10(b). Insecticide screening data card.

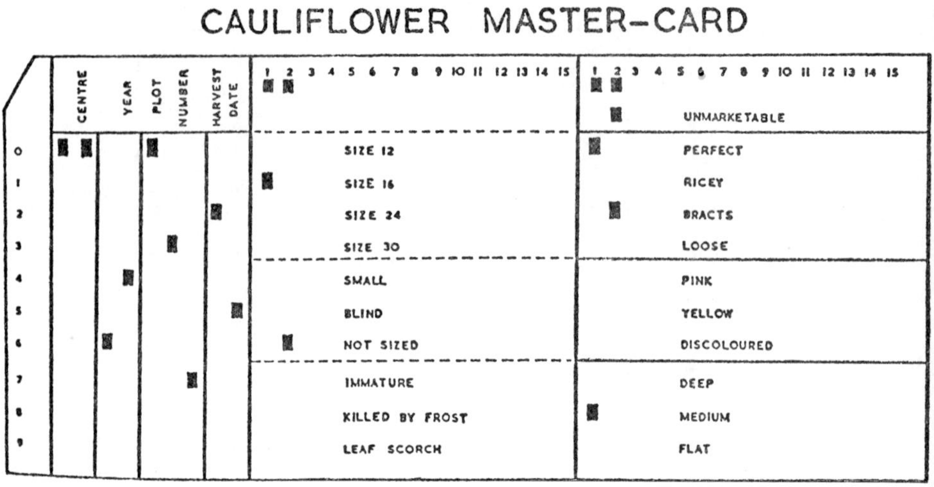

CAULIFLOWER MASTER-CARD

FIG. 10(c). Port-a-Punch card according to Berry *et al.* (1966).

punched card (Berry *et al.*, 1966). In this case, the data can be entered manually by piercing the required pre-scored position(s).

The availability of data in this form enables them to be tabulated either via a sorter/tabulator or via the computer (Fig. 11). The data, after transfer from punched card to magnetic tape, constitute a file which can be used to search, for example, for chemicals which show a certain desired combination of test results. A more extensive set of variables may require a series of data cards, as shown in Fig. 12, for the recording of information on field trials involving the use of pesticides. This type of approach is also described by Waldo *et al.* (1964).

In the cases mentioned the data were represented on punched cards in fixed field format. In other cases, the use of a variable length record may be required for efficient storage. As an example of this one could mention the complete description of a chemical structure. A structure can be depicted in fixed field arrangement using a fragmentation code; such a coding however cannot provide a complete description of the molecule. Various means are available to store within the computer system complete, unambiguous and unique structure descriptions. One of the most efficient methods for this purpose is a notation system which represents the structure as a linear string of characters, the length of which will obviously vary with the composition and complexity of the structure concerned. Fig. 13 gives an example of a chemical structure, its representation in IUPAC notation (I.U.P.A.C. Commission on Codification, etc., 1961) and its internal representation for computer use (Polton, 1969). All notations in this case

COMPOUNDS ACTIVE AGAINST AEDES AEGYPTI

Compound No.	Primary data	M.d.	A.a.	P.c.	P.m.	P.b.	A.p. or M.v.	T.t.
wL192450P	AABAAAA	30	800		50	80	40	600
wL22301	AAAAAAA	15	500	25	2	< 1	40	40
wL22231	AAAAAAA	5	500	20	4	< 1	10	250
wL218510P	AAAAAAA	3	400	25	10	15	60	50
wL218260P	AAAAAAA	60	400	50	10	3	150	250
wL217300P	AAAAAAA	< 1	400	10	5	15	25	30
wL22351	AAAAAAA	15	300	10	2	40	80	30
wL21870	AAAAAAA	10	300	5	4	7	< 3	30
wL216950P	AABAAAA	4	300		10	10	50	25
wL18465	AAAAAAA	25	300	100	60	300	15	1200
wL21167	AAAAAAA	30	250	200	700	600	50	250
wL218300P	AAAAAAA	10	200	7	2	10	2	80
wL207290P	AAAAAAA	10	200	20	60	100	15	100
wL217980P	AAAAAAA	7	150	30	15	30	50	80
wL217550P	AAAAAAA	20	150	10	4	30	200	500
wL19507	AAAAAAA	20	150	15			10	< 70
wL194770P	BAAAAAA		150				10	150
wL193890P	AAAAAAA	7	150	20	10	30	7	200
wL18508	CAABBAA		150	15			7	150
wL17962	AAAAAAA	30	150	30	30	300	10	2000
wL22230	AAAB AA	7	100	< 6			10	125
wL209100P	AAAAAAA	15	100	25	25	40	30	25
wL207960P	AAAAAAA	40	100	40	60	300	8	25
wL18505	AAAAAAA	25	100	40	80	100	7	200
wL13560	AAAA CC	15	100	50	150			
wL127300P	AAAA CC	20	100	100	150			
wL196240P	AAAAAAA	2	80	3	15		4	50
wL194150P	AAABAAA	7	80	20		15	30	200
wL190110P	AAAAAAA	10	80	50	80	100	10	1500
wL16252	AAAA AA	25	80	50	40		50	400
wL218990P	BABAAAA		60		1	< 1	3	20
wL219040P	AAAAAAA	3	60	7	4	< 1	15	60
wL207300P	AAAAAAA	10	60	15	80	100	< 4	40
wL196360P	CAAAAAA		60	7	10	< 3	60	20
wL195280P	AAAAAAA	40	60	3	100	50	80	100
wL14289	AAAA AA	15	60	25	15		5	200
wL215340P	AAAAAAA	20	50	5	20	80	50	20
wL210970P	BABC AA		50				4	50
wL207400P	AAAAABC	4	50	15	100	100		
wL194170P	CAAAACC		50	10	10	25		
wL18879	CACC CC		50					
wL18464	AAAAAAA	15	50	40	60	300	15	350
wL18071	AAAAAAB	3	50	7	15	25	2	
wL15352DE	CAAA AB		50	25	20		10	
wL14981	AAAA AA	25	50	150	30		30	100
wL13561	AAAA CC	10	50	50	150			

M.d.	Musca domestica		A.a.	Aedes aegypti (larvae)
P.c.	Phaedon cochleariae		P.m.	Plutella maculipennis (larvae)
P.b.	Pieris brassica (larvae)		A.p.	Acyrthosiphon pisum
T.t.	Tetranychus telarius		M.v.	Megoura viciae

FIG. 11. Tabulation of biological properties from punched cards.

CARD TYPE 1	Experimental Status and Soil Type
cc 1–11	Trial code number
12	Card type code
13–14	Card sequence number
15–16	Experimental status code
17–19	Previous history code
20	Residues
21–60	Experimental design
61–78	Soil type

CARD TYPE 2	Fertilizer Treatment and Rainfall
cc 1–11	Trial code number
12	Card type code
13–14	Card sequence number
15–47	Fertilizer treatment
48–80	Rainfall

CARD TYPE 3	Application and Treatments
cc 1–11	Trial code number
12	Card type code
13–14	Card sequence number
15–16	Method of application code
17–22	Date of application
23–27	Volume applied
28	Unit of measurement code
29–44	Compound
45	Formulation type code
46–52	Formation number
53–61	Batch number
62	Unit of measurement code
63–68	Dosage
69–74 75–80	Further dosage

CARD TYPE 4	Crop
cc 1–11	Trial code number
12	Card type code
13–14	Card sequence number
15–20	Date sown
21–25	Depth of planting
26–35	Crop species code
36–50 51–65 66–80	Repeat of information in cc 21–35 for further crop species

CARD TYPE 5	Pests
cc 1–11	Trial code number
12	Card type code
13–14	Card sequence number
15–17	General pest code
20–29	Specific pest code
30–39 40–49 50–59 60–69 70–79	Repeat of information in cc 20–29 for other pest species

Fig. 12. Recording of information on field trials.

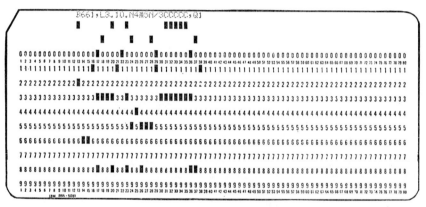

Cipher: normal   B6₂Ch3 1̲0̲N4:5N/3C₅Q

Cipher: internal representation : B661,L3.10.N4: N/3CCCCC,Q1

FIG. 13. Coding and keypunching of a chemical structure using the IUPAC notation.

would start in column 13 but they would not end in a fixed position as the length of the notation as recorded might vary from less than 10 to over a 100 characters; instead the end of the notation is indicated by a special character, in this case a blank.

Search for specific chemical characteristics (sub-structures) takes place by examination of the sequence of characters present in the notation (Dammers and Polton, 1968). When required, the notation can be expanded by the computer into an atom-connection table which displays fully the structural relationships of all atoms present in the structure. An extensive literature on the use of notation systems for this purpose is now in existence, in particular as regards the Wiswesser notation system, widely used in the U.S.A. (National Research Council Committee on Chemical Information, 1964, 1969; Lynch, 1968; Smith, 1968; Hyde et al., 1967; Thomson et al., 1967).

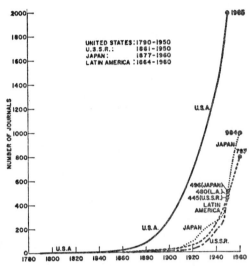

FIG. 14. Growth in number of biological journals (from Conrad, 1965).

The rapidly increasing use of such coding systems arises from the need of research organizations to store and search large files of chemical structures related to their own research activities. Computers are more and more being used in the operation of such data storage and retrieval systems (Durachta *et al.*, 1965). Similarly, their use is rapidly expanding with regard to associated activities in the field of literature information, bibliography and current awareness.

III. LITERATURE INFORMATION/STORAGE AND RETRIEVAL

A number of factors have contributed to making the task of keeping up with the literature in a particular field an onerous one. In the first place, the literature has undergone, and is still undergoing, considerable expansion (Fig. 14). Perhaps the expansion is not as fast as in the case of chemistry where the volume of literature tends to double every 8 years, but the microbiological literature appears to grow faster than the biological literature in general (Conrad, 1965). Secondly, many microbiologists now tend to be much more concerned than before with fringe areas, e.g. biochemistry and biochemical engineering. Furthermore, as in other research fields, it appears to become more difficult to adhere to the routine of consulting regularly abstracting journals, maintaining private indexing systems, etc.

Computers were expected as far back as the mid-50s to play an important role in easing the literature information problem. The early optimism proved rather unfounded, partly as a result of inadequacy and cost of the hard- and software available at the time; however since the mid-60s the situation has been changing rapidly. The progress achieved is due not only to the availability of more useful computer systems but also to a re-appraisal of what we need in the way of literature retrieval and awareness services and of the difficulties encountered in meeting such demands by the more conventional methods (Dammers, 1968). In fact, there are now a variety of ways in which computers are proving of distinct benefit to the scientist in coping with his literature task.

1. The use of computers to produce KWIC indexes (IBM, 1962) is now well established in a number of fields, e.g. chemistry ("Chemical Titles"), biology ("BASIC", see Fig. 15), etc. More sophisticated forms, which not only rely on bibliographic information in the title but make use of specially assigned keywords or terms, are in use in medicine (the MEDLARS system operated by the U.S. National Library of Medicine), in biology ("Biological Abstracts Previews" supplied by the Biosciences Information Services, Philadelphia), in chemistry ("CA Condensates" issued by the Chemical Abstracts Service, Columbus) etc. (see Appendix IV).

In most cases the production of these indexes is seen as part of the overall development towards computer-aided journal production. A very large abstracting organization, the Chemical Abstracts Service, Columbus, Ohio, is expected to have completed changeover to computer production of its abstract journal by the early 70s (Tate, 1967).

Other organizations, e.g. the National Library of Medicine, Bethesda, and the Institute of Scientific Information, Philadelphia (Elias *et al.*, 1968) already rely completely on computer production of some or all of their publications, e.g. Index Medicus, Science Citation Index.

2. The computer production of KWIC indexes or variants, such as KWOC in which the keyword is used as heading for all the references which contain the keyword concerned (Fig. 16), is now a straight-forward matter. Much attention has been paid to improving presentation by producing a printed output comparable with conventionally produced indexes by using say 1000 or more different print characters rather than the 48 or 64 provided by the high speed printers; considerable effort is also being devoted to producing by computer an index structure which might approach the sophistication of those produced at present manually by organizations such as the Chemical Abstracts Service (Armitage and Lynch, 1968).

3. Search of a KWIC index is quite effective if one's interest can be adequately described and references located via one or only a few keywords. It becomes, however, more laborious if one needs to consider also a

DIAGNOSIS

R HUMAN/ INACCURATE	DIAGNOSIS ON PRIMARY PULMONARY CANCE 62599
RLY	DIAGNOSIS ON PULMONARY CANCER/ AN EA 62627
Y GLAND CLINICAL COURSE	DIAGNOSIS TREATMENT HUMAN/ CARCIN ON 62825
EURIN OMAS DIFFERENTIAL	DIAGNOSIS WITH MALIGNANT TUMORS OF T 62586
RAY	DIAGNOSIS/ LUNG CALCIFICATIONS IN X- BP 545
YSTO URETHROGRAPHY AS A	DIAGNOSTIC AID IN STRESS INCONTINENC 61226
S PLEOPTICS AND RELATED	DIAGNOSTIC AND TREATMENT REGIMES 9-1 BP 514
ICE HUMAN/ NEW	DIAGNOSTIC ASPECTS OF THE GASTRIC JU 60917
PATHOLTEC-TM STRIPS IN	DIAGNOSTIC BACTERIOLOGY/ EVALUATION 63488
	DIAGNOSTIC LABORATORY HEMATOLOGY/ BP 520
OF MAEDI IN SEARCH FOR	DIAGNOSTIC LABORATORY METHODS USE 63478
AR DISEASE HUMAN/ THE	DIAGNOSTIC PROBLEM IN CEREBRO VASCUL 61128
PENICILLIN ANTI INFECT/	DIAGNOSTIC PROBLEMS AND NEW THERAPEU 63790
ROM THE NIPPLE IN WOMEN	DIAGNOSTIC PROBLEMS AND THEIR TREATM 61369
PREPARING ANTIGENS FOR	DIAGNOSTIC PURPOSES FROM CULTIVABLE 63518
NST PHOTOMETER/ A RAPID	DIAGNOSTIC TEST FOR PATHOLOGICAL HYP 60448
UCHIDA KRAEPELIN PSYCHO	DIAGNOSTIC TEST HUMAN DELINQUENT EPI 62012
NSION CLINICAL FEATURES	DIAGNOSTIC TESTS RESULTS OF SURGERY 61129
GNOS HUMAN/ COMPARATIVE	DIAGNOSTICS OF HEPATIC FUNCTION WITH 60906
JOHNIN IN DIFFERENTIAL	DIAGNOSTICS OF MYCOBACTERIAL INFECTI 63513
	DIALYSIS CENTER HUMAN/ ANATOMY OF A 63674
E FROM.BAKERS YEAST ENZ	DIALYSIS ENZ ELECTROPHORESIS INST CH 64306
NT WITH INST PERITONEAL	DIALYSIS HUMAN/ RENAL FAILURE DUE TO 61282
EFECT CORRECTED BY INST	DIALYSIS HUMAN/ UREMIC BLEEDING A RE 61215
	DIALYSIS IN THE HOME HUMAN/ HEMO 63708
EGG WHITE PROTEINS INST	DIALYSIS INST GEL FILTRATION/ INCORP 60754
/ THE INST ELECTRO	DIALYSIS OF ANABAENA-FLOS-AQUAE-A-37 64038
	DIALYSIS/ HARD WATER SYNDROME HUMAN 61271
MAN INST LONG-TERM HEMO	DIALYSIS/ PSYCHOLOGICAL FACTORS LONG 62096
	DIALYSIS/ THE CARDIO VASCULAR SYSTEM 61006
ST	DIALYZERS CURRENTLY IN USE HUMAN/ IN 61224
	DIAMETER ASSOCIATED WITH ILLNESS HUM 60659
REDUCTION OF HAIR SHAFT	DIAMETER CHILD/ EFFECT OF PREDNISONE 61400
VALUE AND THE RED CELL	DIANTHUS-ARMERIA-D AT WOODWALTON FEN 59615
RSUTA-D CATTLE GRAZING/	DIAPHRAGM I EFFECT OF GLUCOSE AND RE 60568
EN PHOSPHORYLASE IN RAT	DIAPHRAGM II EFFECT OF GLUCOSE AND R 60569
EN PHOSPHORYLASE IN RAT	DIAPHRAGM MUSCLE IN-VITRO/ THE EFFEC 60687
UCOSE METABOLISM IN RAT	DIAPHRAGM/ THE RELATIONSHIP BETWEEN 60682
SS IN ISOLATED RAT HEMI	DIAPHRAGM/ THE RELATIONSHIP BETWEEN 60683
OF LITHIUM ION RAT HEMI	DIAPHRAGMATIC HERNIAS/ CIRCULATORY E 61109
IN PATIENTS WITH LARGE	DIAPHRAGS CARBON-14/ EFFECT OF FREE 61592
ABOLISH OF ISOLATED RAT	DIAPHRAGS IN A SOLUTION CONTAINING 61586
ED AND UNSTIMULATED RAT	DIARRHEAL AGENT HUMAN ENTAMOEBA-HIST 63762
AND ANTI AMEBIC AN ANTI	DIARRHEAS HUMAN/ SEROLOGICAL RESPONS 63487
E IN CHOLERA-LIKE	DIASTASE/ OLIGO NUCLEOTIDE STUDIES I 64425
CHROMATOGRAPHY ENZ TAKA	DIASTASE/ STUDIES ON POLY NUCLEOTIDE 64489
WITH ENZ RNASE ENZ TAKA	DIASTASE/ STUDIES ON POLY NUCLEOTIDE 64490
MARY STRUCTURE OF ENZ TAKA	DIATARY CHANGES IN THE SURMULLET MUL 60308
S/ DIURNAL AND SEASONAL	

DILUTION

ICROSCOPY HUMAN/ ON THE	DIFFERENTIAL DIAGNOSIS BETWEEN CHRON 60652
RADIO PHOSPHORUS-32 FOR	DIFFERENTIAL DIAGNOSIS OF EVE TUMORS 62620
F THE SCALP COW/ ON THE	DIFFERENTIAL DIAGNOSIS OF TRAUMATIC 60665
TRIGEMINAL NEURIN OMAS	DIFFERENTIAL DIAGNOSIS WITH MALIGNAN 62586
SMISCHIN AND JOHNIN IN	DIFFERENTIAL DIAGNOSTICS OF MYCOBACT 63513
SIS RAT ADIPOSE TISSUE/	DIFFERENTIAL EFFECTS OF PROSTAGLANDI 60722
PROVED BY INVESTIGATING	DIFFERENTIAL EXCITATION AND LUMINESC 64078
IN CANOIDA-PELLICULOSA/	DIFFERENTIAL INDUCTION OF 2 ENZ GLUC 64301
TER-SCHREGER BANDS INST	DIFFERENTIAL INTERFERENCE MICROSCOPE 61712
ELLITUS IN INDIA HUMAN/	DIFFERENTIAL MOBILIZATION OF NONESTE 61464
IAN-SARC OMA VIRUSES VI	DIFFERENTIAL MULTIPLICATION OF UNINF 62758
MPHETAMINE CENT STIM ON	DIFFERENTIAL REINFORCEMENT OF LOW RA 62341
E CONTROLLABLE NEGATIVE	DIFFERENTIAL RESISTANCE IN NITELLA-T 64287
S IN HUMAN DENTINE/ THE	DIFFERENTIAL STAINING OF PERI TUBULA 61708
ORPUS CERVIX AND VAGINA	DIFFERENTIAL SURVIVAL RATES A HYPOTH 62661
T LIGHT MICROSCOPY INST	DIFFERENTIAL THERMAL ANALYSIS INST X 60490
MMINUTED MEAT EMULSIONS	DIFFERENTIAL THERMAL ANALYSIS OF FAT 60837
AF RUST ON THE STANDARD	DIFFERENTIATED WHEAT-M VARIETIES/ INHE 59829
SELECTION BY CHEMICALLY	DIFFERENTIATED RACES OF LICHENS RANA 63917
/ USE OF SAFRANIN-O FOR	DIFFERENTIATING BRUCELLA-SUIS FROM O 63472
	DIFFERENTIATION BOOK/ THE EVOLUTION 59733
VE INHIBITION OF FLORAL	DIFFERENTIATION IN CHENOPODIUM-RUBRU 64238
METABOLISM DURING CYTO	DIFFERENTIATION IN THE CELLULAR SLIM 64395
R10 LACTOSE/ THE RAPID	DIFFERENTIATION OF ENTEROBACTERIA BY 63077
STOCLADIELLA-EMERSONII/	DIFFERENTIATION OF ENZ GLUCOSE-6 PHO 64153
RA ON THE MORPHOLOGICAL	DIFFERENTIATION OF LENSES IN CHICK E 62904
AT/ CONTRIBUTION TO THE	DIFFERENTIATION OF NERVE AND GLIAL C 61787
LE ELUTRIATING PROCESS/	DIFFERENTIATION OF PELLETS MADE FROM 60826
FIA-D WITH REFERENCE TO	DIFFERENTIATION OF SCLEREIDS ENZ CYT 64307
F CERTAIN WOODY PLANTS/	DIFFERENTIATION OF THE APEX OF SYMPO 64150
SMENT OF THE FUNCTIONAL	DIFFERENTIATION OF THE GERMINAL EPIT 61457
POSSIBLE FACTOR IN CELL	DIFFERENTIATION/ SEQUENTIAL DNA REPL 59790
OF BOVINE LEUKOSIS/ THE	DIFFICULTY IN INTERPRETING RESULTS O 62755
LCULI HUMAN/ INST X-RAY	DIFFRACTION ANALYSIS OF 464 URINARY 61285
MAL ANALYSIS INST X-RAY	DIFFRACTION INST IR SPECTROSCOPY INS 60490
Y INST SCAN/ INST X-RAY	DIFFRACTION NEW HIGH-SPEED TECHNIQUE 60026
RIL ANGLE BY INST X-RAY	DIFFRACTION PINUS-RADIATA-G/ MEASURE 64699
ID LAMELLAE/ INST X-RAY	DIFFRACTION STUDY IN WATER OF LIPIDS 61192
ATER SYSTEMS INST X-RAY	DIFFRACTION/ DETERMINATION OF INTERN 64586
EM RAT AGING INST X-RAY	DIFFRACTION/ SYNTHETIC HYDROXY APATI 61636
OF THE DETERMINATION OF	DIFFUSABLE CALCIUM RAT/ CONTRIBUTION 61502
TUBULAR ALTERATIONS IN	DIFFUSE RENAL DISEASE III QUANTITATI 61266
DURING THE TREATMENT OF	DIFFUSE TOXIC GOITER HUMAN/ EXCRETIO 61578
ECTION OF EXTRACELLULAR	DIFFUSIBLE SUBSTANCES BACTERIAL ENZ 63072
AINING ON THE PULMONARY	DIFFUSING CAPACITY DURING SUBMAXIMAL 60613
E PROTEINS/ INST IMMUNO	DIFFUSION ANALYSIS OF HUMAN MONKEY A 63137
GUE VIRUS DRIED BY INST	DIFFUSION AND INST LYOPHILIZATION/ H 63094
NEOUS SYSTEMS/ CATIONIC	DIFFUSION IN CLAY MINERALS I MOHOGEN 64624

FIG. 15. Specimen page of Biological Abstracts KWIC index: BASIC.

ACRIFLAVINE
    FASCIOLIASIS IN CATTLE IN THE BELGIAN CONGO.=

AEROSOL OT 100%
    AEROSOL OT 100%, A WETTING AGENT FOR MOLLUSCICIDES.=

AFRICA
    MORPHOLOGICAL STUDY ON THE JAPANESE LIVER FLUKE COMPARED WITH THE AFRICAN SPECIMENS.=
    CONTROL OF FASCIOLIASIS.=

ALASKA
    RECENT LIMNAEIDAE: THEIR VARIATION, MORPHOLOHY, TAXONOMY NOMENCLATURE AND DISTRIBUTION.=

ALCOHOL
    EFFECT OF VARIOUS AGRICULTURAL CHEMICALS ON THE VIABILITY OF THE METACERCARIAE OF FASCIOLA

ALGERIA
    STUDY OF A CASE OF HEPATIC DISTOMATOSIS IN ALGERIA.=

ALLANTOLACTONE
    THE PARASITICIDAL ACTION OF INULA HELENIUM AND ALLANTOLACTONE ON FASCIOLA HEPATICA IN VITRO.=

AMINES
    CHEMOTHERAPY OF FASCIOLIASIS IV. ACTION OF AROMATIC AMINES.=

AMINO ACIDS
    THE AMINO ACID COMPOSITION OF THE PROTEINS AND DISTRIBUTION OF FATTY ACIDS IN THE LIPIDS OF EGGS OF
    THE NATURE OF THE AMINO AND KETO ACIDS SEPARATED BY FASCIOLA HEPATICA IN VITRO.=
    EXCHANGE OF AMINO ACIDS BETWEEN THE MOTHER COW AND ITS FETUS UNDER NORMAL CONDITIONS AND WITH

AMPHIPEPLA CUMINGIANA
    MONNIGS VETERINARY HELMINTHOLOGY AND ENTOMOLOGY.=

AMPULLARIA SP.
    MONNIGS VETERINARY HELMINTHOLOGY AND ENTOMOLOGY.=

ANAEMIA
    RADIOISOTOPE STUDIES ON THE ANAEMIA PRODUCED BY INFECTION WITH FASCIOLA HEPATICA.=
    ACUTE FASCIOLIASIS IN HORSES AND ITS DIFFERENTIATION FROM EQUINE INFECTIOUS ANAEMIA.=

ANTIGEN
    STUDIES ON THE DIAGNOSIS OF FASCIOLIASIS I. ANTIGENS FOR THE PRECIPITATION TEST. II. THE
    ISOLATION OF A COMPLETE LIPOID ANTIGEN FROM FASCIOLA HEPATICA.=
    CONTRIBUTION TO THE DIAGNOSIS OF PARAGONIMIASIS BY INTRACUTANEOUS REACTION WITH THE ANTIGENS OF
    INTRADERMAL REACTION AND COMPLEMENT-FIXATION REACTION IN HUMAN FASCIOLIASIS.=

ANTIMONY
    LIVER FLUKES IN FRANCE AND THEIR TREATMENT.=
    THE SEPTICEMIC FORM OF FASDIOLA HEPATICA INFECTION.=

FIG. 16. Example of KWOC index. (Liver fluke bibliography, Shell Research Ltd., Sittingbourne, 1968.)

number of synonyms and associated keywords. Hence it was obvious to move to the next step which is to let the computer do the matching of a set of keywords, including synonyms, associated keywords, representing an "interest profile", with the words occuring in the literature references.

Several such SDI (Selective Disseminarion of Information) systems are now in existence for this purpose following early systems such as that described by Sage *et al.* (1965). They are operated also on a commercial basis and some of these may be of particular interest to the microbiologist, e.g. the CBAC (Chemical Biological Activities) service operated by the Chemical Abstracts Service, Columbus (Zabriskie and Lynch, 1966) and the ASCA service provided by the Institute of Scientific Information, Philadelphia (Garfield and Sher, 1967). The former covers specifically literature dealing with the interaction of chemicals and biological systems, the latter provides complete coverage of some 1600 scientific journals, including many concerned with microbiology. Several such services have

1. Single term, one parameter	(SODIUM)
2. Two or more terms, one parameter	(SODIUM or POTASSIUM or LITHIUM)
3. Two parameters	(SODIUM) and (CHLORIDE)
4. Multi-term parameters, two or more parameters	(SODIUM or POTASSIUM . . .) and (CHLORIDE or BROMIDE) and . . .
5. NOT logic	(SODIUM or POTASSIUM) and (CHLORIDE or BROMIDE) not (IODIDE)
6. Weighting factor	[SODIUM (10) or POTASSIUM (5)] and [CHLORIDE (15) or BROMIDE (10)] Question weight = 16
7. Truncation e.g. QUIN*	will accept quinone, quinones, quinoline etc.
QUIN	will accept hydroquinone, benzquinolines.

FIG. 17. Some SDI search types as used with Chem. Abstracts tapes.

now also been established in the U.K. (Kent, 1967; Somerfield, 1967; Harley, 1966; Barraclough, 1967) (see Appendix IV for further details).

The advantages of such systems are obvious; they allow rapid alerting to new literature, sometimes even prior to the arrival of the printed journal, they also scan a much wider range of literature than is available in one's own local library and they enable the alerting to be specific to the users' needs. On the other hand, they are limited by the type of information available for scanning, often only titles, and by the search techniques used at present.

The systems now in operation enable matching of groups of terms against a file held on magnetic tape or disc in the computer system. In framing the search profile AND/OR- and NOT-logic can be used, also weighting and truncation of the search terms is possible (Fig. 17, see also Chemical Abstracts Service, 1967). Furthermore, one can select on the basis of authors' names, journal titles, keywords (CA Condensates), subject codes (MEDLARS, Biological Abstracts Previews), etc. Hence already quite versatile strategies for computer searches are feasible.

Fig. 18 gives a profile and Fig. 19 a corresponding print-out for literature on a specific biochemical topic. In fact this provides a good example of the type of output the user was presented with in the early stages of SDI; an example of a more recent output format is given in Fig. 20. In this case the user receives the references printed on card slips, which he can file if desired; in addition he receives for each reference selected a response card

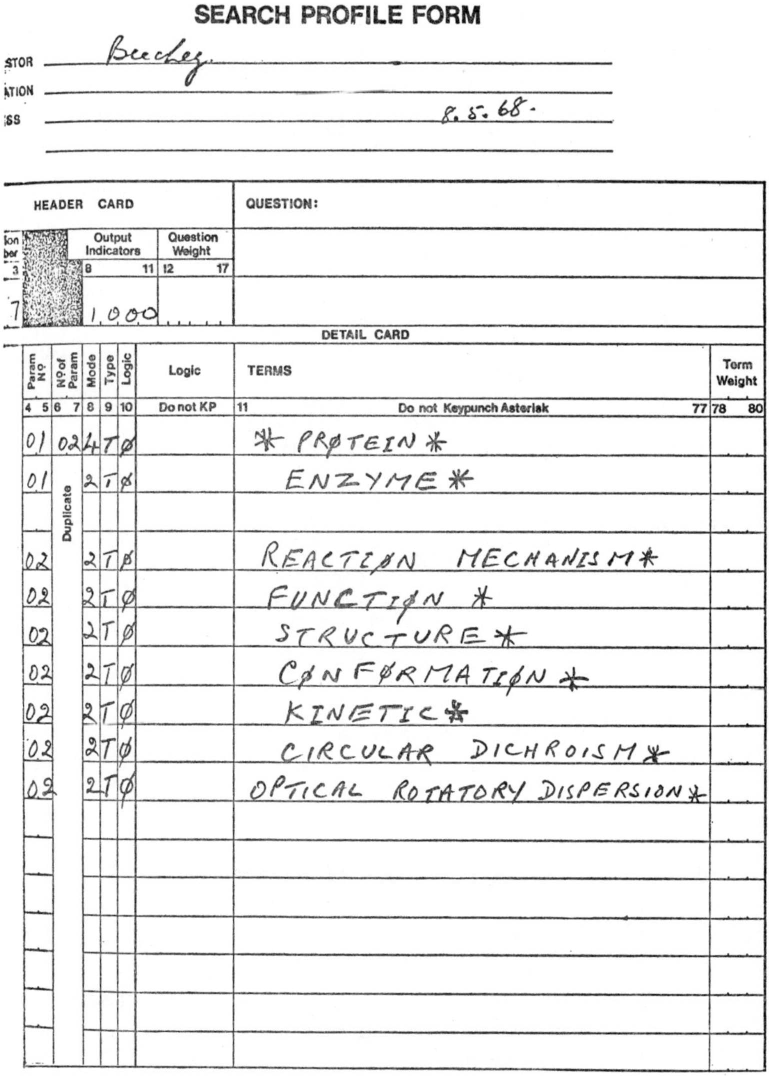

SEARCH PROFILE FORM

STOR _____ Beechey. _____

ATION _____

SS _____ 8. 5. 68. _____

HEADER CARD			QUESTION:
ion ber	Output Indicators	Question Weight	
	8 11	12 17	
7	1.000		

				DETAIL CARD			
Param N°	N° of Param	Mode	Type	Logic	Logic	TERMS	Term Weight
4 5	6 7	8	9	10	Do not KP	11 Do not Keypunch Asterisk 77	78 80
01	024	T	Ø			✳ PRØTEIN ✳	
01	2 Duplicate	T	Ø			ENZYME ✳	
02	2	T	Ø			REACTIØN MECHANISM✳	
02	2	T	Ø			FUNCTIØN ✳	
02	2	T	Ø			STRUCTURE ✳	
02	2	T	Ø			CØNFØRMATIØN ✳	
02	2	T	Ø			KINETIC✳	
02	2	T	Ø			CIRCULAR DICHROISM✳	
02	2	T	Ø			OPTICAL ROTATORY DISPERSION✳	

FIG. 18. Typical search profile.

or simply a duplicate copy which he can return after having indicated the relevance of the reference or his wish to receive a full text copy of the paper.

Research work, providing the basis for more sophisticated systems, is being done by a number of workers, for example, at Cornell and Harvard by Salton and Lesk (1965), at Cambridge by Sparck-Jones and Needham

```
ABBI-A-0125-0932   MATSUMURA S          STUMPF PK
                   FAT METABOLISM IN HIGHER PLANTS.  PARTIAL PRIMARY
                   STRUCTURE OF SPINACH ACYL CARRIER PROTEIN.=
                        68              932-41
BBAC-A-0150-0676   JI TH                HESS JL            BENSON AA
                   CHLOROPLAST MEMBRANE STRUCTURE. ASSOCIATION OF PIGMENTS
                   WITH CHLOROPLAST LAMELLAR PROTEIN.=
                        68              676-85
EBAC-A-0160-0151   FORMANEK H           ENGEL J
                   OPTICAL ROTATORY DISPERSION OF A RESPIRATORY HEME PROTEIN
                   OF CHIRONOMUS THUMMI.=
                        68              151-8
BBAC-A-0160-0188   COTTON RGH           GIBSON F
                   BIOSYNTHESIS OF TYROSINE IN AEROBACTER AEROGENES.
                   EVIDENCE FOR A SUBUNIT STRUCTURE OF THE PROTEIN
                   CONVERTING CHORISMATE INTO 4-HYDROXY PHENYL PYRUVATE.=
                        68              188-95
BBRC-A-0031-0699   GOTTO AM             LEVY RI            ROSENTHAL AS
                   BIRNBAUMER ME        FREDRICKSON DS
                   STRUCTURE AND PROPERTIES OF HUMAN BETA LIPO PROTEIN AND
                   BETA APO PROTEIN.=
                        68              699-705
BIJO-A-0108-0C9PA  TRUMAN DES           CLAYTON RM         CAMPBELL JC
                   SUBUNIT STRUCTURE OF CHICK LENS PROTEINS.=
                        68              9P
BIOF-A-0013-0396   LICHTENSTEIN GI      PIVCVAROV AP       BOBODZHANOV PK
                   ROSANTSEV EG         SMOLINA NB
                   DYNAMIC STRUCTURE OF PROTEINS AND ENZYMES STUDIED BY
                   SPECIFIC LUMINESCENT AND PARA MAGNETIC LABELS.=
                        68              396-400
BIOF-A-0013-C428   AKSENTSEV SL         NISENBAUM SD       KONEV SV
                   DEPENDENCE OF PROLONGED AFTERGLOW OF PROTEINS ON THE
                   SECONDARY STRUCTURE OF THEIR MOLECULES.=
                        68              428-32
JHOB-A-0034-0251   ECHOLS H             GINGERY R          MOORE L
                   INTEGRATIVE RECOMBINATION FUNCTION OF BACTERIOPHAGE
                   LAMBDA. EVIDENCE FOR A SITE SPECIFIC RECOMBINATION
                   ENZYME.=
                        68              251-60
JTBI-A-0019-0215   CARVEY IG
                   TRANSIENT PHASE KINETICS OF ENZYME REACTIONS.=
                        68              215-31

            -PAGES PRINTED FOR QUESTION NUMBER-057    001
```

Fig. 19. Print-out from CT No. 15, 1968 according to profile, Fig. 18.

(1968), at Lehigh University by Hillman (1968), etc. It should be stressed that the above only indicates some of the many activities in this field. Activities of this type are now proceeding in a great number of organizations in several countries. Cost per profile may be in the range of £30–£150 per annum (\$100–\$500) depending on number and type of search terms used, number of references retrieved, size of the file searched, etc. Computer operated SDI has undoubtedly still many defects but as pointed out by Savage (1967) it appears to represent the least expensive, most effective and most easily evaluated system usable as a base for information services. It is, however, essential that it be operated in a highly adaptive manner if its advantages are to be realized and maintained.

4. In order to provide computer operated SDI facilities to their own research workers, an increasing number of large organizations (governmental and industrial) are making use of magnetic tapes obtained from outside sources.

C.A. 73(13) NO. 062552X   251
MOCKEL JJ. DUMONT JE, COLLYN L.
(SCH. MED., UNIV. BRUSSELS, BRUSSELS, BELG.).
INFLUENCE OF ENERGY-COUPLING INHIBITORS ON THE RES
PIPATION OF TIGHTLY-COUPLED HUMAN SKELETAL MUSCLE
MITOCHONDRIA. = =
EUP. J. CLIN. INVEST.
VOLUME 0001(0001), PAGE 0032–0009 YEAR 1970
CODEN EJCIB
INHIBITORS ENERGY COUPLING MITOCHONDRIA
UNCOUPLING AGENTS MITOCHONDRIA
ENERGY COUPLING INHIBITORS MITOCHONDRIA
MITOCHONDRIA ENERGY COUPLING INHIBITORS

C.A. 73(13) NO. 062554Z   251
DAVIES DD. KENWORTHY P.
(SCH. BIOL. SIC., UNIV. EAST ANGLIA, NORWICH, ENGL.).
ALPHA-OXOGLUTARATE. GLYOXYLATE CARBOLIGASE ACTIVI
TY OF PLANT MITOCHONDRIA. = =
J. EXP. BOT.
VOLUME 0021(0067), PAGE 0247–0057 YEAR 1970
CODEN JEBOA
OXOGLUTARATE CLYOXYLATE CARBOLIGASE
ENZYMES PLANT MITOCHONDRIA
MITOCHONDRIA PLANT ENZYMES
PLANT MITOCHONDRIA ENZYMES
CARBOLIGASE OXOGLUTARATE GLYOXYLATE
PYRUVATE OXIDN ENZYMES

FIG. 20. Print-out from CA Condensates tape Vol. 73 No. 13.

In this case, the organization concerned takes the responsibility for carrying out the computer search themselves, using either the search programme provided with the tapes or their own search programmes (Corbett, 1967; Dammers, 1968; National Research Council of Canada, 1967). This type of operation is perhaps only economical when one has to satisfy a demand for say 100 profiles in a particular organization. The cost of obtaining the tapes and searching them should then be rather less than the cost of having this work done as customer searches by the organization supplying the tapes. However, such an assessment ignores some other important considerations. Operation under one's own control can provide greater flexibility and adaptability; also speed is likely to be greater. Another consideration is that by doing the searches oneself one can preserve the selected references in machine-readable form and use them to build specific subject files held in the computer system. On the other hand one should expect organizations, dedicated to and specifically equipped for the provision of SDI services, to be in a better position to apply more advanced search techniques; they should also, as a rule, be better placed to cope with retrospective search requirements. It would seem therefore that we might progress towards a situation in which the various information handling activities are shared between the information service and the user organization.

Such a mid-way approach is already coming into existence in those cases where user organizations receive output from searches on magnetic tape for further processing and dissemination within their own organization.

5. The indications are that we may be moving towards more personalized computer operated information systems, i.e. relatively small systems with an increase of perhaps at most 500 literature references per annum.

Examples of such systems are those described by Lipsett and Blair (1968) at the National Research Council of Canada concerning a current bibliography on energy transfer in polyacene solid solutions; by Church-house (1967) dealing with a current awareness service on computer science literature at the Atlas Computer Laboratory, Chilton, to take some specific systems, operated in essence under direct control of the scientists concerned. The approach at Shell Research, Sittingbourne, and some of its economic implications has been dealt with by Dammers (1967, 1968).

A generalized scheme for providing a computer operated personal literature system might be represented as indicated in Fig. 21. The input of the system is either via scanning of magnetic tape files such as those provided by Chemical Abstracts Service, Institute for Scientific Informa-tion, etc., or via scanning of literature in print (abstract journals, primary journals, etc.). The resulting bibliographic files are relatively small as they cover only highly specialized literature, i.e. they are likely to contain say 2000 to 3000 references and to grow on average by 500 references per annum. Their maintenance and use can be achieved in a number of ways:

(a) If there are no direct access facilities, the search is likely to be initi-ated via the input of search conditions on punched cards; output would be via high speed printers. Updating would also be via punched cards.

In this case, it will be useful to provide at say quarterly or half-yearly intervals a KWIC index of the information stored. This can then be used for most day-to-day searches instead of the direct computer search.

(b) If the system is operated as an on-line system, the user might be able to access the system via a teletype (TTY), allowing either data to be entered on to the file or required information to be printed out. Under time-sharing operating conditions, the user could have direct

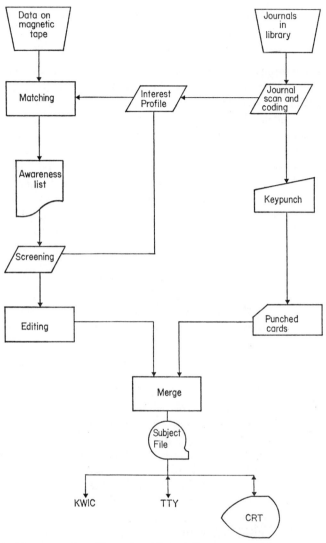

FIG. 21. Computer handling of published literature using magnetic tape and printed journal input.

access to the file, probably held on disc, whenever he required. In this case, the need to prepare periodic KWIC indexes would tend to disappear. Still more convenient might be the system whereby the user can have relevant parts of the file displayed on a CRT (cathode ray tube) device enabling him to scan the file rapidly for relevant information.

6. Various systems of the type described or its variants are now already in or coming into operation.

In view of this, the following questions seem worth posing:

(i) Is it economical? The answer to this obviously depends very much on the environment in which the system is expected to operate in particular with regard to the computer facilities (hard- as well as software) available. For the personal reference file system executed in its simplest form, i.e. whereby the scientist selects references or obtains them via a magnetic tape data base search, has them where necessary keypunched, put on his file, receives periodic KWIC indexes and carries out occasional computer searches, one can estimate, that the running cost of the system would probably not exceed 3% of the cost of employing the scientist served (including overheads). Hence such a system would pay for itself if it saved the scientist about one hour per week. In many cases one is likely to find that the scientist tends to spend rather more than this on the maintenance and use of his private literature collection and index.

(ii) How relevant is this approach in dealing with microbiological literature? On a purely personal level, a system of the type outlined can be operated by selection of relevant papers from the printed literature. One might, however, like to use eventually magnetic tape services covering the field of microbiology. Such rather specific literature collections on magnetic tape are already available covering mass spectrometry, pesticides, selected topics in biochemistry, etc. The total number of references in microbiology is of the order of 20,000 publications per year, hence of the same magnitude as, for example, the CBAC (Chemical Biological Activities) service now provided by the Chemical Abstracts Service. The production of a magnetic tape service for microbiological literature would therefore appear to be by no means an unrealistic possibility. Perhaps the relevant microbiological societies might like to consider how far this can be considered desirable and whether it could be brought about by co-operative action of the societies concerned.

IV. SOME GENERAL COMMENTS WITH SPECIAL REFERENCE TO RECENT DEVELOPMENTS

The rate at which computer applications in data and literature information handling will increase is likely to be high. This will be brought about partly by the need to increase labour efficiency in research, partly as a result of increased experience in computer use and last but not least by the rapidly increasing availability and the declining cost of computer capacity. As a result the areas in which computer use is becoming feasible and economic are increasing fast. It is perhaps of interest to outline, against this general background of increasing computer use, some of the developments which have become particularly noteworthy during the past 2 to 3 years.

In the first place one might indicate some of the problem areas; time-sharing, whilst it has made considerable strides, has remained well behind the expectations of the mid- and late sixties. Most systems now in operation lack generality and are more expensive to operate than anticipated. To a large extent such shortcomings arise from the difficulties and cost involved in developing efficient software for the much more complex systems now required, and in developing the software one of the major obstacles encountered appears to be our lack of knowledge regarding the way real life systems operate. This deficiency is becoming painfully apparent every time one starts trying to implement such systems on computers (Dammers, 1970b).

On the other hand small and cheap computers have become available more readily than generally expected and this has fostered the development of special purpose systems with small computers dedicated to a specific application. In many cases such systems have proved not only easier to implement than those based on the use of large general purpose computer facilities, they also tend to be more economical to operate though they may be rather limited in their capabilities.

Developments such as the above have tended to direct attention towards a network approach in which a small dedicated computer may be linked to, e.g. a larger laboratory computer and this in turn to a much larger installation, an approach which enables the advantages of both the small dedicated and the larger general purpose system to be combined in an adaptive manner (Krugers, 1970).

As regards information handling by computer, developments have been fast, resulting in systems such as SDI being used in many research establishments (e.g. Rowlands, 1970). There would now appear to be wide acceptance of not only the need but also the feasibility of computer use to cope with the mounting problems in library operation and use.

Novel methods of data analysis such as pattern recognition have come strongly to the fore in recent years (Nilsson, 1965; Watanabe, 1969). They have shown considerable promise in some areas (Ingram and Preston, 1970), whilst their methodology and value in others still remains to be explored (Minsky and Papert, 1969).

Particularly noteworthy is the fact that recently several systems have come into operation which go well beyond data analysis as such and move into the realm of artificial intelligence. As examples of such development one might mention the Heuristic Dendral system under development at Standford University (Buchanan et al., 1969) and the OCSS system developed at Harvard University (Corey and Wipke, 1969). The former system interprets mass spectra and predicts the chemical structures that are likely to have given rise to the spectra observed. The system admittedly is as yet restricted to a rather limited range of organic compounds but even in this narrow field it has been found to produce results comparable to those obtained by experienced mass spectroscopists. The latter system is designed to establish feasible pathways to be followed in the synthesis of complex organic molecules.

It is a characteristic of such advanced programmes that they need to incorporate a formalization of the theory and expertise relating to the area in which they are intended to operate. Hence they require intimate involvement of users in their development (Buchanan et al., 1970).

This need for close involvement of the user in system/programme development is becoming increasingly apparent in computer applications in general. It is essential if one wants to arrive at computer operated systems that match acceptable operational and economic performance with satisfactory adaptation to users needs. The original expectation that a universal, relatively easy to use programming language might ease this development has all but disappeared; such a language now appears to be as elusive as the Holy Grail. Even so much better interactive languages are becoming available and as an example of these one might mention the POP-2 language developed at the University of Edinburgh (Burstall and Popplestone, 1968), a language that appears capable of handling a wide range of data structures, both numeric and non-numeric, combining many of the useful features of the more commonly used programming languages. It is also attractive in that the user of POP-2 can steadily progress from learning a simple subset, through higher subsets to the full language thus allowing gradual involvement and development of experience which is so essential in computer applications.

Considerable strides have been made during the past few years with regard to widening the range of computer applications in research. It is also obvious that the main potential for applications remains as yet unexplored. Perhaps only through the involvement of the motivated user can one hope that this potential will be exploited more rapidly and effectively than has been the case in the past. The computer is presenting him with an additional task but one which is also likely to present substantial rewards. It should greatly reduce the repetitive element in research work and considerably increase its output of meaningful results. It can open the way to a highly adaptive form of experimentation, one in which the research worker will have the ability to interact with and control his experiments to a degree as yet only feasible in exceptional cases. Rather than diminish it should augment the importance of the human element in scientific experimentation.

REFERENCES

Alexander, D. C., and Wortzman, D. (1968). "Computers and Biomedical Research", 1, 348–365.

A.M.A. (1966). *J. Am. Med. Ass.*, 196, 109–166.

Armitage, Janet E., and Lynch, M. F. (1968). *Inform. Stor. Retr.*, 4, 101–111.

Aron, J. D. (1967). *IBM Systems Journal*, 6, 49–67.

Barber, D. L. A. (1967). *In* "The Collection and Processing of Field Data". A CSIRO Symposium, (Ed. E. F. Bradley and O. T. Denmead), pp. 579–586. Interscience Publishers.

Barlow, G. E. (1967). *In* "The Collection and Processing of Field Data". A CSIRO Symposium (Ed. E. F. Bradley and O. T. Denmead), pp. 407–436. Interscience Publishers.

Barraclough, Elizabeth D. (1967). *In* "Organization and Handling of Bibliographic Records by Computer". Proceedings of the University of Newcastle-upon-Tyne Seminar, July 1967 (Ed. N. S. M. Cox and M. W. Grosse), pp. 75–91. Oriel Press Ltd., Newcastle-upon-Tyne.

Berry, G., Cleaver, T. J., Nelder, J. A., and Salter, P. J. (1966). Methods of recording data in the laboratory and field. *Expl. Agric.*, 2, 69–80.

Buchanan, B. G., Sutherland, G. L., and Feigenbaum, E. A. (1969). "Machine Intelligence 4" (Ed. B. Meltzer and D. Michie), pp. 209–254. Edinburgh University Press, Edinburgh.

Buchanan, B. G., Sutherland, G. L., and Feigenbaum, E. A. (1970). "Machine Intelligence 5" (Ed. B. Meltzer and D. Michie), pp. 253–280. Edinburgh University Press, Edinburgh.

Burstall, R. M., and Popplestone, R. J. (1968). *In* "POP-2" Papers. Oliver and Boyd, Edinburgh.

Cavins, J. F., and Friedman, M. (1968). *Cereal Chem.*, 45 (2), 172–176, March.

Chemical Abstracts Service (1967). Preparation of search profiles, pp. 41. American Chemical Society.

Churchhouse, R. F. (1967). The Atlas Laboratory information retrieval project, pp. 6. Atlas Computer Laboratory, Chilton.

Conrad, G. M. (1965). *Bact. Rev*, 29, 523–533.

Corbett, L. (1967). *J. Doc.*, 23 (2), 150–151.

Corey, E. J., and Wipke, W. T. (1969). *Science*, 166, 178–192.

Dammers, H. F. (1967). *In* "Proceedings F.I.D./I.F.I.P. Conference on Mechanized Information Storage, Retrieval and Dissemination", Rome, June 14–17, 1967, pp. 415–436. North Holland Publishing Company, Amsterdam.

Dammers, H. F. (1968). *Inform. Stor. Retr.*, 4, 113–131.

Dammers, H. F. (1970a). *Inform. Stor. Retr.*, 6, 17–28.

Dammers, H. F. (1970b). *In* "Data Organization for Management and Access", pp. 1–12. British Computer Society, London.

Dammers, H. F., and Polton, D. J. (1968). *J. Chem. Doc.*, 8, 150–160.

Durachta, C. W., Schenk, C. E., Dick, R. G., and Sturtevant, F. M. (1965). *Bact. Rev*, **29**, 560–576

Elias, A. W., Revesz, G. S., and Foeman, G. H. (1968). *J. Chem. Doc.*, **8**, 74–80.

Estrin, Thelma (1968). "Data Acquisition and Processing in Biology and Medicine", **5**, 117–136. Pergamon Press.

Fraser, J. W. (1968). *Analyt. Chem.*, **40**, 26A–40A.

Garfield, E., and Sher, I. H. (1967). *J. Chem. Doc.*, **7**, 147–153.

Gillard, P. O., and Lamb, D. (1967). *In*: "The Collection and Processing of Field Data". A CSIRO Symposium (Ed. E. F. Bradley and O. T. Denmead), pp. 541–557. Interscience Publishers.

Harley, A. J. (1966). U.K. Medlars Information Retrieval Service—A handbook for users, pp. 66. National Lending Library for Science and Technology, Boston Spa, Yorkshire, England.

Hillman, D. J. (1968). *Inform. Stor. Retr.*, **4**, 219–238.

Hyde, E., Matthews, F. W., Thomson, Lucille, H., and Wiswesser, W. J. (1967). *J. Chem. Doc.*, **7**, 200–204.

IBM (1962). General information manual—Keyword-in-Context (KWIC) indexing.

Ingram, M., and Preston, K. (1970). *Scient. Am*, **223**, No. 5, pp. 72–82.

I.U.P.A.C. Commission on Codification, Ciphering and Punched Card Techniques (1961). "Rules for I.U.P.A.C. Notation for Organic Compounds". Longmans, Green and Co., London.

Joseph, E. C. (1968). "Computers: Trends Toward the Future". I.F.I.P. Congress, Edinburgh, August 1968. Invited Papers, pp. 145–157.

Kent, A. K. (1967). An experiment in computer-based chemical information retrieval and dissemination. Chemical Society Research Unit in Information Dissemination and Retrieval, University of Nottingham.

Kienitz, H., and Kaiser, R. (1968). *Z. Anal. Chem.*, **237**, 241–263.

Knight, K. E. (1965). Ph.D. Thesis, Carnegie Institute of Technology.

Knight, K. E. (1966). Changes in computer performance. *Datamation*, September 1966, pp. 40–54.

Knight, K. E. (1968). Evolving computer performance. *Datamation*, January 1968, pp. 31–35.

Krugers, J. F. (1970). *Chem. Weekblad*, **66**, No. 51, 26–36.

Lindberg, D. A. B. (1965). *Bact. Rev.* **29**, 554–559.

Lipsett, F. R., and Blair, F. D. (1968). *J. Chem. Doc.*, **8**, 26–29.

Lockerman, P. C., and Knutsen, W. D. (1967). *Comm. ACM*, **10**, 658–764.

Lynch, M. F. (1968). *Endeavour*, **27**, 68–73.

Macey, J. Jr. (1965). Analog-digital conversion systems. "Computers in Biomedical Research", **2**, 3–34. Academic Press.

Maskell, B. M. (1968). Batch Fermentation. Elliott-Automation series: Automation in Action. London, February 1968.

Minsky, M., and Papert, S. (1969). "Perceptrons. An Introduction to Computational Geometry". MIT Press, Cambridge, Mass.

National Research Council Committee on Chemical Information (1964). "Survey of Chemical Notation Systems". Publication 1150. National Academy of Sciences —National Research Council, Washington, D.C.

National Research Council Committee on Chemical Information (1969). "Chemical Structure Information Handling. A Review of the Literature 1962–1968", Publication 1733. National Academy of Sciences, Washington.

National Research Council of Canada (1967). NRC–SDI system. Private communication received from J. Brown and P. Wolters via AWRE, Aldermaston.

Nilsson, N. J. (1965). "Learning Machines. Foundations of Trainable Pattern-Classifying Systems". McGraw-Hill, New York.

Orr, C. H., and Norris, J. A. (Eds.) (1970). "Computers in Analytical Chemistry". Plenum Press, New York and London.

Polton, D. J. (1969). Inform. Stor. Retr., 5, 7–25.

Price, D. G. (1967). Whither keypunch. Datamation, June 1967, pp. 32–34.

Rowlands, D. G. (1970). Inform. Stor. Retr., 6, 53–71.

Sackman, H. (1967a). "Computers, Systems Science and Evolving Society", p. 202. Wiley.

Sackman, H. (1967b). "Computers, Systems Science and Evolving Society", p. 225. Wiley.

Sage, C. R., Adderson, R. R., and Fitzwater, D. R. (1965). Am. Doc., 16, 185–200.

Salton, G., and Lesk, M. (1965). Comm. ACM, 8, No. 6.

Savage, T. R. (1967). Am. Doc., 18, 242–246.

Schmidt, D. U. (1966). Techniques in amino-acid analysis. Technicon Monograph No. 1. Technicon Instruments Company Ltd., Chertsey.

Smith, E. G. (1968). "The Wiswesser Line-Formula Chemical Notation". McGraw-Hill, New York.

Somerfield, G. A. (1967). Aslib Proc., 19, 255–259.

Sparck-Jones, K., and Needham, R. M. (1968). Inform. Stor. Retr., 4, 91–100.

Tate, F. A. (1967). Chem. Eng. News, 45 (4), 78–88, 90.

Thomson, Lucille, H. Hyde, E., and Matthews, F. W. (1967). J. Chem. Doc., 7, 204–209.

Tukey, J. W., and Wilk, M. B. (1966). Data analysis and statistics: An expository overview AFIPS Conference Proceedings, 29 (1966 Fall Joint Computer Conference), pp. 695–709. Spartan Books, Washington, D.C.

Van Oorschot, J. L. P., and Belskma, M. (1961). Weed Res., 1, 245–257.

Waldo, W. H., Hamm, P. C., Hannah, L. H., Dunn, P. V., and Billman, R. C. (1964). J. Chem. Doc., 4, 218–220.

Watanabe, S. (Ed.) (1969). "Methodologies of Pattern Recognition". Academic Press.

Weinwurm, G. F. (1965). Research in the management of computer programming, SP-2059, May 1965. Systems Development Corporation, Santa Monica, California.

Zabriskie, K. H., and Lynch, M. F. (1966). J. Chem. Doc., 6, 30–33.

APPENDIX I

GLOSSARY

Analogue/digital conversion (ACD)

The conversion of signals, usually from instruments or transducers and presented as voltage variations, into digital units/pulses. The basis of analogue-to-digital conversion is the comparator circuit. This circuit compares an unknown voltage with a reference voltage and indicates which of the two is larger.

Analogue processing (analogue computer)

A form of computation in which variables are represented and manipulated as continuously variable physical quantities. The analogue computer provides a model of the system being studied. The physical form of the analogue may be similar to that of the system, but more often the analogue is based solely on the mathematical equivalence of the interdependence of computer variables and the variables in the physical system.

Batch processing

A form of computer processing in which jobs are dealt with strictly serially, i.e. a new job is not processed until the previous one is completed. In contrast with this, multi-programming or time-sharing processing permits the processor, under control of its executive programme, to deal with several jobs at the same time.

Blocking

The recording of several records in a block, for example, on magnetic tape. The blocks may vary in length and are separated by an inter-block gap. Instructions for processing operate on one tape block and it is usually not possible to read or write less than one block (except in the case of incremental tape units). The magnetic tape is stopped and started when the inter-block gap is under the read-write head of the tape transport.

Boolean algebra (Boolean logic)

An algebra for dealing with the truth of logical propositions. Operators are AND, OR, NOT, etc.

Named after George Boole, an English mathematician (1815–1864), Boolean algebra is relevant to the design of switching networks in computers as well as to the formulation of search strategies in information retrieval.

Character

Any individual letter, number or special symbol from a character set. An 8-bit representation of a character would allow $2^8 = 256$ different characters to be represented. Present high speed printers, however, are as a rule still limited to at most $2^6 = 64$ different characters.

A digit is a single character that represents an integer, i.e. in decimal notation one of the characters 0 to 9 (decimal digits). A bit is a digit in binary notation, usually 0 or 1.

Compilation

The production of a machine language programme by translating a set of instructions written in a high-level language such as FORTRAN or COBOL. This translation from source language to object language is done by the compiler, a computer programme which translates the source statements, provided by the programmer, selects sub-routines and assembles the parts into an object programme.

Data acquisition (system)

A peripheral system that collects data at source for processing and/or storage in the computer system. The data acquisition system may incorporate the means to transform data, carry out data reduction, etc. The larger systems can handle data obtained concurrently from a variety of sources, e.g. instruments, and are likely to contain a small computer to deal with the various data channels.

Data reduction

The transformation of information (raw data), usually experimentally derived, with the object of eliminating redundant or non-relevant information, where necessary applying error-detection and correction. The result usually is a much reduced set of data in a form suitable for scientific computation, statistical analysis, control purposes or storage and subsequent retrieval.

Digital computer

An information processing system in which the characters or symbols handled by the system are processed internally in binary representation. Its basic functions are to store, retrieve and transform symbols and condition transformations on the values of symbols. It performs these functions according to a list of instructions stored within the system.

Historically digital computers have been used predominantly for arithmetic tasks; this is no longer so. In fact, we are now rapidly moving towards a situation in which only a fraction of the information processing tasks performed by digital computers will be concerned with primarily arithmetic operations.

Feed back control (system)

A system in which the value of some output quantity is controlled by feeding back the value of the controlled quantity in such a way that the value of the controlled quantity is brought closer to a desired value.

Fixed field representation

A method of data recording and storage in which particular data are always stored in certain specified locations in a record, for example, on punched cards (one or more specified card columns), on magnetic tape, etc.

FORTRAN

An acronym for FORmula TRANslator, a programming language designed for writing programmes to solve problems which can be stated in terms of arithmetic procedures. It is the most popular of the algebraic procedure-oriented languages.

There are many versions of FORTRAN, e.g.

> FORTRAN II—An improvement over the original FORTRAN, with such additions as the use of sub-routines and additional format control.

> FORTRAN IV—An expanded version of FORTRAN II, which includes additional functions, type statements, and complex arithmetic and logical operations.

(See also Ware, this Volume, p. 1, for a description of various programmes.)

Fragmentation code

A coding procedure whereby a given code represents only one aspect or feature of a given entity.

For instance, in the case of chemical structures one might use in the case of monochloracetic acid, $Cl.CH_2.COOH$, three different codes to indicate the presence of chlorine, of a C_2 chain and of a carboxylic group.

By contrast, a coding system such as the IUPAC notation would provide one code only, i.e. C_2XiCh2, representing all features of the structural formula.

Hardware

The physical equipment of a computer configuration. Contrasted with software.

Interface

A common boundary or link between computer systems or parts of a single system. "Interface" involves compatibility between system components and hence may be concerned with the design of the system and equipment, codes, transfer speed, tape format and other points of possible difference. An interface also exists between man and machine, and much attention has been paid in recent years to the development of systems involving enquiry points, data terminals and display consoles.

KWIC index (Keyword-in-context index)

A computer produced index. The main steps in the preparation of such an index, e.g. from titles of papers, are as follows:

1. Select keywords from titles; unwanted words, e.g. "in", "the", etc. are eliminated by comparison with a stored list of "forbidden words".
2. Sort keywords in alphabetical order.
3. Print each keyword in the middle of the page, one keyword to a line. The remainder of the line is filled with text preceding or following the keyword in the original title. During this step keywords which, though significant, are considered non-relevant, can be suppressed via reference to a stop-list, provided with the programme.

KWOC index (Keyword-out-of-context index)

A computer produced index. Its preparation is similar to that for the KWIC index except that a keyword, common to a number of entries, is now printed as a heading to the listing of the entries concerned.

On-line operation

An on-line system is one in which a peripheral device, a terminal, operates under the control of and is directly connected to the central processing unit. Communication can be, for example, via a telephone line. In its more advanced forms, input data enter the computer directly from their point of origin and output data are transmitted directly to where they are used.

Relocation

Movement or loading of programmes or part of programmes from one location in core to another. This can be achieved by programming or special circuitry.

Software

The programming systems required to operate a computer. Includes executive programmes, compilers, assemblers, diagnostic routines, various utility programmes such as sorts, application programmes, etc.

Sorter/tabulator

Equipment used in a punched card operated system for sorting, listing.

Teletype

An electric typewriter capable of manual operation to produce hard copy and used as a terminal for transmitting to and receiving from the computer system information in a readable format.

It may also have attached to it a punch card reader for handling papertape.

Time-sharing

In general, the use of a given device by a number of other devices, one at a time, in rapid succession.

With regard to computer systems, it usually means that the central processor deals with a number of users programmes', at the same time by allocating to each small time-slices in rapid succession. The sequence in which the sharing takes place is automatically controlled by the executive programme and can either be predetermined or can be arranged on a request basis, within a priority scheme or not.

One of the aims of time-sharing is to provide a quicker response to users from the computer system, in particular as far as small jobs is concerned. Another aim is to achieve better utilization of the central processor by eliminating, where feasible, idling time which, for example, can occur when the processor is waiting for data to be read in from tape, disc or peripheral devices.

Transducer

Any device which converts input energy into output energy of another form. The most important class of transducer in instrumentation is the one in which the output is electrical in nature, because of the ease with which transmission, amplification and transformation of the output can be accomplished.

Utility programmes

Programmes which provide a support function in operations such as compiling, actual job runs, etc. Utility programmes are general purpose programmes designed to perform functions such as file conversion, house-keeping (e.g. storage, print or load programmes), aid in programme testing (e.g. error-detection), sorting, etc. Strictly speaking, sorting is a specific type of file conversion; however, it is so important in its own right that it is dealt with as a separate entity.

APPENDIX II

SOME SOURCES FOR COMPUTER PROGRAMMES
(PROGRAMME LIBRARIES)

The total number of computer programmes now available is very substantial indeed and is likely to be well in excess of 100,000 worldwide. Efforts have been made to publish comprehensive international directories† which aim to locate a significant proportion of these programmes. In general though, the user in search of a suitable programme, might try sources such as those indicated below:

† Directory of Computer Programmes, Science Associates Inc.

1. Computer manufacturers (and their users' groups)

As yet perhaps still the main source. They, in particular the larger ones, have available or access to considerable libraries of programmes, including both utility and a wide variety of standard application programmes.

The adoption, by some manufacturers, of an "unbundling" policy, whereby users are charged separately for the computer plus systems software on the one hand and applications software on the other, means that many application programmes may no longer be available free of charge.

2. National sources

In the U.S.A. the ACM (Association for Computing Machinery, 211 East 43 Street, New York, NY 10017) acts as a focal point. Its journal "Communications of the ACM" contains a section on algorithms which publishes fully documented programmes, mostly in ALGOL but more recently also in FORTRAN. The number of programmes thus published is still relatively modest, i.e. of the order of 500.

In the U.K. the BCS (British Computer Society, 29 Portland Place, London, W.1) does publish programmes in its journal but the main focal point for guidance on availability of programmes is the NCC (National Computing Centre, Quay House, Quay Street, Manchester 3). It also provides liaison on the BMD set of statistical programmes, i.e. a substantial collection of FORTRAN programmes, emanating from the Biomathematics Department, University of California, Los Angeles. The NCC index now covers nearly 5000 programmes and is rapidly expanding.

3. Specialized sources

Various research groups are co-operating in collecting and disseminating programmes relevant to their field of activities. As examples of such co-operative effort one might mention:

"Classification Programs Newsletter", distributed by the Medical Research Council Microbial Systematics Research Unit, University of Leicester, Leicester, England (first issue published March 1966).

"Taxometrics", a newsletter dealing with mathematical and statistical aspects of classification. Compiled by L. R. Hill, M.Sc., National Collection of Type Cultures, Central Public Health Laboratory, Colindale Avenue, London, N.W.9.

4. Published compilations of subject specific programmes

In view of the importance computer-use has attained in various subject fields there is a tendency to publish compilation of programmes applicable to specific subject areas. As an example one might mention:

P. A. D. de Maine and R. D. Seawright
Digital computer programs for physical chemistry
Macmillan, New York, 1963.

Hopefully this type of literature information will become as common as compilations dealing with research methods, data collections, etc.

APPENDIX III

SUPPLIERS OF COMPUTER EQUIPMENT

Suppliers of computers and peripheral equipment are so numerous that it is impossible, within the limitations of the present Chapter, to give a comprehensive listing. Nevertheless, it was felt useful to list some of the internationally known computer manufacturers, as well as some of the companies supplying peripherals and those marketing the small scientific computers which are now being installed at a rapidly increasing rate. For each of the manufacturers included some products or product types have been given but again this listing is not comprehensive.

British Olivetti Ltd. 30 Berkeley Square London, W.1.	Programma 10, P.203
Burroughs Corporation 6071 Second Avenue Detroit 32 Michigan 48232 U.S.A.	B.500, B.2500, B.3500 B.6500, B.7500, B.8500, etc.
Burroughs Machines Ltd Heathrow House Bath Road Cranford Hounslow Middx.	
California Computer Products Inc. 305 N. Muller Street Anaheim California 92803 U.S.A.	Graph plotters
Computer Technology Ltd. Eaton Road Hemel Hempstead Herts.	Modular One
Control Data Corporation 8100 34th Avenue South Minneapolis Minnesota 55420 U.S.A.	3000 and 6000 Series, etc.
Cossor Electronics Ltd. The Pinnacles Elizabeth Way Harlow Essex.	Visual Displays (DIDS 400 Display System)
Creed and Company Ltd. Hollingbury Brighton Sussex	Tape readers, punches, teletypes, etc.

Digital Equipment Corporation   PDP 8, PDP 9, PDP 10, etc.
146 Main Street
Maynard
Massachusetts 01754
U.S.A.

Digital Equipment Company Ltd.
3 Awkwright Road
Reading RG2 0LJ.

Electronic Associates Inc.   Analogue computers
185 Monmouth Parkway
West Long Branch
New Jersey 07764
U.S.A.

Electronic Associates Ltd.
Victoria Road
Burgess Hill
Sussex

Ferranti Ltd.   ARGUS computers and display systems, etc.
Hollinwood
Lancs.

General Electric   200, 400, 600 Series, etc.
P.O. Box 2918
Phoenix
Arizona 85002
U.S.A.

Hewlett Packard   HP 2114, 2115/2116, etc.
1501 Page Mill Road
Palo Alto
California 94304
U.S.A.

Hewlett Packard
224 Bath Road
Slough
Bucks.

Honeywell Inc.   H. 516, H. 1800, H. 4200, etc.
Old Connecticut Path   Series 32
Framingham
Massachusetts 01702
U.S.A.

Honeywell Ltd.
Great West Road
Brentford
Middx.

International Business Machines Corp. 555 Madison Avenue New York New York 10022 U.S.A.	360 Series, 1800, 1130, 370 Series, etc.
International Computers Ltd. I.C.L. House Putney London, S.W.15	System 4, I.C.T. 1900 Series, etc.
Mohawk Data Sciences Corporation P.O. Box 630 Harter Street Herkimer New York 13350 U.S.A.	MDS (Magnetic tape) data encoders, etc.
Mohawk Data Sciences— Great Britain Ltd. Prudential House Wellesley Road Croydon CR9 3LD Surrey.	
National Cash Register Co. Main and K Streets Dayton Ohio 45409 U.S.A.	390, 500 Series Century Series, etc.
National Cash Register Co. Ltd. 206 Marylebone Road London, N.W.1.	
Radio Corporation of America Camden New Jersey 08101 U.S.A.	Spectra 70 Series
Raytheon Company Spring Street Lexington Massachusetts U.S.A.	Display systems, Memories, etc.
Raytheon Overseas Ltd. Shelley House Noble Street London, E.C.2.	
Sanders Associates Inc. Nashua New Hampshire U.S.A.	Graphic displays

7

Scientific Control Corporation
14008 Distribution Way
Dallas
Texas 75234
U.S.A.

660–2, 670–2, 2700, etc.

Scientific Data Systems
1649 17th Street
Santa Monica
California 90404
U.S.A.

Sigma 7, SDS 940, etc.

Scientific Data Systems
I.L.I. House
Olympic Way
Wembley Park
Middx.

Teletype Corporation
55555 Touhy Avenue
Skokie
Illinois 60076
U.S.A.

Teletypes

Sperry Rand Corp.
Univac Division
Sperry Rand Building
New York
New York 10019
U.S.A.

1106, 1107, 1108, 1110;
418; 9000 Series, etc.

Sperry Rand Ltd.
Univac Division
Remington House
65 Holborn Viaduct
London, E.C.1.

University Computing Company
44 Gordon Square
London, W.C.1.

Computer Services

Varian Data Machines
2722 Michelson Drive
Irvine
California 92664
U.S.A.

Cope 45
620/i, etc.

Wang Laboratories Inc.
836 North Street,
Tewksbury
Massachusetts 01876
U.S.A.

300 Series

APPENDIX IV

SOME CURRENT COMPUTER OPERATED LITERATURE INFORMATION SERVICES

As might be expected, most of the use made of the computer operated literature information services is in the U.S.A. It has, in fact, been estimated that by now perhaps around 50,000 users are participating in the U.S.A. in computer operated SDI.

Some of the major facilities of this type are listed below. Services operated by an institute or company for its own use only have not been included.

A. Chemical Abstracts Service (American Chemical Society) Columbus, P.O.B. 1378, Ohio 43210

The Chemical Abstracts Service (CAS) is moving towards complete computer production of its publications.

Currently, the following combinations of printed and computer services are available:

1. *Printed current awareness services with computer tapes available:*

(a) *Chemical-biological activities* (CBAS). This service monitors ca. 650 journals for papers concerned with the interaction of organic compounds (drugs, pesticides, etc.) with biological systems (man, other animals, plants, micro-organisms etc.). Included are studies of metabolism and *in vitro* chemical reactions of biochemical interest. The bi-weekly printed issues as well as the tapes contain informative digests for ca. 16,000–17,000 selected papers per annum, and can be searched for subject terms, journal titles, authors, molecular formulae and registry numbers.

(b) *Chemical titles* (CT). The bi-weekly printed issues and tapes cover titles (ca. 125,000/annum) selected from ca. 650 journals. Search in this case restricted to subject terms appearing in the title as well as author names and journal titles.

(c) *Polymer science and technology* (POST). Covers papers from ca. 460 journals as well as patents from 25 countries. The tape as well as the printed version, issued bi-weekly, provides for each paper, report or patent an informative digest (ca. 20,000/annum) which can be searched for subject terms; in addition, one can search for authors, journal titles, molecular formulae etc. There are two sections POST–P, covering patents literature and POST–J, covering journal literature.

2. *Machine-readable current awareness services using computer tape*

(a) *CA condensates* (CAC). Covers titles, bibliographic citations and keyword index terms for all abstracts published in Chemical Abstracts (ca. 250,000 abstracts/annum). This is a magnetic tape service which corresponds with the printed weekly issue of Chemical Abstracts.

(b) *Basic journal abstracts* (BJA). Printed issues and tapes which cover complete abstracts (ca. 10,000/annum) from 35 chemical and chemical engineering journals. Hence in this case the full text of the abstracts can be searched for relevant subject terms, molecular formulae, etc.

3. *Machine-readable indexes on tape*

(a) *CA registry system.* This system is intended to cover all chemical structures mentioned in Chemical Abstracts to date. The system covers at present ca. $1\frac{3}{4}$

million structures, for each of which a complete structure description (in atom connection table representation) is available on magnetic tape for computer search. (b) *CA patent concordance*. A concordance relating to patents published in Chemical Abstracts from Vol. 56 (1962) onwards.

4. *Machine-readable library reference and record keeping tools*

Comprehensive list of periodicals for chemistry and chemical engineering. Covers ca. 25,000 journal titles and over 5000 monographs, including locations of these publications in over 400 of the world's major resource libraries.

Subscribers are encouraged to acquire the machine-readable files for use on their own computer systems. For subscribers without access to the necessary computer equipment, Chemical Abstracts provides search services on CAS computers for the tape services mentioned under 1 to 3 above.

B. National Library of Medicine (NLM)
Washington, D.C.

NLM has since 1964 operated a computer-based medical literature analysis and retrieval system (MEDLARS). The system used human indexers to assign the indexing terms according to the Library's thesaurus of terms "Medical Subject Headings" (ca. 7000 main headings).

The major product of the system is the printed "Index Medicus", a comprehensive monthly subject and author index to much of the world's biomedical journal literature (ca. 200,000 titles/annum, each of which appears three or four times under different headings).

A second type of product is the demand bibliography on a specialized medical subject, a retrospective search generated in response to an enquiry from an individual clinician or scientist. Many thousands of such demand searches are carried out each year producing on average 100–200 citations per search.

The third product is the recurrent bibliography, which provides citations to more specific and limited subject areas on a regular basis. They are produced in co-operation with leading national public and private professional groups, e.g. the Index to Dental Literature, a joint production of the NLM and the American Dental Association, or the Index to Rheumatology, produced co-operatively with the American Rheumatism Association.

MEDLARS is operated on a decentralized basis. Apart from the central system at Washington, there are five university-based MEDLARS stations in the U.S.A. (Harvard, UCLA, University of Michigan, University of Colorado and the University of Alabama). In addition, some stations have been established abroad, e.g. National Lending Library, Boston Spa, England, and Karolinska Institute, Stockholm) which are providing individual bibliographic services to local users via use of the MEDLARS tapes.

C. Biosciences Information Service of Biological Abstracts (BIOSIS)
2100 Arch Street, Philadelphia, Pa. 19103

Since 1969 BIOSIS is supplying the BA Previews tapes, corresponding to each issue of Biological Abstracts and Bio Research Index. The tapes contain abstract number, title, index terms, authors' names, CROSS codes, biosystematic index codes and primary journal reference and are available for distribution approximately one month earlier than the corresponding printed issues. As with CA Condensates nearly 250,000 items per year are covered by the tapes which are supplied on a bi-weekly basis (monthly for the Bio Research Index).

In 1970 BIOSIS announced a further magnetic tape service, the Toxitapes implemented as part of the Specialized Information Service programme of the National Library of Medicine. Two tapes will be released quarterly, one covering Industrial Toxicology and the other Pharmaceutical Toxicology at the rate of 2000–3000 citations per year each.

D. Institute for Scientific Information (ISI)
325 Chestnut Street, Philadelphia, Pa. 19106

Since 1965 the Institute has operated its ASCA (Automatic Subject Citation Alert) system. It makes use of the input to Science Citation Index, which covers around 1900 journals in the fields of chemistry, biomedicine, physics, etc. About 300,000 current articles are entered into the system each year.

Via the ASCA system a subscriber can have his "interest profile" matched each week at Philadelphia against new entries (ca. 6000 items); he receives a weekly printed report of current articles. In the selection, the following options can be used; presence in the title of specific terms or phases, presence of given author names, journal titles, names of organizations at which the work was done, citation of a given paper, book, thesis, patent or author. ISI has also established a computer operated search and alert system for information on chemical structures included in their "Index Chemicus" publication. (ca. 150,000 structures/annum).

E. Excerpta Medica Foundation
119–123 Herengracht, Amsterdam-C, Netherlands

The Excerpta Medica service covers ca. 80,000 abstracts (200,000 citations) annually, selected from 3000 biomedical journals. Like Index Medicus (MEDLARS) the Excerpta Medica system is fully computer based resulting in a wide variety of services provided, i.e. printed publications and their magnetic tape versions, current awareness and retrospective searches by computer, specialist publications, etc.

As an example of one of the specialist services provided one might mention the Comprehensive Drugs Literature Tape Service which covers, on magnetic tape, all available information on drugs from the bio-medical literature.

F. National Drug Code Directory Magnetic Tape Extract

In connection with the service, mentioned earlier and provided by Excerpta Medica, it is of interest to indicate a corresponding service from the U.S. Clearinghouse for Scientific and Technical Information (National Bureau of Standards, Department of Commerce, Springfield, Virginia 22151).

It covers the drug information supplied to the U.S. Food and Drug Administration by pharmaceutical companies co-operating in the implementation of the National Drug Code (NDC) System. Each product is assigned a 9-character code; on the Directory tapes these are associated with the product name(s), manufacturer or repackager, dosage form, route of administration, strength and the trade packages in which the product is marketed.

G. National Agricultural Library (NAL)
U.S. Department of Agriculture, Washington, D.C. 20250

NAL is making available magnetic tape files, corresponding with their "Bibliography of Agriculture" (ca. 150,000 papers/annum), which is no longer distributed by the NAL in printed form.

Within the NAL the Pesticides Information Centre produces the Pesticides Documentation Bulletin, covering ca. 30,000 papers/annum.

H. INSPEC (Information service in physics, electro-technology and control)
Institution of Electrical Engineers, Savoy Place, London, W.C.2

This service is the first comprehensive computer-based abstracting and current awareness service in the U.K. It is concerned with the computer-aided production of "Science Abstracts", which in fact consists of three abstract journals covering physics, electrical and electronics engineering, and control, together with the associated current awareness periodicals called "Current Papers". The machine-readable data-base is used, among others, to provide a weekly SDI service for some 600 research workers in electronics.

I. COMPENDEX
Engineering Index Inc., 345 East 47th Street, New York, NY 10016

Covers ca. 5500 engineering publications monthly. Current awareness (profile) searches are carried out for customers; tapes are supplied to customers requiring to carry out their own searches.

J. American Petroleum Institute (API)
555 Madison Avenue, New York, NY 10022

The API Central Abstracting and Indexing Service has since early 1964 been issuing to subscribers magnetic tapes covering journal literature, papers presented at meetings and patents relevant to petroleum refining and the petrochemical industry.

About 150 journals are covered and the number of journal articles and papers included is around 3000–4000 per year; in all over 60,000 publications are recorded in the system.

K. MARC (Machine-Readable Catalogue)
Library of Congress, Card Division, Building 159, Navy Yard Annex, Washington, D.C. 20541

This catalogue on magnetic tape, issued by the Library of Congress on a weekly basis, covers the bibliographic [information for ca. 60,000 books/monographs published annually in the English language. Coverage is gradually being extended to include non-English language literature via co-operation with appropriate organizations in the countries concerned.

L. Derwent Publications Ltd
Rochdale House, 128 Theobalds Road, London, W.C.1

Provides magnetic tape files corresponding with its various printed documentation bulletins, i.e. RINGDOC, FARMDOC, PLASDOC, AGDOC, etc., covering journal and patent literature in a number of subject areas of interest to the chemical industry.

M. INTREDIS (Register system for literature retrieval in forest pathology)
Pesticides Information Center, U.S. Department of Agriculture, National Agricultural Library, 14th and Independence Avenue, Washington, D.C. 20250

A tape service covering forest pathology literature from 1930 to date. In addition to the supply of tapes, retrospective searches are provided.

N. Mass Spectrometry Data Centre
Atomic Weapons Research Establishment, Aldermaston, Eerkshire, England

Was established in 1966 to provide internationally a comprehensive data and information service to all users of mass spectrometry. Covers around 200 journals in the fields of chemistry, physics, geology and biology. Computer facilities are used in the production of the monthly Mass Spectrometry Bulletin, the corresponding tape files being available for retrospective retrieval. Tapes containing data on and references to actual spectra can be made available to subscribers for their own use.

O. Gas Chromatography Literature
Preston Technical Abstracts Company, 909 Pitner Avenue, Evanston, Illinois 60202

A service covering the gas chromatography literature from 1952 onwards (over 15,000 publications).

Users can subscribe to the complete tape file with semi-annual updates or have individual searches carried out.

The above listing has dealt principally with organizations producing machine readable data bases and providing computer search facilities using such data bases. In recent years a considerable number of information centres have been established, which restrict themselves' to the latter task, i.e. searching magnetic data base(s). The prime example of this type of operation is perhaps the Information Science Centre at the University of Georgia (Athens, Georgia 30601) which makes use of a dozen magnetic tape data-bases (covering chemistry, biology, engineering, etc.) to service over a thousand users.

Similar centres, albeit it on a more modest scale, have been or are being set up in other countries, e.g. in the U.K. the United Kingdom Chemical Information Service (UKCIS) (The University, Nottingham NG7 2RD), whilst at present dealing principally with data-bases obtained from the Chemical Abstracts Service, Columbus (see A above), is gradually widening its scope to provide a computer search service covering biological topics as well.

The services mentioned in the above account form only a small part of the various computer operated literature information services now in operation. Because of the rapid expansion in this type of activity it is obviously not feasible to provide a comprehensive listing. The main purpose has been to indicate the range of services now available from large international services covering wide subject fields to highly specialized services dealing with relatively narrow fields. The increasing use of computer facilities in journal production and in the operation of documentation services, if properly exploited, should provide the research worker with a more convenient and more effective means of utilizing the ever expanding volume of literature.

CHAPTER IV

Principles of Biological Assay

M. ROBERTS AND C. B. C. BOYCE

Shell Research Limited, Woodstock Agricultural Research Centre,
Sittingbourne, Kent

I. INTRODUCTION

It is well recognized that the response of living matter to stimuli can be extremely specific and that the use of the biological indicator often has few peers in qualitative assay methods. On the other hand the value of the biological assay, or bioassay as it is commonly called, as a sound quantitative method of analysis is not always appreciated. It is true that because of the complexity of living material, biological assays are subject to far greater variability than are physical or chemical methods of analysis. However, variation of this sort can be considerably reduced by good experimental design, as we intend to show in this Chapter.

It is important to design bioassay experiments properly as it is rare for a comprehensive statistical analysis to make up for any deficiencies there may be, whereas a well conceived experiment will often give useful and valid conclusions even without full statistical analysis of the data.

We shall discuss factors which influence the precision of bioassay techniques, such as the magnitude and number of doses of the material to be tested, the choice of organism for the assay, as well as the number used and the way that they are allocated to the doses. We shall also discuss some of the methods available for the analysis of the results because it is the considerations of the analysis of the dose/response relationship which govern the principles of design.

We shall only be able to discuss the subject briefly within the constraints of a short Chapter but, fortunately, there are several books to which the reader can refer for a much more comprehensive treatment. Some of the most notable of these are: "Probit Analysis", Finney (1952), "The Statistics of Bioassay", Bliss (1952), and "Statistical Methods in Biological Assay", Finney (1964).

II. TYPES OF BIOASSAY

Bioassays can be classified into several types depending on the nature of the responses that are observed. The simplest type, which is usually the least practical, is the *direct assay* in which each subject receives a continually increasing dose until its tolerance level is reached and it responds. The dose just sufficient to cause a response is then measured directly, and by repeating the exercise on several subjects a mean effective dose, together with a measure of its precision, can be calculated. This method is usually impractical for several reasons. There may be practical difficulties associated with applying continually increasing doses; there may be a time lag between the administration of the effective dose and response, during which time the dose has been further increased, thereby biasing the observations; or the response to a continually increasing dose may be different from that of the same quantity administered in a single dose because of the subject's ability to metabolize the material being assayed. Consequently, it is usually necessary to adopt a procedure in which the subjects receive a range of single doses and observations are made of the degree of response at each dose level which are then used to derive the dose/response relationship.

One such type of assay is known as the "*quantal assay*", because the subject's response is all-or-nothing, as in a mortality assay where, at a given time, a subject has either survived or died. In this case the degree of response cannot be deduced from the response of the individual subjects, but all the subjects receiving identical treatments have to be pooled into groups to give the observed percentage responses at each dose. The responses for this type of assay are particularly characterized by having well defined limits, viz. 0 and 100%.

In contrast, the *quantitative assay* has continuously graded responses so that each subject gives a direct measure of the degree of response. Growth-inhibition assays are of this type. A common difficulty with quantitative assays is that one of the extreme responses is usually not well defined and has to be estimated from measurements on control subjects. For example in a growth-inhibition assay the minimum growth will be zero but the maximum growth will not have a clearly defined limit and will need to be estimated by including subjects which receive zero dose and then calculating their mean growth. The amount of growth for the treated subjects can then be expressed as percentages of the mean growth of the control subjects. As the extreme response is determined experimentally, and is itself subject to error, the precision of the observed percentage responses will also include these errors and will therefore be reduced.

Another type of assay, the *scored response assay*, is really a hybrid form of the quantal and quantitative assays and has responses which are graded by means of a scoring or rating system which indicates the degree of response. Strictly speaking, these are quantitative assays but they have well defined response limits and if the observations are aimed at providing a measure of percentage response the results should be analysable by very similar methods to those used for analysing quantal assays.

The design considerations for quantal and quantitative assays are much the same, as they will tend to have similar dose/response relationships and similar relationships between response and the size of the experimental errors. The quantitative assay has an advantage in having analysable results for each subject but this is offset by the precision of the assay results having to be estimated from the experimental data whereas the precision of the quantal response can usually be derived theoretically.

III. THE DOSE/RESPONSE CURVE

The dose/response relationships which provide the basis for the design and analysis of bioassays can take many forms, and while there is not often a theoretical basis for deriving them, a vast accumulation of experience shows that they work well in practice. There is however an underlying coherence between the most common forms of the dose/response curve. This can be illustrated by applying a progressive series of restraints to the most general form of the empirical relationship between dose and response:

$$\text{Response} = \text{function}\,(a + b\,\text{dose}^\lambda) \qquad (1)$$

where a and b are constants to be determined from the data and λ is a constant which is characteristic of the assay.

Many assays have relationships with $\lambda = 1$, while those described by equation (2), which is the limiting form of equation (1) as λ approaches zero, are even more common.

$$\text{Response} = \text{function } (a + b \log \text{dose}) \qquad (2)$$

Experience shows that most assays described by equations (1) and (2) are of the sigmoidal form illustrated in Fig. 1. Thus in a quantal assay a few subjects respond at the lower end of the dose scale, the majority respond in the middle dose range, and at the upper end of the dose scale all but a few subjects have responded. It is mathematically difficult to estimate the dose/response relationship quantitatively with the curve in this form but this can be overcome by transforming the units of both scales so that the dose/response relationship becomes linear. Using the power transformation $x = \text{dose}^\lambda$ for equation (1) and the logarithmic transformation $x = \log$ dose for equation (2) simplifies the dose/response relationship to:

$$\text{Response} = \text{function } (a + bx) \qquad (3)$$

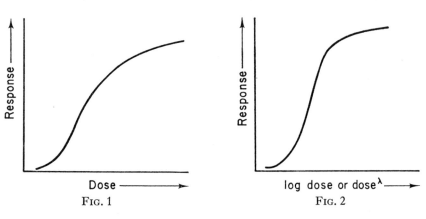

FIG. 1   FIG. 2

The relationship is now of the symmetrical sigmoidal form illustrated in Fig. 2, and to reduce this to a linear form we need to be able to describe the response function. A number of ways of doing this have been proposed of which the method of probits is the most commonly used. Its derivation need not concern us and we shall simply accept that it is a mathematical device based on the assumption that the tolerance of individual subjects to the transformed dose follows a Normal (or Gaussian) distribution. It is sufficient for our purposes to accept that tables are available for translating percentage responses directly into probit responses ("Biometrika Tables", 1958, and Fisher and Yates, 1963) and that probability graph paper is available with percentages printed on the probit scale so that it is possible to plot results directly without reference to a table of probits (see Table IV, p. 171 and Fig. 4).

Several other methods for transforming the response scale have been advocated, e.g. the logit and angle transformations (Finney, 1964, Chapter 17) but these methods give very similar results to those of the probit method and as the transformation used will have no practical influence on the design we will not discuss them further. Strictly speaking, these methods of transformation are only applicable to quantal assays, but in practice they can also be valuable for analysing quantitative assays.

We can now formulate two important types of dose/response relationships, both linear and both based on equation (1), as:

$$\text{Probit response} = a + bx \tag{4}$$

where $x = $ log dose for one, and $x = $ dose$^\lambda$ for the other.

However, not all assays require transformation of the response scale and there is an important group of bioassays in which the function of dose on response is unity. For these, equation (1) immediately simplifies to:

$$\text{Response} = a + b \text{ dose}^\lambda \tag{5}$$

which in its limiting form, as λ approaches zero, reduces to:

$$\text{Response} = a + b \text{ log dose} \tag{6}$$

Finally, when $\lambda = 1$, equation (5) becomes:

$$\text{Response} = a + b \text{ dose} \tag{7}$$

so that we can add three further linear forms of the dose/response relationship based on equation (1):

$$\text{Response} = a + bx \tag{8}$$

where $x = $ dose$^\lambda$, log dose, or simply dose.

As the dose/response relationships given by equations (4)–(8) are linear, the constant b measures the slope of the relationship.

The vast majority of biological assays will comply with one of the five dose/response relationships represented by equations (4) and (8). As might be expected, the complexity of the relevant dose/response relationship tends to parallel the complexity of the organism used to measure the response. For example, assays depending on whole animals tend to comply with the most complex dose/response curve and require the probit response/log dose or power dose transformation, whereas for the assay based on single cell organisms the response may be directly proportional to the dose so that no transformation of either scale is required.

A. The dose/response parameters

Let us assume that the validity of one of the dose/response relationships has been established and that the constants in the relationship have been calculated, together with the estimate of their precision (the details of the methods for doing this are described on p. 163 *et seq.*). We can then show how the relationship can be used to derive a number of parameters, for example the dose required to produce a particular response and its precision, or the relative potency of two samples.

If we let the relevant dose/response relationship be:

$$y = a + bx \tag{9}$$

where $y =$ the transformed response and $x =$ the transformed dose, and let EDp be shorthand for the p% effective dose and m be the EDp in its transformed units, then

$$m = \frac{y(\text{p}) - a}{b} \tag{10}$$

Now a is estimated as $\bar{y} - b\bar{x}$, where $\bar{y}$ is the mean transformed response and $\bar{x}$ is the mean of the transformed doses. In many cases the various observations will not have equal precision and therefore $\bar{y}$ and $\bar{x}$ will be weighted means.

It follows that:

$$m = \frac{y(\text{p}) - \bar{y}}{b} + \bar{x} \tag{11}$$

The EDp is then found by the detransformation of m. The variance† of m can be calculated from:

$$\text{variance } (m) = \frac{1}{b^2} \left[\text{variance } (\bar{y}) + (m - \bar{x})^2 \text{ variance } (b) \right] \tag{12}$$

The precision limits of EDp will depend on p approximately as illustrated in Fig. 3, the actual point at which the variance is minimal depending on the distribution of responses obtained for the treatment groups.

As the actual responses are not known before testing, the minimum point will tend to vary, but over a series of experiments the most precisely defined dose will be for 50% response, particularly in well designed experiments. On *a priori* grounds therefore the 50% response (ED50) will often be chosen as the parameter of interest.

In order to calculate the relative potency (α) of two preparations of the same material which differ only in strength, we use the following property of the dose/response relationships: if the dose for p% response with

† Variance is a standard measure of precision which is used to calculate a number of different practical measures of precision such as fiducial limits.

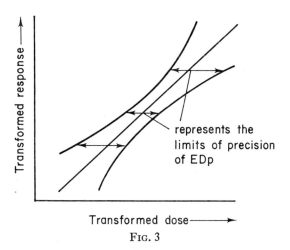

Transformed dose ⟶

FIG. 3

preparation B is α times the dose for p% response with preparation A then preparation A has α times the potency of preparation B,

i.e.
$$\alpha = \frac{\text{EDp}\,(B)}{\text{EDp}\,(A)} \qquad (13)$$

and this is constant for all values of p.

When the power transformation is used the responses are given by:

$$y(p) = a_1 + b_1\,[\text{EDp}\,(A)]^\lambda \text{ for preparation } A$$

and $\qquad y(p) = a_2 + b_2\,[\text{EDp}\,(B)]^\lambda \text{ for preparation } B$

For zero dose of either preparation both responses must be the same so $a_1 = a_2$, hence:
$$b_1\,[\text{EDp}\,(A)]^\lambda = b_2\,[\text{EDp}\,(B)]^\lambda \qquad (14)$$

from which we obtain:

$$\alpha^\lambda = \left[\frac{\text{EDp}\,(B)}{\text{EDp}\,(A)}\right]^\lambda = \frac{b_1}{b_2} = m_{1,\,2} \qquad (15)$$

When no dose transformation is required (i.e. $\lambda = 1$) this simplifies further to:

$$\alpha = \frac{b_1}{b_2} = m_{1,\,2} \qquad (16)$$

Consequently assays of the type involving equations (15) and (16) are known as *Slope Ratio* assays.

The variance of $m_{1,\,2}$ is calculated from the expression:

$$\text{variance}\,(m_{1,\,2}) = \frac{1}{b_2{}^2}\,[\text{variance}\,(b_1) + m_{1,\,2}{}^2\,\text{variance}\,(b_2)] \qquad (17)$$

When the log transformation is used, for equal responses, we have:

$$a_1 + b_1 \log [\text{EDp } (A)] = a_2 + b_2 \log [\text{EDp } (B)] \tag{18}$$

Now $\log \alpha = \log \text{EDp } (B) - \log \text{EDp } (A)$ which must be independent of p, and as the above expression also holds for all values of p, b_1 and b_2 must be equal, i.e. the relationships are parallel. If b is the common slope, it follows from (18) that:

$$\log \alpha = \frac{a_1 - a_2}{b} \tag{19}$$

As before, a_1 is estimated as $\bar{y}_1 - b\bar{x}_1$, and a_2 as $\bar{y}_2 - b\bar{x}_2$, where $\bar{y}_1$, $\bar{y}_2$ are the mean responses for each material and $\bar{x}_1$ and $\bar{x}_2$ are the mean log doses.

$$\therefore \log \alpha = \frac{\bar{y}_1 - \bar{y}_2}{b} - \bar{x}_1 + \bar{x}_2 = m_{1,\,2} \tag{20}$$

which gives the relative strengths of the preparations. The variance of $m_{1,\,2}$ can be calculated from the expression:

$$\text{variance } (m_{1,\,2}) = \frac{1}{b^2} [\text{var } (\bar{y}_1) + \text{var } (\bar{y}_2) + (m_{1,\,2} + \bar{x}_1 - \bar{x}_2)^2 \, \text{var } (b)] \tag{21}$$

IV. DESIGN OF BIOASSAYS

A. Choice of doses

The fitting of any straight line is most efficient when the points on the transformed dose axis are equally spaced. The optimum spacing between the doses will therefore depend on which transformation is appropriate, i.e. the doses should be equally spaced on a linear, logarithmic or power scale. The actual interval used in any particular assay is determined by the slope of the dose/response curve and the number of dose levels necessary to achieve an acceptable level of precision.

The slope of the dose/response curve measures the rate at which the magnitude of the response changes with increasing dose, and in practice it can vary considerably. As it is such a fundamental factor in the selection of doses, much the simplest policy for choosing a suitable range of doses is to run a pilot experiment. The alternative of running a single experiment with a large range of doses and small increments between them is very costly in time and effort.

It is desirable to cover a wide range of responses to define the dose/response relationship precisely but in a full statistical analysis the transformed observations are usually weighted according to the degree of precision, and the extreme values have little weight, particularly when the basic dose/response curve is sigmoidal. For example, in probit analysis virtually no weight is given to the extreme responses of 0 and 100% and very little to those outside the 5 to 95% range. Therefore a successful assay will include responses of 5% and 95% for the extreme doses and concentrate on doses which give responses within this range. An adequate number of doses giving responses in this range are required to be confident of the validity of the dose/response transformations. Furthermore, in some cases the precision of the parameters may have to be estimated from the data and then it will be a great advantage to have tested several dose levels. As a rough guide at least four observations in the 5–95% response range should be aimed at.

B. Choice and allocation of subjects

There may be a variety of species from which the test subjects can be chosen when the bioassay is used in the analytical sense, as in the standardization of potency and in monitoring the purification of natural products. In this case the choice depends on balancing the accuracy obtainable with a given species against the availability of the species and the complexity of the assay. If it is economical to do so it is best to use the species with the least variability between subjects and therefore with the steepest dose/response curve. But whatever species is used every effort should be made to see that the subjects are as homogeneous as possible. For example, they should be bred under standard conditions and should be of uniform size and age. Naturally, the more subjects that can be used the more precise the result will be, but equal numbers should be used at each dose level as this helps to ensure that no point biases the result and has the additional advantage that it can simplify the analysis if one of the approximate methods is used.

To avoid any unsuspected or uncontrollable lack of uniformity, the subjects should be randomly allocated to the doses. A convenient way to do this is to allocate a random order to the doses, using a set of random tables, and then treat the subjects as they come to hand. For example, if ten subjects are to be used at each of six dose levels then ten random orders of the six doses should be selected and the first subject allocated to the first dose of the first random order, the second subject to the second dose of the first order and so on until the sixtieth subject is allocated to the last dose of the tenth random order.

Random allocation of subjects minimizes the possibility of a systematic deviation about the dose/response line arising from biases in the selection of subjects and so guards against false conclusions being inferred about the form of the relationship. However, allocation of subjects can be further refined if the subjects can be divided into relatively homogeneous groups before testing. For example, groups could be made up of litter mates of the same sex or from the same batch, as these are likely to have more similar responses than are those from a more varied background. Thus if ten subjects were to be tested at each of six dose levels the subjects could be allocated by forming ten homogeneous groups each containing six subjects and then randomly assigning one subject from each group to each dose level. Each group of subjects would then cover all dose levels and the mean response at each level would not be biased by differences between groups. Of course this sort of design depends on being able to form groups each containing as many subjects as doses. There are several other ways left of improving design, for example Latin squares and balanced incomplete blocks, but these are outside the scope of this Chapter and can be referred to in the texts recommended above (see p. 154).

C. Relative potency

So far we have concentrated on the design of assays which involve testing several doses of a single material. Situations often arise however where materials have to be assayed relative to one another. In these cases the design principles which have already been discussed concerning choice of doses, allocation of subjects, etc., are simply extended to incorporate a number of further considerations.

When the problem is to measure potency with respect to a standard sample of the same material it is normally assumed that one test sample is merely a dilution of the other and that the diluents have no biological activity. Their relative potency will therefore be independent of the method used to assay them. This simple concept is valuable because it leads to an absolute value of potency which is independent of arbitrary units. Logically it would be convenient to calibrate the assay by determining a precise dose/response curve for the standard and subsequently bioassaying only the unknown. Unfortunately bioassays are rarely sufficiently consistent to make this feasible and so the unknown and standard have to be assayed in parallel. It is best to arrange the assay so that both samples are used in the same effective dose range with the mean response being as near as possible to 50%. Ideally both samples should be treated essentially as replicates, i.e. the same number of doses, spaced similarly, each with the same number of subjects, should be used.

D. Environmental control

Small differences in temperature, humidity, light intensity, pH, etc., may lead to a change in the sensitivity of the subject as well as to unsuspected changes in the effective dose. The environmental conditions of the test should therefore be as uniform as possible, but to avoid any systematic variation, e.g. a temperature gradient, the subjects or groups of subjects should be placed randomly in the holding area.

E. Natural responses and control groups

The response observed in a quantal assay is often a summation of the effect of the stimulus together with that of a natural, background response, in which case the subjects responding naturally are effectively not part of the test and their response has to be subtracted from the total response (see p. 175 *et seq.*). Also in quantitative assays, such as the growth inhibition type, it may be necessary to use the natural or control response to define one of the end points, which will frequently be maximum growth (see p. 182 *et seq.*).

If, as will usually be the case, the natural response rate is not known beforehand, it will have to be determined experimentally. A control group of subjects receiving zero dose (or the same treatment apart from the active ingredient) should therefore always be included in an assay to check whether there is a natural response and if so to provide the data to make the necessary corrections. The optimum number of subjects to use, like most things in a bioassay, depends on the property being examined and so cannot be stated specifically. However, it is a good working rule to have at least as many subjects in the control group as there are in each of the groups receiving treatment.

It will be obvious that the maximum utilization of subjects will occur when control response is at a minimum. Therefore one of the considerations in selecting a particular assay procedure will be a low natural response.

V. ANALYSIS OF BIOASSAY DATA

We showed earlier (p. 158) how various parameters of interest can be derived from the basic dose/response relationship and in fact it is the derivation of this relationship which is central to all analyses of bioassay data. Once a curve has been fitted and an estimate of its precision obtained only one or two further steps are usually needed to calculate the required parameters and their precision. However, a number of factors affect the exact form of the estimation of the relationship; whether the response is quantal or quantitative; the number of responses which are some distance from the extreme responses and so lie on the steep, almost linear part of the sigmoid curve; or whether the precision varies with response, making the assignment of weights to the responses necessary. The effects of these factors will be shown in the following examples which illustrate the various methods of estimating the dose/response relationships.

We shall limit ourselves to the more elementary types of analysis which will not be beyond the scope of the non-statistician. The most comprehensive methods of analysis require some statistical knowledge or access to a computer which is programmed to do the analysis, consequently some sources of programmes are given later (p. 186).

A. Analysis of quantal assays

Some of the methods available for analysing quantal assays will be exemplified by using the following data which were obtained by Bond, Boyce and French (1969) during purification studies on *Bacillus thuringiensis* exotoxin:

TABLE I

Dose of exotoxin (ml)	$\log_{10}$ (dose × 100)	Number of larvae treated (n)	Number responding (r)	% response $p(= r/n \times 100)$	Empirical probit y
0·4	1·60	20	20	100	∞
0·2	1·30	20	19	95	6·64
0·1	1·00	20	16	80	5·84
0·05	0·70	20	10	50	5·00
0·025	0·40	20	2	10	3·72
0·01	0	20	1	5	3·36
Control		20	0	0	—

In assays of this type for which the response is all or nothing (in this case the inhibition of development of *Musca domestica* (house fly) larvae) experience has shown that the probit transformation of response and the logarithmic transformation of doses are usually the best transformations to use. The form of analysis then used is called "Probit Analysis", though this term is sometimes also used in a generic sense to cover cases when the logit and angle transformations are adopted. The percentage responses at each dose are first calculated (column 5) and these are then transformed to empirical probits (column 6) by reference to Table IX of Fisher and Yates (1963) or Table 6 of "Biometrika Tables" (1958).† These are conventionally referred to as empirical since they refer to actual observed responses and this distinguishes them from the expected probits which are the probits predicted by the fitted dose/response relationship. The doses are multiplied by 100 and converted to logarithms (the factor of 100 is used for convenience to give positive logarithms). The analysis is then basically concerned with estimating a and b in the dose/response relationship:

$$\text{Probit response} = a + b \log_{10} (\text{dose} \times 100)$$

† See also Table IV, p. 171 this Chapter.

1. *Graphical method*

For this method the responses are plotted against dose level, the curve is fitted by eye and the required parameters are read from the graph. In some assays there may be enough points on the linear part of the sigmoid curve for satisfactory results to be obtained by plotting the % response

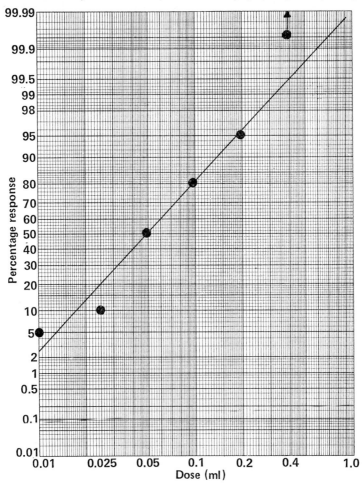

FIG. 4. Graphical analysis of quantal assay data.

on a linear scale against the transformed dose values. However, it will usually be a simple matter to obtain the empirical probits from tables and plot them against transformed doses, or, as we have done in Fig. 4, to use probability paper which gives percentage response on the probit scale and doses on the transformed scale.

The 0·4 ml dose level gave 100% response and so has an infinite probit value which is off the scale of the graph and it is therefore ignored in fitting the dose/response curve. The linear relationship which can be fitted by eye to the remaining five points suggests that the choice of the probit/log dose transformation is justified.

The ED50 can then be read directly from the graph. In this case the dose corresponding to 50% response on the fitted line is 0·051 ml.

The slope of the relationship, b, can be obtained by considering two points on the line (x_1, p_1) and (x_2, p_2) and calculating:

$$b = \frac{y(p_1) - y(p_2)}{\log(x_1) - \log(x_2)}$$

where $y(p)$ is the probit for p% response.

We can choose points which simplify the denominator in this expression so that:

$$b = \frac{y(80·0\%) - y(2·3\%)}{\log(0·1) - \log(0·01)}$$

$$= \frac{5·84 - 3·00}{1}$$

$$= 2·84.$$

Litchfield and Fertig (1941) have given an approximate method for calculating the variance† of the transformed ED50. This depends on the points being more or less evenly distributed about the 50% response, there being approximately equal numbers of subjects at each dose level, and the responses being in the range 5%–95%. Their formula is:

$$\text{Variance (log ED50)} = \frac{1}{b^2(N/2)},$$

where N is the total number of subjects tested.

As the extreme point was not used in fitting the line we satisfy the conditions of the approximation. Twenty subjects were tested at each of the remaining five doses and therefore $N = 100$.

Therefore:

$$\text{Variance (log ED50)} \frac{1}{2·84^2(100/2)}$$

$$= 0·00248$$

† See footnote p. 158.

Therefore the approximate 95% fiducial limits for log (ED50) are:

$$\log (0.051) \pm 1.96\dagger \sqrt{0.00248}$$
$$= \bar{2}.7076 \pm 0.0976$$
$$= \bar{2}.6100 \text{ to } \bar{2}.8052$$

Transforming back to the original units gives

ED50 $= 0.051$ ml with 95% fiducial limits 0.041 to 0.064 ml.

It is also possible to check that the observed responses do not deviate significantly from the fitted line. Deviations about this line are known as "heterogeneity" and its significance is assessed by means of a factor called the heterogeneity χ^2 which is calculated from the data shown in Table II.

TABLE II

Heterogeneity calculations

Dose of exotoxin (ml)	Expected % response (100P)	Expected no. affected (nP)	Observed no. affected (r)	Deviation (r − nP)	$\dfrac{(r-nP)^2}{nP(1-P)}$
0·4	99·4	19·88	20	0·12	0·12
0·2	95·5	19·1	19	−0·1	0·01
0·1	80·0	16·0	16	0	0
0·05	49·0	9·8	10	0·2	0·01
0·025	19·0	3·8	2	−1·8	1·05
0·01	2·3	0·46	1	0·54	0·65
			Heterogeneity χ^2_4		1·84

The expected percentage responses (100P) are read from the graph as the percentages predicted by the fitted line for each dose tested. From these the expected numbers of subjects responding are calculated as nP where n is the number of subjects in the dose group, which in this case was 20. The observed number affected in each group (r) is written down from Table I and the deviation of the observed from the expected number affected $(r - nP)$ is worked out. The heterogeneity χ^2 can then be

† The factor 1·96 which multiplies the square root of the variance is derived from the Normal distribution. If a parameter has true value μ and estimates of it are Normally distributed with variance σ^2, then 95% of the estimates will lie in the range $\mu \pm 1.96\sigma$, hence there is a 95% probability that μ will lie within $\pm 1.96\sigma$ of its estimated value. This probability is called fiducial probability and the limits $\pm$ 1·96σ about the estimate are called the fiducial limits of the value of the parameter. Limits can be calculated for other percentage probabilities and Table I of Fisher and Yates (1963) gives the relevant multiplying factors.

calculated from the expression:

$$\chi_\gamma^2 = \sum \frac{(r-nP)^2}{nP(1-P)}$$

where γ is called the degrees of freedom and is two less than the number of treatment groups. Therefore in our example $\gamma = 4$ and $\chi_4^2 = 1\cdot84$.

The significance of this figure is obtained from Fisher and Yates (1963) Table IV, Distribution of χ^2. It is considered to be significant at the level α if the heterogeneity χ^2 is greater than the value given at the intersection of the α probability column and the degrees of freedom row (n in the Tables). The 0·05 probability value for 4 degrees of freedom is given as 9·488 which is clearly not exceeded by the calculated heterogeneity χ^2 and so we conclude that there is no significant heterogeneity in this example. We therefore have no reason to doubt either the validity of our chosen dose/response model or the proper randomization of the subjects.

2. Unweighted regression method

This method is very similar to the graphical method with the exception that the line is fitted by calculation instead of by eye. This is done by considering only those points with responses in the range 5% to 95% and doing a linear regression of empirical probits (y) on the logarithms of concentration or as we shall do, to avoid negative values, on the logarithms of $100 \times$ dose (x).

The y and x values are written down as shown in Table III and the sums over the treatment groups of y, y^2, x, x^2 and xy are calculated, ignoring the groups with extreme responses (shown in brackets).

TABLE III

Empirical probit (y)	log (dose × 100) (x)
(∞)	(1·60)
6·64	1·30
5·84	1·00
5·00	0·70
3·72	0·40
3·36	0

$\Sigma y = 24\cdot56$ $\Sigma x = 3\cdot40$
$\Sigma y^2 = 128\cdot3232$ $\Sigma x^2 = 3\cdot3400$
                $\Sigma xy = 19\cdot4600$

Also note that the number of doses, k, $= 5$.

The sums of squares and products corrected for the mean values, Syy, Sxx, Sxy, are then calculated.

$$Syy = \Sigma y^2 - (\Sigma y)^2/k = 128\cdot3232 - \frac{(24\cdot56)^2}{5} = 7\cdot684$$

$$Sxx = \Sigma x^2 - (\Sigma x)^2/k = 3\cdot3400 - \frac{(3\cdot40)^2}{5} = 1\cdot028$$

$$Sxy = \Sigma xy - (\Sigma x)(\Sigma y)/k = 19\cdot4600 - \frac{(3\cdot40)(24\cdot56)}{5} = 2\cdot759$$

The mean x and y values, $\bar{x}$ and $\bar{y}$, are also calculated:

$$\bar{y} = \frac{\Sigma y}{k} = 4\cdot912; \quad \bar{x} = \frac{\Sigma \bar{x}}{k} = 0\cdot680.$$

The slope, b, of the dose/response relationship is given by:

$$b = \frac{Sxy}{Sxx} = \frac{2\cdot759}{1\cdot028} = 2\cdot68$$

and the intercept, a, by: $a = \bar{y} - b\bar{x} = 3\cdot090$.

To estimate the precision of these values, we use the property that over the 5% to 95% response range, the average variance of a probit is approximately $2/n$, where n is the number of subjects tested in the corresponding treatment group. If there are approximately equal numbers of subjects in each group, then the variance of each probit will be nearly constant and equal to $2/\bar{n}$ where $\bar{n}$ is the average number of subjects per treatment group.

In each of our treatment groups $n = 20$ and therefore variance (y) $\simeq 2/20 = 0\cdot1$

Now the variances of the constants in the dose/response relationship can be calculated as follows:

$$\text{variance } (\bar{y}) = \frac{\text{variance } (y)}{k} = \frac{0\cdot1}{5} = 0\cdot02$$

$$\text{variance } (b) = \frac{\text{variance } (y)}{Sxx} = \frac{0\cdot1}{1\cdot028} = 0\cdot0973$$

and variance $(a) = $ variance $(\bar{y}) + \bar{x}^2$ variance (b)

$$= 0\cdot02 + 0\cdot68^2 \times 0\cdot0973$$

$$= 0\cdot0650.$$

The dose/response curve and its precision have now been estimated and we can go on to derive the ED50 and its 95% fiducial limits using equations (11) and (12).

$$\log (100 \times ED50) = \frac{5\cdot0 - 4\cdot912}{2\cdot68} + 0\cdot68 = 0\cdot713$$

therefore: $$ED50 = 0\cdot052 \text{ ml.}$$

$$\text{Variance of } \log (100 \times ED50) = \frac{1}{2\cdot68^2} [0\cdot02 + 0\cdot0973 (0\cdot713 - 0\cdot68)^2]$$

$$= \frac{1}{2\cdot68^2} (0\cdot02 + 0\cdot0001)$$

$$= 0\cdot00280$$

Therefore

$$95\% \text{ fiducial limits for } \log (100 \times ED50) = 0\cdot713 \pm 1\cdot96 \sqrt{0\cdot00280}$$

$$= 0\cdot713 \pm 0\cdot104$$

$$= 0\cdot609 \text{ to } 0\cdot817$$

Transforming back to the original units gives ED50 = 0·052 ml with 95% fiducial limits 0·041 to 0·066 ml.

Because the log (ED50) was very close to the mean of the log doses tested, the precision calculations were essentially the same as those used in the Litchfield and Fertig (1941) approximation employed in the graphical method. However, the calculations here are not limited to obtaining the precision of the ED50 but can be applied to any percentage response desired, which was not possible before.

The test for heterogeneity is carried out as for the graphical method with the slight difference that the expected responses are calculated from the fitted line instead of being read from the graph. The value obtained is $\chi_4^2 = 1\cdot78$.

3. *Approximate weighted regression method*

An important characteristic of data from quantal assays is that the precision of a probit response varies with the level of response, a characteristic which is ignored in the graphical and unweighted regression methods of analysis. The variance of a probit response is equal to $1/nw$ where n is the number of subjects tested to obtain the observed response and w is a factor called the weighting coefficient which is dependent on the response but independent of n. These coefficients are tabulated by Fisher and Yates (1963) [Tables IX 2 and IX 3] and we give below (Table IV) the values for a restricted number of percentage responses:

TABLE IV

% response	Probit	w	% response	Probit	w
0	∞	0			
5	3·36	0·226	55	5·13	0·632
10	3·72	0·343	60	5·25	0·622
15	3·96	0·425	65	5·39	0·602
20	4·16	0·490	70	5·52	0·576
25	4·33	0·539	75	5·67	0·539
30	4·48	0·576	80	5·84	0·490
35	4·61	0·602	85	6·04	0·425
40	4·75	0·622	90	6·28	0·343
45	4·87	0·632	95	6·64	0·226
50	5·00	0·637	100	∞	0

The derivation of these weighting coefficients is discussed more fully by Finney (1952). We only need to know their use, which is to assign weights, nw, to the probit responses.

Table V shows the empirical probits (y), logarithms of $100 \times$ concentration (x) and their weights (nw). The weighted probits, the weighted log concentrations, and the sums over all the treatment groups of nw, nwy, nwy^2, nwx, nwx^2 and $nwxy$, are then calculated.

TABLE V

Empirical probit (y)	log (conc. $\times 100)$ (x)	Weight (nw)	nwy	nwx
∞	1·60	0	0	0
6·64	1·30	4·52	30·01	5·88
5·84	1·00	9·80	57·23	9·80
5·00	0·70	12·74	63·70	8·92
3·72	0·40	6·86	25·52	2·74
3·36	0	4·52	15·19	0

$$\Sigma nw = 38\cdot44 \quad \Sigma nwy = 191\cdot65 \quad \Sigma nwx = 27\cdot34$$
$$\Sigma nwy^2 = 997\cdot9624 \quad \Sigma nwx^2 = 24\cdot7840$$
$$\Sigma nwxy = 151\cdot0410$$

The sums of squares and products corrected for the weighted mean values are then calculated as follows:

$$Syy = \Sigma nwy^2 - \frac{(\Sigma nwy)^2}{\Sigma nw} = 42\cdot4545$$

$$Sxx = \Sigma nwx^2 - \frac{(\Sigma nwx)^2}{\Sigma nw} = 5\cdot3387$$

$$Sxy = \Sigma nwxy - \frac{(\Sigma nwy)(\Sigma nwx)}{\Sigma nw} = 14\cdot7322$$

and the weighted mean values are given by:

$$\bar{y} = \frac{\Sigma nwy}{\Sigma nw} = 4\cdot986 \quad \bar{x} = \frac{\Sigma nwx}{\Sigma nw} = 0\cdot711$$

The slope of the dose/response curve is given by:

$$b = \frac{Sxy}{Sxx} = 2\cdot76$$

and the intercept by:

$$a = \bar{y} - b\bar{x} = 3\cdot024$$

We stated earlier that the probit response, y, has variance $1/nw$, and from this it can be shown that:

$$\text{variance}(\bar{y}) = \frac{1}{\Sigma nw} = 0\cdot0260$$

$$\text{variance}(b) = \frac{1}{Sxx} = 0\cdot187$$

and

$$\text{variance}(a) = \text{variance}(\bar{y}) + \bar{x}^2 \text{ variance}(b)$$

$$= 0\cdot026 + 0\cdot711^2 \times 0\cdot187$$

$$= 0\cdot1205.$$

As with the previous method, we have estimated the dose/response curve and its precision, and in the same way we can go on to use equations (11) and (12) to derive the ED50 and its 95% fiducial limits:

$$\log(100 \times \text{ED50}) = \frac{5\cdot0 - 4\cdot986}{2\cdot76} + 0\cdot711 = 0\cdot716$$

Therefore:

$$\text{ED50} = 0\cdot052 \text{ ml.}$$

$$\text{Variance of } \log(100 \times \text{ED50}) = \frac{1}{2\cdot76^2} [0\cdot026 + 0\cdot187(0\cdot716 - 0\cdot711)^2]$$

$$= \frac{1}{2\cdot76^2} [0\cdot026 + 0\cdot000005]$$

$$= 0\cdot00341$$

Therefore:

$$95\% \text{ fiducial limits for log } (100 \times ED50) = 0.716 \pm 1.96\sqrt{0.00341}$$
$$= 0.716 \pm 0.114$$
$$= 0.602 \text{ to } 0.830.$$

Transforming back to the original units gives ED50 = 0.052 ml with 95% fiducial limits 0.040 to 0.068 ml.

The test of heterogeneity can now be carried out without reference to the graph, as follows:

$$\chi_3 = Syy - \frac{Sxy^2}{Sxx} = 1.80$$

which is again clearly not significant. There are only 3 degrees of freedom for χ^2 in this case, because by giving the highest dose zero weight this result was effectively discarded, leaving one less result on which to test for significant deviations from linearity.

4. *Maximum likelihood method*

This is the most comprehensive form of analysis which takes into consideration all relevant factors such as the further concept of "working probits". This method is beyond the scope of this Chapter and is described by Finney (1952) who explains the procedure and concepts fully in the main part of "Probit Analysis" and gives the method of computing the analysis in Appendix I and the mathematical basis of the method in Appendix II.

Applying the procedure to our data gives the following results:

$$\bar{y} = 5.088 \text{ with variance } 0.0254$$
$$\bar{x} = 0.749$$
$$b = 2.89 \text{ with variance } 0.199$$
$$a = 2.923 \text{ with variance } 0.137.$$

Equation (11) is again used to derive the ED50.

$$\log (100 \times ED50) = \frac{5.0 - 5.088}{2.89} + 0.749 = 0.719$$

Therefore:

$$ED50 = 0.052 \text{ ml.}$$

Ninety-five per cent fiducial limits for log $(100 \times ED50)$ can be derived from the more exact and more complicated formula described by Finney

(1952) in "Probit Analysis", Chapter 4, paragraph 19:

$$\text{limits} = m + \frac{g}{1-g}(m-\bar{x}) \pm \frac{1\cdot96}{b(1-g)}\sqrt{(1-g)\,\text{var}\,(\bar{y})+(m-\bar{x})^2\,\text{var}\,(b)} \qquad (22)$$

where the notation is that of Section III.A and $g = \dfrac{1\cdot96^2\,\text{var}\,(b)}{b^2}$

The limits in this example are therefore

$$0\cdot719 - \frac{0\cdot092 \times 0\cdot030}{0\cdot908} \pm \frac{1\cdot96}{2\cdot89 \times 0\cdot908}\sqrt{0\cdot908 \times 0\cdot0254 + 0\cdot030^2 \times 0\cdot199}$$

i.e. $0\cdot719 - 0\cdot003 \pm 0\cdot114$
i.e. $0\cdot602$ to $0\cdot830$.

Transforming back to the original units gives ED50 = 0·052 ml with 95% fiducial limits 0·040 to 0·068 ml.

The test for heterogeneity is calculated the same way as in the approximate weighted method from the weighted, corrected sums of squares and products. We find the heterogeneity $\chi^2 = 2\cdot03$ with 4 degrees of freedom, which is again clearly not significant.

5. *Discussion of the methods*

All four methods described give almost identical answers (Table VI) for our example, though because such good data are not always obtained in practice this does not imply that the methods are all equally good. Even with this example, the results approach closer to the maximum likelihood solution for each successive method and one should normally use the most comprehensive method possible. Although this may seem laborious, it will usually require little effort compared with that put into carrying out the bioassay itself, and even when maximum precision of the dose/response parameters is not required it may be possible to economize on the total effort by using this method and a smaller amount of experimental data.

TABLE VI

Method	ED50	95% fiducial limits	Slope b	χ^2	Degrees of freedom
Graphical	0·051	0·041–0·064	2·84	1·84	4
Unweighted regression	0·052	0·041–0·066	2·68	1·78	4
Approx. weighted regression	0·052	0·040–0·068	2·76	1·80	3
Max. likelihood	0·052	0·040–0·068	2·89	2·03	4

The unweighted regression and approximate weighted regression methods have been described mainly to illustrate simply the various concepts which are involved in the mathematically complex maximum likelihood method, so that in practice the choice of method is usually likely to lie between the graphical and maximum likelihood methods, depending on the computational facilities available. Later, in Section VI, we also discuss how the availability of a computer can make the maximum likelihood analysis a simple task.

The fiducial limits formula (22) can also be used with both the simpler regression methods, but not with the graphical method as it requires the calculation of the variance of the slope b. The earlier calculation procedures are related to the exact formula in that they assume g is zero which is only a good approximation when the variance of b is small compared with b, i.e. the line is well defined with little scatter of the individual points about it. The approximation may also be poor when the parameter m is not near $\bar{x}$, the mean of the transformed doses.

Alternative, quick methods of analysis have been proposed by Spearman (1908), Dragstedt and Lang (1928), Behrens (1929), Karber (1931), Gaddum (1933), Reed and Muench (1938), and Thompson (1947). These are described and commented on in detail by Finney (1964) Chapter 20, Sections 6–12. Generally they impose restrictions on the experimental design and give only limited information from the analysis.

6. Methods when natural responses occur

When a proportion of the test subjects respond naturally to zero dose, the sigmoid curve will not approach zero percentage for low doses, but will approach the natural response percentage. If this percentage is not known beforehand it will have to be estimated by having a control group of subjects which receive zero dose, but in either case the full maximum likelihood solution is more complicated than that without natural responses and so we refer the reader to the exposition given by Finney (1952) of the method in Chapter 6 of "Probit Analysis".

An approximate adjustment for natural responses is available, however, for the three simpler methods of analysis which we described and it can often be satisfactorily applied also to the maximum likelihood solution. If the natural response rate is known to be $c\%$, or if r_0 respond out of a total of n_0 control subjects and it is considered that $100r_0/n_0 = c\%$ is a satisfactory estimate of natural response rate, then $c\%$ of each treatment group will respond naturally and so effectively will not be part of the experiment. If r subjects respond out of n in the treatment group then the effective response to the treatment is $r - nc/100$ subjects out of $n - nc/100$

subjects treated. Thus the true response percentage is

$$\frac{r - nc/100}{n(1 - c/100)} \times 100\%$$

a formula which is commonly known as Abbott's Formula (Abbott, 1925).

One obvious difficulty with this approach is that for low doses one can obtain apparent responses which are less than n, the natural response rate, and so an effective response which is negative is obtained. Such doses will of course be extreme response doses and so will have little or no weight attached to them. The results for all doses up to the highest dose giving an apparent response less than or equal to the natural response rate should therefore be discarded. However, one can often regard these results as further information on the natural response rates.

For the bioassay of *Bacillus thuringiensis* exotoxin described earlier, the mean control response was 2·5%, but for simplicity we ignored this when analysing the results. Let us now assume for the sake of argument that two out of the 20 control subjects responded, i.e. the natural response rate was 10%, which is greater than the percentage observed for 0·01 ml dose and equal to that for 0·025 ml. Discarding these dose levels from the main set of data and including them with the controls gives an estimated natural response rate of five out of 60 i.e. $c = 8·3\%$. This figure can then be used to adjust the observed responses by Abbott's Formula as shown in Table VII.

TABLE VII

Dose of exotoxin (ml)	Number of larvae treated, n	Number responding r	$\frac{nc}{100}$	$n - \frac{nc}{100} = n'$	$r - \frac{mc}{100} = r'$	% response $p\left(=\frac{r'}{n'}\right)$
0·4	20	20	1·66	18·34	18·34	100
0·2	20	19	1·66	18·34	17·34	94·5
0·1	20	16	1·66	18·34	14·34	78·2
0·05	20	10	1·66	18·34	8·34	45·5

The methods of analysis previously described can now be applied to the revised figures n', r', and p. The maximum likelihood solution, for example, gives an ED50 of 0·055 ml with 95% fiducial limits 0·029 to 0·075 ml.

7. Heterogeneity

If the heterogeneity χ^2 is significant this may imply that the dose/response transformation is not valid, and a modification of the dose transformation will usually be adequate to overcome this problem with quantal assays. An inspection of the data plotted graphically will often highlight a systematic deviation from linearity and may suggest an appropriate transformation. If there is no evidence for a more suitable transformation it is likely that the heterogeneity arises from other factors such as non-random allocation of subjects. In this case the χ^2 value has to be used to adjust the estimates of the precision of the parameters in the dose/response curve, $\bar{y}$, a and b, by multiplying the variances by S^2 where

$$S^2 = \frac{\text{heterogeneity } \chi^2}{\text{degrees of freedom}}$$

This is equivalent to estimating the precision from the data instead of theoretically and so account has to be taken of the amount of data available by replacing the multiplying factor for fiducial limits (1·96 for 95% limits) with Student's "t" factor (Fisher and Yates, 1963, Table III). Not surprisingly this often causes the fiducial limits to be considerably widened, and it is one reason why we suggested testing several dose levels so that reasonably satisfactory estimates of variation can be obtained if necessary.

This procedure is illustrated in the example of a quantitative assay given on p. 182.

B. Analysis of relative potency assays

We will concentrate on assays based on the log dose/probit response transformation but, rather than work through examples of the various methods of analysis, we will outline the methods and give a single example.

We have shown on p. 160 that when the log dose transformation is used the dose/response curves for the materials must be parallel, and the common slope for the curve is estimated with only slight modification to the methods of analysis already described.

For the graphical method, the lines are fitted parallel by eye to the data sets, and the doses corresponding to a convenient response level are read off and substituted in equation (13). The precision of the relative potency estimate, α, is then given by an extension of Litchfield's and Fertig's (1941) approximation (p. 166):

$$\text{Variance} (\log \alpha) = \frac{2}{b^2} \left(\frac{1}{N_1} + \frac{1}{N_2} \right)$$

where N_1, N_2 are the total numbers of subjects tested for each preparation, less any discarded for responses outside the 5% to 95% range.

The test for heterogeneity is carried out as described in the single preparation example by calculating the deviations of all the treatment groups for each preparation and then calculating the heterogeneity χ^2 which will have degrees of freedom $= M - R - 1$, where M = total number of treatment groups and R = number of preparations.

For the unweighted regression method, the sums of squares and products Syy, Sxy and Sxx are calculated separately for the individual preparations as before. These values are then summed over the preparations and the pooled slope is calculated from:

$$b = \frac{\Sigma Sxy}{\Sigma Sxx}$$

This value has approximate variance $= \dfrac{2}{\bar{n}\Sigma Sxx}$

where $\bar{n}$ is the average number of subjects per treatment group, provided there is a roughly even distribution of points about the 50% response for each preparation and approximately equal numbers of subjects in each treatment group.

The approximate weighted regression method has a similar modification in which the weighted sums of squares and products are calculated separately for each preparation and then:

$$b = \frac{\Sigma Sxy}{\Sigma Sxx}$$

which has variance $= \dfrac{1}{\Sigma Sxx}$

Heterogeneity $\chi^2 = \Sigma Syy - \dfrac{(\Sigma Sxy)^2}{\Sigma Sxx}$

with degrees of freedom $= M - R - E - 1$

where, as before, M = total number of treatment groups

$\qquad\qquad\quad R$ = number of preparations

and $\qquad\qquad E$ = number of extreme responses.

The full analysis is again done by the method of maximum likelihood and is described by Finney (1952) in Chapter 5 of "Probit Analysis".

1. *An example of a relative potency assay*

In our example of a single quantal assay, the data were extracted from a much larger exercise in which the activities of several preparations of *Bacillus thuringiensis* exotoxin were measured and we can illustrate the relative potency calculations with the following data from this experiment:

TABLE VIII

Preparation	Dose of exotoxin (ml)	$\log_{10}$ (dose $\times 100$)	Number of treated larvae (n)	Number responding (r)	% response $p(=r/n \times 100)$	Empirical probit y
A	0·4	1·60	20	20	100	∞
	0·2	1·30	20	19	95	6·64
	0·1	1·00	20	16	80	5·84
	0·05	0·70	20	10	50	5·00
	0·025	0·40	20	2	10	3·72
	0·01	0	20	1	5	3·36
B	0·4	1·60	20	20	100	∞
	0·2	1·30	20	18	90	6·28
	0·1	1·00	20	16	80	5·84
	0·05	0·70	20	9	45	4·87
	0·025	0·50	20	5	25	4·33
	0·01	0	20	1	5	3·36

The two preparations, A and B, from two stages in the purification of the exotoxin were made up at 0·05 mg/ml and 17 mg/ml respectively so as to be approximately equally potent. The relative potency of material A to material B is therefore:

$$\alpha = \frac{17\text{EDp}(B)}{0\text{·}05\text{EDp}(A)} = \frac{340\text{EDp}(B)}{\text{EDp}(A)}$$

This is a slight modification of equation (13) to take account of the different concentrations of the materials.

As before, the probit transformation is used for responses and the logarithmic doses and the graph of response against dose is given in Fig. 5, where the lines are those estimated by the maximum likelihood method. The parameters estimated by this method are:

$$b = 2\text{·}63,\ \text{variance}(b) = 0\text{·}0801$$
$$\bar{y}_1 = 5\text{·}098,\ \text{variance}(\bar{y}_1) = 0\text{·}0235$$
$$\bar{y}_2 = 5\text{·}104,\ \text{variance}(\bar{y}_2) = 0\text{·}0235$$
$$\bar{x}_1 = 0\text{·}754,\ \bar{x}_2 = 0\text{·}743$$

These values are then substituted in equation (20):

$$m_{1,\,2} = \frac{5\text{·}098 - 5\text{·}104}{2\text{·}63} - 0\text{·}754 + 0\text{·}743$$
$$= -0\text{·}002 - 0\text{·}011$$
$$= -0\text{·}013$$

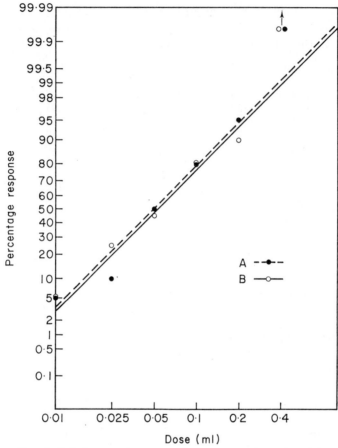

Fig. 5. Relative potency assay of two preparations A and B.

The 95% fiducial limits for $m_{1,\,2}$ are calculated from the following extended version of equation (22).

$$\text{limits} = m_{1,\,2} + \frac{g}{1-g}\,(m_{1,\,2} + \bar{x}_1 - \bar{x}_2)$$

$$\pm \frac{1\cdot96}{b(1-g)}\sqrt{(1-g)\,[\text{var}\,(\bar{y}_1) + \text{var}\,(\bar{y}_2)] + (m_{1,\,2} + \bar{x}_1 - \bar{x}_2)^2\,\text{var}\,(b)} \qquad (23)$$

The limits in this example are therefore

$$-0\cdot013 - \frac{0\cdot0445 \times 0\cdot002}{0\cdot9555} \pm \frac{1\cdot96}{2\cdot63 \times 0\cdot9555}\sqrt{\begin{array}{l}0\cdot9555\,(0\cdot0235 + 0\cdot0235)\\ + 0\cdot002^2 \times 0\cdot0801\end{array}}$$

i.e. $-0\cdot178$ to $0\cdot152$.

In this example, relative potency α is given by:

$$\log \alpha = \log 340 + m_{1,\,2}$$
$$= 2.532 - 0.013$$
$$= 2.519$$

which has 95% fiducial limits:

$$\log 340 - 0.178 \text{ to } \log 340 + 0.152$$

i.e. $2.532 - 0.178 \text{ to } 2.532 + 0.152$

i.e. $2.354 \text{ to } 2.684.$

Transforming back to the original units gives the relative potency of solution A to solution B as 330 with 95% fiducial limits 226 to 483.

C. Slope ratio assays

In the slope ratio assay for the relative potency of different preparations of the same material all the dose/response relationships are described by the single model:

transformed response $= a + b_1 (\text{dose}_1)^\lambda + b_2 (\text{dose}_2)^\lambda + \ldots b_n (\text{dose}_n)^\lambda$

This is derived by considering each treatment as made up of a non-zero dose of one preparation together with zero doses of the other preparations. The common intercept, a, is the transformed response for zero dose of all preparations, i.e. for the control dose.

The method of analysis, which makes use of multiple regression techniques, is complicated, particularly when there are more than two preparations, and is beyond the scope of this Chapter, so the reader is referred to Williams (1959); Crow, Davis and Maxfield (1960); Finney (1964); and Draper and Smith (1966). The calculations are best carried out on a computer and programmes for multiple regression analyses are available for most computers.

D. Analysis of quantitative assays

With quantitative assays there is a greater chance that the dose/response curve will not be sigmoidal than there is with quantal assays. If such a case is met it means that there will probably not be any limits to the degree of response and it will usually not be possible to estimate the dose required to cause a given percentage response. These curves will only be useful in relative potency experiments, or in estimating the dose required to cause a given response on an absolute, as opposed to a percentage, scale. However, despite this complication, the sigmoid form of relationship is still very common in quantitative assays arising from the situation where responses only occur within a limited range of values.

If the extreme responses are well defined the precision of the responses will usually follow a similar pattern to that for quantal responses with very little variability at the extremes and most variability around the 50% response. In this case, very good results will be obtained by the methods described for quantal assays with the modification that the precision will have to be estimated by making use of the heterogeneity χ^2 value as shown in the example following.

Often one of the extreme responses is not well defined and has to be estimated by observing the responses of a number of untreated subjects. The mean control response, R_C, can then be taken as a satisfactory exact value and all the percentage responses can be expressed as:

$$\frac{R_C - R_T}{R_C} \times 100$$

where R_T is the observed response.

Doses for which responses are obtained outside the control limits can be discarded or pooled with the zero dose results to give a better estimate of the control response. This will generally be satisfactory provided the variation at the end point is small compared with the variation at the middle of the response range. If this provision does not hold there is a considerable risk that doses which normally give substantial responses will be discarded because they contain results outside the response range.

For relative potency assays the definition of the extreme responses presents no problem as we are only interested in the relative levels of the relationship. The quantal assay method of analysis can be used in cases where the sigmoid relationship is relevant but this may be difficult, because of the pattern of variation or because insufficient natural response data are available for example. In such a case it may be possible to consider just the linear part of the curve and analyse the data without transforming the responses.

1. Example of a quantitative assay

Five dose levels of a plant growth regulator were tested in triplicate on cotton plants to estimate the dose required to cause a 10% reduction in growth.

Observations of growth made by weighing the fully grown plants are shown in Table IX.

There are a large number of control results because the data come from a larger experiment in which other compounds were tested. The control

TABLE IX

Dose kg/hectare	Weight of plant (g)		
	Replicate 1	Replicate 2	Replicate 3
0·4	94·3	85·5	85·9
1	80·7	68·0	69·0
2	39·5	69·2	8·7
4	39·2	28·9	31·3
8	7·1	21·5	7·2
	94·9	77·2	89·6
	91·0	88·0	90·4
	85·2	70·5	96·5
0	89·0	69·0	86·2
	61·7	80·0	84·7
	78·8	85·3	65·0
	79·1	56·9	85·8
	89·7	83·0	81·7
	82·2	69·5	92·2
	83·5	78·5	79·5

mean was 81·5 and as the 0·4 dose level contained results greater than control they had to be discarded. They could have been included with the control results but as there were already thirty control observations this was not thought to be worthwhile.

A plot of weight against log dose suggests a sigmoid relationship so that it is likely that the probit transformation on response will be satisfactory. The percentage reductions in weight shown in Table X are plotted in Fig. 6 on probit/log paper.

TABLE X

Dose	Log dose	% weight reductions		
0·4	—	—	—	—
1	0	1·0	16·6	15·3
2	0·30	51·5	15·1	89·3
4	0·60	51·9	64·5	61·6
8	0·90	91·3	73·6	91·2

This indicates that the transformed dose/response relationship is reasonably linear and it can therefore be derived by the methods given already for the quantal assay by letting the % weight reduction correspond to r, the number of subjects responding. To do this we arbitrarily let the number of

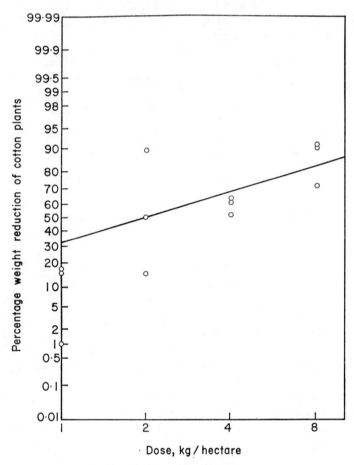

FIG. 6. A quantitative assay.

subjects, n, tested be 100. This gives the correct relationship but because the precision is dependent on n, which has been arbitrarily chosen, the variances derived have to be adjusted by means of the heterogeneity χ^2.

We will not restate all the steps again here but by using the maximum likelihood method the following results are obtained before adjustment by the heterogeneity χ^2.

$\bar{y} = 5{\cdot}035$ with variance $0{\cdot}00159$

$\bar{x} = 0{\cdot}442$

$b = 2{\cdot}24$ with variance $0{\cdot}0163$

χ^2 was $181{\cdot}0$ with 10 degrees of freedom.

Two types of variation can contribute to the heterogeneity: the variation between replicate results at the same dose level, and the fitting error due to deviations of the dose means from the relationship. If the weight reductions at each dose level are summed and the single total response results for each dose level used to fit the relationship, the heterogeneity χ^2 obtained will be the value for the fitting error only. This can then be subtracted from the total variation value, to obtain the variation resulting from the replication. A test of non-linearity can then be made by comparing the fitting error with the replicates error.

In our example summing over the three replicates at each dose level give the following results:

TABLE XI

Dose (kg/hectare)	Weight reduction, r	Maximum possible reduction, n
0·4	—	—
1	32·9	300
2	155·9	300
4	178·0	300
8	256·1	300

Applying the maximum likelihood analysis gave $\chi^2 = 33.83$ with 2 degrees of freedom with the other estimates as before.

Data in Table XII show the individual χ^2 values which were divided by their degrees of freedom and their F-ratio formed:

TABLE XII

Source of variation	Degrees of freedom	χ^2	Mean square	F-ratio
Fitting error	2	33·83	16·92	0·92
Replicates error	8	147·17	18·40	
Total	10	181·00		

For the fitting error to be significant its mean square would need to be much greater than the replicates error mean square, that is the F-ratio would need to be much greater than unity. The critical values for the F-ratio are tabulated in Fisher and Yates (1963) Table V, and in this case the value is 4·5 so it is clear that the fitting error was not significant.

The adjustments to the variances of the dose/response parameters are therefore done by multiplying by the total χ^2 divided by 10.

Therefore:

$$\text{variance}(\bar{y}) = 0.00159 \times 18.1 = 0.0288$$

$$\text{and variance}(b) = 0.0163 \times 18.1 = 0.295$$

Equation (11) is then used as before to derive the ED10:

probit for 10% response = 3.72 (see Table IV).

Therefore

$$\log(\text{ED10}) = \frac{3.72 - 5.035}{2.24} + 0.442 = -0.145 = \bar{1}.855$$

$$\text{ED10} = 0.72 \text{ kg/hectare.}$$

The 95% fiducial limits are obtained from equation (22) as

$$-0.145 - \frac{0.587 \times 0.292}{0.708} \pm \frac{2.23\dagger}{2.24 \times 0.708} \sqrt{0.708 \times 0.0288 + 0.587^2 \times 0.295}$$

i.e. -0.878 to $0.104 = \bar{1}.122$ to 0.104.

Transforming back to the original units gives the dose for 10% depression of cotton growth = 0.72 kg/hectare with 95% fiducial limits 0.132 to 1.27 kg/hectare.

E. Analysis of scored response assays

The data will consist of scores for each subject, the score giving a measure of the degree of response of the subject according to some predetermined scale. In this respect they will be like quantitative assays but will be simplified by having well defined maximum and minimum scores. Because of this, the dose/response curves are usually sigmoidal, particularly if the scores are intended to estimate percentage responses. Such data can then be simply analysed by the methods for quantal assays taking the maximum score as n, the number of subjects tested, and the scores themselves as r, the number of subjects responding. Once again the precision needs to be estimated by making use of the heterogeneity χ^2 in exactly the same way as shown in the example of a quantitative assay given above.

VI. USE OF COMPUTERS

We mentioned earlier that the method of analysis used will depend to some extent on the availability of a computer with suitable programmes.

---

† Instead of using the multiplier derived from the Normal distribution, Student's "t" factor is used as the variance has been estimated from the data. Fisher and Yates (1963), Table III, give 95% "t" value for 10 degrees of freedom as 2.23. This value is also used instead of 1.96 in calculating the value for g of 0.292.

With such facilities a full arithmetical analysis can be obtained having spent only a few minutes punching the data on to cards or paper tape. The cost of computer time will usually be more than offset by the time that would have been spent doing the analysis by hand and there is the advantage that the risk of error in the calculations will be considerably reduced.

Sokal (1958) has discussed the use of computers for Probit Analyses, but in spite of spectacular advances recently in the use of computers, the provision of good statistical programmes has tended to lag behind. The following programmes are suitable for carrying out analyses of bioassay data though all were written to accept quantal data as input and to obtain the maximum likelihood solution.

(a) *BMD 03S, biological assay: probit analysis programme,* written in FORTRAN IV, will fit single relationships using the probit transformation with allowance for known or estimated natural responses. The programme is part of a comprehensive package of statistical programmes edited by W. J. Dixon of the University of California, Los Angeles, and manuals are published by the University of California Press in the U.S.A. and the Cambridge University Press in England.

(b) *Simple probits,* written in Extended Mercury Autocode, will fit single relationships using the probit transformation with allowance for known natural response. The programme, written by M. J. R. Healey and G. J. S. Ross, is one of the library programmes of Rothamsted Experimental Station, Harpenden, England, and is coded ORION/27.

(c) *Parallel logits,* written in Extended Mercury Autocode, will fit relationships using the logit transformation with facility for fitting several parallel relationships. The programme, written by D. A. Williams and C. W. Fearne, is another of the Rothamsted library programmes and is coded ORION/19/EXT.

(d) *Maximum likelihood programme (MPL),* written in Extended Mercury Autocode, is a general programme, capable among other things of fitting single or up to three parallel lines using either probit or logit transformations and making allowance for known or estimated natural response. It will also give a solution of Wadley's Problem.† Written by G. J. S. Ross, the programme is again one of the Rothamsted library programmes and is coded ORION/25.

(e) *Probit analysis,* written in FORTRAN IV, will fit single or several parallel relationships with allowance for known or estimated natural responses. It

† Finney (1952), "Probit Analysis", §50, pp. 203–205.

was written by D. L. Holmes of Shell Research Ltd, Woodstock Agricultural Research Centre, Sittingbourne, England.

(f) *IBM biology assay parallel line programme* written in FORTRAN II, will fit single or several parallel relationships. The authors were B. S. Lee and S. P. Young and further details are available from the Program Library, Technical Information Centre, IBM (U.K.) Ltd, 101 Wigmore Street, London, W.1, England.

(g) *ICT probit programme*, written to run on the ICT 1300 series computers, will fit single probit lines. Further details are available from the Subroutine Library, International Computers Ltd, Bridge House North, London, S.W.6, England, and the programme is coded M/03/11/12.

VII. PRECISION OF BIOASSAYS

In previous Sections we have freely referred to measures of precision such as variance and fiducial limits, but strictly, the figures derived apply only to the variation obtained within an experiment in which the subjects used have been randomly allocated amongst the treatment groups. The values cannot be used indiscriminately and it should not be assumed that assays carried out on different occasions, even in the same laboratory, will give results which agree within the precision limits calculated for a single experiment. On another occasion, a new sample of subjects will be used whose tolerances may differ from those of the previous occasions and such differences can only be minimized by having carefully regulated breeding procedures and closely standardized assay conditions. Even then long-term changes in tolerance levels are difficult to eliminate completely.

Burges (1967) has reported the results of a collaborative programme in which a number of laboratories bioassayed three standard preparations of *B. thuringiensis* spore-crystal mixture against a variety of insect species. He found considerable variation between the results of different contributors even using the same test species and he suggests that assay technique and possibly insect stock are significant factors in this variation, which emphasizes the importance of having fully standardized techniques.

This problem can be illustrated by use of data obtained during the purification of the *B. thuringiensis* exotoxin (Bond, Boyce and French, 1969). Two dilutions (*A* and *B*) were assayed together on four separate occasions in a house fly assay. The experimental data were analysed by the maximum likelihood method using parallel probit/log dose relationships and the ED50 values are given in Table XIII.

TABLE XIII

Occasion	Solution A		Solution B		Ratio A/B	95% fiducial limits
	ED50, μg	95% fiducial limits	ED50, μg	95% fiducial limits		
I	2336	1601–3409	5·3	3·6–7·7	443	344–569
II	1501	1028–2191	4·8	3·3–7·0	313	220–447
III	1128	773–1646	2·9	2·0–4·3	386	270–550
IV	1206	826–1760	3·3	2·3–4·9	361	253–514

Clearly the values obtained at different times do not agree within the calculated precision limits, up to 100% differences being obtained, while the fiducial limits suggest that the ED50 values are precise to about 70%. However the potency ratio A/B obtained on each occasion showed much better agreement. For this reason it is common practice to carry out comparative assays together and if possible to express potency in terms of a standard.

From this experiment it was also possible to obtain estimates of the amount of testing required to make given differences significant. Table XIV gives the approximate numbers of replicates (each of six doses with 20 larvae at each dose) which are needed for differences between ED50s of 10%, 20% and 30% to be significant at the 5% level.

TABLE XIV

% difference	10%	20%	30%
2 sided test†	29	8	4
1 sided test†	20	6	3

† The two sided test is used when one wants to know if two ED50s are significantly different from each other, e.g. if the two ED50s are A and B, and one is testing whether either of the situations $A>B$ or $B>A$ is significant. The one sided test is used when only one of these situations is of interest, e.g. when one is testing if $A>B$ but it is of no interest if $B>A$ however large this difference may be.

Sometimes "relative potency" experiments are also undertaken with test materials which are chemically distinct. However, this concept may provide only a partial answer to increasing precision because there is no guarantee that the variation of the subject's responses resulting from their own variability or that of the assay conditions will be parallel for the different materials. Consequently the potency ratio of a material with respect to a standard may itself vary from one occasion to another. The best policy to adopt in this case is to carry out the crucial comparisons in a single assay and if this is not practicable every effort should be made to standardize the assay so as to reduce variation in the absolute potencies. As a check a standard can be included and if it behaves abnormally the experiment should be repeated. In this case the standard is used in a sense as a control.

REFERENCES

Abbott, W. S. (1925). *J. econ. Ent.*, **18**, 265–267

Behrens, B. (1929). *Arch. exp. Path. Pharmak.*, **140**, 237–256.

Biometrika Tables for Statisticians, Vol. 1. (1958). Second Edition. University Press, Cambridge.

Bliss, C. I. (1952). "The Statistics of Bioassay". Academic Press, New York.

Bond, R. P. M., Boyce, C. B. C., and French, S. J. (1969). *Biochem. J.*, **114**, 477.

Burges, H. D. (1967). "Insect Pathology and Microbial Control". Proceedings of the International Colloquium on Insect Pathology and Microbial Control. Wageningen, The Netherlands, September 5–10, 1966, pp. 306–337. The North Holland Publishing Co., Amsterdam.

Crow, E. L., Davis, F. A., and Maxfield, M. W. (1960). "Statistics Manual", Chapter 6, pp. 168–183. Dover Publications, New York.

Dragstedt, C. A., and Lang, V. F. (1928). *J. Pharmac exp. Ther.*, **32**, 215–222.

Draper, N. R., and Smith, H. (1966). "Applied Regression Analysis", Chapter 2, pp. 44–85. John Wiley and Sons, New York.

Finney, D. J. (1952). "Probit Analysis", Second Edition. University Press, Cambridge.

Finney, D. J. (1964). "Statistical Methods in Biological Assay", Second Edition. Charles Griffin and Co., London.

Fisher, R. A., and Yates, F. (1963). "Statistical Tables for Biological, Agricultural and Medical Research", Sixth Edition. Oliver and Boyd, Edinburgh.

Gaddum, J. H. (1933). Reports on Biological Standards. III. Methods of Biological Assay Depending on a Quantal Response. Medical Research Council, Special Report Series no. 183.

Kärber, G. (1931). *Arch. exp. Path. Pharmak.*, **162**, 480–487.

Litchfield, J. T., and Fertig, J. W. (1941). *Johns Hopkins Hosp. Bull.*, **69**, 276–286.

Reed, L. J., and Muench, H. (1938). *Am. J. Hyg.*, **27**, 493–497.

Sokal, R. R. (1958). *J. econ. Ent.*, **51**, 738–739.

Spearman, C. (1908). *Br. J. of Psychol.*, **2**, 227–242.

Thompson, W. R. (1947). *Bact. Rev.*, **11**, 115–145.

Williams, E. J. (1959). "Regression Analysis", Chapter 3, pp. 23–40. John Wiley and Sons, New York.

CHAPTER V

Methods for Studying the Infectious Properties and Multiplication of Bacteriophage

D. KAY

*Sir William Dunn School of Pathology, University of Oxford,
South Parks Road, Oxford*

I. INTRODUCTION

Bacteriophage has now been studied for over 50 years since its discovery by F. W. Twort in 1915 and there is no sign that the interest in the subject has even reached its peak let alone begun to diminish. From being a bacteriologist's curiosity the study of phage has passed through a number of stages. The dramatic bacteriolytic property fascinated the early workers and led to many unsuccessful attempts to use phage therapeutically. In the 1930s interest developed in the physical properties of phage, its particle size, rate of adsorption to the host bacteria and its chemical composition. Attention was directed to the relationship between specific phage receptors and bacterial somatic antigens. A great impetus was given to phage research by the American workers led by Delbruck who identified and quantitated the basic steps of phage multiplication, adsorption, followed by the latent period and ending in the sudden release or "burst" of progeny, phage. These workers focused their attention on a single group of phages, the "T" group, and their host *Escherichia coli* B and encouraged others to do the same. As a result of this leadership studies on the T phages proceeded apace rather to the exclusion of work on other bacterium-phage systems. Inevitably the most detailed knowledge about phage concerns the T phages and a few others which also attack *E. coli*. There is however no reason to believe that the principles of phage multiplication discovered in this limited system do not apply in the broad outlines and largely in the finer details to all bacterium-phage systems.

The advent of the electron microscope in the 1940s led to undreamt of revelations in which phages, previously considered as just particles of nucleoprotein were found to have fascinating morphologies. They were seen, in many cases, to be "tadpole-like" in shape and the terms "head" and "tail" were used to describe their component parts. The development of superior staining methods and the improvement of the microscope led in the late 1950s and subsequently to the identification of still finer morphological details of phages some of which possess highly complex structures which are concerned in attachment to, and injection of DNA into, the host cell.

The biochemistry of phage multiplication began in earnest when S. S. Cohen introduced the use of radioactive isotopes into the study of the sources of the material from which the progeny phages were built. These studies were further helped by the discovery that the DNA of the T-even phages contained the previously unknown base hydroxymethyl-cytosine instead of cytosine. Phage nucleic acid could now be positively identified in infected cells.

The illuminating experiment of Hershey and Chase (1952), which established beyond all doubt that the DNA of the phage was the germinal substance, began the long and continuing task of unravelling the function of the nucleic acids.

Another shaft of light was thrown on to a perplexing area of phage study by the experiments of Lwoff and colleagues who elucidated the properties of lysogenic phage. The phenomenon of lysogeny is probably more widespread in nature than that of virulent phage and the lysogenic phages have proved very useful in the study of both phage and bacterial genetics. The first experiments on the genetics of phage were done by Hershey and Rotman in 1948. Subsequent genetic experiments have yielded a rich harvest of information including the evidence for the triplet nature of the genetic code (Crick *et al.*, 1961). Work with conditional lethal mutants of phage has revealed how, in the infected cell, the various component parts of the particle are assembled step by step and how this assembly can take place automatically *in vitro*.

It is clear when the original papers are studied that a very great deal of ingenuity has been applied to the study of phage and that it would be an enormous task to review and record all the worthwhile methods. The first attempt to collect the methods used in phage study was made by Mark H. Adams in 1950 and his monograph was brought up to date by others and published posthumously in his book "Bacteriophages" in 1959. This book is still the authoritative account of the basic methods used in the study of phage and should be read by all who contemplate work in this field.

In preparing this Chapter the author has drawn not only on Adams' book but also on the phage literature, the methods of colleagues and a little of his own observations. But the literature on phage is now so vast that it would be idle to suggest that this Chapter contains a complete account of phage methodology to date. It is believed that the methods recorded here are valuable ones and that the references given will lead the reader further into the literature in which more techniques will be found.

II. ASSAY PROCEDURES

No study of bacteriophage can proceed far without the use of a reliable, readily performed and sufficiently accurate assay procedure. The purpose of the assay is to determine the number of infective particles in a specimen of phage and the result is expressed as plaque forming units (p.f.u.) per ml. All the procedures depend on the ability of a single phage particle, when brought into contact with the host bacteria growing in a thin layer in a Petri plate, to lyse one cell and release sufficient progeny to lyse the surrounding cells until a visible clear area or "plaque" is formed. Each plaque is assumed to derive from only one phage particle and so by counting the plaques the number of p.f.u./ml can be obtained.

It has been shown for a few phages that, under favourable conditions, the number of p.f.u./ml approximates closely to the number of morphological particles as determined in the electron microscope. There are several sources of error in the plaque assay and these will be discussed later (p. 199) but in general it must be assumed that the number of p.f.u./ml in a particular specimen of phage is rather lower than the actual number of phage particles present.

A. Plaque assay for virulent phage

Bacteriophages can be divided into two groups, virulent and lysogenic. The former always produce lysis and plaques while the latter may not produce plaques except under special conditions. Assay procedures for lysogenic phage will be considered in a separate section (p. 197).

1. *The two layer method*

This is the most commonly used method and was described by Adams (1950) in a chapter entitled "Methods of Study of Bacterial Viruses" which is a standard reference work. It was designed for work with *E. coli* but it is suitable for all the enteric bacteria and for many others. It should be borne in mind that for bacteria with special growth requirements the media and conditions described below will have to be modified.

(a) *Bottom layer*. Petri plates 9 cm diameter, are poured with 25–30 ml of nutrient 1·5% agar on a level bench. If the agar is not of uniform thickness the plaque size will vary across the plate and increase the counting error. If a suitable bench is not available a sheet of $\frac{1}{4}$ in. (6–7 mm) plate glass mounted on a tripod with adjustable screw legs (Fig. 1) should be set up and levelled with a spirit level.

The nutrient agar can be a mixture prepared by a manufacturer and made up according to the instructions or it can be made up by the user as required. In that case it is convenient to prepare a stock of 3% agar in water and store it sterilized in 250 ml lots in 500 ml screw capped bottles. Sterile nutrient broth is also prepared at double strength and stored in 250 ml quantities. To prepare plates the agar is melted in the autoclave, the nutrient broth is poured in together with any additives (see Modifications, p. 201), and the plates poured. This method ensures that the temperature of the nutrient agar just before pouring is about 55°C and so reduces the amount of condensation which forms in the plates. It is not necessary to measure the agar into each plate as sufficient manual skill to get 17–20 plates from 500 ml agar is soon developed.

Frequently freshly poured plates exude moisture and are useless for phage assay. They should be stored at room temperature for 2–3 days at least, in a cupboard, but if they are still not dry they can be placed open and inverted at 37°C for an hour or two.

(b) *Top layer*. A soft agar is used for the top layer. It is made with the same nutrient broth as the bottom layer but with the agar concentration reduced to 0·7%. Before use the agar is melted and 2·5 ml lots are dispensed into

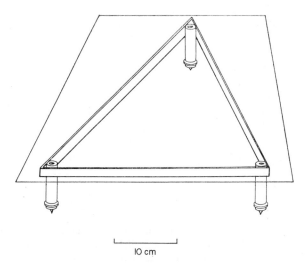

10 cm

FIG. 1. Levelling table.

test-tubes which are kept at 46°C in a water bath so that the agar remains molten. It is easier to handle the agar if it is kept a little warmer but its temperature should not exceed 50°C to avoid killing the bacterial inoculum. The agar concentration and volume can be varied for special purposes (see Modifications, p. 201).

(c) *Bacterial inoculum.* Adams (1950) advocates washing the bacteria from the surface of an agar slant with 5 ml of broth and using one drop per tube of melted agar. Any procedure which gives a suspension of bacteria, preferably in the log phase, but certainly not in an advanced stationary phase, containing from 5×10^8–2×10^9/ml is suitable. Overnight cultures of *E. coli* for example in nutrient broth (10 ml) can be grown in 50 ml conical flasks or rapidly growing cells can be grown in aerated tubes or in "T" tubes. These are specially made glass vessels (Fig. 2) in which 10 ml of culture can be agitated in a water bath equipped with mechanically rocked bar (60 strokes/min) to which they can be attached by clips. When it is required to measure the O.D. of the culture one arm of the "T" is inserted into a suitable holder in an absorptiometer (e.g. Hilger "Spekker" with modified cell holder). In this way the growth of a culture can be followed without the necessity of taking samples.

(d) *Procedure.* The phage to be assayed is diluted appropriately (see Accuracy of the Plaque Assay, p. 199) and 1 ml is added to a tube of melted top layer agar together with one to four drops of bacterial suspension (Pasteur pipette). The contents are mixed by rolling the tube between the hands

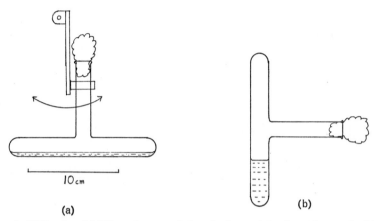

FIG. 2. "T" tube. (a) The tube containing the bacterial culture is attached by a spring clip to a bar which can be mechanically rocked to aerate the culture. The tube hangs in a water bath. (b) The opacity of the culture can be measured by inserting the tube into a photometer.

(avoid bubbles) and poured into a plate containing bottom agar. The plate is rocked to distribute the agar evenly, laid on a level surface to set and then incubated at a suitable temperature (usually 37°C but can be varied, see Modifications, p. 201). The plaques are sometimes countable after 4 h but it is usual to incubate the plates overnight.

2. The single layer method

A considerable economy of working can be achieved by using the single layer method but the efficiency of plating (p. 200) is lower than with the two layer method.

Petri plates containing nutrient agar are prepared as for the two layer method but particular care must be taken to ensure that they are sufficiently dry. This is best achieved by storage at room temperature in the dark for a few days. The plates are seeded with host bacteria by flooding the surface with a few ml of culture from a Pasteur pipette. Immediately, the plates are held at an angle and the excess fluid withdrawn. A bacterial concentration of 2×10^8/ml is suitable.

If the plates are sufficiently dry they will absorb the fluid in less than 5 min but if this is not so they can be dried in an inverted position at 37°C. Drying at a higher temperature produces a hard "skin" on the surface of the agar and does not give a useable plate.

The phage to be assayed is diluted and applied to the seeded plates by means of calibrated discardable Pasteur pipettes. These are made as required by inserting the slightly tapered, drawn out end of a pipette into a hole drilled in a piece of steel. (A piece of $\frac{3}{4}$ in. × $\frac{1}{8}$ in. silver steel is drilled with a No. 55 drill, 0·052 in. diameter, and hardened. Alternatively an engineer's drill gauge may be used.) The glass is marked with the edge of a piece of triangular section carborundum stick, withdrawn from the hole and broken at the mark. If pressure is applied gently to the vertically held pipette it will deliver drops of about 0·025 ml with sufficient accuracy. One pipette can be used for a series of dilutions of one phage specimen provided that one begins with the highest dilution and that the dilutions are at least five-fold. The number of drops that can be accommodated on one plate is at least four and with care this can be increased to six or even more. In order to count the plaques, which are very small, it is advisable to use a lower power microscope and a viewing box (see Plaque Counting Equipment, p. 198).

B. Plaque assay for lysogenic phage

Lysogenic phages can be assayed by the same methods as for virulent phage. This may seem surprising since every initial infection which results in lysogeny would fail to produce a plaque. Nevertheless it is generally found that if conditions are used in which bacterial growth is optimum the lytic response is predominant and a satisfactory plaque count can be made. There must always be some doubt whether all the phage particles produce plaques but provided a standard method is strictly adhered to the count will probably be a constant proportion of the active particles present.

It is worthwhile noting the phenomenon described by Boyd (1951) in which phage "A" causes lysis of a strain of *Salmonella typhimurium* in liquid culture when the multiplicity of infection is one or less but when the multiplicity is raised to 10 the fraction of cells rendered lysogenic reached almost 100%. When lysogenic phages are plated out it is sometimes found that the yield of plaques increases as the dilution decreases in the usual way but that if still more phage is applied to a plate then the yield of plaques falls until a situation is reached where the plates receive a high dose of phage but no plaques are visible. It would be advisable when assaying a lysogenic phage of unknown titre to test a wide range of dilutions.

Ogawa and Tomizawa (1967) have used the following method to assay phage. Infected cells or induced lysogenic cells were added to a test-tube containing melted soft agar, 100 μg penicillin per ml and penicillin resistant indicator bacteria and layered on a plate supplemented with 100 μg of penicillin per ml. The plates contained peptone (10 g) and sodium chloride (2·5 g) per litre and agar (1%). The soft agar consisted of the same medium solidified with 0·6% agar. Penicillin stops multiplication of the bacteria and finally kills them, but it does not inhibit phage multiplication in infected or induced bacteria. Thus phage multiplication in the cells to which

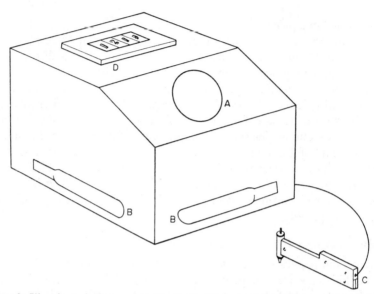

Fig. 3. Illuminated plaque counter. A Petri plate with plaques to be counted is inverted over hole A and is illuminated obliquely by 25 W lamps B. The plaques are marked by pen C which, through a microswitch, operates electromagnetic counter D each time the pen is depressed.

penicillin was added can be measured. The method is essential for the detection of suppression of multiplication of λc1 by the immunity substance in non-lysogenic cells. For measuring the efficiency of induction of cells lysogenic for λ, and especially for a *ts* mutant, this method has the advantage of reducing the background caused by the spontaneous induction after plating.

C. Plaque counting equipment

The counting of plaques, especially in large numbers, is greatly facilitated by some type of mechanical aid. With the two layer method the size of the plaques should be such that they can be easily seen by the unaided eye provided the plates are properly illuminated. A form of simple dark ground illumination is best and can easily be constructed as shown in Fig. 3. The plates to be counted can be inverted on the illuminator and each plaque marked with a pen. If the pen is attached to a microswitch the number of plaques can be automatically recorded. Failing this a hand tally can be used. There are several varieties of commercially made colony counters available which can be used for plaque counting. Some of these depend on making an electrical connection with each plaque as it is counted. In this case the plates would be laid on the illuminator the right way up.

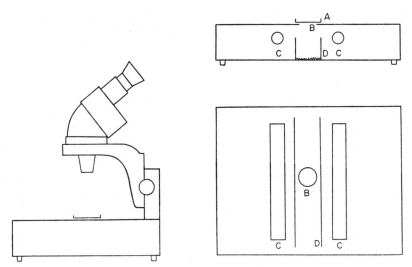

Fig. 4. Illuminated counter for small plaques. A Petri plate A is placed over hole B in a metal box which forms the base of a binocular microscope. The plate is illuminated obliquely by fluorescent lamps C and the plaques are observed against a dark background formed by velvet lined baffles D. A magnification of 5–8 times is adequate.

For counting the plaques produced by the single layer method some form of illuminator and magnifier is necessary. A suitable design is given in Fig. 4. This apparatus is extremely useful for examining the morphology of plaques and colonies.

D. Accuracy of the plaque assay

The plaque assay is subject to statistical errors which are unavoidable and to experimental errors which can be reduced to a minimum by proper technique.

As a preliminary check on the plating technique the relationship between the count obtained and the relative dilution should be determined. It should be possible to show a linear relationship from 20–30 plaques to 300 plaques per plate. Above this figure the relative count will fall due to overlapping of plaques while below the lower figure the sampling error will be unacceptably high. The precision of the assay depends on the number of plaques counted. For example with a plaque count of 100 the coefficient of variation is 10% but for 25 plaques it is 20%.

The overall accuracy of the assay is affected by the extent of the dilution which has to be made before counting, the effect of the diluent and the delay, if any, between dilution and pouring the assay plate. Often, high titre phage, which might contain up to 10^{14} particles per ml, has to be counted and this necessitates dilutions of up to $1 : 10^{12}$. This can be done with acceptable accuracy in $1 : 100$ steps by running 0·1 ml into 9·9 ml of diluent but inevitably the greater the number of steps the larger the dilution error.

There is always a danger that the phage will be inactivated during the mixing of each dilution, which is usually done by drawing the mixture up and down several times in a pipette. This danger can be minimized by the inclusion of some protein such as gelatin or serum albumin (0·01%) in the diluent (Adams, 1948). A very satisfactory phage diluent is nutrient broth which can be diluted to half strength with water. Buffer solutions can be used provided some protein is added and calcium in the case of some phages which are inactivated in the presence of phosphate buffer. Distilled water is not suitable.

When dilutions have been made they should be plated immediately to avoid losses due to adsorption to the walls of the glassware.

1. *Efficiency of plating*

The term efficiency of plating (e.o.p.) has been used in two different ways. Properly it should mean the proportion of viable phage particles which actually form plaques but sometimes it has been used to mean the number of plaques that appear on a particular host as a fraction of the (larger) number which appear on the most efficient known host.

Ellis and Delbruck (1939) have proposed the following method for determining the e.o.p. It depends on the chances of an individual phage particle adsorbing to a bacterium in a liquid culture being greater than to a bacterium on the surface of an assay plate. The phage is diluted in broth (in which there are no known adsorption cofactor or nutritional deficiencies) so that there is somewhat less than one infectious particle per ml and distributed to give, say, 50 samples of 1 ml each. Each sample is inoculated with a few hundred bacteria and incubated overnight. Next day the tubes are assayed to determine whether phage is present or not (actual titre not required). The proportion of samples containing no phage is determined and the average number of phage particles per sample is calculated from the Poisson distribution

$$P_0 = e^{-n}$$

where P_0 is the fraction of samples containing no phage and n is the average number of particles per sample. In a typical example 23 out of 40 plated samples gave no plaques so $P_0 = 0·57$ and $n = 0·56$ particles per sample. From a direct assay the number of particles per sample was 0·22 and so the e.o.p. was $0·22/0·56 = 0·39$.

A useful statistical study of efficiency of plating has been made by Williams (1968).

E. Laboratory precautions with bacteriophage

It is appropriate to discuss the laboratory precautions which should be taken with work on phage in the Section dealing with assay methods because it is most frequently when scanning the assay plates that any deficiencies in technique become obvious. The trouble usually observed is that the assay plates are completely lysed or carry more plaques than could reasonably be expected. The reason for this is that some stray phage has reached the plate and this is due to some error in technique.

In addition to the normal bacteriological precautions appropriate to the organism being studied it is essential to guard against the laboratory becoming contaminated with phage. This danger is not very great with the larger phages such as the T-even ones but can be serious with the smaller ones such as ØX174 and the RNA phages. It seems that the larger phages are easily inactivated if spilled material is allowed to dry on the benches but that the smaller ones are more resistant. It is possible to contaminate a room with small phages to such an extent that it is impossible to work with the host bacteria and be certain that the cultures will not become accidentally infected.

The following precautions are worth taking. Any spilled phage should be treated with a strong disinfectant such as "Deosan" (chlorine containing) before it has a chance to dry. No phage should be poured down the sink and all phage contaminated glassware should be sterilized before cleaning. Disposable Petri dishes should be autoclaved before disposal.

If work is contemplated in which large amounts of phage will have to be processed then it is preferable to conduct this work in a room well away from that used for setting up bacterial cultures or making phage assays.

All materials and apparatus used for phage assay work should be sterile and stored well away from areas where phage at high concentration is handled.

F. Modifications to the plaque assay procedures

The conditions under which the plaque assay is conducted can be varied over a wide range. Some of the variations can be used to improve the accuracy or readability of the assay while others can be used to investigate fundamental aspects of phage behaviour.

1. *Agar concentration*

If the agar concentration in the top layer is decreased the diameter of the plaques will increase. and *vice versa*. It is sometimes useful to raise the agar concentration when assaying phages like T3 and T7 which normally give very large plaques. In this way a convenient number of plaques can be accommodated on a plate whereas otherwise they would overlap and obscure each other.

As agar is not a standard product with precise properties and as the way in which it is made up can affect the strength of the gel it is advisable to examine the effect of concentration on plaque numbers and appearance before choosing which type of agar to use.

2. *Chemically defined media*

A chemically defined medium can be substituted for the nutrient broth in both the top and bottom layers. In this way the adsorption cofactor of phage T4 was discovered (Anderson, 1945) when it was found that the titre of the phage was much reduced when it was plated on minimal agar. The addition of L-tryptophan at as little as 100 μg/ml to the agar was sufficient to restore the plaque count to what it was on nutrient agar. The tryptophan is now known to act by releasing the tail fibres from a tightly wrapped conformation around the tail sheath so that they become extended from the tail tip and can make contact with the bacterial phage-receptor sites. A full account of this is given by Brenner *et al.* (1962).

3. *Additions to complex media*

Many phages are affected by divalent metal cations with the result that the plaques are either less in number or less easily counted unless the cation concentration is increased above that which is present in the nutrient agar normally. The plaque forming ability of ØX174, T1, T5 and ZJ/2 can be improved by the addition of 2mM $CaCl_2$ to the agar in both the top and bottom layers. On the other hand the presence of too much calcium can diminish the clarity of the plaques given by the T-even phages and others of similar morphological type. In this case the addition of 20mM sodium citrate is beneficial. Citrate is also useful in selectively inhibiting Ca-requiring phages of the T1 and T5 type when isolating Ca-independent phages from natural sources where the two varieties occur together. (Kay and Fildes, 1962).

The small RNA phages R17, MS2, f2, etc., do not give plaques when plated in the presence of RNase. The addition of the enzyme at 1 μg/ml to the top layer is sufficient to do this. This is a rapid method for identifying RNA phages and checking their purity. Should a specimen give plaques in the presence of the enzyme then there is reason to question its homogeneity.

4. *Mixed indicators*

The strain of bacteria on which the phage is plated is sometimes called the indicator strain. Considerable use has been made of mixtures of two different indicator strains of the same organism in work on phage mutants.

Phage resistant bacterial mutants, known as indicator strains, can be used to assay one phage in the presence of others provided the resistance pattern has been chosen appropriately. The efficiency of plating in the presence of the non-plaque forming phage should be checked as it is possible for this phage to kill the indicator and so block plaque formation by the other one. By the use of mixed indicators B/1, 5 and B/3, 4, 7 it was possible for Delbruck (1945) to demonstrate the mutual exclusion effect when bacteria were mixedly infected with immunologically unrelated phages T1 and T7. The assay plates were poured with mixtures of the two indicator strains which are resistant to one of each of the two phages. Except for a few due to overlapping all the plaques produced when the mixedly infected cultures were plated out were turbid showing that a cell could be infected by only one of the two phages. On the other hand when bacteria were mixedly infected with two immunologically related phages in the group T2, T4, T6, then clear plaques were given on the appropriate mixed indicator strains showing that bacteria could be infected by two strains of phage and could liberate both.

The uses which have been made of this system of phage assay are very numerous and have had far reaching effects on the understanding of phage genetics. They are discussed at length by Hopwood (Volume 7B).

5. *Temperature of incubation*

Phage assay plates should be incubated at a standard temperature in order to give consistent results. This should be chosen with the growth requirements of the host bacteria in mind. However bacteria will grow over a range of temperatures and by their careful choice it has been possible to discover and study the temperature sensitive phage mutants. Examples of these are the T4 mutants described by Edgar and Lielausis (1964) which form plaques at 25°C but not at 42°C. Temperature sensitive mutants of M13, a filamentous phage, have been described by Pratt *et al.* (1966). For these the permissive temperature was 32–33°C and the non-permissive 42°C. The presence of *ts* mutants among wild type plaques was revealed by first incubating the plates at 33°C for 5 h and then shifting to 42°C. The *ts* mutant plaques remained small while the wild type continued to enlarge.

6. Detection of lysozyme mutants

During the intracellular multiplication of certain phages an enzyme is synthesized which has properties very similar to those of egg white lysozyme. This is called phage lysozyme (Koch and Dreyer, 1958) and it is probably concerned with the release of the progeny phage by digesting the rigid murein component of the cell walls. Lysates of coliphage T4 contain the lysozyme and its action can be demonstrated on prepared cell walls. It does not act on living cells when tested *in vitro*. An ingenious method of demonstrating the lysozyme and detecting phage mutants which lack it or which possess it only in an imperfect form was described by Streisinger *et al.* (1961).

Plates were poured by the two layer method as if to assay the phage. After the plaques had formed the plates were inverted and a little chloroform was placed in the lid. This killed the bacteria and permitted the lysozyme, which diffuses away from the plaques, to digest the cells and produce clear halos around the plaques. Mutants lacking the lysozyme produced no halos.

G. Protoplast methods

The normal course of infection of a bacterial cell by phage involves the passage of the viral nucleic acid through the cell wall and the cytoplasmic membrane into the cytoplasm beneath. The cell wall is a barrier through which the phage nucleic acid can pass only if it is injected by the whole phage particle. If naked phage nucleic acid is presented to bacterial cells it is incapable of infecting them.

Under suitable conditions the bacteria can be deprived of their walls leaving osmotically sensitive objects which have been termed protoplasts. According to the definition of Brenner *et al.* (1958) the term protoplast should be reserved for structures, usually derived from Gram-positive organisms, which are totally devoid of cell wall residues. The analogous structures derived from Gram-negative bacteria, where cell wall remnants are still present, should be called spheroplasts (see Hughes, Wimpenny & Lloyd, this Series, Volume 5B).

Once the cell wall has been removed the protoplast may become susceptible to naked nucleic acid obtained from phage particles. The restriction imposed by the phage receptors in the cell wall no longer applies and it is possible for nucleic acid from phages other than those to which the cell is sensitive to enter.

1. Infectious ØX174 DNA in K12 protoplasts

In only a few cases has it been shown that naked phage nucleic acid can infect protoplasts and give rise to complete progeny phage. A method for demonstrating this with ØX174 has been described by Guthrie and Sinsheimer (1960). These authors prepared protoplasts from *E. coli* C or K12 by the following procedure and from *E. coli* B by the procedure of Fraser *et al.* (1957) (see p. 206).

Broth (modified 3XD, Fraser and Jerrell, p. 214) was inoculated with bacteria and aerated until there were 5×10^8/ml. These were used to inoculate another aerated culture (dilution 1 : 25) which was grown to between 2 and 6×10^8/ml. A 20 ml sample was centrifuged at 1000 *g* for 10 min at room temperature and the cells were taken up in 0·35 ml sucrose solution (0·5M) to which is added in order, 0·1 ml Tris buffer, pH 8·1, (0·25M), 0·01 ml lysozyme (crystalline, Worthington Biochemical Co., 2 mg/ml in water) and 0·02 ml EDTA (acid, 4% in water). The cells were converted to protoplasts in 10 min at room temperature. It is important that the cells are not washed or chilled before use. The protoplasts are diluted 1 : 5 in nutrient broth (see p. 215) containing 2% bovine serum albumin (BSA). and finally 1 : 4 in nutrient broth to reduce the albumin concentration.

Subviral preparations of ØX174, one of which was free nucleic acid, were stored in a solution containing 0·1M KCl in 0·001M Tris, pH 7·5 and diluted 1 : 10 in 0·01M Tris pH 8·0–8·3. An equal volume of protoplast suspension was added and the mixture was kept at 37°C for 10–15 min. At this point the infective centres could be assayed or incubation could be continued for a further 90 min after dilution 1 : 5 in nutrient broth when the mixture was titred for mature phage. It is important that the concentration of BSA should be below 0·2% during the incubation of infected protoplasts for the maximum yield of phage.

The infected protoplasts were assayed by the two layer method using the following materials. The bottom layer consisted of (per litre) Tryptone (10 g); KCl (2·5 g); NNaOH (6 ml), NaCl (2·5 g) and agar (10 g). Sterile M CaCl₂ (1 ml) was added to each litre after autoclaving. The top layer contained nutrient broth and 1% agar. After the melted top layer agar (2·5 ml) had been pipetted into the plating tubes 0·15 ml of sterile 30% BSA and 0·2 ml of plating bacteria were added.

2. *Protoplasts of* E. coli *B*

For preparing protoplasts from *E. coli* B the method of Fraser and Mahler (1957) is suitable. The bacteria were grown in 3XD medium (Fraser and Jerrell, see p. 214) to 2×10^8/ml, centrifuged and washed twice in 0·1M Tris buffer (Tris brought to pH 8·0 with 5% HCl) and resuspended at 5×10^8/ml in protoplasting medium (5 ml). This consisted of sucrose (171 g) dissolved in a little less than 1 litre of distilled water to which M Tris (30 ml) was added, the pH brought to 8·0 with 5% HCl and the volume made up to 1 litre. Lysozyme was then added (0·05 ml of 1 mg/ml in water) and the mixture swirled gently for 2 min at room temperature. 0·025 ml of EDTA (acid, 4% in water) was added and after a further 10 min the cells were largely converted to protoplasts.

3. *Improved method of protoplasting* E. coli *B*

In an improved procedure Fraser *et al.* (1957) increased the bacterial concentration in the protoplasting medium to 5×10^9/ml, raised the lysozyme to 0·1 ml of 1 mg/ml for each ml of cells and raised the EDTA to 0·2 ml of a 1% solution per ml cells. Protoplasts prepared by this procedure were used to test the ability of DNA from urea-inactivated phage T2 to produce infective phage. The DNA was prepared by treating 3 ml of T2 at 5×10^{11}/ml with 27 ml 8M urea dissolved in 0·1M NaCl adjusted to pH 8·2 with HCl. After 1 h at 37°C when the activity had been reduced to a negligible amount, the mixture was dialysed at 2°C overnight against 3 litres of 0·1M NaCl and for 4–6 h against another 3 litres of saline. The product (0·5 ml) was mixed with an equal volume of protoplasts and kept at room temperature for 10 min before plating for infective phage.

4. *Genetic recombination between urea-disrupted mutant T4 and T4 DNA*

Later it was found that purified T2 and T4 DNA cannot infect protoplasts to give rise to infective phage but that urea-disrupted phage preparations can do so. This matter was investigated by Van de Pol *et al.* (1961) who showed that genetic recombination can take place between purified phage DNA and an intact phage genome multiplying in spheroplasts. Veldhuisen *et al.* (1962), continuing these investigations, made spheroplasts from *E. coli* B grown on a minimal salts medium with 0·5% glucose. The cells at 10^9/ml were stored overnight in the cold and converted to spheroplasts by the method of Denes and Polgar (1959). The cells (90 ml) were added to 210 ml of the medium in which they were grown containing sucrose (20%), magnesium sulphate (hydrated) (0·20%) and penicillin (1000 units/ml). The mixture was gently shaken for 2 h at room temperature by which time 95% of the cells had been converted to spheroplasts.

Disrupted phage (T4 rII, a deletion mutant, 5×10^{12}/ml) was prepared by dilution 1 : 20 in 4M urea containing 2% bovine serum albumin followed by dialysis against 0·1M NaCl containing 0·02M Na citrate. DNA was prepared from the wild type (T4 rII⁺) by the method of Mandell and Hershey (1960). Equal volumes of DNA and spheroplasts were mixed and kept at 37°C. After 30 min 0·1 volume of disrupted T4 rII was added and the mixture stood at 37°C for 3–4 h. It was then plated on *E. coli* B, which gives plaques with both mutant and wild type and on *E. coli* K, which is sensitive only to the wild type. It was shown that disrupted mutant phage particles and DNA from the wild type in spheroplasts induces the production of a small number of wild type phage. It has also been shown that the spheroplasts could be prepared from *E. coli* B, K or KS/4 a mutant resistant to T4 (Van Arkel *et al.*, 1961).

5. *Infectious RNA*

A method for the assay of RNA from phage MS2 is described by Strauss (1964). A bacterial protoplast stock from *E. coli* K12 (strain W6) is made as described by Guthrie and Sinsheimer (1963) (see p. 205 for details) except that the PAM medium, which should contain 1 g glucose/litre, is added 30 sec after the addition of EDTA to the resuspended cells. The stock, which contains about 10^9 protoplasts/ml may be chilled and used for at least 24 h without loss of efficiency.

For assay, 0·4 ml of protoplast stock at room temperature is added to an equal volume of an RNA solution (see p. 222 for preparation), in a 37°C water bath, in 0·05M Tris buffer pH 7·0 (measured at 37°C). Thirty seconds later, 3·2 ml of PAM medium is added. After 2·5 h incubation at 37°C the protoplasts are disrupted by adding a few drops of chloroform and shaking vigorously. The phages thus released are titred.

The time of dilution of the RNA-protoplast mixture with the PAM medium is critical. The optimum time occurs from 30 to 45 sec after addition of the protoplasts to the RNA. The yield of phage is about one plaque-forming particle per 50 molecules of viral RNA input.

The bacterial protoplasts are prepared as follows (Guthrie and Sinsheimer, 1963). *E. coli* K12 W6 was grown in 3XD medium (p. 205) with aeration. A 20 ml (5×10^8/ml) sample was centrifuged and the pellet was resuspended in 0·35 ml of 1·5M sucrose. The following solutions are then added, in order, with gentle shaking after each one; 0·17 ml of 30% BSA (Armour), 0·02 ml of lysozyme (crystalline, Worthington Biochemical Co., 2 mg/ml in 0·25M Tris, pH 8·1), 0·04 ml of 4% EDTA and 10 ml of PA medium (see p. 218). After the mixture has been incubated at room temperature 10–15 min, 0·2 ml of 10% magnesium sulphate (hydrated) is added to complex the EDTA and stop the reaction. This is the protoplast stock and can be kept at room temperature for an hour or may be stored on ice for several hours.

Infection of the protoplasts is carried out as follows. Protoplast stock (0·4 ml) is added to the DNA preparation (in this case from ØX174, see below for extraction method) preferably dissolved in or diluted in 0·4 ml of 0·05M Tris (pH 8·1). After 10–20 min at 37°C, 3·2 ml of PAM medium (see p. 218), pre-warmed to 35°C are added and mixed. If infective centres are to be assayed, dilution is made through a solution made of 1 vol. of PAM medium, 2 vol. of 1·5M sucrose and 0·3 vol. of 30% BSA. Top agar for plating contains PAM medium, 2–3% BSA and 0·8% agar. For assay of phage yield, the infected protoplasts are incubated at 37°C for 90–120 min. They are then opened, either by freezing and thawing three times (in dry ice-acetone) or by a 1 : 100 dilution into water or 0·05M borate buffer and titrated for phage.

The DNA was extracted from ØX174 by treating one volume of phage in 0·1M borate buffer with 1 volume of phenol previously equilibrated with 0·1M tetraborate buffer. Before mixing both the phage and the phenol were brought to 70°C. They were then shaken and reheated to 70°C alternately for 3 min. After cooling to room temperature the mixture was centrifuged at 1000 g for 5 min to separate the layers. The aqueous layer was extracted with phenol twice at room temperature and the three phenol layers were serially re-extracted with 0·5 volume of 0·1M borate. The two aqueous layers were combined and the residual phenol was extracted by shaking three to five times with an equal volume of ether at 0°C. The ether was removed by dialysis or by bubbling nitrogen through the sample. Such extractions of DNA can be successfully carried out on as little as 0·1 μg (10^{10} particles) of virus if 1 mg of BSA is added per ml of virus suspension.

6. *Phage multiplication in cell-free systems*

It should be noted that in contrast to methods described above where phage replication takes place in intact protoplasts it is possible for phage DNA, in this instance from phage λ, to cause the production of infective virus in either mechanically disrupted bacteria (Mackal, Werninghaus and Evans, 1964) or in osmotically ruptured protoplasts (Zgaga, 1967).

III. PREPARATION OF PHAGE STOCKS

In this Section the methods for growing phage on the scale of a few litres will be discussed. The preparation of stocks on a smaller scale is dealt with by Billing (this Series, Vol. 3B) and on a larger scale by Sargeant (this Series, Vol. 5B).

It is essential when working with any phage that a stock should be laid down for reference and as a source from which a working stock can be prepared at infrequent intervals. The preparation and preservation of small stocks of this kind has been described by Billing (this Series, Vol. 3B). In the case of the *E. coli*-typhoid phages the author has found that storage of centrifuged broth lysates in screw-capped sample bottles at 4°C with a crystal of thymol to prevent microbial growth has been entirely satisfactory. Several bottles of reference stock should be prepared and only one of these used to prepare working stocks. Phage should not be propagated serially or from single plaques (once the initial selection has been made) as both methods run the risk that mutants might be selected.

A. Identity and homogeneity of phage stocks

Some procedure should be sought to identify any new phage or even a well-known one on which it is intended to begin work. This is especially important where several different phages are in use in one laboratory because of the ease with which cross contamination can occur.

In the case of the *E. coli* phages for example phage resistant bacterial strains can be isolated very easily against most of the seven and it is found that resistance occurs against groups of phages, e.g. B/1,5; B/3,4; B/3,4,7 as well as singly, B/2; B/6. With the aid of a set of mutant bacteria it is possible to identify with certainty all the T phages and this scheme could be repeated with most other groups of phages.

A difficulty exists here with the RNA phages and the filamentous phages. Although a number of each of these types of phage has now been isolated the receptors on the bacteria to which they attach are located on the sex pili and are (except for Qβ and the I phages, Meynell and Datta, 1967), probably identical. It has not been possible to obtain a set of mutants which will distinguish between all of the RNA phages or all of the filamentous ones.

Antiserum is useful for testing the identity and homogeneity of a phage. Thus phages can be compared by examining the K values obtained by inactivating them with antiserum

The homogeneity of any preparation of phage should always be examined in the electron microscope. In this way not only is some idea of its cleanliness obtained but the presence of contaminant phages can be seen, if present to the extent of about 1% or more.

B. Preparation of phage on a moderate scale

This Section deals with the growth of phage on the scale of a few tens of ml to a few litres. In general phage multiplication is greatest in cultures which are rapidly growing but the total yield of phage depends also on the actual number of cells which undergo infection and lysis. In most types of apparatus used for phage growth, such as shake flasks and simple aerated vessels, the oxygen supply cannot match the needs of the culture above a certain cell density. Above this density the growth rate of the bacteria falls and usually lysis is poor and the yield of phage low. The means of raising the oxygen supply to match the needs of dense cultures is dealt with by Sargent (this Series, Vol. 5B) but where lower yields per unit volume of culture are acceptable quite simple apparatus will serve.

1. *Apparatus*

On the scale of a few tens of ml the "T" tube (see p. 196) which can grow 10 ml per tube, is very convenient. Bacterial growth and lysis can be followed without danger of contamination due to opening the vessel.

Cultures of up to a few hundreds of ml can be grown in shake flasks. These are usually conical (Erlenmeyer) flasks of 1–2 l capacity in which 100–200 ml of culture is agitated on a reciprocating or rotary shaking machine.

Many published methods for the growth of phage mention that the cultures were aerated. This usually means that air was passed into the culture but the precise means that were used is rarely described. If it is decided to aerate a culture then a suitable vessel of a comparatively tall cylindrical shape must be fitted with a bung which carries the air inlet tube, an air outlet tube and a sampling port. The air should be supplied from a large compressor capable of maintaining a steady pressure and both inlet and outlet pipes should be fitted with filters. These can be made of wide bore tubing packed with cotton wool. It should be borne in mind that the effluent air will contain both bacteria and phage as an aerosol and it is the purpose of the outlet filter to prevent escape of this into the atmosphere. Tests should be made from time to time to see that this is so, particularly if the more stable varieties of phage are being grown (see p. 201).

Cultures of up to 1 litre at a time can be grown very conveniently without the danger of aerosol formation in the rotating flask apparatus described by Mitchell (1949). Five litre round flasks containing 1 litre of medium are each mounted on a rotating table inclined at 45°C so that they can be kept in continuous motion about the long axis. The motion causes the medium to form a thin film around the bowl of the flask and ensures a degree of aeration sufficient to permit exponential growth up to about 1×10^9 cells/ml. The original Mitchell design used a pair of arms fitted into the flask by means of a rubber bung to cause a current of air to pass into the flask but these have always proved rather fragile and the author has found that they can be dispensed with and diffusion through the cotton wool plug can be relied upon to supply all the requirements of the culture. The apparatus is either mounted in a hot room or a hot box can be built around the rotating platform.

2. *Culture media*

A great many culture media have been devised for the growth of bacteriophage. These media have to satisfy two main criteria, they must be adequate for the growth of the host bacteria and they must provide suitable conditions for the attachment, penetration, multiplication and release of the phage. In many cases these requirements are easily met with common culture media but there are numerous instances where special media have had to be devised.

The following list of media has been included in this Chapter because they have often been developed to meet specific requirements which are referred to in other parts of the text and they give a cross section of the various types which have been formulated.

Contents to Table of Culture Media

Culture Media

"F" medium (*Anderson*, 1948)

NH$_4$Cl	1·0 g
MgSO$_4$.7H$_2$O (a)	0·1 g
KH$_2$PO$_4$	1·5 g
Na$_2$HPO$_4$	3·5 g
Lactic acid (a)	9·0 g
Water	1·0 litre

Adjust pH to 6·8 with NaOH, autoclave.

"N" medium (*Anderson*, 1948)

Difco Nutrient Broth	8 g
NaCl	5 g
Water	1 litre

"M9" medium (*from Adams*, 1959)

NH$_4$Cl	1·0 g
MgSO$_4$7H$_2$O (a)	0·13 g
KH$_2$PO$_4$	3·0 g
Na$_2$HPO$_4$	6·0 g
Glucose (a)	4·0 g
Water	1 litre

Friedlein medium (*Weidel*, 1951)

NH$_4$Cl	1·0 g
MgSO$_4$.7H$_2$O	0·1 g
KH$_2$PO$_4$	1·5 g
Na$_2$HPO$_4$	3·55 g
Lactic acid	10·2 g
NaOH	3·5 g
Water	1 litre

Adsorption medium (*Hershey and Chase*, 1952)

NaCl	4·0 g
K$_2$SO$_4$	5·0 g
KH$_2$PO$_4$	1·5 g
Na$_2$HPO$_4$	3·0 g
MgSO$_4$	1mM
CaCl$_2$	0·1mM
Gelatin	0·01 g
Water	1 litre
	pH 7·0

(a) Autoclave separately.

Medium for preparing phage labelled with ^{32}P and ^{35}S
(*Hershey and Chase*, 1952)

Sodium lactate	70mM
Glycerol	4·0 g
NaCl	5·0 g
KCl	2·0 g
NH$_4$Cl	1·0 g
MgCl$_2$	1mM
CaCl$_2$	0·1mM
Gelatin	0·01 g
Phosphorus (as orthophosphate)	10 mg
Sulphur (as MgSO$_4$)	10 mg
Water	1 litre
	pH 7·0

The growth of *E. coli* in this medium is not accompanied by any serious alteration in the pH. ^{32}P or ^{35}S at specific activities of 0·5 and 8 mc/mg is added to the medium before inoculation with bacteria.

Tris buffered medium (*Hershey*, 1955)

Used for preparing radioactive phage T2

Glucose (sterilized separately)	2·0 g
NaCl	5·4 g
KCl	3·0 g
NH$_4$Cl	1·1 g
CaCl$_2$	0·011 g
MgCl$_2$	0·095 g
Tris	12·1 g
KH$_2$PO$_4$	0·087 g
Na$_2$SO$_4$	0·023 g
FeCl$_3$	0·00016 g

pH adjusted to 7·4 with HCl, final volume 1 litre.

For growing radioactive phage uniformly labelled ^{14}C glucose, ^{32}P orthophosphate or ^{35}S sulphate was substituted for the unlabelled constituents. The bacteria were grown for three generations in the labelled medium before infection with phage.

Peptone broth (*Hershey, Dixon and Chase*, 1953)

Difco Bacto-peptone	10 g
NaCl	3 g
Glucose	1 g
MgSO$_4$	1mM
CaCl$_2$	0·1mM
P (as phosphate buffer, pH 7·0)	5 mg
Water	1 litre

Glycerol-Casamino-acids medium, 3XD (Fraser and Jerrell, 1953)
Used by Fraser and Jerrell for the growth of coliphage T3 and by Eigner *et al.*
(1963) for ØX174.

Na_2HPO_4	10·5 g
KH_2PO_4	4·5 g
NH_4Cl	1·0 g
$MgSO_4$	0·3 g
$CaCl_2$ (molar solution)	0·3 ml
Gelatin (1% solution)	1·0 ml
Casamino-acids	15·0 g
Glycerol	30·0 g

The following precautions should be taken when making up this medium (Fraser
and Mahler, 1957). The Ca_2Cl_2 should be diluted and added last when the volume is
nearly complete. The pH should be 7·0 or slightly lower and there should be no
calcium contaminating the distilled water.

Maaløe and Hannawalt used this medium to grow *E. coli* 15T⁻ and supplemented
the medium with thymine (2 µg/ml), uracil (10 µg/ml) and arginine (20 µg/ml)
as required. For incorporation of ¹⁴C thymine this compound 9·5 mc/m-mole)
was added to 0·0159 µmole/ml.

MS broth (Davis and Sinsheimer, 1963)
For growth of coliphage MS2.

Bacto-tryptone (Difco)	10 g
NaCl	8 g
Bacto-yeast extract	1 g
Water	1 litre
Autoclave and add	
Glucose solution (10%) sterile	10 ml
$CaCl_2$ (M) solution, sterile	2 ml
Thiamine hydrochloride 10 mg/ml, sterile	1 ml

TPG medium (Sinsheimer et al., 1962)
Used for labelling ØX174 with deuterium, ¹⁵N and ³²P, with appropriate additions.

NaCl	0·5 g
KCl	8·0 g
NH_4Cl	1·1 g
$CaCl_2$ (0·1M)	1·0 ml
$MgCl_2.6H_2O$	0·2 g
Tris†	12·1 g
KH_2PO_4	0·023 g
Na pyruvate	0·8 g
Na_2SO_4 (0·16M)	1·0 ml

Dissolve in 1 litre of water, adjust to pH 7·4 with HCl and autoclave. Then add
to each 100 ml the following sterile solutions.

$FeCl_3.6H_2O$ (1 µg/ml)	0·1 ml
Glucose (0·1 g/ml)	2·0 ml

† 2 amino-2-hydroxymethylpropane-1 : 3-diol.

TPG3A medium (*Sinsheimer*, 1966)
Used for growing ØX174.

Dissolve in 1 litre of water 5·4 g of a mixture of 20 natural L-amino-acids (Nutritional Biochemicals Corporation). Dissolve in 500 ml of water NaCl, 1·0 g; KCl, 16 g; NH_4Cl, 2·2 g; Tris, 24·2 g; KH_2PO_4, 2·0 g; Na pyruvate, 1·6 g. Mix and add 2 ml of $MgCl_2.6H_2O$ (20% w/v); 0·2 ml of M $CaCl_2.2H_2O$; 100 ml of adenine (50 mg/100 ml) and 2·0 ml of 0·16 M Na_2SO_4.

Adjust pH to 7·4, make up to 2 litres and autoclave. After autoclaving add 2·0 ml of $FeCl_3.6H_2O$ (1 mg/10 ml of sterile water) and 20·0 ml of 20% (w/v) sterile glucose solution.

Modified 3XD medium (*Guthrie and Sinsheimer*, 1960)
Used for protoplast preparation.

This is the glycerol-Casamino-acids medium of Fraser and Jerrell (p. 214) but with the KH_2PO_4 reduced to 0·9 g and the Na_2HPO_4 reduced to 2·1 g/litre.

Nutrient broth (*Guthrie and Sinsheimer*, 1960)
Used for protoplast preparation.

Casamino-acids (Difco)	10 g
Nutrient broth (Difco)	10 g
Glucose	1 g
Sucrose	100 g
Water	1 litre

After autoclaving add sterile 10% $MgSO_4$ (anhydrous), 10 ml.

H medium (*Maaløe and Hannawalt*, 1961)
Used by Ray *et al.* (1966) for growing phage M13.

Dissolve in 1 litre of water

Tris	12·0 g
KCl	2·0 g
NH_4Cl	2·0 g
$MgCl_2.6H_2O$	0·5 g
Na_2HPO_4	0·05 g
Na_2SO_4	0·02 g
HCl (conc)	7·5 ml
Glucose	0·05%

KC broth (*Sinsheimer* et al., 1962)
Used for growing ØX174

KCl	100 mg
Bacto-tryptone (Difco)	200 mg
$CaCl_2$ (0·01M)	1 ml
Make up to 20 ml.	

D-TGL medium (*Sinsheimer* et al., 1962)

Used for growing ØX174 labelled with deuterium. For a final volume of 20 ml the following amounts are used.

KCl	100 mg
NaCl	30 mg
NH_4Cl	5 mg
K_2HPO_4	0·6 mg
$Na_2SO_4 . 10H_2O$ (113 mg in 1 ml D_2O)	20 μl
Glycerol	0·03 ml
Na lactate 50% solution	5 μl

Dissolve in 3 ml D_2O and evaporate to dryness. The residue is dissolved in 16 ml D_2O, 0·2 g Tris is added and the pH is adjusted to 7·1–7·3 first with concentrated HCl and then with a 1N dilution of 12N HCl in D_2O. Then add 20 μl of a solution containing 100 mg of $MgCl_2 . 6H_2O$ in 1 ml D_2O, 10 μl of a solution of 8 mg $FeCl_3 . 6H_2O$ in 2 ml D_2O and 1·47 mg $CaCl_2 . 2H_2O$. The volume is then made up to 20 ml with D_2O and sterilized by filtration through a millipore filter itself sterilized in ultraviolet light.

Tris buffered gylcerol, Casamino-acids medium (*Capecchi*, 1966)

Used for labelling phage R17 with ^{14}C in the protein and ^{3}H in the RNA.

Casamino-acids	5·0 g
NaCl	5·0 g
NH_4Cl	1·0 g
Glycerol	4 ml
$MgSO_4$	1mM
K_2HPO_4	0·3mM
$FeCl_3$	10 μM
Tris	10mM
$CaCl_2$	0·1mM
Water	1 litre
pH adjusted to 7·5	

MGM medium (*Lanni*, 1961)

Used for growing phage T5.

Maleic acid	5×10^{-2}M
Glucose	5 g
NH_4Cl	1 g
P (as orthophosphate)	40 mg
S (as Na_2SO_4)	27 mg
KCl	2·0 g
Gelatin	0·1 g
$FeSO_4 . 7H_2O$	0·5 mg
$MgSO_4$	10^{-4}M
Water	1 litre

The maleic acid is first adjusted to pH 7·3 and the final pH should be 7·15.

Tris-glucose-Casamino-acids medium (Nomura, Okamato and Asano, 1962)

Used for labelling RNA in T4-infected *E. coli* B with ^{32}P and ^{14}C (in uracil).

Tris, pH 7·4	0·1M
NaCl	0·08M
KCl	0·02M
NH$_4$Cl	0·02M
KH$_2$PO$_4$	$6·4 \times 10^{-4}$M
Na$_2$SO$_4$	$1·6 \times 10^{-4}$M
MgCl$_2$	10^{-3}M
CaCl$_2$	10^{-4}M
FeCl$_3$	2×10^{-6}M
Glucose	0·2%
Casamino-acids, vitamin free	0·1%

Tryptophan (50 μg/ml) was added to permit adsorption of T4. ^{32}P was added when required at 1–5 mc/24 ml. ^{14}C uracil (1·2 mc/m-mole) was added at 1·6 μg/ml.

λ Broth (Davison and Freifelder, 1966)

Used for the preparation of λ phage.

Tryptone	1%
NaCl	0·5%
MgCl$_2$	0·01M

Lysing medium (Hershey, 1957)

KCN	0·81 g
MgCl$_2$	0·12 g
Gelatin	0·13 g
Indole	0·13 g
Water	1 litre

pH 8 with H$_3$PO$_4$.

"L" broth (Levine, 1957)

Bacto Tryptone	1%
Yeast extract	0·5%
NaCl	0·05%
Glucose	0·01%

pH 7·0 with N NaOH.

Modified TPG medium (Oeschger and Nathans, 1966)

Used for preparing phage-specific proteins in cells inhibited with actinomycin.

KCl	0·11M
NaCl	8·0mM
NH$_4$Cl	0·05M
Tris	0·1M
Na$_2$SO$_4$	0·16mM
KH$_2$PO$_4$	1·0mM
Na pyruvate	0·073M
CaCl$_2$	0·1mM

MgCl$_2$	1·0mM
FeCl$_3$	2 $\mu\mu$M
Thiamine	10 mg
Glucose (sterile solution, added separately)	2 g
Water	1 litre

pH 7·4 with HCl

"K" medium (Weigle, Meselson and Paigen, 1959)

Double strength M9 medium (see p. 212)	100 ml
3% Casamino-acids treated with decolorizing charcoal to remove ultraviolet absorbing material	100 ml
NaCl	0·1 g
MgSO$_4$	0·06 g
Glucose	0·4 g

PA and PAM medium (Guthrie and Sinsheimer, 1963)

Used for preparing protoplasts of E. coli K12 and for the assay of infectious ØX174 DNA.

PA medium contains per litre:

Casamino-acids	10 g
Nutrient broth (Difco)	10 g
Glucose	10 g
Sucrose	100 g

PAM medium is PA medium with 0·2% MgSO$_4$ added after autoclaving.

3. Phage growth

In order to avoid long and often unreproducible lag periods it is best to inoculate media for phage production with enough of a log phase culture to give not less than 2×10^7 cells per ml. Bacterial growth will then begin with scarcely any delay and can be allowed to reach 2×10^8 but not more than 5×10^8 cells per ml before the phage inoculum is put in. A choice will have to be made of the multiplicity of infection. A high one (one or more) will result in most of the progeny phage being produced by the first round of multiplication by which time most of the bacteria will have been infected and lysed. A low multiplicity can be used and the phage concentration be allowed to build up as each round of multiplication is succeeded by another. The main advantage of this method is that small phage inocula can be used as, for example, when a new phage is being prepared and a sufficiently large stock for high multiplicity infection has not yet been obtained. It has the disadvantage that the progeny are the result of an unknown number of phage generations.

In the case of the T-even phages the multiplicity of infection should not be allowed to exceed two to three to avoid lysis-from-without which would give a negligible yield of phage. Also in the T-even phages use can be made of the property of lysis inhibition. This matter is discussed further in the Section on Lysis, p. 248, but in essence it means that if the r or rapid lysis mutants of the T-even phages are avoided and the r^+ mutants used lysis will occur rather slowly and the yield of phage will be much higher than if the r mutant was used.

The growth of lysogenic phage does not appear to present any special difficulty. Davison and Freifelder (1966) prepared phage λ by adding 5×10^9 particles and 0.01M $MgCl_2$ to 5 ml of $E.$ $coli$ W3110 grown overnight in λ broth (see p. 217). This inoculum was added to 500 ml of λ swirled on a rotary shaker for 6 h at 37°C and then treated with chloroform. The phage was precipitated by adding 25 g ammonium sulphate per 100 ml lysate and purified by several cycles of differential centrifugation. It was stored in a solution of 0.1M NaCl, 0.01M Tris (pH 7.5) and 0.001M $MgCl_2$.

Some phages tend to be difficult to grow unless the procedure described by other workers who have successfully grown them are followed. One of these is ØX174 for which a method has been described by Sinsheimer (1966).

Inoculate 2 litres of TPG3A medium (see p. 215) in a 10 litre flask with 100 ml of $E.$ $coli$ C406 grown from a slant to 4–5×10^8/ml and aerate vigorously at 37°C. When the cell density reaches 2–3×10^8/ml add wild type ØX174 to give a multiplicity of infection of three. Thirty minutes later add 10 ml of disodium versenate adjusted to pH7. Foaming will begin about 10 min later. Allow lysis to continue until the culture clears 5–7 h later. The titre of the lysate should be 4–12×10^{11}/ml.

4. *Isotopically labelled phage*

Many phage investigations have been made possible only by the use of isotopically labelled phage particles, host bacteria or media.

(a) *T4 labelled with* ^{32}P *and* ^{35}S. The experiments of Hershey and Chase (1952) on the independent functions of phage nucleic acid and protein used radioactively labelled phage T4 which was prepared by a procedure described in outline on page 213. By this method the phage became generally labelled in either the protein or the nucleic acid but should it be necessary to label only particular components of the macromolecules different procedures have to be used.

(b) *ØX174 labelled with* ^{14}C *in the pyrimidines*. Hall and Sinsheimer (1963) studied the chemical structure of the DNA from phage ØX174 and required phage labelled in the pyrimidines of the nucleic acid. It should have been possible to do this using a pyrimidine requiring mutant of the host organism and supplementing the medium with labelled uracil but unfortunately the mutant gave too small a yield of phage. The problem was overcome by using the normal host, *E. coli* C, preventing the endogenous synthesis of pyrimidines by adding azauracil and thereby causing it to utilize labelled uracil.

The bacteria were grown in 1 litre of minimal medium TPG (Sinsheimer *et al.*, 1962) (p. 214) to which 6-azauracil (25 μg/ml) and uracil (5 μg/ml) had been added. After the culture had grown to 3×10^8/ml the cells were quickly collected by filtration on to a 142 mm HA filter (Millipore Filter Co., Bedford, Mass., U.S.A.) and resuspended in fresh, prewarmed TPG medium to which azauracil and ^{14}C-2-uracil (1 μg/ml, 18·1 mc/mM) had been added. The bacteria were infected with phage at a ratio of three infective particles per cell and incubated for 20 min when 5 ml of 0·1M EDTA (pH 7·0) were added to minimize readsorption of released virus. Ninety minutes after infection pancreatic DNase, 1 mg and RNase, 1 mg were added to the lysate and incubation continued for an additional 2 h. The phage was purified by a procedure described in Chapter 2 and 7×10^{13} virus particles were obtained with a radioactivity of $1·5 \times 10^6$ counts/min. The specific activities of the thymidylic and deoxycytidylic acid isolated from the phage were found to be equal.

(c) *ØX174 labelled with* ^{15}N *and* ^{32}P. In order to prepare ØX174 labelled in nitrogen and phosphorus Sinsheimer *et al.* (1962) used the following procedure. TPG medium (p. 214) was made up with ^{15}NH$_4$Cl instead of the usual NH$_4$Cl. To 75 ml, 10 mc of ^{32}P (carrier free) which had been evaporated to dryness over KOH and CaCl$_2$ and redissolved in 5 ml of sterile ^{15}N TPG medium, was added together with an inoculum of *E. coli* C^1 which had been adapted to growth in TPG medium. The initial cell titre was $3–5 \times 10^7$/ml and the culture was aerated through a sintered glass bubbler until it had risen to $6–7 \times 10^8$/ml. Phage ØX174 diluted in ^{15}NH$_4$Cl (1 ml) enough to give a multiplicity of three was then added and the culture aerated for a further 75 min by which time lysis had occurred and progeny titre was $4–6 \times 10^{10}$/ml.

(d) *MS2 labelled with* ^{15}N *and* ^{32}P. A variant of this procedure is given by Davis and Sinsheimer (1963) for the preparation of the RNA phage MS2 labelled with ^{15}N and ^{32}P. *E. coli* C3000 was grown to 5×10^8/ml with vigorous aeration in ^{15}N–TPG medium. To 9 ml of this medium containing 2 mc of carrier free ^{32}P sodium phosphate 0·3 ml of the culture was added. When the bacterial titre reached $1–1·5 \times 10^8$ cells/ml the culture was infected with 0·1 ml of the ^{15}N TPG medium containing sufficient MS2 to give a multiplicity of 10. Aeration was continued for 2–3 h until the culture cleared. The titre of the lysate was 10^{12} phage/ml or more.

(e) $\emptyset X174$ *labelled with* D, ^{15}N *and* ^{32}P. In order to label $\emptyset X174$ with deuterium, ^{15}N and ^{32}P Sinsheimer *et al.* (1962) used the following procedure. First *E. coli* C was adapted to growth in D–TGL medium prepared as described on p. 216 by inoculating 10 ml and aerating for 2 days with air passed through a D_2O bubbler. 0·1 ml of this culture was used to inoculate 4·5 ml of medium and allowed to grow overnight. 0·2 ml of this culture which contained 1×10^9 cells/ml was then used to inoculate 100 ml of D-TGL to which 10 mc of ^{32}P (dried down and redissolved in 5 ml D-TGL) had been added. After 17 h aeration at 37°C the culture contained 4×10^8 cells/ml and was then infected with $D^{15}N$-labelled phage at a multiplicity of 0·2. It cleared after 4–6 h. The phage used to infect the culture had been previously enriched in deuterium and ^{15}N by the following method. From a lysate made in $D^{15}N$ medium with normal phage the heavier particles were selected by density gradient centrifugation. These were used to infect another culture which was again centrifuged to separate the denser phage. After several cycles a phage preparation of homogeneous density was obtained and it was this which was used to infect the $D^{15}N^{32}P$ culture.

(f) *T2 labelled with* ^{14}C, ^{32}P or ^{35}S. Hershey (1955) described the preparation of phage T2 labelled with either ^{14}C, ^{32}P or ^{35}S. Bacteria (*E. coli* H) were allowed to grow for three generations in the labelled media (see p. 213) up to 5×10^8/ml before infecting with phage. Occasionally bacteria were transferred to radioactive medium just before infection. The phage was purified by differential centrifugation.

The amino-acids of phage T4D were specifically labelled by allowing *E. coli* BB or CR63 to grow exponentially in M9 medium (p. 212) up to 5×10^8/ml, infecting with phage at a multiplicity of 4–5 and 11 min later inducing lysis inhibition by superinfection. At this point 2 μc of ^{14}C lysine (uniformly labelled, 100 μc/mmole) was added. It was shown that incorporation of label into phage continued linearly for 8 min.

To permit labelling of other amino-acids the medium was supplemented with 0·4 μc/ml of arginine, proline, glutamic acid, threonine or methionine.

(g) *T2 labelled with* ^3H. Phage T2 was labelled with ^3H thymine for autoradiographic purposes by the following method (Kahn, 1964). *E. coli* B3 (thymine requiring) was grown in the Tris-buffered glucose medium described by Hershey (1955, see p. 213) supplemented with Casamino-acids (Difco) 0·5 g/litre, uracil 20 μg/ml, deoxyadenosine 250 μg/ml and thymine 5·5 μg/ml. The cells were centrifuged, washed once, diluted and resuspended in the same medium containing ^3H thymine (10·1 c/mmole). The total volume was 0·2 ml. A control non-radioactive culture was set up at the same time and its growth followed. When the optical density had increased by a factor of ten to about 1×10^8 cells per ml phage T2H was added to a multiplicity of 0·2. At the same time fluorodeoxyuridine (5 μg/ml) was added to inhibit thymidylate synthetase. Seventy minutes later 2 ml of lysing medium without KCN (Hershey, 1957, p. 217) and a few drops of chloroform were added. Aeration was continued for a few minutes to remove the chloroform. The yield was 300 particles per infecting phage.

(h) *P22 heavily labelled with* ^{32}P. Hartman and Kozinski (1962) prepared very heavily labelled ^{32}P phage P22 by growing it in a radiation-resistant strain of *Salmonella typhimurium* which had been selected for survival in the highly radioactive medium. The medium used consisted of glucose and Casamino-acids buffered with Tris but it contained only 5 μg P/ml (one fifth of the normal amount). Carrier-free ^{32}P (200–400 mc/mg P) was added.

(i) *R17 labelled with* ^3H *in the RNA*. The RNA of phage R17 was labelled with ^{3}H by growth in a glycerol-Casamino-acids medium (p. 216) (Capecchi, 1966). *E. coli*, Hfr 1 (a *met⁻* strain) was grown to 2×10^8/ml, 0·1 mc of ^{3}H uracil/litre was added and the culture infected with R17 at a multiplicity of 5. After 3 h aeration at 37°C the phage titre was 1–2×10^{12}/ml. The lysate was made 2·5M with ammonium sulphate and stood at 4°C overnight to precipitate the phage, which was collected by centrifugation at 5000 *g* for 25 min and resuspended in SSC (0·15M NaCl and 0·015M Na citrate, pH 7). After clarification by low speed centrifugation the phage was again precipitated, this time by the addition of one third of a volume of cold methanol and kept at $-10°$C for 2·5 h. The precipitate was spun down at 5000 *g* for 25 min, resuspended in SSC and centrifuged at low speed. It was finally banded in CsCl ($n^{25} = 1·374$) (see p. 274 in Kay, Chapter VI, this Volume, for typical procedure) for 16 h at 39,000 rpm and the denser of the two bands taken. The product gave 520 counts/min/μg of RNA.

(j) *R17 labelled with* ^{14}C *in the protein*. The protein of phage R17 was labelled by growth in medium containing ^{14}C-phenylalanine. The bacteria were grown in the same medium as was used for labelling the RNA of the phage with tritium (Capecchi, 1966) except that the Casamino-acids were replaced by a mixture of amino-acids omitting phenylalanine. ^{14}C-phenylalanine (200 μc) was added at the time of infection. After purification the product had a specific activity of 80 counts/min/μg phage.

(k) *ØX174 labelled with* ^{14}C *in the purines*. The purines of ØX174 were labelled by growing the phage in a medium supplemented with 8[^{14}C]-adenine (Sedat and Sinsheimer, 1964).

(l) *T4 labelled with* ^{13}C *and* ^{15}N

Phage T4 was labelled with ^{13}C and ^{15}N by growth in a medium containing [^{13}C ^{15}N]-algal protein hydrolysate (Roller, 1964).

IV. THE MAIN FEATURES OF PHAGE MULTIPLICATION

In this Section phage adsorption and related topics, the burst size, eclipse period, methods for studying intracellular phage and the lysis of infected cells will be discussed.

A. Adsorption

The first step in the interaction between a phage particle and its host cell is specific adsorption. In this a special part of the phage anatomy, frequently at the tip of the tail but presumably some area of the capsid in the case of isometric phages, comes in contact with an area on the bacterial surface which corresponds sufficiently to allow an irreversible combination to be made between the two. This is called adsorption and it is specific because only the host bacteria carry the correct receptor areas to which the phage can attach. In general phages rarely attach to insusceptible strains of bacteria.

1. *Measurement of adsorption*

Adsorption can be measured in two basic ways. The amount of phage unadsorbed in a mixture of phage and bacteria can be determined or conversely the number of infected cells can be counted. If sufficient measurements are taken during the period of adsorption a curve can be plotted and the kinetics of adsorption studied.

The amount of free phage in a mixture can be determined after centrifugation to sediment the cells together with the attached phage. A bench centrifuge is suitable. In this type of experiment a bacterial culture, generally in the log phase, but any physiological condition can be studied, is taken and a sample removed for a cell count (counting chamber, viable cell count or optical density referred to a standard curve). The adsorption can be followed either in the vessel in which the culture grew (e.g. a "T" tube, p. 196) or in a test-tube. Phage is now added to the culture in a ratio generally less than one per cell, and to a similar volume of diluent or culture medium (see p. 199) which is assayed to find the input, P_0. At intervals samples are withdrawn from the mixture diluted 1 : 10 (say 0·5 ml plus 4·5 ml) in centrifuge tubes and spun for 5 min to bring down the cells and any attached phage. Depending on the bacterial concentration it may or may not be possible to see the sedimented cells but even so they will have been thrown down and if a sample of the supernatant fluid is carefully removed from near the top of the tube on the inner side the free phage concentration (P_t) can be determined without admixture with the bacterial cells.

Further samples are taken as required but it might not be possible to take many due to the length of time it takes to dilute, centrifuge and assay each one. To overcome this it is possible to collect all the samples needed, dilute them immediately in ice cold diluent and store them at 4°C until all can be centrifuged together.

If a plot of the log % free phage is made against time a straight line is generally obtained down to about 1% or less free. Should the line vary appreciably from linearity it might be that the phage is inhomogeneous. If the bacterial concentration is known the rate of adsorption, K, can be calculated.

$$K = \frac{2 \cdot 3 \log P_0/P_t}{B.t}$$

where P_0 is the initial phage count, P_t is the free phage at t min and B is the bacterial concentration (cells/ml). This constant will apply only under standard conditions of temperature, ionic environment and of the bacterial culture.

Another method for the determination of phage adsorption uses antiserum to remove the free phage. The preparation of antiphage serum is given on p. 225. This method actually determines phage which has become serum insensitive due to adsorption on to and, more likely, penetration into the host cell. Phage and bacteria are mixed as before and samples are taken at zero time and at intervals and diluted 1 : 10 in serum at such a concentration that 99% of the phage is inactivated in 5 min (temperature 37°C). The mixture is then assayed for phage after further dilution to lower the serum concentration below that at which it would affect plaque formation. The plaque count is due solely to infected bacteria and knowing the input phage concentration the fraction adsorbed at any time can be calculated. All adsorption experiments with bacteria in growth media must be completed before the end of the latent period.

A very simple method to determine unadsorbed phage is to shake samples of the phage/bacteria mixture with a few drops of chloroform. The infected cells are killed but the free phage is unharmed.

An indirect method for determining the amount of phage adsorbed makes use of the Poisson distribution (Adams, 1950).

$$P_{(r)} = \frac{n^r}{r!} e^{-n}$$

where $P_{(r)}$ is the proportion of bacteria in the phage/bacteria mixture which adsorbs r phage particles and n is the multiplicity of infection. Only $P_{(0)}$, the proportion of bacteria uninfected, i.e. adsorb no phage, can be determined. First the number of bacteria is determined by plating out suitably diluted specimens, then the phage is added and after time for adsorption the number of bacteria still able to form colonies is determined. It is necessary to spread the plates used for the colony count with sufficient antiphage serum to inactivate any free phage and any which might be released from infected cells.

$$P_{(0)} = e^{-n}$$

and hence n can be found and knowing the phage input the amount adsorbed can be calculated.

The Poisson distribution does not apply with sufficient accuracy when n exceeds 2 but Dulbecco (1949) has devised a method to overcome this objection.

The indirect method using the proportion of surviving bacteria to determine the adsorption rate of phage to bacteria is particularly useful where the phage has been previously inactivated, for example by ultraviolet light, but is still capable of causing cell death (see Luria, 1947).

(a) *Preparation of antiphage serum.* Bacteriophages are generally very good antigens and antibodies to them can be easily detected and assayed because they render the phage inactive by interacting with the adsorptive organ of the phage particle. The phage preparation used as antigen should be as free of bacterial debris as possible and can be suspended in nutrient broth, phosphate buffer or normal saline. Good results are obtained in rabbits by injection intravenously of 0·1 ml of phage at 1×10^{11}/ml at weekly intervals over a period of four weeks. A test bleeding from the ear vein is taken 1 week later and serum prepared and tested. If this is satisfactory more blood can be taken from the ear vein (5–10 ml with care) or greater volumes can be taken by cardiac puncture. Serum is prepared from the blood by standing it at 37°C in the sterile bottle in which it was collected until the clot has retracted. The serum, which should show no sign of haemolysis, should be stored in the refrigerator. If more serum is required at a later date the rabbits can be kept, given a booster dose of the same phage preparation and bled a week later (see Kingham, this Series, Vol. 5A).

(b) *Assay of antiphage serum.* The serum can be diluted in the same medium as that used for the phage. A mixture of phage at 1×10^6/ml and serum at a dilution of 1 : 100, 1 : 1000 or even more is made and immediately assayed for phage. It is then stood at 37°C and assayed for phage at intervals of 5 min. The samples are diluted for the assay and this effectively stops the antibody reaction. If the serum is active it will be found that a plot of log of the fraction of phage surviving against time is a straight line.

The activity of the phage can be described in terms of the "K" value. at constant temperature,

$$K = 2 \cdot 3 \frac{D}{t} \times \log \frac{P_{(0)}}{P}$$

where D is the final dilution of the serum in the test mixture (e.g. 100), $P_{(0)}$ is the concentration of phage at the beginning and P is the concentration at time t min later. The value of K may lie between a few tens and a few thousands and is a useful characteristic of the sample of serum. Once it is known it can be substituted in the above equation to obtain the dilution needed to inactivate any proportion of a phage specimen in a given time.

(c) *Antibody blocking power.* The property of antibody or serum blocking power (SBP) was first described by De Mars *et al.* (1953). It is defined as the power of a material to combine with the neutralizing antibody of an antiphage serum and thereby reduce its phage neutralizing titre. Such power is present in phage particles and in non-infectious ultrafiltrable material present in most phage lysates. This ultrafiltrable material turned out to be phage tail fibres in the case of the T-even phages.

Mixtures of the material to be tested and antiserum to the whole phage were incubated at 48°C for 4 h. Then a constant amount of whole phage was added and the mixture again incubated for 4 h. Finally each mixture was tested for active phage.

Tube No.	Contents		Assay of test phage	% titre of test phage
1	Broth		$7 \cdot 7 \times 10^5$	100
2	Serum		$2 \cdot 2 \times 10^4$	3
3	Serum $+ 7 \cdot 0 \times 10^9$ T2		$7 \cdot 7 \times 10^5$	100
4	Serum $+ 2 \cdot 3 \times 10^9$		$4 \cdot 8 \times 10^5$	62
5	Serum $+ 7 \cdot 7 \times 10^8$		$1 \cdot 8 \times 10^5$	23
6	Serum $+ 2 \cdot 6 \times 10^8$		$4 \cdot 3 \times 10^4$	6
7	Serum $+ 8 \cdot 7 \times 10^7$		$1 \cdot 6 \times 10^4$	2
8	Serum $+$ ultrafiltrate of T2 lysate 1 : 3		$1 \cdot 7 \times 10^5$	22
9	Serum	1 : 9	$5 \cdot 3 \times 10^4$	7
10	Serum	1 : 27	$2 \cdot 5 \times 10^4$	3

The serum was a 1 : 40,000 dilution and the phage added in tubes 3–7 was ultraviolet inactivated. It can be seen that the more T2 or ultrafiltrate was added to the serum the less the test phage was inactivated.

2. *Factors affecting the adsorption of phage to bacteria*

The following factors have been found to affect the rate of adsorption of phage to sensitive bacteria; the ionic environment, organic compounds acting as adsorption co-factors or antagonists, the physiological state of the cells and the temperature.

(a) *The ionic environment.* The adsorption of phage to host bacteria is highly dependent on the concentration of mono-and divalent cations in the environment. This was investigated by Puck *et al.* (1951) for the T phages and more recently Tzagoloff and Pratt (1964) found it necessary to know the ionic requirements of the filamentous phage M13. As noted by Stent (1963) "it is of great practical importance in bacteriophage work to ascertain the optimal ionic conditions for adsorption of any virus under study since (depending on circumstances) it is sometimes essential to achieve rapid infection of bacterial cultures, and at other times highly desirable to create conditions which *prevent* rather than promote optimal phage adsorption".

Puck *et al.* (1951) found that when T1 and *E. coli* B were mixed in distilled water no adsorption took place nor did it in 10^{-4}M phosphate buffer, pH 6·8. Increasing amounts of NaCl were then tested in 10^{-4}M buffer and it was found that the rate of adsorption rose to a maximum at 0·005M and then fell again until at 0·05M it was fairly low. Almost identical response curves were given by LiCl, KCl and NH$_4$Cl. When divalent cations Ca^{++}, Ba^{++} and Mn^{++} were tested the same shape of curve was found but its peak was displaced by a factor of 10 towards lower concentrations. In the case of T2 and T4 no adsorption took place in plain Difco nutrient broth but when 0·1M NaCl was added the rate of adsorption rose to the maximum predicted from theoretical considerations.

With M13 Tzagoloff and Pratt (1964) had to use bacteria at 5×10^9/ml in order to measure the rate of adsorption because of the few adsorption sites on the cells (now known to be the F- or sex-pili). The cells were suspended in water after washing on a Millipore HA filter and NaCl was added to aliquots to give a series of concentrations from 0·01 to 0·8M. Phage was added to give 8×10^5/ml and the cell-phage mixtures held at 0°C for 200 min. The unadsorbed phage was assayed by the chloroform method (see p. 224) every 40 min and the average adsorption rate calculated. As with the T phages a curve with a maximum was obtained, this time at a molar ionic strength of about 0·1.

Another example of the importance of knowing the ionic requirements for adsorption is given in the paper of Davis and Sinsheimer (1963) where these authors were studying the transfer of parental nucleic acid from the RNA phage MS2 to the progeny. The bacteria, *E. coli* C3000, were grown and infected with phage in a calcium-containing medium, MS broth (p. 214). It was necessary to include calcium to permit adsorption. Ten minutes later when 90% of the cells had been infected the culture was centrifuged and the cells were resuspended in the same broth, less calcium, in the cold. The cells were again sedimented and taken up in Ca-minus broth. Finally a quantity of warm aerated Ca-minus broth was added and the culture aerated at 37°C until it lysed. In earlier tests it had been shown that even when the bacteria in Ca-minus broth were mixed with phage at a multiplicity of 10^4 phage per cell there was no detectable diminution of the phage titre. Under these conditions Davis and Sinsheimer could be sure that there would be no loss of progeny phage by adsorption to bacteria as yet unlysed or to bacterial debris.

(b) *Temperature.* Puck *et al.* (1951) studied the rate of adsorption of T1 at temperatures from 5°C to 50°C and found that although there was a maximum at 37°C adsorption continued over the whole range falling to a quarter at 50°C and a thirtieth at 5°C. With M13 Tzagoloff and Pratt found that the rate of attachment increased two-fold from 0°C to 25°C, remained approximately constant to 37°C and fell off abruptly by 45°C. This decline was found to be due to the inactivation of the attachment sites on the cells.

(c) *Adsorption co-factors.* The requirement of coliphages T4 and T6 for L-tryptophan as an adsorption co-factor was first described by Anderson (1945). Several other substances including phenylalanine, di-iodotyrosine, tyrosine and norleucine are also effective at higher concentrations but D-tryptophan is inactive. Anderson (1948) also showed that the tryptophan acts upon the phage and not the bacteria. Subsequent work by Brenner *et al.* (1962) and Kellenberger *et al.* (1965) has shown that tryptophan reacts with the tail fibres to relax their binding around the tail sheath. This needs one molecule per fibre and results in the fibres being out-stretched from the tail tip in which position they can engage the receptor sites on the bacterial surface. The tail fibres of T2 and of non-tryptophan requiring mutants of T4 and 6 are already extended under normal physiological conditions.

Certain mutants of T4 have been described by Delbruck (1948) which also require tryptophan as an adsorption cofactor. However the activating effect of the tryptophan can be antagonized by indole. Complications might arise because indole is a breakdown product of tryptophan produced by certain strains of *E. coli* and the presence of variable amounts of indole affect the results of experiments on the activation of phage with tryptophan in the presence of bacteria.

(d) *Physiological condition of the host bacteria.* Very little work has been done on this subject since Delbruck (1940) described the effect on phage adsorption of cultural conditions on the phage adsorption rate constants. He showed that a strain of *E. coli* grown in broth with aeration up to

1×10^9/ml or without aeration for 24 h gave low values of the rate constant, approx. 5×10^{-10} cm³/min. Growth with aeration up to 10^8/ml gave 10×10^{-10} while a 30 h broth culture diluted 1 : 10 in fresh broth 30 min before the experiment gave a still higher value of 23×10^{-10} cm³/min. Even higher constants were obtained when the bacteria were tested while growing rapidly in the logarithmic phase. For example with cells at $1\cdot3 \times 10^6$/ml the constant was 310×10^{-10} cm³/min.

Factors which were believed to affect phage adsorption were the size of the cells which would give an increase in cell surface area and the motility of the cells which is greatest under the most favourable physiological conditions and would increase the chances of a cell colliding with a phage particle.

It should be borne in mind that any variation in the cultural conditions under which bacteria are grown can affect the antigenic structure of the cells and, since the phage receptors are often identical with the antigens or parts of them, then these variations might affect the ability of the cells to adsorb phage. Another possibility is that alteration in cultural conditions can affect the synthesis of pili and flagella. For example while *E. coli* C 3000 F+ will produce F pili at 37°C it does not do so at 25°C and consequently bacteria grown at this temperature can not absorb filamentous phage nor can they produce plaques on assay plates.

3. *Receptor substances*

The specific attachment of phage particles to host bacteria is mediated through certain macro-molecules on the surface of the cells. These are called receptors and have been extensively studied by Weidel (1958) and Jesaitis and Goebel (1955). Apart from adsorption the receptors are also concerned with penetration, the passage of the phage genome from the particle into the cell, since the reaction of the phage particle with the receptor triggers off the release of the phage DNA.

In the same way that most phage adsorptions to bacteria are irreversible the reaction between phage particles and receptors *in vitro* is also irreversible. This is fortunate because the reaction results in the inactivation of the phage and is therefore susceptible of exact measurement. Early studies on phage receptors showed that they were related to the somatic antigens of the cells (Burnet, 1934; Goebel and Jesaitis, 1952) and this concept has been developed so that considerable light has been shed on the chemical basis of antigenic variation and on the mutational changes which result in phage resistance.

Phage receptors must reside in the cell wall but this was only established with certainty when Weidel (1951) prepared the cell walls of *E. coli* free of cytoplasmic material and showed that they could still bind specifically and reversibly phage T2, 3, 4 and 7. His method is described on p. 231. The cell wall could be fractionated by phenol treatment to give an outer layer which amounted to 80% of the dry weight of the wall composed of a mixture of lipoprotein and lipid and an inner layer, the rigid part of the wall, containing glucose, L-gala-D-mannoheptose, glucosamine, muramic acid, lipid, alanine and diaminopimelic acid (Weidel, 1955). These two layers must be arranged in a manner which allows the inner one to be exposed since it is available to the phages.

The inner layer was found to contain the receptors for phages T3, 4 and 7 but those for T2 and 6 were lost.

It is often found that resistance to phages T3, 4 and 7 is acquired simultaneously as the result of a single step mutation and that it is due to the failure of the adsorption to take place. Examination of the inner layer from resistant mutant bacteria showed that the sugar L-gala-D-mannoheptose was completely absent and it is presumed that this compound is necessary in the macromolecular structure for it to act as a receptor for these three phages.

The receptor for phage T5 was also isolated by Weidel *et al.* (1954) from the whole cell wall. It is a spherical particle, 300 Å diameter, consisting of a core of lipopolysaccharide surrounded by lipoprotein. It inactivates T5 by combining with the tail tip of the phage and so blocking adsorption to the host.

Unlike the mutants resistant to T3, 4 and 7 receptors from mutants to T5, which are frequently also resistant to T1, could not be distinguished chemically or serologically from those prepared from the sensitive strains. In this case the mutation must have resulted in a much more subtle change than that found in the T3 resistant mutants.

Further examination of the cell walls of *E. coli* by Weidel *et al.* (1960) revealed that they consist of three layers. The innermost one, the "R" layer, is responsible for the rigidity of the cell wall but carries no phage receptors. It is composed of muramic acid, glucosamine, alanine, glutamic acid, and diaminopimelic acid and is easily disintegrated by lysozyme or by the "lysozyme" carried by phage T2. The middle layer composed of lipopolysaccharide is non-rigid and carries the receptors for phages T3, T4 and T7. The outer layer contains the receptors for phages T2 and T6 and is composed of lipoprotein.

The cells used by Weidel *et al.* (1960) were found not to contain any heptose in the lipopolysaccharide layer of their cell walls in contrast to those prepared earlier (Weidel, 1954) which did. It appears that the heptose is only present in cells grown in the Friedlein medium (p. 212) which contains lactate as the sole carbon source. In the later work (Weidel *et al.*, 1960) the cells were grown on a defined medium in which the carbon source was glucose. This observation, which has not been studied further, emphasizes the complexity of bacterial cell walls whose composition can vary not only according to presence or absence of specific phage receptor substances but also in response to the composition of the culture medium.

(a) *Preparation of cell walls.* Cell walls free of cytoplasmic material were prepared by Weidel *et al.* (1960) from *E. coli* B grown in a defined medium of unstated composition containing glucose as source of carbon. The other components of the medium were probably those of the Friedlein medium (p. 212). The cells were harvested at the onset of the stationary phase and stored in the deep freeze. The frozen cells (60 g) were suspended in water (400 ml) and rapidly extracted with $0\cdot1$N NaOH (200 ml) as described by Weidel *et al.* (1954). The mixture was immediately neutralized by passing in CO_2 gas and treated with DNase (1 $\mu g/ml$) to break down the DNA which was interfeing with further purification by its viscosity. The cells were sedimented at 10,000 g and extracted twice more with alkali. They were then suspended in $0\cdot4\%$ w/v sodium dodecyl sulphate (SDS) (120 ml) and shaken in a Mickle shaker (Salton and Horne, 1951) with glass beads ($0\cdot17$ mm diameter), 10 ml in each cup, for 1 h. The beads were allowed to settle out and the supernatant fluid was centrifuged at 4000 g for 15 min to remove unbroken cells. The cell walls were then spun down at 22,000 g for 30 min and were washed six times in water by centrifugation. Examination in the electron microscope showed how well the cytoplasmic material had been removed and if this were not sufficiently complete the cells were again treated with SDS in the Mickle shaker and washed with water. This treatment removed some protein and lipid from the outer layer of the wall.

(b) *Separation of lipopolysaccharide from the "R" layer.* Weidel *et al.* (1960) removed the lipopolysaccharide from the cell wall preparation by treatment with phenol. The moist sediment of cells obtained above was transferred to a glass-stoppered 300 ml Erlenmeyer flask with the help of 10 ml water. The suspension was made homogeneous by shaking and 90% w/w phenol (80 ml) was added in several portions with vigorous shaking. Solid phenol was then added until all the water droplets had dissolved and vigorous shaking continued for 1 h. The opaque suspension was centrifuged at 35,000 g for 45 min and the supernatant containing mostly protein was discarded. The extraction of the sediment with 90% phenol was repeated with 80 ml once and 40 ml twice shaking each time for 1 h and centrifuging at 35,000 g for 45 min. The final sediment was carefully resuspended in 30 ml water so as to make it as homogeneous as possible and dialysed against water to remove the phenol. The dialysed material was then spun at 6000 g for 10 min in swinging buckets to bring down the cell walls and leave an opalescent supernatant containing the lipopolysaccharide.

The sediment was washed in water several times until the supernatant was clear and then treated with 0·4% SDS (80 ml) in the Mickle shaker. Unhomogenized material was removed by centrifugation at 5000 g for 10 min and the "R" layer thrown down at 22,000 g for 30 min and washed six times with water to remove SDS. The yield was 150 mg. It was the intention of the authors to prepare purified cell "R" layers and the receptor content of the lipopolysaccharide was not described but it can be inferred that it contained the receptors for T3, T4 and T7 and that it could be recovered from the opalescent supernatant obtained after centrifugation of the dialysed phenol treated material by centrifugation at 25,000 g which causes it to sediment readily.

(c) *Preparation of T5 receptors.* Weidel *et al.* (1954) prepared T5 receptors from *E. coli* grown in Friedlein medium containing lactate (p. 212) by shaking a suspension of 30–40 g of cells in 200 ml water with 0·1N NaOH. After neutralization by passing in carbon dioxide gas the mixture was centrifuged at 12,000 g for 30 min to bring down the bacteria. The supernatant fluid was then adjusted to pH 4·0 with acetic acid and the precipitate collected by low speed centrifugation. It was taken up in 0·067M phosphate buffer pH 8·0 (30 ml) and found to contain the particulate, 300 Å diameter, receptors for T5.

(d) *Phage receptors from* Shigella sonnei. A lipocarbohydrate complex containing the receptors to phages T2, T3, T4, T6 and T7 was obtained from the somatic antigen of *Shigella sonnei* by Jesaitis and Goebel (1955). Bacteria were grown in the medium of Dole (1946) and treated with 1% formaldehyde overnight at room temperature to sterilize them. The cells were then spun down and dried from the frozen state. The antigen was extracted by treating the cells with 7M urea at 5°C for 24 h (Baker *et al.*, 1949) followed by sedimentation of the cells at 16,000 g for 30 min, filtration of the supernatant through a Berkefeld "N" filter and dialysis to remove the urea. After freeze drying 1·57 g of crude antigen was obtained from 110 g of cells.

The antigen (3·0 g) was then treated with 90% phenol (70 ml) for 30 min at room temperature with stirring and dialysed against several changes of water for 3 days at 5°C. The antigen is now dissociated into protein which precipitates and a lipocarbohydrate fraction which remains in solution. The protein is removed by centrifugation and the lipocarbohydrate is again dialysed and finally freeze dried (yield 2·2 g).

(e) *Assay of receptor substances.* The inactivation of phage by isolated receptor substances follows a first order reaction as is shown by the straight lines obtained when the log of the surviving phage is plotted against time. The slope of this line depends on the concentration of the receptor material

(Weidel, Koch and Bobosch, 1954) and can be used to compare the strengths of different receptor preparations.

Jesaitis and Goebel (1955) showed that the lipocarbohydrate of *Shigella sonnei* not only inactivated phage T4, it caused the release of the phage DNA. This resulted in an increase in the viscosity of the mixture which could be measured in a viscometer.

The receptor for phage 0–1 has been isolated from *Salmonella minnesota* R60 by Lindberg (1967) using the phenol method of Westphal, Luderitz and Bister (1952). The acetone killed and dried bacteria which had been grown in M9 medium (p. 212), were treated with phenol and the aqueous layers were collected. The residual phenol was removed by washing five times in ice cold ether and the ether was removed by passing a stream of nitrogen through the solution. The opalescent solution was freeze-dried. If a 2% solution in water was centrifuged at 105,000 g for 4 h, a sediment of lipopolysaccharide was obtained. After washing twice with distilled water the preparation (LPS) was freeze dried.

A solution of LPS was diluted in M9 in two-fold steps and mixed with phage at 2×10^3/ml. After incubation at 37°C for 4 h the residual phage was assayed and compared with a control of the same phage in M9 alone. The activity of the lipopolysaccharide was expressed as the concentration of LPS (dry w/vol) which caused 50% inhibition of the phage.

Treatment of the LPS with 0·5% sodium deoxycholate in Tris buffer (0·1M, pH 8·0) at 4°C overnight resulted in the loss of the phage inactivating power but on dialysis against three changes of Tris buffer and five of M9 the activity was largely restored. In the electron microscope it was observed that deoxycholate disaggregated the lipopolysaccharide particles into elements which were too small to be seen but that after removal of the deoxycholate these elements reassociated themselves into short rods and spherical and irregular particles. Before disaggregation the LPS consisted of long filaments of constant width about 100 Å.

4. *Adsorption in the electron microscope*

In order to observe adsorbed phage particles in the electron microscope it is necessary to use a fairly high multiplicity of infection. If an average of 20 or so particles per cell become adsorbed there will be a good chance of finding some cells with the particles in positions where they can be seen.

The adsorption of phage to whole cells (Anderson, 1953), cell walls (Kellenberger and Arber, 1955), isolated receptors (Weidel and Kellenberger, 1955), bacterial flagella (Meynell, 1961) and pili (Caro and Schnoss, 1966; Crawford and Gesteland, 1964) has been studied. Any of the standard procedures for applying specimens to grids and producing adequate specimen contrast can be used (Kay, 1965). Useful information can also be obtained from sections of bacteria carrying adsorbed phage (Milne and Trautner, 1967; Simon and Anderson, 1967a).

B. The single step growth experiment

A classic experiment to study the release of phage from infected bacteria under conditions where no readsorption could occur was devised by Ellis and Delbruck (1939). It is called the single step growth experiment and enables one to measure two important parameters of phage multiplication, the latent period and the average burst size. It is applicable to all phages which are released spontaneously from the infected cells, that is where infection results in cell lysis or phage leakage without obvious lysis. The effect of a wide range of variables such as medium composition, temperature, multiplicity of infection, inhibitors, etc., can be studied.

Before attempting to do an accurate experiment a rough estimate of the latent period and burst size should be made using the same procedure so that suitable dilutions can be decided upon. A typical experiment using *E. coli* B and T2 is performed as follows.

Bacteria are grown exponentially to about 5×10^7/ml in a broth medium in which adsorption occurs rapidly. Phage is added in a ratio of 1 to 10 cells to give a multiplicity of infection of about 0·1. After 5 min adsorption the unadsorbed phage is inactivated by dilution 1 : 10 in antiphage serum (see p. 225) at a concentration sufficient to neutralize 95% of the phage in 5 min. After 5 min at 37°C to allow the serum to act the mixture will contain both infected and uninfected bacteria but very few free phage. If incubation is continued phage will be released and will immediately attach to the remaining bacteria, in which case it will be impossible to determine the actual yield of phage from the cells infected at the beginning of the experiment. To overcome this the infected cells are diluted to such an extent that adsorption of the released phage is negligible. Immediately after the serum has been allowed to act the mixture is diluted 1 : 10^3 or 10^4 in medium warmed to 37°C. This dilution is termed the First Growth Tube (FGT) and is incubated at 37°C. Another dilution is made, a further 1 : 10^2 in medium, the Second Growth Tube (SGT) and also set at 37°C. Both tubes are assayed for phage at intervals of say 2 min.

It is found that the phage titre in the FGT remains constant for the first 21 min and then suddenly increases. The counts in the SGT steadily increase in the period from 23 to 32 min and then remain constant. From the average phage count during the latent period and the dilution of the FGT the number of infected bacteria in the adsorption tube can be calculated. The constant final titre divided by the number of infected cells gives the average burst size and the latent period can be determined to ± 1 min.

If the input of phage P_0 is known the percentage adsorbed can be calculated and the average multiplicity of infection, n. At low multiplicities (see p. 225) the distribution of phage particles amongst the bacteria obeys the Poisson distribution

$$P_r = \frac{n^r}{r'} e^{-n}$$

where P_r is the proportion of bacteria adsorbing r phage particles and so the number of bacteria that are singly and multiply infected can be found. For example if $n = 0.08$ the proportion on cells singly infected is 0.074 and doubly infected is 0.003, 4% of the total infected cells. This percentage can easily be varied by altering the multiplicity of infection.

It is found that burst sizes usually lie in the range from a few tens to a few hundreds but in the case of the RNA phages (MS2, R17, etc.) burst sizes up to 20,000 have been obtained. Some phages such as the filamentous ones (ZJ/2, f1) do not show a rapid release from the infected cells but appear to leak out over a period of time (see p. 249). It is not always necessary to use antiserum to remove free phage as this can be determined separately and subtracted from the counts in the FGT and SGT.

C. Penetration

Following the irreversible attachment of the phage particle to the host bacterium the phage nucleic acid penetrates into the cell leaving the protein capsid outside. This observation, which holds good for all phages so far examined was made by Hershey and Chase (1952) in a classic experiment. The principle of this was to determine what happened to the radioactivity when phage radioactively labelled in the nucleic acid or in the protein was allowed to adsorb to bacteria and then subjected to shear forces in a mixing apparatus with rapidly rotating blades. It had been shown by Anderson (1953) that particles of phage T2 attached to bacteria tail first and it was expected that when subjected to shear the particles would be torn off. The nucleic acid of the phage was labelled with ^{32}P and as this is the only phosphorus compound in the phage it is clear that the presence of radioactivity would indicate only nucleic acid or its breakdown products. Similarly the phage protein was labelled with ^{35}S which, being localized in the sulphur-containing amino-acids would indicate only the presence of phage protein or degradation products.

1. The Hershey and Chase experiment

Full experimental details of this experiment were not given in the original publication but the omitted details are easily inferred.

Bacteria (*E. coli* H) were grown in broth, centrifuged and resuspended in adsorption medium (see p. 212). Radioactive phage was added and a few minutes allowed for adsorption. The phage remaining unadsorbed was removed by centrifugation and the sedimented cells were resuspended in a solution containing $MgSO_4$, 1mM; $CaCl_2$ 0·1mM and gelatin 0·1 g/litre. This low salt medium was necessary to prevent readsorption of ^{35}S containing material to the bacteria. The bacteria were then subjected to shear in a semimicro size Waring blendor running at 10,000 rpm for periods of 1 min with brief cooling in ice water between each treatment. It was found that almost all the removable ^{35}S came off in 2 min. The cells were then sedimented by low speed centrifugation and the radioactivity of the supernatant fluid and of the sedimented cells was determined. It was found that the amount of extracellular ^{35}S rose to 80% of that added while the ^{32}P increased only slightly to 15%. The free ^{35}S was present as more or less intact phage protein coats but their removal did not affect the ability of the infected cells to form plaques. It was therefore clear that phage protein and nucleic acid have independent functions and that the protein part of the particle has no further role to play after adsorption has taken place.

The detached material containing ^{35}S was shown to be phage membranes because it could be sedimented at 12,000 *g*, precipitated by antiphage serum (in the presence of unlabelled active carrier phage) and adsorbed to bacteria under the same conditions as for whole phage.

2. *Passage of the T-even phage genome into the host cell*

The Hershey and Chase experiment showed that only the phage DNA had to enter the cell to ensure multiplication of the phage and it was therefore confirmed that the genetic information of the phage resided in its nucleic acid. The observation of Anderson (1953) that the T-even phages adsorb by the tips of their tails and the further studies (Kellenberg *et al.*, 1965) which show the retraction of the tail sheath and the passage of the hollow tail core into the cell leave no doubt that the DNA passes through the tail core. The time taken for the transferrence of the complete genome is probably a few seconds but the mechanism by which this piece of DNA, 20 Å wide but about 50 μm long is propelled is as yet unknown.

From work of Weidel (1958) it is clear that the bacterial cell wall constitutes a considerable barrier for the DNA to pass. The outer layers which contain the phage receptors do not possess any particular mechanical strength and one can easily imagine the force of the contracting sheath pushing the core through them. The inner rigid layer composed of murein which maintains the shape and integrity of the cell is another matter as this is mechanically strong and normally withstands a pressure of several atmospheres within the cell (Mitchell and Moyle, 1956). Passage of the core or the DNA through this layer might be facilitated by the phage tail lysozyme which specifically attacks certain bonds in the murein. However, as there are mutant T4 phages which do not carry lysozyme but which are nevertheless capable of infecting the host cells, it must be possible for the DNA to penetrate without the help of lysozyme.

3. *Penetration of T5 DNA*

Coliphage T5 is a member of a widespread group of phages which are morphologically similar. They possess an icosahedral head and a flexible tail which lacks a contractile sheath. The penetration of T5 DNA into *E. coli* B was studied by Luria and Steiner (1954) who found that it took several minutes for the DNA to pass completely into the cell and that calcium was necessary for the initiation of phage development. In the absence of calcium adsorption and penetration still occurred, the cells were killed and underwent nuclear disintegration but did not give rise to any progeny phage.

It seems that the transfer of T5 DNA into the host is both slow and subject to a natural temporary interruption (Lanni, 1960; McCorquodale and Lanni, 1964) at about 8% transfer. Phage-bacterium complexes in which this small amount of DNA had been transferred were called FST (first step transfer) complexes and could be prevented from producing progeny phage by blending. Stabilized complexes which were unaffected by blending could be produced if sufficient time was allowed after adsorption. The host cells at 5×10^9/ml suspended in a buffer containing 10^{-3}M $CaCl_2$ were infected with T5 at a multiplicity of 5 and incubated at 37·5°C without aeration for 10 min. If the cells were then diluted in ice cold buffer (MGM, p. 216, less glucose and NH_4Cl but with 10^{-3}M $CaCl_2$) they would be held at the FST stage but if they were diluted 50-fold in calcium supplemented MGM (see p. 216) and incubated for a further 7 min the complexes had passed into the stabilized form. From the FST complexes a part of the phage DNA, about 8%, could be extracted but from the stabilized complexes the whole intact T5 DNA molecule could be obtained (Lanni, McCorquodale and Wilson, 1964).

The DNA was extracted by freezing and thawing in the presence of lysozyme together with treatment with SDS. This is described on p. 245.

4. *Penetration of RNA phage nucleic acid*

Zinder, Valentine, Roger and Stoeckenius (1963) examined a group of phages, active on *E. coli* K12 (F+ or Hfr), which had been isolated by Loeb (1960). They found that one of them, f2, which contained RNA instead of DNA, was completely prevented from forming plaques if as little as 1 $\mu g/ml$ ribonuclease was incorporated into the agar used for plating. A possible mechanism for this inhibition has been suggested by Valentine and Wedel (1965). The receptors for phage f2 and other RNA phages such as R17, MS2 and Qβ reside along the sides of the F pili which are carried by the F$^+$ and Hfr strains of coli (Crawford and Gesteland, 1964). It is believed that in order to enter the cell the RNA passes along the inside of the hollow pilus but in the period of time between leaving the phage capsid and entering the pilus the RNA is exposed to the medium and it is then that the RNase can degrade it.

Valentine and Wedel (1965) distinguished between injection which is the RNase sensitive step and penetration which is the passage of the RNA into the cell so that it becomes impossible to remove it by blending. Adsorption of ^{32}P-labelled f2 phage to *E. coli* K12 F$^+$ was allowed to proceed at 0°C then warmed up to 37°C. The RNA does not leave the phage capsid at 0°C and is not sensitive to RNase at this temperature. At intervals of a few minutes samples were taken, treated with RNase (40 $\mu g/ml$), and incubated at 37°C for a total of 15 min. Samples of 1 ml were then diluted in 20 ml water at 0°C to prevent further phage adsorption and blended for 2 min to remove adsorbed but as yet unpesnetrated phage. The blended cells were collected by centrifugation, precipitated with 5% cold trichloroacetic acid and counted for radioactivity derived from the penetrated RNA after collection on glass filter pads. It was shown that over a period of 10 min after raising to 37°C the phage RNA which could not be removed by the action of RNase or blending gradually increased until it equalled that of the control without RNase.

5. *Penetration observed in the electron microscope*

Examination of the interaction of the T-even phages with *E. coli* B has shown that the particles adsorb by the tips of their tails (Anderson, 1953; Kellenberger and Arber, 1955). It is also known that these phages can be caused to retract their tail sheaths by chemical treatment (Kellenberger and Arber, 1955; Kozloff *et al.*, 1957) and that the central hollow core is then revealed. It is therefore tempting to liken the phage particle to a hypodermic syringe in which the tail core, like a hollow needle, is forced through the cell wall by the contraction of the sheath (see Stent, 1963, p. 108).

If phage particles are allowed to adsorb to empty cell walls instead of whole cells it is possible to observe in shadowed preparations that the heads have been drawn down towards the walls and that the sheaths have contracted and become thickened. The tail spikes can also be seen but it is very difficult to decide whether they have penetrated the wall or whether they are merely lying on the surface.

By the combined use of negative staining and thin sectioning Simon and Anderson (1967a) were able to analyse the mechanism of adsorption and penetration of coliphages T2 and T4. The initial attachment takes place when the distal ends of the long tail fibres make contact with the cell surface. This is followed by a repositioning of the phage particle so that the short tail pins which were at first more than 1000 Å away from the surface are brought into close proximity with the cell wall. The tail sheath contracts and the base plate is pulled away from the cell wall along the tail spike or needle. At this stage the tail pins are no longer visible but short tail fibres (370 Å long) connect the baseplate directly with the cell wall. The long tail fibres remain attached in their original places. The needle appears to penetrate about 120 Å into the cell wall and to reach the area between the wall and the protoplasmic membrane immediately underneath it. Simon and Anderson (1967a) suggest that the DNA released under the cell wall passes through the protoplasmic membrane in much the same way as naked phage DNA can penetrate and infect protoplasts (Guthrie and Sinsheimer, 1960).

Simon and Anderson (1967a) with T2 and T4 and Milne and Trautner (1967) with subtilis phage SP50 observed the leakage of fibrils (probably DNA) from the tips of phage particles which had penetrated the cell walls. These authors used thin sectioning methods. Both Milne and Trautner and Simon and Anderson (1967b) using sections of infected cells cut at grazing incidence with the walls were able to show the six-pointed star structures with which both these phages make intimate contact with their hosts.

Little information concerning the mode of penetration of phages without contractile tail sheaths is available but it is known that all the tailed phages adsorb by the tips of their tails (see review by Bradley, 1967).

D. Intracellular multiplication

Multiplication of phage proceeds intracellularly under the direction of the nucleic acid injected by the infecting phage. The effect on the activities of the host cell is characteristic of the particular phage and may vary from drastic interference as shown by the T-even phages where the host nucleoplasm is totally broken down, to a negligible effect as shown by filamentous phage where cellular multiplication can continue at the same time as phage multiplication and release (Hoffmann-Berling and Mazé, 1964). However in all phage infections in which multiplication occurs replication of the nucleic acid takes place with the production of up to several thousand copies. This involves the synthesis of many new enzymes, e.g. specific nucleic acid polymerases and where novel nucleic acid bases are required, as in the T-even phages (Wyatt and Cohen, 1953) where 5-hydroxymethyl cytosine is found and in subtilis phages (Kallen, Simon and Marmur, 1962; Roscoe and Tucker, 1966), enzymes involved in their synthesis make their appearance. The synthesis of phage structural components, all proteins, proceeds at the same time as that of the nucleic acid but begins slightly later. The number of structural components depends on the complexity of the phage particle and varies from one or two in the case of the RNA phages to a large but as yet unknown number in T-even phages. In addition there may be morphogenetic proteins which aid the condensation of the nucleic acid and the assembly of the subunits which form the phage capsid but which are not incorporated into the structure (Wood and Edgar, 1967).

In order to study the processes going on inside infected cells it is necessary to break them open, isolate the products of interest and assay them. The method used will depend on the organism concerned, the degree of degradation of the products which can be tolerated, the speed and completeness of their release and the extent to which any reagents used might affect subsequent analytical procedures.

Cytological changes can be followed in the intact cells by light microscopy and in fixed, sectioned cells by electron microscopy.

Both physical and chemical methods have been used to disrupt infected cells. The physical methods include sonication, vibration with glass beads, grinding with abrasive and sudden decompression. The chemical methods used have been chloroform treatment, lysozyme, lysis from with out by heterologous phage, strong glycine solution, phenol extraction, toluene, trichloracetic acid extraction and treatment with surface active compounds.

Table of materials extracted from phage-infected bacteria

Page	Material
241, 243	Intracellular phages T1, T3, T4, T7
241	Phage-specific protein
241	Phage-induced enzymes
242	Ribosomal and soluble RNA
244	Degraded DNA
243	Protein
244	TCA soluble polypeptides
244	Infectious DNA
245	DNA fragments
246	Infectious RNA

1. *Methods of disruption of infected cells*

(a) *Sonication.* Bacterial cells can be broken open by sonication (Hughes *et al.*, this Series, Vol. 5B) and this method was first used to release intracellular phage by Anderson, Boggs and Winters (1948). They were only able to study the smaller coliphages T1, T3 and T7 because the larger ones did not survive sonication. The infected cells were treated with 0·01M KCN to inhibit further phage multiplication, cooled to 0°C, sonicated for 5 min and then assayed for phage. It is necessary to determine the conditions for a high degree of cell disruption by examination of the cells in the light microscope and by plating out for a colony count. The susceptibility of the phage to inactivation under the same conditions should also be determined.

Radioactively labelled phage-specific proteins were isolated from *E. coli* C3000 infected with phage f2 (RNA) by Nathans *et al.* (1966) after the cells had been broken by sonication. Host bacteria were grown in a modified TPG medium (see p. 214) to which amino-acid supplements were added as required. In order to shut off bacterial RNA and protein synthesis the cells were treated sequentially with EDTA and actinomycin D. Log phase cells grown in modified TPG medium to 8×10^8/ml were centrifuged at 20°C and washed once in 0·12M Tris-HCl (pH 8·0). The pellet was resuspended in the same buffer at one tenth the original volume of culture and the cell suspension kept at 4°C for 0·5–2 h. The chilled cells were then mixed with an equal volume of EDTA (0·4mM)–Tris-HCl (0·12M, pH 8·0), prewarmed to 41°C. After 3 min at 41°C, the cells were transferred to 10 volumes of modified TPG medium prewarmed to 37°C, containing actinomycin, required amino-acids, and twice the usual amount of Ca^{2+}, Mg^{2+} and Fe^{3+} salts. After shaking for 5 min at 37°C, the cells were ready for infection with phage. It was found that 5·5–6·5 μg/ml actinomycin was sufficient to give nearly complete inhibition of host protein and RNA synthesis but allowed adequate phage infection. A multiplicity of 10 or 20 was used. After 50 min the labelled cells were centrifuged at 10,000 *g* for 5 min washed once in cold saline containing non-labelled amino-acids and the cell pellet was resuspended in a small volume of water. The cells were broken by sonication for 3 min and all labelled protein was solubilized by addition of one tenth volume of glacial acetic acid, freshly deionized urea to a concentration of 0·5M, SDS to 1% and mercaptoethanol to 0·01M. After incubation at 37°C for 60 min, the solution was centrifuged at 30,000 *g* for 10 min, and the supernate, which contained all the radioactive protein, was passed through coarse G25 Sephadex equilibrated with 20% sucrose, 0·1% SDS and mercaptoethanol (0·01M). The proteins were then separated by polyacrylamide gel electrophoresis and the radioactivity determined by autoradiography or by elution in 0·1% SDS and scintillation counting.

A considerable variety of ultrasonic disintegration apparatus is available but in general one giving an output of 60–100 W at about 20 kHz is suitable.

(b) *Grinding with abrasive.* Alumina powder can be used as an abrasive to break open cells. In one method the infected bacteria were sedimented in the centrifuge and then mixed with sufficient alumina to give a dry crumbly mixture. This was transferred to a mortar and ground. A few strokes of the pestle caused the mixture to become liquid indicating that the cells had been ruptured. It is necessary to wash the alumina or neutralize it before use to remove alkalinity.

Flaks and Cohen (1957) prepared cell-free extracts of T6-infected *E. coli* by grinding the bacteria with alumina 15 min after infection in an aerated synthetic medium. The ground cells were extracted with 0·1M phosphate buffer, pH 7·0 and the extract dialysed against 0·01M phosphate pH 7·0, and treated with Dowex-1 chloride resin. This extract was used in the study of new enzymes induced in the bacteria by the infecting phage.

A more detailed description of the method of breaking cells with alumina is given by Sekiguchi and Cohen (1964).

A bacterial suspension containing at least 5×10^{10} cells was chilled rapidly by pouring it on to crushed ice. The cells were collected by centrifugation, washed once in 0·05M Tris-chloride buffer, pH 7·5, and disrupted by grinding with Alcoa alumina A301 (0·5 g/litre/10^{11} cells). The ground paste was extracted with a buffer containing 0·05M Tris, pH 7·5, and 0·01M 2-mercaptoethanol (5 ml/litre/10^{11} cells), and unbroken cells, cell debris and alumina powder were removed by two successive centrifugations at 10,000 g and 40,000 g for 20 min each. All these procedures were carried out at 2°C to 4°C. Deoxycytidylate hydroxymethylase, thymidylate synthetase, dihydrofolate reductase and phage lysozyme were assayed in the extracts. The lysozyme assay is described on p. 252.

Nomura, Okamato and Asano (1962) extracted ribosomal and soluble RNA from *E. coli* B infected with T4B by the following procedure which uses alumina grinding and SDS treatment.

Samples of the culture were poured on to crushed ice and about 1×10^{11} uninfected cells were added to act as carrier. The cells were centrifuged, the pellet ground with alumina and extracted with Tris buffer (0·01M, pH 7·3) containing 10 μg/ml DNase and Mg^{2+} (usually 10^{-4}M) The extracts were acidified with acetic acid to pH 5·2, treated with SDS (0·2%) for 3 min at 37°C, and then shaken with an equal volume of phenol saturated with 0·05M acetate, pH 5·2–0·01M MgCl$_2$ solution. After centrifugation the RNA was precipitated with 2 volumes of alcohol, dissolved in a mixture of 0·02M acetate (pH 5·2)–0·02M KCl–0·01M MgCl$_2$ and precipitated with alcohol. Finally the precipitate was dissolved in the same acetate-KCl-MgCl$_2$ and dialysed against several changes of the same solution overnight.

(c) *Chloroform treatment.* Séchaud and Kellenberger (1956) showed that by shaking a phage-infected culture with a few drops of chloroform the cells are rapidly lysed and the intracellular phage are released. This method succeeds when the infection has proceeded some way and sufficient phage-induced lytic enzyme has accumulated within the cells. It does not work with uninfected cells.

(d) *Lysis-from-without.* When *E. coli* B is allowed to adsorb a large number of any of the T-even phages rapid lysis of the cells ensues. Advantage of this phenomenon was taken by Doermann (1948a, 1952) to disrupt phage infected bacteria and follow the intracellular multiplication of the phage.

E. coli B grown to 10^8/ml and concentrated to 10^9/ml to permit rapid adsorption was mixed with T4r at 10^8/ml. After 2 min the remaining free phage was removed by dilution 1 : 10 in anti-T4 serum. After a further 4 min three dilutions were prepared (1 : 100, A; 1 : 2×10^3, B; 1 : 2×10^5, C) and incubated at 37°C. Samples taken from tubes B and C were assayed for phage at intervals and provided data from which the latent period and burst size could be calculated.

Samples from tube A (0·1 ml) were also taken at intervals and diluted in 1·9 ml of lysing medium which consisted of growth medium supplemented with 0·01M KCN to inhibit further phage multiplication and 4×10^9 particles of phage T6 per ml to cause lysis-from-without. The mixture was kept at 0°C for 10 min then at 37°C for 30 min and plated on B/6, a mutant of B resistant to T6 but still susceptible to T4. In this way the fate of the infecting phage from about the ninth minute after adsorption was studied. The disappearance of infectivity, known as the "eclipse phase" was discovered and the reappearance of phage particles at about the 14th minute was observed.

Hershey and Melechen (1957) isolated intracellular phage from *E. coli* H infected with T2H by treatment of 2·5 ml samples of the culture with 1·5 ml of the same phage which had been killed by ultraviolet light and 0·05 ml of M KCN. After 10 min in the cold the tubes were warmed to 36°C for 30 min and then refrigerated overnight to complete the lysis. Heat-killed cells of a non-adsorbing strain were then added as a carrier and the mixture was diluted to 10 ml with a solution of peptone (0·1%), NaCl (0·3%), $MgSO_4$ (0·001M) and digested for two successive periods of 20 min at 36°C first with 0·1 mg of DNase and then 1 mg pancreatin. Bacterial debris was centrifuged down at 5000 rpm for 10 min and the phage was then sedimented at 15,000 rpm for 35 min. The phage recovery was 87%. Labelled protein in the pellets was assayed for radioactivity after precipitation and washing in 0·3M TCA, the precipitate was dissolved in dilute NH_4OH and sampled on to planchets containing a slight excess of acetic acid. Before precipitation with TCA 0·2 ml of 1% serum albumin was added to each tube (1 ml) and one drop of albumin was added at each wash.

(e) *Extraction with trichloracetic acid*. Hershey, Dixon and Chase (1953) extracted the DNA from *E. coli* infected with phage T2 and determined its purine and pyrimidine composition.

The bacteria were grown in peptone-broth (see Media, p. 213) with aeration at 37°C to 2×10^8 cells/ml, sedimented resuspended in non-nutrient adsorption medium (see p. 212) and infected with phage at a multiplicity of 5. The infected cells were then resedimented and transferred to warm aerated broth to give a concentration of 2×10^8/ml. The bulk of each culture (650 ml) was taken for extraction of DNA. It was mixed with one tenth its volume of 3M TCA and 2 ml of 1% serum albumin (to improve the packing quality of the precipitate), and chilled. When well cooled the cells were spun down and rinsed into a single tube with small amounts of 0·1N NaOH and water. They were reprecipitated with 0·3M TCA and fractionated by the methods of Schmidt and Thannhauser (1945) and Schneider (1945). The precipitate was warmed for 15–18 h at 37°C in 5 ml N NaOH and reprecipitated cold with 5 ml N HCl and 1 ml 3M TCA. After washing in the cold with 0·3M TCA the precipitate was extracted twice in 0·3M TCA at 90°C for 15 min. An aliquot was used for the diphenyl-amine reaction (p. 246) and the remainder was heated at 100°C for 1 h to decompose the TCA, evaporated to dryness by heating in a current of air and finally dried in a vacuum desiccator. This material was used for base analysis after acid hydrolysis (p. 246).

TCA extraction yields DNA in denatured condition and if intact nucleic acid is required other methods (p. 244–246) have to be used.

Eddleman and Champe (1966) extracted acid soluble material from T4 infected *E. coli* with TCA. At 30 min after infection the cells were quickly chilled to 4°C and sedimented in a chilled rotor at 11,000 *g* for 5 min. The pellet was resuspended in 0·5 ml cold water and then acidified with 0·5 ml ice cold 10% TCA. After standing at 4°C for 30 min the precipitate was removed by centrifugation at 11,000 *g* for 20 min and subjected to analysis. Amber mutants blocked in head formation fail to produce these acid soluble polypeptides.

(f) *Lysozyme treatment*. Ray, Bscheider and Hofschneider (1966) isolated infectious forms of phage specific DNA from *E. coli* K12 infected with the filamentous phage M13. An exponentially growing culture in H medium (p. 215) containing 10^{-3}M phosphate, 5·0 mg/ml glucose and 1·0 mg/ml vitamin-free Casamino-acids at $6–7 \times 10^7$ cells/ml was infected with purified M13 at $3–5 \times 10^8$/ml. The infected bacteria were chilled by the addition of ice and were collected by filtering the culture through a membrane filter (Membranfilter, Göttingen; Group 50). A 90 mm filter was used for each 150 ml of culture at 1–2 $\times 10^8$ cells/ml. The bacteria were washed twice on the filter with 10 ml of NT (0·1M NaCl, 0·01M Tris, pH 8) and resuspended in NT at a final concentration of 1–2 $\times 10^9$ cells/ml. The cells were further purified by low speed centrifugation at 4°C and by resuspension of the bacterial pellet in NET (NT containing 0·01M EDTA) at 1–2 $\times 10^9$ cells/ml. The purified bacteria which now contained only 3–15 plaque forming units per cell were lysed by the addition of 2 mg lysozyme per 10 ml suspension, incubation at 37°C for 15 min and the addition of 0·5 ml of 20% sodium dodecyl sulphate per 10 ml of bacteria. One half volume of 3M NaClO₄ was added and incubation at 37°C continued for 15 min. The preparation was frozen and stored overnight.

The DNA was purified by thawing the crude lysate and removing the denatured protein by shaking with an equal volume of chloroform-octanol (9/1), followed by low speed centrifugation at room temperature. The aqueous phase was removed and the procedure repeated. This nucleic acid preparation was dialysed against 0·58M NaCl and 0·05M phosphate buffer, pH 6·7. Ribonuclease (5 ×crystallized) was added at 20 μg/ml and the mixture incubated at 37°C for 40 min. It was then dialysed against several changes of 0·58M NaCl and 0·05M phosphate buffer, pH 6·7, overnight. The ribonuclease was removed by shaking with an equal volume of phenol, centrifuging and removing the aqueous phase. Phenol was removed by three extractions with ether followed by aeration for 1 h at 37°C. This material was used in infectious DNA assays which are described in the same paper.

(g) *Lysozyme and freezing and thawing*. Lanni, McCorquodale and Wilson (1964) extracted intact T5 DNA molecules from infected cells of *E. coli* F which had been prepared by the method described on p. 237. The cells were centrifuged at 5°C and gently resuspended in an ice-cold solution of 0·05M EDTA plus 0·15M NaCl (EDNA). Lysozyme (100 μg/ml) and redistilled 2-mercaptoethanol (0·015M) was added to cells at about 3·3 $\times 10^9$/ml which were frozen in a dry ice alcohol bath and stored overnight at −25°C. The suspensions were then subjected to four cycles of thawing (5 min at 37·5°C) and freezing (3 min in dry ice-alcohol). After the fifth freezing the lysed suspensions were allowed to thaw and incubated at 37·5°C for 30 min. SDS was then added (2 mg/ml) and the lysates were rocked very gently by hand until almost water clear. They were then centrifuged at 8000 rpm for 10 min at room temperature and analysed by zone centrifugation in sucrose gradients.

(h) *Treatment with sodium dodecyl sulphate (SDS)*. Davis, Pfeiffer and Sinsheimer (1964) extracted infective RNA from cells of *E. coli* C3000. The bacteria were grown to 2 $\times 10^8$/ml in MS broth (see p. 214) and infected

with phage MS2 at a multiplicity of five. At various intervals samples of
5 ml or more were chilled, centrifuged down and washed and resuspended
in 1·2 ml of cold 0·1M tris buffer, pH 7·0. All operations were carried out
at 0°C. To the resuspended cells was added 0·4 ml of a 10% aqueous solution of recrystallized SDS. After 5 min standing, with occasional vigorous
shaking on a Vortex mixer, the cells were frozen and thawed three times.
The opened cells were then usually assayed for viable phage (MS2 is not
inactivated by this concentration of detergent).

To this solution was added an equal volume of phenol (previously equilibrated with 0·1M Tris, pH 7·0). The mixture was shaken on a Vortex mixer
for 2 min, then centrifuged at 25,000 g for 15 min. The denatured protein formed a tight band at the interface, and the aqueous layer was easily
removed with a capillary pipette. The aqueous layer was then re-extracted
twice with phenol as before, and then extracted four times with ether
or precipitated three times with ethanol. If any infective phage particles
were detected in the RNA preparation, the process was repeated but as a
rule none were found.

(i) *Explosive decompression.* Fraser (1951) used explosive decompression in
which cells were placed in a pressure vessel and subjected to a high pressure of nitrous oxide gas. When the pressure was rapidly released the
cells were ruptured. A similar procedure was used by Levinthal and
Fisher (1952).

2. *Analytical methods*

Many studies on the intracellular multiplication of phage involve
analytical procedures which are of general use. For example the determination of nitrogen, phosphorus, sulphur, nucleic acid bases and sugars and
protein. These methods will be found in the appropriate text books and
are described by Strange, Phipps and Herbert (this Series, Vol. 5B).
Some references will be given. There are some procedures which have
been developed to assay enzymes found in phage-infected bacteria. Again
these will be given in reference only. Certain analytical procedures have
been given in other parts of this Chapter. These are determination of
antibody blocking power (p. 226) which measures certain phage specific
proteins synthesized in infected cells and phage-induced lysins (p. 250).

Purine and pyrimidine bases	Hershey, Dixon and Chase (1953)
Deoxyribose (DNA)	Burton (1956)
Nitrogen, phosphorus, pentose	Cohen (1948)
Phage-induced enzymes	Volkin and Astrachan (1956)
	Hershey and Burgi (1956)

Putnam and Kozloff (1950)
Maaløe and Watson (1951)
Flaks and Cohen (1959a)
Flaks and Cohen (1959b)
Flaks, Lichtenstein and Cohen (1959)
Kornberg, Zimmerman, Kornberg and Josse (1959)
Koerner, Smith and Buchanan (1959)
Kornberg (1960)
Keck, Mahler and Fraser (1960)
Barner and Cohen (1959)
Haruna and Spiegelman (1965a, b)
de Ward (1964a, b)
Short and Koerner (1965)

See also reviews by: Wittman and Scholtissek (1966)
Erikson and Franklin (1966)
Borek and Srinivasan (1966)
Hayes (1967)

3. Cytological changes

The cytology of phage-infected bacteria can be studied in the light and electron microscopes. Luria and Human (1950) used Giemsa stain in an examination of *E. coli* infected with the T group of phages and showed that in the case of the T-even phages within 5 min of infection the nuclei were disrupted into small blocks of chromatin material which collected at the periphery of the cell. Later on, toward the end of the eclipse period the cells became filled with chromatin which was presumably the DNA of the progeny phage (see also Kellenberger, 1962).

The effect of various amber mutants of phage T4 on *E. coli* was examined by Epstein *et al.* (1963) with the light microscope in order to determine whether they could cause nuclear disruption. Samples of infected cells were added to an equal volume of a 40% solution of polyvinylpyrrolidine (PVP) containing 10% formaldehyde. Within 10 min after the addition of the formaldehyde the cell samples were examined in the phase contrast microscope under oil immersion (magnification ×1250). The PVP provides a medium with sufficient refractive index to permit visualization of the cell nuclei and the formaldehyde fixes the cells. The cells should be examined quickly because they become progressively opaque. Cells infected with wild type phage pass through three clearly distinguishable phases which correspond to (1) uninfected cells with nuclei of normal appearance, (2) nuclear disruption and (3) a stage of general transparency which normally corresponds to the development of the pool of vegetative phage DNA.

The advantage of the light microscopical methods is that they are very rapid but of course little detail can be seen in the cells. For greater detail examination in the electron microscope is necessary. The conditions under which the bacterial nucleoplasm is preserved during fixation and embedding were studied by Kellenberger *et al.* (1958). Their procedure works well for a variety of organisms and should be adhered to strictly.

E. Cellular lysis and release of progeny phage

1. *Optical methods*

The clearing of turbid suspensions of bacteria by the action of phage is a dramatic phenomenon and has attracted attention over the whole period of time during which phage has been studied. The immediate cause of the loss of turbidity is the dissolution or lysis of the cells which accompanies the release of progeny phage and it is mediated by the development within the cells of a phage-induced lysin. In some cases, for example coliphage T4, the lytic enzyme is a variety of lysozyme (Koch and Dreyer, 1958) while in another, phage f2, the coat protein of the virus particle itself has a lytic effect (Zinder and Lyons, 1968).

Lysis can be followed by measuring the optical density of the bacterial suspensions in an absorptiometer. Frequently a spectrophotometer is used at a wavelength in the region of 500 nm but this is not necessary and a simple absorptiometer using white light (e.g. the Hilger "Spekker") is quite satisfactory. With this instrument and a modified cell carrier cultures in "T" tubes (see p. 196) can be measured without the need to take samples. It is not possible to place much meaning on figures from lysing cultures obtained with any absorptiometer because of the difficulty of relating optical density to cell counts under those conditions. The optical properties of suspensions of particles such as bacteria do not follow Beer's Law and the optical properties of bacterial fragments produced by lysis are unknown so it is not possible to use the optical density of a lysing culture to determine the fraction of cells lysed. However the fall in optical density can be taken as the beginning of mass lysis and the degree of fall with the same phage/cell system under closely similar conditions can be taken as a measure of the relative amount of lysis.

It is also possible to observe individual cells lysing in the light microscope. This was used in the study of lysogeny made by Lwoff and Gutman (1950) (see p. 255 where more details are given). It is essential that the slide carrying the infected cells be kept at the proper temperature. This can be achieved by the use of either a hot stage, or by placing the microscope in a hot box or by setting it up in a hot room. Hanging drop cultures can be made on cover slips placed over well-slides and made air tight by painting grease round the edges of the slide. It is necessary to use phase contrast or dark ground illumination.

2. *Electron microscope methods*

The act of lysis cannot be watched in the electron microscope but cells in the act can be fixed and examined. For example lysing cells can be fixed by adding formalin to give a final concentration of 1% formaldehyde and then placed on grids and shadowed or negative stained. Internal details of the cells can be observed in thin sections. Frequently cells which are swollen or ruptured at one point are seen together with a large amount of cell debris in which progeny phage particles can be distinguished. An interesting observation which is the exception to this is the release of the filamentous phage M13 (Hofschneider and Preuss, 1963). No obvious cell lysis takes place but large numbers of particles can be seen to be leaking out of the cells.

3. Rate of phage release

The rate of phage release from an infected culture can be followed by the plaque assay procedure and the effect of cultural conditions on it can be studied. The release of phage can be affected by the phenomenon of lysis inhibition which is exhibited by the T-even coli-phages. Mutants of T2 which caused rapid lysis of the host bacteria, *E. coli* B were isolated by Doermann (1948b). These were termed *r* mutants while the wild type r^+ caused a much slower fall in the turbidity of the culture and a slower rise in the titre of released phage. This effect is due to the reinfection of already infected cells by phage from those cells which lyse first. The sequence of events which lead to lysis of the cells is somehow arrested when the superinfection takes place towards the end of the latent period thus delaying the moment of lysis. The yield of phage is much greater than with *r* mutants, because maturation continues while the cells are intact.

Bode (1967) has investigated the effect of multiplicity of superinfection on lysis inhibition with T4B and *E. coli* S/6/5 using a continuous filtration method described on p. 257. The time interval between primary and superinfection had little effect on the length of lysis delay but with increasing rate of superinfection the length of lysis delay decreased.

Mukai, Streisinger and Miller (1967) have examined the effect of certain mutants of T4 which lack active lysozyme on *E. coli* B and BB. It appears that about 30 min after infection the bacterial metabolism is interrupted and that this is not due to lysozyme being produced in the cells. Lysis of infected bacteria is due to digestion of the cell walls by phage lysozyme but though this enzyme is present from 8 min it only lyses the cells after metabolism has ceased. Lysis is thus triggered by the cessation of metabolism and is accomplished by lysozyme.

4. Lysins

Lysis of individual cells takes place suddenly. A cell which appears normal one moment has disappeared the next (see Lwoff and Gutman, 1950).

Occasionally swollen, protoplast-like objects are seen but these soon disintegrate. Lysis is caused by the action of substances synthesized under the direction of the infecting phage nucleic acid on the rigid component of the cell wall. In the case of coliphage T4 an enzyme called phage lysozyme is produced. This enzyme acting on the murein component of cell walls releases breakdown products characteristic of the action of ordinary (egg white) lysozyme. The synthesis of this enzyme begins about 8 min after infection but lysis does not occur until 25 min. Presumably during this time the lysozyme is acting on the murein but the damage is made good by the normal cell wall synthesizing system. Only when the balance between synthesis and degradation is upset by the continually increasing amount of intracellular lysozyme does the cell suffer catastrophic breakdown.

Some phages such as coliphage T3 give plaques which are very large and consist of a clear central area surrounded by a less clear halo. In the early days of phage research Sertic (1929) showed that in this sort of plaque only the clear central area contained phage while a non-infective lysin could be extracted from the halo. This could lyse bacteria which had been killed by chloroform. More recently Streisinger et al. (1961) have used this method to demonstrate a diffusible lysozyme emanating from plaques of phage T4 (see p. 204)

These authors have also demonstrated the lytic action of phage lysozyme on isolated cell walls. The enzyme was prepared from phage lysates and mixed with purified cell walls. The turbidity of the suspension was followed and it was found that the time taken to cause a 50% reduction was a linear function of the enzyme concentration.

The enzyme was prepared by infecting aerated 10 ml broth cultures of E. coli B (4×10^8 cells/ml) at 30°C with five phages per cell. After 25 min chloroform (1 ml) was added and air was vigorously blown through the culture which lysed after 5 min. Centrifugation at 26,000 g in the cold removed most of the phage and the bacterial debris leaving a supernatant containing the enzyme. This was stored in the cold overnight and then tested.

Cell walls were made as described by Weidel (1951) (see p. 231) except that the digestion with trypsin (10 μg/ml) was carried out in water continually adjusted to pH 8·0 with NaOH. The digestion was continued until the rate of uptake of NaOH resembled that before the addition of trypsin. Chymotrypsin (10 μg/ml) was then added and digestion continued as with trypsin. At the completion of digestion the pH was lowered to 6·5 and the walls were washed as described by Weidel. The walls were stored frozen but were heated to 100°C for 10 min prior to use.

The activity of lysozyme synthesized in E. coli THU infected with T6r$^+$ was determined by Sekiguchi and Cohen (1964). Strain THU is a colicin resistant variant of *E. coli* 15 H⁻T⁻. The lysozyme was extracted from the cells by grinding with alumina as described on p. 242.

Chloroform treated cells of strain THU were prepared by suspending the bacteria in a chloroform saturated buffer for 30 min with occasional shaking, and the treated cells were washed three times in Tris buffer (0·05M). They were used the same day. In the assay the chloroform-treated cells were incubated with an appropriate amount of extract in 0·05M Tris pH 7·8 (3 ml total volume) at 25°C and the decrease in turbidity was measured at 450 nm at 0·5 min intervals for 5 min. The concentration of the chloroform-treated cells in the reaction mixture was adjusted to an optical density of 0·6. The reaction proceeded at a linear rate until the optical density had decreased by 65% and there was a good linear relationship between the change in turbidity and the amount of extract used.

F. *In vitro* Morphogenesis of phage

It has now been demonstrated on several occasions that component parts of phage particles are capable of self assembly *in vitro*. No enzymes are needed and the process can be extremely efficient when purified component parts are used. In order to obtain supplies of phage component parts, use has been made of conditional lethal mutant phages. These are mutants which under the appropriate conditions of temperature (temperature sensitive, *ts*) or in permissive host bacteria (amber, *am* or ochre) give rise to normal progeny (or functionally active ones) but which at unsuitable temperatures or in non-permissive hosts fail to produce some particular gene product and so fail to produce active progeny. However they do accumulate the products controlled by the unmutated genes. In the well-studied example of *E. coli* phage T4 more than 75 genes have been identified by the use of *ts* and *am* mutants and a genetic map has been constructed (Wood and Edgar, 1967). Of these some 40 have morphogenetic functions. The products of these mutant phages in non-permissive hosts or conditions have been examined in the electron microscope and identified as heads, tails without fibres, base plates, tail fibres, incomplete heads, complete particles less tail fibres and so on. If the products of each mutant are mixed together in pairwise combination it is found that in certain cases complete phage particles are spontaneously formed. In this way the morphogenetic mutants have been classed into 13 complementation groups and a morphogenetic pathway for the assembly of phage components has been drawn. First the prolate icosahedral head complete with DNA is constructed step by step while simultaneously the tail consisting of core, baseplate and contractile sheath is assembled. The head and tail now come together spontaneously. Meanwhile the tail fibres are being made and these now attach to the head plus tail structure to make a complete infective phage particle.

Other work of the same nature has shown that phage P22 of *Salmonella typhimurium* (Israel *et al.*, 1966) and phage λ of *E. coli* (Weigle, 1966) can also be assembled *in vitro*.

1. *Phage P22*

Phage P22 of *S. typhimurium* is less complicated in structure than T4. It consists of a polyhedral head to which is attached a small base plate which appears to consist of a central core around which are arranged six spikes. Phage heads were prepared by growing bacteria (LT2) carrying a temperature sensitive c_2 mutant prophage in L broth (p. 217) at 25°C with aeration to 4×10^8/ml. The cells were sedimented and resuspended in L broth at 10^8/ml prewarmed to 40°C. At this temperature the prophage is thermally induced. Aeration was continued until lysis occurred. The lysate contained 10^{10} active phage and $3–4 \times 10^{10}$ heads/ml. The active phage was removed by repeated adsorption to bacteria at 10^9/ml at 37°C for 1 h in the presence of 0.01M NaCN to prevent phage multiplication. The heads were recovered by sedimentation at 19,000 rpm for 90 min and banded in CsCl.

Phage tail parts were prepared by growing bacteria to 10^8/ml in M9 medium (p. 212) and infecting with a multiplicity of 10 with a *ts* mutant $G5c_1$. After 35 min the culture was rapidly chilled by pouring over ice and quickly concentrated by centrifugation at 17,000 rpm for 5 min. The viscous pellet was resuspended in one hundredth of the original volume of buffered saline and frozen twice in a bath of acetone and dry ice. The lysed cells were treated for 10 min with DNase (10 μg/ml) at room temperature. Debris and active phage particles were removed by centrifugation at 17,000 rpm for 60 min. Further purification was made by zone sedimentation of a 1 ml sample on a 5–20% sucrose gradient in a Spinco SW25 rotor for 25 h at 25,000 rpm at 25°C. This mutant, G5, grows normally at 25°C but at 37°C is defective. A double mutant $G5c_1$ was used to prevent lysogenization.

The preparation of heads without base plates lacked antibody blocking power (p. 226) and it was clear that base plates were responsible for SBP. The tail parts preparation did contain SBP and in the electron microscope consisted of spindle shaped molecules about 50×180 Å bearing little resemblance to the tail structure of mature phage.

Active phage was formed when a mixture of heads (containing 2.5×10^5 p.f.u./ml) and tail parts (3.23×10^3 p.f.u./ml) was kept at room temperature for a few hours when it was found to contain 1.93×10^{11} p.f.u./ml. In the electron microscope the phage particles were indistinguishable from wild type particles.

2. Phage λ

A number of conditional lethal mutants of phage λ have been isolated by Campbell (1961) and used by Weigle (1966) to prepare phage components. These λ *sus* (suppressor sensitive) mutants grow on the permissive strain of *E. coli* K12 C600 but they do not grow on the restrictive strain 594 (this is strain 3350 made resistant to streptomycin). However these mutants can lysogenize strain 594. Various strains of 594 each made lysogenic for one of 12 different *sus* mutants (in genes A to M less F, which was leaky) were grown in K medium (p. 218) and were ultraviolet induced at 2×10^8 cells per ml. After induction the cells were maintained at 37°C under vigorous aeration and 90 min later chloroform was added. The cultures lysed completely and were then filtered and tested for sterility. All the lysates were tested in pairwise combination by adding 0·1 ml of each to 0·8 ml of K medium and standing at room temperature for 60 min. The mixtures were assayed for active phage on the permissive strain C600. It was found that any of the lysates of mutants A–E produced active phage when mixed with lysates of mutants G–M but that within each of these groups no complementation took place. Mutants in genes A–E are blocked in head formation and yield only tails while mutants in genes G–M are blocked in tail formation and their defective lysates contain only heads. It appears that all factors necessary for the *in vitro* assembly of complete phage are present in the head and tail structures as purification by sucrose density gradient centrifugation does not affect their ability to form active phage.

3. Phage T4

The *in vitro* morphogenesis of phage T4 has been studied extensively by Edgar and Wood (1966) and Wood and Edgar (1967). Tail-fibreless particles were prepared by the growth of the multiple *am* mutant X4E defective in the tail fibre genes 34, 35, 37 and 38 in a culture of *E. coli* B/5 infected with a multiplicity of 4 and aerated for 3 h at 30°C. The culture was lysed with chloroform and the defective particles were purified by two cycles of high and low speed centrifugation and resuspended in buffer (Na_2HPO_4, 0·039M; KH_2PO_4, 0·022M; NaCl, 0·07M and $MgSO_4$, 0·01M at pH 7·4). The particle concentration was estimated from the optical density at 265 nm assuming $OD_{265} = 1·0$ for a suspension of $1·2 \times 10^{11}$ particles per ml.

Extracts of phage-infected bacteria containing tail fibres were made by infecting B/5 with mutant phage of the desired genotype (e.g. 23) at 30°C and aerating vigorously for 30 min. The bacteria had been grown at 37°C in broth and cooled to 30°C before the addition of phage. At 30 min the cultures were rapidly cooled by pouring into large iced Erlenmeyer flasks and the cells were concentrated 200 times by centrifugation at 5000 g for 8 min. The viscous pellet was resuspended in buffer containing DNase (10 μg/ml). The resuspended pellet was frozen in dry ice-ethanol, thawed at 30°C and either used immediately or refrozen at -70°C and stored at -20°C.

When mixtures of the tail-fibres less heads, 8×10^{11} particles/ml, and the bacterial extracts were mixed together in equal volume at 30°C active phage particles were formed as shown by a gradual increase (three orders of magnitude) in titre on CR63 over the period of 1 h.

4. Phage R17

Phage R17 contains two major components: a single RNA molecule of molecular weight $1 \cdot 1 \times 10^6$ and approximately 180 identical coat protein subunits of molecular weight 14,000. The RNA is single-stranded and is enclosed in an isometric capsid. There is no tail or any obvious organ of attachment. Attempts to reconstitute the virus from RNA and protein subunits produced virus-like particles but they were not infective. Genetic studies with *am* mutants of R17 showed that there was a cistron which could be distinguished from those coding for coat protein and RNA synthetase. It therefore became apparent that another protein was concerned in the synthesis of active virus particles. This is the "A" protein and has been isolated by Roberts and Steitz (1967) who were able to show that by mixing phage RNA, coat protein and the "A" protein active phage particles were assembled *in vitro*.

The three components were isolated from complete phage which had been grown on strain S26, an Hfr strain of *E. coli*, and purified by the method of Gesteland and Boedtker (1964) with the addition of a second CsCl banding step. The RNA was purified from a suspension of phage at a concentration of $3 \cdot 4$ mg/ml in TSE at pH $7 \cdot 0$ by three phenol extractions followed by three ethanol extractions (TSE buffer contains $0 \cdot 02$M Tris-HCl, $0 \cdot 15$M NaCl, and $0 \cdot 001$M ethylenediaminetetra-acetate). The RNA was finally dissolved in TSE, pH $7 \cdot 0$ at $1 \cdot 0$ mg/ml. For the preparation of coat protein 1 volume of R17 at 17 mg/ml in $0 \cdot 15$M NaCl, $0 \cdot 015$M Na citrate, pH $7 \cdot 0$, was added gradually to 2 volumes of glacial acetic acid at 0°C. The precipitated RNA was removed by centrifugation and the supernate was dialysed against three changes of 10^{-3}M acetic acid. This procedure yielded a stable protein solution at a concentration of $1 \cdot 1$ mg/ml at pH $4 \cdot 2$. The "A" protein was prepared by dissolving purified phage in 6M guanidinium chloride, dialysing into 8M urea and chromatographing the mixture on a cellulose phosphate column. The "A" protein was eluted with a linear NaCl gradient and was dissolved in 8M urea, 0·05M Tris HCl, pH 8·5 and 0·2M NaCl. The concentration of "A" protein was 1·0 mg/ml. Dialysis membranes were prepared by boiling successively in 2% Na_2CO_3, distilled water, 0·002M EDTA and distilled water again.

The reconstitution experiments were made by combining the three components in the presence of 5·7M urea, dialysing against two changes of buffer (TSE, pH 9·0 supplemented with 1% β mercaptoethanol and 0·01M $MgCl_2$) for at least 2 h and then assaying for phage. It was shown that the addition of "A" protein gave a yield of active phage several hundredfold greater than that given by the RNA and coat protein together.

V. BACTERIOPHAGE GROWTH IN INDIVIDUAL CELLS

There have been two general approaches to the growth of phage in individual cells. One of these, elegantly used by Lwoff and Gutman (1950) to solve several perplexing aspects of lysogeny was to use a micromanipulator to place single cells in micro-droplets of medium while observing them under the microscope. When cell division occurred the daughter cells could be transferred to other droplets and samples from the droplets could be withdrawn for phage assay. The other method is a statistical one in which infected cells are diluted to such an extent that in any small sample the probability of finding a cell is such that only a negligible fraction of samples contains more than one. The cells are not observed in the microscope but any phage which they release can be determined by plating out the whole of the fluid in which they were suspended. A variant on this method is that used by Hutchison and Sinsheimer (1963) to determine whether ØX174 was released as a burst or whether it leaked out of the cells over a period of time. Single cells were held on membrane filters with pore size sufficient to pass the phage particles. At regular intervals the medium bathing the cell was sucked through and assayed for phage. These methods will be discussed in detail.

A. Micromanipulation method

Lwoff and Gutman (1950) studied individual cells of the lysogenic organism *Bacillus megaterium* strain 899, in an attempt to elucidate several puzzling features of lysogeny. It was known that cultures of this organism, and indeed all lysogenic bacteria, always contained free phage but that if the cells were washed and broken open no phage was ever present intracellularly. Lwoff and Gutman placed single washed cells in micro-droplets of medium and allowed them to divide. In one experiment 22 daughter cells were removed as they separated and then the entire droplet was assayed for phage. None was found. In another type of experiment a washed cell was allowed to divide and the daughter cells were removed and plated on sensitive bacteria. Almost all of them gave plaques showing that the lysogenic property is maintained through many generations in the absence of free phage. In a further type of experiment bacteria were allowed to multiply in microdroplets and their number recorded at short intervals. Small samples from the droplets were removed from time to time and assayed for phage. It was found that occasionally phage suddenly appeared but that on closer examination it became clear that this only happened if one of the cells disappeared, that is, lysed. The lysis that liberated phage always took place very rapidly while occasional cells which swelled and lysed slowly never released any phage.

As a result of these studies the well-known theory of lysogeny was postulated in which the bacteria all carry a non-infective structure, the prophage, which endows them with the ability to give rise to infective phage. In only a small fraction of the cells is this ability expressed and when it is those cells lyse and release infective phage in the same manner as cells infected with virulent phage.

The full details of the technique of micromanipulation are too complex to describe here and the reader is referred to Johnstone (this Series, Vol. 1) and to the standard textbook by de Fonbrune (1949). For handling the bacteria Lwoff and Gutman used a micromanipulator fitted with a pipette which was sufficiently finely adjustable that single bacteria or volumes of 10^{-5} mm^3 could be withdrawn. A special cell was made consisting of a well-slide to which two pieces of glass 12×7 mm, $1 \cdot 5$ mm thick had been cemented on either side of the depression. A sterile cover slip previously cleaned in nitric acid and distilled water, was covered with a thin layer of paraffin. With a fine drawn Pasteur pipette several rows of droplets 500–800 μm diameter were placed on the slip beneath the oil. The slip was then inverted on to the slide so as to lie across the two glass strips and was sealed in place with more paraffin. A few drops of water were placed in the well to insure against evaporation of the microdrops. The whole assembly was mounted on a microscope stage and the pipette held in the micromanipulator was inserted through the paraffin seal into the microdrops. The apparatus was kept at 37°C in an incubator box. Bacteria were transferred from drop to drop by moving the micromanipulator but for sampling bacteria or culture medium the contents of the pipette were expressed into a wider bore Pasteur pipette held near to it. This pipette which already held a drop of medium was then withdrawn and its contents assayed. The results are discussed further by Lwoff (1953).

The same technique was used by Hoffman-Berling and Mazé (1964) to study the release of filamentous phage from *E. coli* K12. Single infected cells were followed for several generations and the daughters were separated and placed in fresh droplets of medium. Samples of the medium were assayed for phage and it was found that cells could continue to release phage without interferring with growth and cell division.

B. Dilution methods

The phage liberated by single cells can be examined without actually observing the cells in a microscope. If the infected cells are highly diluted in a suitable culture medium so that there are fewer than one per ml and then samples of 1 ml are taken and allowed to lyse the phage produced can be assayed by plating out the whole sample. It can be shown from the Poisson distribution that if the average number of cells/ml is 0·3 then a large proportion of the samples will be uninfected, some will contain only one cell and very few will contain two or more. By this means Ellis and Delbruck (1939) showed that the phage yield from individual cells varied over a wide range.

An interesting variation on this idea was that used by Hutchison and Sinsheimer (1963) to determine whether phage ØX174 was released from its host cells in a sudden burst or whether it leaked out slowly without concomitant cell lysis. It was necessary to test this point because it was possible to show with mass cultures that phage appeared in the medium before any diminution of the turbidity of the cells, and that the release took place over a period of time longer than the minimal latent period.

Cells of *E. coli* C were starved and then infected with ØX174 at a multiplicity of 0·1. From then on all operations were performed in a room maintained at 37°C. Phage growth was initiated by dilution in broth (KC, see Media, p. 215). Further dilutions were made so that in a sample of 1 ml only three infected cells would be expected. Such samples were placed in a membrane filter (Millipore, Type HA, 25 mm diameter, pore size 0·45 μm) and washed a few times with broth to remove any free phage. The bacteria settled on the filter and the phage were washed through. Before the end of the latent period regular washes of the filter were begun and continued at intervals of 1 min. Each wash consisted of two 1 ml portions of broth which were rapidly drawn through and collected for phage assay. It had previously been determined that one wash would recover 90% of phage added to the filter and that the remaining 10% could be recovered by repeated washing. The results showed clearly that the phage was released in discrete bursts shorter than the interval between the washes but that the latent period varied greatly from one infected cell to another, values of 11 min to over 40 min being recorded.

Bode (1967) used a multiple filtration apparatus consisting of water-jacketed holders fitted with Schleicher and Schuell Type B6 membrane filters which had been washed repeatedly in saline and finally soaked in 30% bovine serum albumin solution. Medium was pumped out of the filters by a four place peristaltic pump and was replaced by prewarmed medium. The flow rate was 0·5 ml/min.

He was studying the effect of multiplicity of infection on the lysis inhibition produced in *E. coli* S/6/5 by various mutants of T4D.

REFERENCES

Adams, M. H. (1948). *J. gen. Physiol.*, **31**, 417–431.
Adams, M. H. (1950). *In* "Methods in Medical Research" (Ed. J. H. Comroe), Vol. 2, pp. 1–73. Year Book Publishers Inc., Chicago.
Adams, M. H. (1959). "Bacteriophages". Interscience, New York.
Anderson, T. F. (1945). *J. Cell. comp. Physiol.*, **25**, 17–26.
Anderson, T. F. (1948). *J. Bact.*, **55**, 637–649.
Anderson, T. F. (1953). *Cold Spring Harb. Symp. quant. Biol.*, **18**, 197–203.
Anderson, T. F., Boggs, S., and Winters, B. C. (1948). *Science*, **108**, 18.
Baker, E. E., Goebel, W. F., and Perlman, E. (1949). *J. exp. Med.*, **89**, 325–338.
Barner, H. D., and Cohen, S. S. (1959). *J. biol. Chem.*, **234**, 2987–2991.
Bode, W. (1967). *J. Virol.*, **1**, 948–955.
Borek, E., and Srinivasan, P. R. (1966). *A. Rev. Biochem.*, **35**, 275
Boyd, J. S. K. (1951). *J. Path. Bact.*, **63**, 445–457.
Bradley, D. E. (1967). *Bact. Rev.*, **31**, 230–314.
Brenner, S., Dark, F., Gerhardt, P., Jeynes, M. H., Kandler, O., Kellenberger, E., Klieneberger-Nobel, E., McQuillen, K., Rubio-Huertos, M., Salton, M. R. J., Tomcsik, J., and Weibull, C. (1958). *Nature, Lond.*, **181**, 1713–1715.
Brenner, S., Champe, S. P., Streisinger, G., and Barnet, L. (1962). *Virology*, **17**, 30–39.
Burnet, F. M. (1934). *J. Path. Bact.*, **38**, 285.
Burton, K. (1956). *Biochem. J.*, **62**, 315–323.
Campbell, A. (1961). *Virology*, **14**, 22–32.
Capecchi, M. R. (1966). *J. molec. Biol.*, **21**, 173–193.
Caro, L. G., and Schnoss, M. (1966). *Proc. natn. Acad. Sci. Wash.*, **56**, 126–132.
Cohen, S. S. (1948). *J. biol. Chem.*, **174**, 281–293.
Crawford, E. M., and Gesteland, R. F. (1964). *Virology*, **22**, 165–167.
Crick, F. H. C., Barnet, L., Brenner, S., and Watts-Tobin, R. J. (1961). *Nature, Lond.*, **192**, 1227–1232.
Davis, J. E., and Sinsheimer, R. L. (1963). *J. molec. Biol.*, **6**, 203–207.
Davis, H. E., Pfeiffer, D., and Sinsheimer, R. L. (1964). *J. molec. Biol.*, **10**, 1–9.
Davison, P. F. and Freifelder, D. (1966). *J. molec. Biol.*, **16**, 490–502.
De Fonbrune, P. (1949). "Technique de Micromanipulation". Masson, Paris.
Delbruck, M. (1940). *J. gen. Physiol.*, **23**, 631–642.
Delbruck, M. (1945). *J. Bact.*, **50**, 151–170.
Delbruck, M. (1948). *J. Bact.*, **56**, 1–16.
De Mars, R. I., Luria, S. E., Fisher, H. and Levinthal, C. (1953). *Annls Inst. Pasteur, Paris*, **84**, 113–128.
Denes, G., and Polgar, L. (1959). *Nature, Lond.*, **183**, 696–697.
De Ward, A. (1964a). *Biochim. biophys. Acta*, **87**, 169–171.
De Ward, A. (1964b). *Biochim. biophys, Acta*, **92**, 286–304.

Doermann, A. H. (1948a). *Carnegie Inst. Wash. Yearbook*, **47**, 176–182.
Doermann, A. H. (1948b). *J. Bact.*, **55**, 257–276.
Doermann, A. H. (1952). *J. gen. Physiol.*, **35**, 645–656.
Dole, V. P. (1946). *Proc. Soc. exp. Biol. Med.*, **63**, 122–126.
Dulbecco, R. (1949). *Genetics*, **34**, 122–125.
Eddleman, H. L., and Champe, S. P. (1966). *Virology*, **30**, 471–481.
Edgar, R. S., and Lielausis, I. (1964). *Genetics*, **49**, 649–662.
Edgar, R. S., and Wood, W. B. (1966). *Proc. natn. Acad. Sci. Wash.*, **55**, 498–505.
Eigner, J., Stouthamer, A. H., van der Sluys, I., and Cohen, J. A. (1963). *J. molec. Biol.*, **6**, 61–84.
Ellis, E. L., and Delbruck, M. (1939). *J. gen. Physiol.*, **22**, 365–384.
Epstein, R. H., Bolle, A., Steinberg, C. M., Kellenberger, E., Boy de la Tour, E., Chevalley, R., Edgar, R. S., Susman, M., Denhardt, G. H., and Lielausis, A. (1963). *Cold Spring Harb. Symp. quant. Biol.*, **38**, 357–392.
Erickson, R. L., and Franklin, R. M. (1966). *Bact. Rev.*, **30**, 267–277.
Flaks, J. G., and Cohen, S. S. (1957). *Biochim. biophys. Acta*, **25**, 667–668.
Flaks, J. G., and Cohen, S. S. (1959a). *J. biol. Chem.*, **234**, 1501–1506.
Flaks, J. G. and Cohen, S. S. (1959b). *J. biol. Chem.*, **234**, 2981–2986.
Flaks, J. G., Lichtenstein, J., and Cohen, S. S. (1959). *J. biol. Chem.*, **234**, 1507–1511.
Fraser, D. (1951). *Nature, Lond.*, **167**, 33–34.
Fraser, D., and Jerrell, E. A. (1953). *J. biol. Chem.*, **205**, 291–295.
Fraser, D., and Mahler, H. R. (1957). *Archs Biochem. Biophys.*, **69**, 166–177.
Fraser, D., Mahler, H. R., Shug, A. L., and Thomas, C. A. (1957). *Proc. natn. Acad. Sci. Wash.*, **43**, 939–947.
Gesteland, R., and Boedtker, H. (1964). *J. molec. Biol.*, **8**, 496–507.
Goebel, W. F., and Jesaitis, M. A. (1952). *J. exp. Med.*, **96**, 425–438.
Guthrie, G. D., and Sinsheimer, R. L. (1960). *J. molec. Biol.*, **2**, 297–305.
Guthrie, G. D., and Sinsheimer, R. L. (1963). *Biochem. biophys. Acta*, **72**, 290–297
Hall, J. B., and Sinsheimer, R. L. (1963). *J. molec. Biol.*, **6**, 115–127.
Hartman, P. E., and Kozinski, A. W. (1962). *Virology*, **17**, 233–244.
Haruna, I., and Spiegelman, S. (1965a). *Proc. natn. Acad. Sci. Wash.*, **54**, 579–587.
Haruna, I., and Spiegelman, S. (1956b). *Proc. natn. Acad. Sci. Wash.*, **54**, 1189–1193.
Hayes, D. (1967). *A. Rev. Microbiol.*, **21**, 369–382.
Hershey, A. D. (1955). *Virology*, **1**, 108–127.
Hershey, A. D. (1957). *Virology*, **4**, 237–267.
Hershey, A. D., and Burgi, E. (1956). *Cold Spring Harb. Symp. quant. Biol.*, **21**, 91–101.
Hershey, A. D., and Chase, M. (1952). *J. gen. Physiol.*, **36**, 39–56.
Hershey, A. D., and Melechen, N. E. (1957). *Virology*, **3**, 207–236.
Hershey, A. D., and Rotman, R. (1948). *Proc. natn. Acad. Sci. Wash.*, **34**, 89–96.
Hershey, A. D., Dixon, J., and Chase, M. (1953). *J. gen. Physiol.*, **36**, 777–789.
Hoffmann-Berling, H., and Mazé, R. (1964). *Virology*, **22**, 305–313.
Hofschneider, P. H., and Preuss, A. (1963). *J. molec. Biol.*, **7**, 450–451.
Hutchison, C. A., and Sinsheimer, R. L. (1963). *J. molec. Biol.*, **7**, 206–208.
Israel, J. V., Anderson, T. F., and Levine, M. (1966). *Proc. natn. Acad. Sci. Wash.*, **57**, 284–291.
Jesaitis, M. A., and Goebel, W. F. (1955). *J. exp. Med.*, **102**, 733–751.
Kahn, P. (1964). *J. molec. Biol.*, **9**, 772–780.

Kallen, R. G., Simon, M., and Marmur, J. (1962). *J. molec. Biol.*, **5**, 248–250.

Kay, D., Ed. (1965). "Techniques for Electron Microscopy". Blackwell Scientific Publications, Oxford.

Kay, D., and Fildes, P. (1962). *J. gen. Microbiol.*, **27**, 143–146.

Keck, K., Mahler, H. R., and Fraser, D. (1960). *Archs Biochem. Biophys.*, **86**, 85–88.

Kellenberger, E. (1962). *Adv. Virus Research*, **8**, 1–61.

Kellenberger, E., and Arber, W. (1955). *Z. Naturf.*, **10b**, 698 *et seq.*

Kellenberger, E., Ryter, A., and Sechaud, J. (1958). *J. biophys. biochem. Cytol.*, **4**, 671 *et seq.*

Kellenberger, E., Bolle, A., Boy de la Tour, E., Epstein, R. H., Franklin, N. C., Jerne, N. K., Reale-Scafati, A., Sechaud, J., Bendet, I., Goldstein, D., and Lauffer, M. A. (1965). *Virology*, **26**, 419–440.

Koch, G., and Dreyer, W. J. (1958). *Virology*, **6**, 291–293.

Koerner, J. F., Smith, M. S., and Buchanan, J. M. (1959). *J. Am. chem. Soc.*, **81**, 2594 *et seq.*

Kornberg, A. (1960). *Science*, **131**, 1503 *et seq.*

Kornberg, A., Zimmerman, S. B., Kornberg, S. R., and Joss, J. (1959). *Proc. natn. Acad. Sci. Wash.*, **45**, 772–785.

Kozloff, L. M., Lute, M., and Henderson, K. (1957). *J. biol. Chem.*, **228**, 511–528.

Lanni, Y. T. (1960). *Virology*, **10**, 514–529.

Lanni, Y. T. (1961). *Virology*, **15**, 127–135.

Lanni, Y. T., McCorquodale, D. J., and Wilson, C. M. (1964). *J. molec. Biol.*, **10**, 19–27.

Levine, M. (1957). *Virology*, **3**, 22–41.

Levinthal, C., and Fisher, H. (1952). *Biochim. biophys. Acta*, **9**, 419–429.

Lindberg, A. A. (1967). *J. gen. Microbiol.*, **48**, 225–233.

Loeb, T. (1960). *Science*, **131**, 932–933.

Luderitz, O., Staub, A. M., and Westphal, O. (1966). *Bact. Rev.*, **30**, 192–255.

Luria, S. E. (1947). *Proc. natn. Acad. Sci. Wash.*, **33**, 253–264.

Luria, S. E., and Human, M. L. (1950). *J. Bact.*, **59**, 551–560.

Luria, S. E., and Steiner, D. L. (1954). *J. Bact.*, **67**, 635–650.

Lwoff, A. (1953). *Bact. Rev.*, **17**, 269–337.

Lwoff, A., and Gutman, A. (1950). *Annls Inst. Pasteur, Paris*, **78**, 711–739.

Maaløe, O., and Hannawalt, P. C. (1961). *J. molec. Biol.*, **3**, 144–155.

Maaløe, O., and Watson, J. D. (1951). *Proc. natn. Acad. Sci. Wash.*, **37**, 507–513.

Mackal, R. P., Werninghaus, B., and Evans, E. A. (1964). *Proc. natn. Acad. Sci. Wash.*, **51**, 1172–1178.

Mandell, J. M., and Hershey, A. D. (1960). *Ann. Biochem.*, **1**, 66–77.

McCorquodale, D. J., and Lanni, Y. T. (1964). *J. molec. Biol.*, **10**, 10–18.

Meynell, E. W. (1961). *J. gen. Microbiol.*, **25**, 253–290.

Meynell, E., and Datta, N. (1967). *Nature, Lond.*, **214**, 885–887.

Milne, R. G., and Trautner, T. A. (1967). *J. Ultrastruct. Res.*, **20**, 267–276.

Mitchell, P. (1949). *Nature, Lond.*, **164**, 846–847.

Mitchell, P., and Moyle, J. (1956). *Soc. Gen. Microbiol. Symp.*, p. 150.

Mukai, F., Streisinger, G., and Miller, B. (1967). *Virology*, **33**, 398–404.

Nathans, D., Oeschger, M. P., Eggen,K., and Shimura, Y. (1966). *Proc. natn. Acad. Sci. Wash.*, **56**, 1844–1851.

Nomura, M., Okamato, K., and Asano, K. (1962). *J. molec. Biol.*, **4**, 376–387.

Oeschger, M. P., and Nathans, D. (1966). *J. molec. Biol.*, **22**, 235–247.

Ogawa, T., and Tomizawa, J.-I. (1967). *J. molec. Biol.*, **23**, 225–245.

Pratt, D., Tzagoloff, H., and Erdahl, W. S. (1966). *Virology*, **30**, 397–410.
Puck, T. T., Garen, A., and Cline, J. (1951). *J. exp. Med.*, **93**, 65–88.
Putnam, F. W., and Kozloff, L. M. (1950). *J. biol. Chem.*, **182**, 243–250.
Ray, D. S., Bscheider, H., and Hofschneider, P. H. (1966). *J. molec. Biol.*, **21**, 473–483.
Roberts, J. W., and Steitz, J. E. A. (1967). *Proc. natn. Acad. Sci. Wash.*, **58**, 1416–1421.
Roller, A. (1964). *J. molec. Biol.*, **9**, 260–262.
Roscoe, D. H., and Tucker, R. G. (1966). *Virology*, **29**, 157–166.
Salton, M. R. J., and Horne, R. W. (1951). *Biochim. biophys. Acta*, **7**, 177–197.
Schmidt, G., and Thannhauser, S. J. (1945). *J. biol. Chem.*, **161**, 83–89.
Schneider, W. C. (1945). *J. biol. Chem.*, **161**, 293–303.
Séchaud, J., and Kellenberger, E. (1956). *Annls Inst. Pasteur, Paris*, **90**, 102 *et seq.*
Sedat, J., and Sinsheimer, R. L. (1964). *J. molec. Biol.*, **9**, 489–497.
Sekiguchi, M., and Cohen, S. S. (1964). *J. molec. Biol.*, **8**, 638–659.
Sertic, V. (1929). *Zentbl. Bakt. ParasitKde* (1), **110**, 125 *et seq.*
Short, E. C., and Koerner, J. F. (1965). *Proc. natn. Acad. Sci. Wash.*, **54**, 595–600.
Simon, L. D., and Anderson, T. F. (1967a). *Virology*, **32**, 279–297.
Simon, L. D., and Anderson, T. F. (1967b). *Virology*, **32**, 298–305.
Sinsheimer, R. L. (1966). *In* "Procedures in Nucleic Acid Research" (Eds G. L. Cantoni and D. R. Davies). Harper and Row, New York.
Sinsheimer, R. L., Starman, B., Nagler, C., and Guthrie, S. (1962). *J. molec. Biol.*, **4**, 142–160.
Stent, G. S. (1963). "Molecular Biology of Bacterial Viruses", p. 92. Freeman, San Francisco and London.
Strauss, J. H. (1964). *J. molec. Biol.*, **10**, 422.
Streisinger, G., Maukai, F., Dreyer, W. J., Miller, B., and Horiuchi, S. (1961). *Cold Spring Harb. Symp. quant. Biol.*, **26**, 25–30.
Twort, F. W. (1915). *Lancet*, ii, **189**, 1251–1252.
Tzagoloff, H., and Pratt, D. (1964). *Virology*, **24**, 374–380.
Valentine, R. C., and Wedel, H. (1965). *Biochem. biophys. Res. Commun.*, **21**, 106–112.
Van Arkel, G. A., van de Pol, J. H., and Cohen, J. A. (1961). *Virology*, **13**, 546–548.
Van de Pol, J. H., Veldhuisen, G., and Cohen, J. A. (1961). *Biochim. biophys. Acta*, **48**, 417–418.
Veldhuisen, G., Jansy, H. S., Alten, J. B. T., Pouwels, P. H., Oosterbaan, R. A., and Cohen, J. A. (1962). *Biochim. biophys. Acta*, **61**, 630–632.
Volkin, E., and Astrachan, L. (1956). *Virology*, **2**, 594–598.
Weidel, W. (1951). *Z. Naturf.*, **6b**, 251 *et seq.*
Weidel, W. (1955). *Hoppe-Seyler's Z. physiol. Chem.*, **299**, 253 *et seq.*
Weidel, W. (1958). *A. Rev. Microbiol.*, **12**, 27–48.
Weidel, W., Frank, H., and Martin, H. H. (1960). *J. gen. Microbiol.*, **22**, 158–166.
Weidel, W., and Kellenberger, E. (1955). *Biochim. biophys. Acta*, **17**, 1–9.
Weidel, W., Koch, G., and Bobosch, K. (1954). *Z. Naturf.*, **9b**, 573 *et seq.*
Weigle, J. (1966). *Proc. natn. Acad. Sci. Wash.*, **55**, 1462–1466.
Weigle, J., Meselson, M., and Paigen, K. (1959). *J. molec. Biol.*, **1**, 379–386.
Westphal, O., Luderitz, O., and Bister, F. (1952). *Z. Naturf.*, **7b**, 148 *et seq.*
Williams, T. (1968). *J. gen. Virol.*, **2**, 13–18.
Wittmann, H. G., and Scholtissek, C. (1966). *A. Rev. Biochem.*, **35**, 299 *et seq.*
Wood, W. B., and Edgar, R. S. (1967). *Scient. Amer.*, **217**, 60–74.

Wyatt, G. R., and Cohen, S. S. (1953). *Biochem. J.*, **55**, 774–782.
Zgaga, V. (1967). *Virology*, **31**, 559–562.
Zinder, N. D., and Lyons, L. B. (1968). *Science*, **159**, 84–86.
Zinder, N. D., Valentine, R. C., Roger, M., and Stoeckenius, W. (1963). *Virology*,
    20, 638–640.

CHAPTER VI

Methods for the Determination of the Chemical and Physical Structure of Bacteriophages

D. KAY

Sir William Dunn School of Pathology, University of Oxford, South Parks Road, Oxford

I. INTRODUCTION

The bacteriophages have been intensively studied by a wide range of techniques since the late 1930s when the subject was reopened by such workers as Schlesinger, Burnet and Delbruck (see Stent, 1963). The first

---

Abbreviations

PFU, plaque forming units; EDTA, ethylene diamine tetracetic acid; MAP, methylaminopurine; HMC, hydroxymethylcytosine; SDS, sodium dodecyl sulphate; RNA, DNA, ribose and deoxyribose nucleic acid; dCMP, dTMP, dUMP, dGMP, dHMP, deoxy cytidine, thymidine, uridine, guanosine, hydroxy-methylcytidine monophosphates.

phages were discovered by Twort in 1915 and the subject was thoroughly studied by d'Herelle in the 1920s, after which interest waned, probably because there were no techniques suitable for their further examination. However with the development of refined biochemical techniques and such apparatus as the ultracentrifuge and the electron microscope the study of all aspects of bacteriophage has been able to proceed apace.

Chemical analysis of the purified virus particles showed that they are all composed almost entirely of protein and nucleic acid but that the latter is either DNA or RNA. The two nucleic acids never occur together in bacteriophages. Some pyrimidine bases and nucleotides unknown in other organisms have been found in phage nucleic acids. The proteins of phage have been shown to be constructed of the same set of amino-acids which are found in the host bacteria and in higher organisms but some phage proteins have been shown to lack one or more of the amino-acids. Recently, phages with a lipid component have been described. Phages also contain, in small amounts, a variety of inorganic cations and in some cases the polyamines putrescine and spermidine are found.

Once the basic chemical composition of phage had been established studies on the macromolecules, the proteins and the nucleic acids, were able to proceed. Methods were devised for the disaggregation of the phage particles into recognizable macromolecular entities. It is now possible, for example, to isolate in pure form the coat proteins and maturation proteins of the small RNA phages and tail sheath and fibre proteins of the large T-even phages have also been prepared. By procedures avoiding denaturation and shearing forces it has been possible to extract intact molecules of DNA and RNA and in some cases show that these molecules can direct the production of active phage when added to a sensitive bacterial protoplast system. In the case of the RNA phages and the filamentous DNA-containing phages the amino-acid sequence in the coat proteins has been determined and studies are now in progress to solve the nucleotide sequence in the phage RNA. There is the prospect that soon the complete sequence codons will be known and it will be possible to relate these precisely to the amino-acid sequence of the proteins as well as to define the functions of the extracistronic codons.

Phages vary in size considerably from the tiny isometric phages such as R17 about 230 Å across to the large *Bacillus subtilis* phages and *Serratia* phages in which the heads may measure 1350 Å from apex to apex. As the size increases so does the apparent structural complexity of the particles. The length of the nucleic acid also increases and from genetic studies it appears that the larger phages possess more genes than the smaller. It appears also that as the size of the particle increases so does the number of genes involved in the formation of the capsid. However by no means all of these code for proteins which eventually become incorporated into the phage capsids. Nevertheless in the more complex phages which have been well studied there may be ten or more different proteins actually built into the structure of the phage particle.

The size and conformation of phage nucleic acid molecules is now well understood. Estimates of the molecular weights of the nucleic acids have been made from ultracentrifugal and light scattering measurements, from direct chemical analysis of the amount of nucleic acid per phage particle and, most strikingly, from the visualization of the whole intact strand by electron microscopy. By the use of the Kleinschmidt technique the DNA strands can be observed and their lengths measured with considerable precision. Then from the known MWU/length relationship for DNA the molecular weight can be calculated.

In all phages yet examined there is only one piece of nucleic acid per phage particle, but, depending on the phage, this may be double-stranded, or single-stranded. In the latter case the strand is always in the form of a closed loop. Information about the strandedness and conformation of DNA does not come solely from electron microscope studies but from a variety of sources involving ultracentrifugation and specific nuclease treatments. Phage DNA has been found to show a surprising number of subtle variations. The T-even phage DNA is linear but circularly permuted while that of T7 is terminally repetitious. Phage λ DNA has single-stranded regions at each end which, because they are complementary in nucleotide sequence, can link together to give a circular form *in vitro.*

The gross structural details of many phages are well documented and simple systems of classification based on morphology have been proposed (Kay, 1963; Bradley, 1965a; 1967). There are however many questions concerning the molecular architecture of the phages which remain unanswered. For example in no case is the arrangement of the capsomeres in the phage capsid understood nor is the way the nucleic acid is packed into the capsid known.

What is clear is that all phages, in common with other viruses, consist of a piece of nucleic acid containing the genetic information for the replication of the virus totally enclosed in a container, referred to as the coat or capsid which is made of protein. The coat affords the genome complete protection against damage by agents such as nucleases which might be present in the surrounding fluid yet the genome can be instantly released and transferred into the host cell when the phage particle makes contact with specific bacterial receptor substances. It is in this respect that bacterial viruses differ most from animal and plant viruses since they often and perhaps invariably possess an organ of attachment to the host cell wall or, in some cases to the flagella or sex pili. It is this interaction between the receptor and the phage particle which results in the release of the phage nucleic acid into the cell leaving the capsid outside. There is an exception to this in the case of the filamentous phages where the whole virus particle enters the cell.

The organ of attachment varies in size, shape, and complexity from phage to phage. It may consist of a single protein molecule or group of molecules at one vertex of the phage capsid, a small spike of protein in the case of coliphage T3, or a complex structure of contractile tubular elements and fibres as in T2. No comparable structures seem to exist in animal and plant viruses. The tubular contractile structure of the T-even phages possesses a helical symmetry in that its protein subunits, though arranged in a series of stacked discs with their planes at a right angle to the axis of the tail, are held together in such a way that each successive disc is rotated slightly with respect to its neighbours. It is at this level that the structure of phage particles is just beginning to be understood.

Very little information has yet been obtained about the arrangement of the protein subunits in phage capsids principally because, unlike the isometric plant and animal viruses, the subunits are not well revealed in the electron microscope. Only in the case of one phage, ØX174, has the electron microscope revealed sufficient detail of the morphological subunits to make it possible to construct a meaningful model of the particle.

The major part of the information concerning phage particle structure has been obtained by electron microscopy but it is important to compare this with information obtained from other sources such as X-ray diffraction light scattering and ultracentrifugal analysis. There are some examples where the data are not entirely in agreement and it may be that the precise size and shape of the particles of phage, as they exist in the aqueous environment, can only be decided by combining information obtained by the use of all relevant techniques.

The aim of this Chapter is to set out the procedures which have been found useful by a wide range of investigators in the determination of the chemical composition and the physical structure of a representative variety of phage particles. No attempt has been made to review the entire literature on the subject, which would at this time be a very large undertaking and so it may be that some procedures that others consider valuable have been omitted. Nevertheless it is believed that the collection of procedures made in this Chapter will provide a good basis for anyone who is interested in phage methodology to see how the analysis is carried out and for anyone who requires to purify and analyse an unknown phage to select methods suitable for his task.

II. SPECIMEN PREPARATION

This Section deals with the methods which have been used to separate and purify the phage in crude lysates of bacteria in order to obtain specimens suitable for chemical and physical analysis. The preparation of the bacterial lysates has been discussed in Chapter V of this Volume.

A. Quantities required

Before any chemical or physical analysis can be undertaken an adequately pure specimen of the phage must be prepared in sufficient quantity. Most of the methods used depend at some stage on differential or density gradient centrifugation in the high speed centrifuge and so it is advisable to begin with sufficient material to give easily visible pellets or bands in the centrifuge tubes. Losses are inevitable in any scheme of purification and these are usually greater with small samples than with large ones. In general therefore the larger the amount of material that can be processed the easier and more complete is the purification. In the case of radioactively labelled phage where the mass of particles may be very small unlabelled carrier phage may be added.

The following are examples of the amounts of phage which were prepared for certain well-known investigations. Wyatt and Cohen (1953) used 35 g of coliphage T6 to separate and crystallize the pyrimidine base 5-hydroxymethylcytosine which replaces all the cytosine in the nucleic acid of that phage. Sinsheimer (1959) accumulated 20 litres of a lysate containing $2–8 \times 10^{11}$ particles of ØX174 per ml before beginning purification. Steitz (1968) purified 300 mg of phage R17 in order to isolate the "A" protein.

A rough estimate of the weight of phage in a preparation can be made if the size of the particle is known and the PFU/ml by comparison with the following figures. Phage T2 which has a head 1150 Å long and 850 Å across and a tail 1170 Å long and 200 Å wide has a particle weight of 5×10^{-16} g. It will take 2×10^{12} particles to weigh 1 mg. The very small phage R17 is about 250 Å diameter and weighs 8×10^{-18} g so about $1·3 \times 10^{14}$ particles will weigh 1 mg.

B. Types of impurities

Bacteriophage lysates contain, in addition to the phage, substances which were derived from the culture medium during and before the growth of the host cells and material released during the growth and lysis of the bacteria. These materials can be divided into two classes, soluble and particulate.

The soluble impurities can be removed by sedimentation of the phage by centrifugation and discarding the supernatant fluid. Later, when a high degree of purity has been obtained, any traces of soluble material can be removed by dialysis.

The particulate impurities consist of bacterial debris resulting from lysis such as pieces of cell wall and membrane, flagella, pili and ribosomes. There may also be degraded phage particles such as empty capsids, tail components and incomplete particles. The purification of phage is principally a matter of separating the phage from the particulate impurities and, provided their sedimentation properties differ sufficiently, there should be no serious difficulty in purifying phage by some form of centrifugation.

C. Purification methods

1. *Concentration*

As it is not usually practicable to centrifuge more than a few hundreds of mls at the speeds required to sediment phage it is often necessary to concentrate the lysates. This can be done by acid precipitation, salt precipitation, evaporation *in vacuo* or by a two-phase extraction procedure (see p. 276).

Herriott and Barlow (1952) precipitated T2r+ at 2×10^{11} PFU/ml by adjusting the pH to 4·0 with N HCl at 5°C. The precipitate was allowed to settle, the majority of the supernatant fluid was syphoned off and the rest was removed by centrifugation at 2400 *g*. The sediment was resuspended in cold saline and brought to pH 6·5 with M NaHCO₃. A concentration of 30 times and a recovery of 92% were achieved.

Sinsheimer (1959) precipitated ØX174, which had been grown in Fraser and Jerrell's medium (p. 214, Chapter V), with ammonium sulphate 280 g/litres and 0·00 25M EDTA. The precipitate was allowed to settle in the cold for 48 h and the supernatant was syphoned off. The sediment was packed by centrifugation at 30,000 *g* for 30 min and resuspended in borate-EDTA (Na tetraborate, saturated solution at 4°C, pH 9·1, 40 parts, 0·1M EDTA, pH 7·0, 1 part). Further purification of this phage is described on p. 275.

It should be noted that phage which has been aggregated by salt does not always settle to the bottom. The filamentous phage f1 (also fd and ZJ/2) float to the surface when treated with ammonium sulphate (Loeb and Zinder, 1961; Zinder *et al.*, 1963).

Lysates of the T-even phages and T5 can be concentrated ten-fold by evaporation *in vacuo*. Standard ground-joint glass chemical apparatus is used. The vacuum is obtained by a water suction pump and boiling of the lysate is promoted by a capillary air leak. Heat is supplied by a thermostatically controlled water bath. Despite the vigorous boiling there is negligible loss of phage activity.

2. Removal of free DNA

Occasionally lysates are noticeably viscous and cannot be easily purified by centrifugation. The viscosity is most likely to be due to DNA liberated from the bacteria by lysis and can be removed by treatment of the lysate with DNase at 0·1–1 μg/ml at 37°C. It is necessary to ensure that the magnesium concentration is about 1 mM. As an alternative to the use of the added nuclease if the lysate is kept overnight in the cold, the small amount of nuclease liberated from the cells will reduce the viscosity.

3. Fluorinated hydrocarbon treatment

Some workers have found it useful to treat concentrated phage lysates with a fluorinated hydrocarbon such as Arcton or Freon. These compounds are liquids which are immiscible with water and after gentle shaking with a suitably buffered phage suspension cause the protein impurities to denature and collect at the interface where they can be removed. Generally the phage is unaffected. This procedure has been used by Rueckert *et al.* (1962), Strauss and Sinsheimer (1963) and Asbeck *et al.* (1969). Strauss and Sinsheimer used Freon-11 to purify phage MS2 (small, RNA-containing). The precipitate formed after treatment of the lysate with 280 g of ammonium sulphate and 25 ml of 0·1M EDTA, pH 7 per litre was mixed with 70 ml (for 7 litres of lysate) of a buffer containing 0·1M NaCl, 0·05M Tris, pH 7·6 and 0·01M EDTA. Freon-11 ($CFCl_3$, Virginia Chemicals and Smelting Co., West Norfolk, Virginia, U.S.A.) 70 ml, was added and the mixture shaken by hand for 3 min. The emulsion was broken by centrifugation at 12,000 *g* for 10 min and the aqueous layer containing about 60% of the initial phage titre was decanted. The Freon layer was extracted with a further 30 ml of buffer to recover a further 5% of the virus. The phage was further purified by CsCl density gradient centrifugation as described on p. 275.

4. Differential centrifugation

Phage particles can be separated from the crude or concentrated lysate by differential centrifugation. A suitable high speed centrifuge is necessary and the procedure consists of a series of alternating low and high speed runs during which the larger debris is sedimented and discarded while the phage remains in suspension then the phage is sedimented while the impurities smaller than phage are left in suspension and discarded. The phage is resuspended and the process repeated until no further improvement in purity is obtained or required. In order to conduct this operation most expeditiously it is necessary to choose the most suitable speeds for the low and high speed runs and if possible to choose the best centrifuge rotor(s).

The factors governing the sedimentation of particles in the centrifuge are related by the following equations (see also Sykes, this Series, Vol. 5B).

The time required for the total precipitation (T_s) in the centrifuge of particles defined by a sedimentation coefficient (s) is given by

$$T_s = \frac{\log_e R_{max} - \log_e R_{min}}{s\,\omega^2}$$

$$s = \frac{d^2\,(1 - \overline{V}\rho)}{18\,\eta\overline{V}}$$

where R_{max}, R_{min} = radial distance to bottom and top of fluid in centrifuge tube,

$\overline{V}$ = partial specific volume of particle,

d = diameter of solvated particle,

ρ = density of solvent,

η = viscosity of solvent, and

ω = angular velocity of rotation.

Combining these two equations

$$T_s = \frac{18\,\eta\overline{V}\,\log_e R_{max} - \log_e R_{min}}{d^2\,(1 - \overline{V}\rho)\,\omega^2}$$

It can be seen that the precipitation time will be greater if the viscosity of the fluid is high and will be lower for high density particles than for low density ones. The above relationships apply only to spherical particles at infinite dilution and hold only approximately under the conditions which apply in practice. For instance the concentration of the particles affects the "effective" viscosity of the fluid and reduces the rate of sedimentation while the fact that many bacteriophage particles are far from spherical again reduces the rate at which they will be sedimented. The dimensions, particle weights and sedimentation coefficients of a number of phages are given in Table I and it can be seen that there is a fifty-fold variation in s and a hundred-fold variation in the particle weights. It is therefore clear that considerably different times and rotor speeds must be used to spin down different phages.

If an estimate of the size of a phage particle can be made from electron microscopy then by comparison with the details given in Table I an approximate sedimentation coefficient can be found. This can be used to calculate the time in hours required for complete sedimentation by the use of the formula

$$t = \frac{k}{s}$$

where k is a constant applicable to a particular rotor running at its maximum speed.

$$k = \frac{\ln R_{max}/R_{min}\ 10^{13}}{\omega^2\ 3600}$$

A selection of k values for rotors in the Spinco range is given in Table II. If speeds less than the maximum are used then the times should be increased in proportion to the squares of the two speeds.

In practice, phage particles comparable in size to coliphage T2, at 10^{11}/ml can be sedimented with little loss by centrifugation at 20,000 rpm for 20 min in a rotor such as the Spinco Type 30. On the other hand the filamentous phage ZJ/2 at 10^{12}/ml is scarcely sedimented at all at the same speed for 2 h in the same rotor. This phage can be completely sedimented at 45,000 rpm for 1 h in the Spinco Type 50 rotor.

A scheme for the purification of phage by differential centrifugation is detailed below.

(i) The crude or concentrated lysate is spun at a low speed sufficient to sediment much of the larger debris but not the phage. (For a phage like T2 5000 rpm for 15 min in the Spinco Type 30 rotor would be suitable.) The sediment can be discarded or, if it contains a significant amount of phage, it can be resuspended in buffer and centrifuged again. The two supernatants are combined.

At all stages the phage titres of the sediments and supernatants should be determined and the recovery calculated.

(ii) The supernatant fluid is next centrifuged at a sufficiently high speed to sediment the phage while the resulting supernatant is discarded.

(iii) The phage-containing sediment is resuspended in a suitable buffer (see Chapter V, page 200) the volume of which is a fraction, say one tenth, of the original lysate. Resuspension can be achieved by gently pipetting the fluid up and down with a Pasteur pipette and rubber bulb. Often resuspension is made easier if the pellet is allowed to stand for some hours covered with the fluid. Sometimes a useful fractionation of the pellet can be made at this stage if it shows two or more distinct layers. The bottom layer usually consists of impurities and can be left undisturbed while the upper layers can be resuspended separately by carefully controlling the flow of fluid from the pipette. As a result an upper and a lower fraction can be obtained.

(iv) The upper fraction might be found to contain mainly damaged or incomplete phage particles and a small amount of perfect particles. In the lower fraction the main bulk of the whole phage would be

TABLE I[†]

Morphological, ultracentrifugal and other data concerning a variety of bacteriophages derived from a number of sources

Phage	Head nm	Tail nm	S_{20w}	Particle weight MWU	Particle density g/cm³	Nucleic acid type	Nucleic acid %	Nucleic acid density g/cm³	Nucleic acid length nm	Nucleic acid MW	Specific absorption
T2	115 × 85[1]	117 × 18[18]	—	$1\cdot2\times10^{7}$[1]		DNA-2	60	1·695	62	$1\cdot3\times10^{8}$	
T2		Sheath 80[1]	114[1], 107								
T2		Bore 80 × 7[1]	31[1]								
T2		Fibres 130 × 2[1]	13[1]								
T4	90[2]	—	1029 ± 31[2]	$3\cdot0\times10^{8}$[2]		DNA-2	60	1·694[16]	—	—	
T3	55[17]	Very short	430 ± 12	$4\cdot9\times10^{7}$[10]		DNA-2	—	1·704[16]	11·93 ± 0·47[3]	—	—
T5	75[17]	180	469 ± 17	—	1·50	DNA-2	50	1·695[16]	—	$4\cdot5\times10^{7}$	
T7	62 ± 1·8	Very short	487	$3\cdot8\times10^{7}$[11]	1·40	DNA-2	25	1·710	12·2	—	6750[13]
ØX174	25[4]	None	114	$6\cdot2\times10^{6}$[5]		DNA-1		1·725		$1\cdot7\times10^{6}$	
fd, f1	800–870[15]	—	40	$1\text{–}1\cdot6\times10^{7}$	1·29	DNA-1	11·3–12·2	1·716[16]	1·25[6]	$2\cdot1\times10^{6}$	
M13	× 50		—								
λ	54–57	140	—	$6\cdot2\times10^{7}$		DNA-2	51·5[8]	1·702[16]	10·8–17·2[7]	48×10^{3} nucleotide pairs	—
PM2	60[9]	None	230	$1\cdot2\times10^{8}$	1·28	—	—	1·702	—	—	
MS2	260[12]	None	81	$3\cdot6\times10^{6}$	1·46 dilute	RNA-1	31·5	1·63[16]	—	3300 nucleotides	8·03[12]
R17	250	None	79–80	$3\cdot6\pm0\cdot3\times10^{6}$	1·38 conc	RNA-1		1·63[16]	—	—	7·66[14]

† A key to the sources of these statistics is on p. 273.

TABLE I—KEY

1. Brenner *et al.* (1959)
2. Cummings (1964)
3. Lang and Coates (1968)
4. Hall *et al.* (1959)
5. Sinsheimer (1959)
6. Bujard (1970)
7. Inman (1967)
8. Buchwald *et al.* (1970)
9. Espejo and Canalo (1968)
10. Bendet *et al.* (1962)

11. Davison and Freifelder (1962)
12. Strauss and Sinsheimer (1963)
13. Richardson, J. P. (1966)
    (molar extinction-phosphorus)
14. Gesteland and Bodtker (1964)
    (E, 260 nm/mg/ml)
15. Marvin and Hohn (1969)
16. Szybalski (1968)
17. Bradley and Kay (1960)
18. Kellenberger *et al.* (1965).

found. Both fractions would then be centrifuged at high speed, the supernatants discarded and the sediments, which will again show the layers but not in the same proportion, are fractionally resuspended and the corresponding whole phage fractions are combined.

(v) The combined fractions are again subjected to low and high speed centrifugation as described in stages (i) to (iii) and the sedimented phage is fractionally resuspended. This process is repeated until adequate purity is obtained.

At all stages of purification it is advisable to examine the fractions by electron microscopy which will immediately show where the majority of the phage particles are and will indicate if any appreciable damage is being caused to them.

If a pellet of homogeneous appearance can be obtained it is probable that the preparation is as clean as can be made by differential centrifugation but if a still better preparation is needed it will be necessary to use a density gradient centrifugation method. This is discussed on p. 274.

Choice of centrifuge rotors. Centrifuge manufacturers now provide a wide range of rotors for their machines and it has become a matter of importance to choose the most advantageous one for a particular purpose. The critical properties of the rotors are their maximum speed, capacity, acceleration to and deceleration from the operating speed. There is also the time taken to load and unload the tubes.

The time required (t h) to completely sediment particles of sedimentation coefficient (s) in a particular rotor running at maximum speed is given by

$$t = \frac{k}{s}$$

as described on p. 270.

TABLE II

Performance details of Spinco centrifuge rotors

Rotor type	Max rpm	No. of tubes	Capacity (ml)*	k value	Acc. time (min)†
65	65,000	8	108	45	8
60 Ti	60,000	8	308	63	20
50 Ti	50,000	12	162	77	13
50·1	50,000	8	308	94	18
50	50,000	10	100	66	7
42	42,000	6	564	156	22
40	40,000	12	162	120	5
30	30,000	12	462	209	11
21	21,000	10	940	398	15
19	19,000	6	1500	776	22

* Total capacity.

† Time to reach max speed, deceleration time is about the same.

The k values, capacities and accleration times for a range of Spinco rotors are given in Table II.

Once some idea of the size of the particles has been obtained from electron microscopy an approximate s value can be calculated or inferred by comparison with those of other similar sized particles (see Table I) and a suitable rotor speed can be selected. If it is necessary to process large volumes, then by adding the time for sedimentation to the acceleration and deceleration times (approx. equal) and the loading and unloading time, a suitable rotor can be chosen to complete the whole volume in the shortest time.

5. *Density gradient centrifugation* (see also Sykes, this Series, Vol. 5B)

Two basic methods are used in density gradient centrifugation. These are the rate zonal method and the equilibrium method. In the former a concentration gradient of a suitable solute in water is formed by a mechanical device which delivers it directly into the centrifuge tube. The solute is usually sucrose but a variety of other substances can be used. The gradient typically varies from 25% at the bottom to 0% at the top. The material to be centrifuged, suspended in the same buffer, is gently pipetted on to the top of the gradient. The volume of the sample is usually not more than one tenth of the capacity of the tube. The gradient is then centrifuged for a time and at a speed sufficient to cause the material of interest to migrate part way down the tube but never to completely sediment it. Different components of the mixture will travel different distances down the tube depending on their densities, sizes and shapes. The function of the gradient is mainly to prevent the remixing of the separated components by thermal and mechanical disturbances. After centrifugation the contents of the tubes are run out dropwise through a pin hole in the bottom and fractionally collected. Each fraction is then assayed for phage or other material of interest. It is not possible to determine sedimentation coefficients directly by this method but they can be estimated by comparison with the positions of specimens of known s value.

In the equilibrium method a density gradient is prepared in the centrifuge tube so that the density about halfway up the tube corresponds to that of the particles being purified. This can be done by preforming the gradient before the run and layering the sample on top or by loading the tube with a homogeneous mixture of the sample and the dense solution and forming the gradient by centrifugation at high speed. In either case the particles will form bands at the level corresponding to their bouyant density. The most frequently used solutions are composed of caesium salts (chloride or sulphate) and the bouyant density found is that of the caesium salt of the material being examined. This is somewhat greater than that of the sodium salt which is the most likely "natural" form.

A very convenient apparatus for the analysis of all forms of density gradients is the Isco analyser. The contents of the tubes are expressed upwards into a measuring head which determines the u.v. absorption by a column of denser liquid pumped in through a hole in the tube bottom. This fluid can be dense sucrose solution or, in the case of the caesium solutions, mercury can be used.

The following examples show how various authors have used the density gradient method to purify different phages.

Coliphage ØX174. Hall and Sinsheimer (1963) took a partially purified suspension of ØX174 in a solution containing 39 parts of saturated sodium borate and one part of 4% disodium EDTA, added tryptone broth to a final concentration of 10% and solid CsCl (0·625 g/g of solution) to give a density of 1·440 g/ml and centrifuged for 4 days at 25,000 rpm in a Spinco 25·1 rotor. After piercing the tube with a fine pin fractions of 19 drops (approx 0·8 ml) were collected. The phage was recovered in fractions 20–29 and was dialysed against three changes of 500 ml of Tris-formate buffer (pH 7·5).

Coliphage MS2 (RNA-containing). Strauss and Sinsheimer (1963) took partially purified phage suspended in 0·1M NaCl and 0·05M Tris (pH 7·6), added CsCl to give a density of 1·38 ± 0·01 and centrifuged for 24 h at 37,000 rpm at 2°C in the Spinco Type 40 rotor (fixed angle). After deceleration without the brake two bands were visible. The lower one containing the phage was removed with a syringe. After a second run the phage was collected by piercing the tube bottom and dialysed against three changes of $0.1M$ NaCl and $0.01M$ Tris (pH 7·6).

Coliphage T4. Kellenberger *et al.* (1965) purified ^{35}S labelled T4 and its amber mutants by centrifugation through CsCl. The phage was concentrated by centrifugation and then layered on to a discontinuous gradient made by gently pouring 0·5 ml quantities of CsCl solution at densities 1·5, 1·45, 1·4, 1·3, 1·2 and 1·1 on to each other in 5 ml Spinco tubes. After centrifugation for 30 min at 28,000 rpm the phage was found to have collected at a density of 1·45 g/ml and was free of bacterial debris and free methionine ^{35}S. The method using discontinuous gradients is often used when no gradient forming apparatus is available and has the advantage of requiring only short centrifugation times. It suffers from the disadvantage of giving less perfect separation of the different components than the other more time consuming methods.

Algal virus LPP–1. Luftig and Haselkorn (1968) partially purified virus LPP–1 by a two-phase extraction method (see below) then centrifuged the suspension in 2 ml lots through a 3–20% sucrose gradient in 0·01 Tris (pH 7·5) and $0.01M$ Mg^{2+} at 20,000 rpm for 40 min in the Spinco SW25 rotor. An opaque band was formed containing the phage. This was removed and dialysed against Tris-magnesium buffer.

6. *Two-phase extraction method*

Luftig and Haselkorn (1968) grew the blue-green alga virus LPP–1 on its host *Plectonema boryanum* and obtained titres of 5×10^9 to 1×10^{10} PFU/ml. As this was rather low they resorted to the use of a two-phase extraction procedure to avoid differential centrifugation of large volumes of lysate.

First the amount of Carbowax 6000 (polyethylene glycol, PEG) needed to separate the algal debris on a small scale was determined. To 100 ml crude lysate 1 ml of 20% Pharmacia dextran sulphate 500(DS), 2·3 g of NaCl and varying amounts of 30% PEG were added. The mixture was stirred and then kept overnight at 4°C. The top layers were then sampled for absorbancy at 650 nm and infectivity. It appeared that 150 ml of 30% PEG per litre of lysate would precipitate the debris and another 150 ml would remove the virus. On the large scale 40 litres of lysate were treated with 150 ml of 30% PEG, 10 ml of 20% DS and 23 g of NaCl per litre. The mixture was agitated and left to stand overnight. The supernatant fluid was decanted and to it were added 150 ml of 30% PEG and 7 ml of 20% DS per litre of the original lysate. After agitation the solution was again allowed to stand overnight. Most of the supernatant fluid was decanted and the dark green interface cake was removed and centrifuged at

5000 rpm for 5 min. The sediment was taken up in a mixture of 47·5 ml of Tris (0·01M, pH 7·5) containing 0·01M Mg^{2+}, 2·5 ml of 20% DS and 7·5 ml of 3M KCl, stirred and stored overnight at 4°C. After centrifugation at 5000 rpm for 5 min a blue supernatant fluid was obtained which contained 65% of the total infectivity of the lysate. The phage was separated from the contaminating blue protein by sucrose density gradient centrifugation.

D. Tests of purity

Various criteria can be used in assessing the purity of a phage specimen. Fortunately most phages retain their infectivity very well during complex purification procedures and it is therefore possible to relate the number of plaque forming units (PFU) per ml (see this Volume, Chapter V) to either DNA or RNA as determined by one of the standard procedures (see p. 278 et seq.) or to the optical density at 260 nm which is also largely a measure of the nucleic acid. Optical density measurements have the advantage of taking little time to make and so viral activity is often quoted against optical density. It is also useful to determine the optical density at 280 nm as well as at 260 nm as the former wavelength is that of protein (due to its content of tryosine and tryptophan); the higher the 260/280 ratio the lower the amount of protein impurity.

Frequent use of the electron microscope should be made during the purification of phage as this will reveal whether the procedures are causing damage to the particles. Any appreciable amount of bacterial or other debris will also be obvious. It would however be unwise to use the appearance of the phage in the electron microscope as the sole criterion of purity.

Important information on the homogeneity of phage preparations can be obtained by the use of the analytical ultracentrifuge. The use of this instrument has been described in several publications (e.g. Svedberg, T. and Pedersen, K. O. (1940); Schachman, H. K. (1959)).

III. CHEMICAL ANALYSIS

The main components of all phages so far examined are protein and nucleic acid and in the vast majority of phages this nucleic acid is DNA. In only one morphological type, the small isometric phages, the nucleic acid is RNA. No phage has been found with both types of nucleic acid. The sugar-phosphate chains in phage nucleic acids do not differ chemically from their counterparts in the nucleic acids of higher forms of life but amongst the bases attached to the sugars some of those found are peculiar to phage. The DNA of the T-even phages contains hydroxymethyl-cytosine (HMC) instead of cytosine while in certain subtilis phages (PBS1 and PBS2) the thymine is substituted by uracil, which is normally found only in RNA, or by hydroxymethyl uracil (SP8). Another peculiarity of phage DNA is also found in the T-even phages where the HMC may be glucosylated. The methylated base 6-methylamino purine has been found in T2, T4 and fd but not in T6 or R17 (Gefter *et al.*, 1966; Hattmann, 1970; Arber and Linn, 1969).

A further complication is that the DNA may be double-stranded and linear or single-stranded and circular. Phage RNA is always single-stranded but there seems no reason why phages with double-stranded RNA should not exist analogous to rheovirus in animals and wound tumour virus in plants.

When the proteins of phage are examined it soon becomes clear that each variety of phage contains more than one species of protein. The small RNA-containing phages are known to contain two proteins but the total number comprising the structure of the much more complex T-even phages is still not known. The identifiable structural components of these phages as seen in the electron microscope are the capsid, the tail sheath, the tail core, the baseplate, the collar and the fibres. Some of these may well consist of more than one protein so the total including possible internal proteins is likely to be in excess of ten.

When the phage proteins are analysed they are found to consist of the well-known set of amino-acids which are found in higher forms of life. No unusual amino-acids have been found though in several well-studied phage proteins certain ones are totally absent.

In addition to the main components several minor ones have been found. These are lipids, polypeptides, polyamines, inorganic ions and some mononucleotides.

This Section will deal with the methods used for analysis of the nucleic acids, proteins and minor components of the bacteriophages.

A. Nucleic acids

Phage nucleic acids, in common with all other nucleic acids, can be analysed for their content of ribose or deoxyribose, phosphate, and purine or pyrimidine bases. The bases may be determined as nucleotides or free bases and from the amounts found the base ratios can be calculated. If the adenine to thymine and the guanine to cytosine ratio are unity it is a good indication that the nucleic acid is double-stranded (further procedures for the determination of the strandedness of nucleic acids are given on page 294).

Total nucleic acid can be determined either spectrophotometrically or by measurement of the ribose or deoxyribose content followed by calculation based on the proportion of the sugar in a standard specimen of the phage nucleic acid. In the case of those phage nucleic acids which contain the bases hydroxymethylcytosine or hydroxymethyluracil, which do not occur elsewhere, determination of the base gives a direct measurement of the nucleic acid.

The percentage of guanine plus cytosine is related to the "melting temperature, T_m" and to the buoyant density and measurements of these parameters can be used to give a rapid measurement of the $\%G + C$ (Schildkraut et al., 1962).

Methods recently developed are enabling the sequence of the nucleotides in MS2 RNA to be determined. These methods will be outlined but for the complete procedure the reader will be referred elsewhere.

1. Total nucleic acid

The content of nucleic acid in a specimen of phage can be calculated from the phosphorus content or the sugar content (deoxyribose or ribose). The sugar and the phosphate are bound to exist in equimolar amounts and the actual ratios found will be a partial check on the accuracy of the estimations. If it is assumed that the four purine and pyrimidine bases are present in equimolar amounts the weight of nucleic acid can then be calculated. Frequently however the ratios of the bases depart from unity and, if the actual base ratios are known, a correction can be made.

A rapid estimation of the amount of nucleic acid in a phage preparation can be made from optical density measurements in the ultraviolet region. The bases in nucleic acid absorb strongly in the region of 260 nm and all nucleic acids show a peak at about that wavelength. Whole phage suspensions also show a peak but the position of the absorption maximum will be affected by the phage protein especially if this comprises a major part of the phage particles. For example the filamentous phage f1 which has only 11% DNA shows a maximum at 270 nm. It was found by Zinder et al. (1963) that a specimen of purified phage f1 containing 4·60 optical density units/ml at 260 nm contained 0·156 mg of DNA/ml. Phage MS2, which contains 31·5% of RNA, gave an optical density of 8·03 at 260 nm at a concentration of 1 mg/ml.

2. Sugar and phosphate

The most frequently used method for the estimation of deoxyribose is that of Burton (1956) in which a blue colour is developed by a diphenylamine-sulphuric acid reagent in the presence of acetaldehyde.

Samples of the specimen to be analysed containing at least 0·15 μg atom of DNA-P with not less than 0·01 μg atom of DNA-P/ml were acidified with 2·5N or 12N $HClO_4$ to a final 0·25N and centrifuged after chilling for 30 min. The precipitate was broken up with a glass rod and stirred with

0·5 ml 0·5N HClO$_4$. A further 3·5 ml of 0·5M HClO$_4$ was added and the suspension was heated at 70°C for 15 min with occasional stirring. The supernatant containing the extracted DNA was poured off and the precipitate was re-extracted in the same way with a further 3 ml of HClO$_4$. After measuring the volume of the combined extracts samples of 1 ml (or 2 ml as convenient) were mixed with 2 vol of the diphenylamine reagent and stood at 30°C for 16–20 h. The OD at 260 nm was measured against a blank containing 0·5N HClO$_4$. Tubes containing standards of purified DNA or deoxyribose were included. The diphenylamine reagent is prepared by dissolving 1·5 g of steam-distilled diphenylamine in 100 ml of redistilled acetic acid and adding 1·5 ml of conc. H$_2$SO$_4$. This is stored in the dark and on the day it is to be used 0·10 ml of aqueous acetaldehyde (16 mg/ml) is added for each 20 ml of reagent required. Distillation of the reagents is not necessary if they give a sufficiently low blank reading.

Ribose is usually estimated by the orcinol reaction as described for example by Ogur and Rosen (1950) or by Dische (1953). To 1·5 ml of the unknown is added 3·0 ml of an acid reagent prepared by adding 0·5 ml of a 10% FeCl$_3$.6H$_2$O to 100 ml of conc. HCl. This is followed by 0·2 ml of a freshly prepared 6% solution of orcinol in 95% ethanol. The mixture is heated in a boiling water bath for 20 min and its optical density read at 665 nm. It should be noted that other sugars give colours with this reagent. Glucose can be allowed for by taking the difference between the readings at 670 nm and 580 nm. The presence of even small amounts of fructose or tetrose renders the determination of pentose by the orcinol method impossible.

Glucose is found in some phages. Methods for determining it are described on p. 283.

Phosphate can be estimated by one of the several methods using molybdate. The method of Fisk and SubbaRow (1925) estimates inorganic and very labile phosphate but has the convenience of simplicity. The method of Berenblum and Chain (1938) in which the phosphomolybdate complex is extracted into isobutanol avoids interference by other colour producing substances. For total phosphate the sample is treated with 1 ml of 5N H$_2$SO$_4$ and evaporated in a test-tube over a flame. The contents become brown. After cooling a drop of 2N nitric acid is added and heating continued until white fumes appear. Nitric acid treatment is repeated until the liquid becomes colourless. After cooling 1 ml of water is added and the tube placed in a boiling water bath for 5 min. After cooling again 1 ml of 2·5% ammonium molybdate in water is added and the solution mixed. 0·1 ml of reducing agent is then added and the volume made up to 10 ml. The optical density at 660 nm is read after 10 min. The reducing agent is made up weekly and consists of an intimate mixture of 0·2 g of 1-amino-2-naphthol-

4-sulphonic acid, 1·2 g Na bisulphite and 1·2 g of Na sulphite of which 0·25 g is dissolved in 10 ml of water. A standard of KH_2PO_4 at 1μmole/ml is used.

3. *The bases of DNA*

The whole phage or the isolated DNA may be subjected to acid hydrolysis to release the bases. Perchloric acid (Wyatt, 1952), hydrochloric acid (Hershey *et al.*, 1953) and formic acid (Wyatt and Cohen, 1952, 1953) have been used. Not more than 15 μlitre of perchloric acid (70%) should be used per mg of DNA unless much protein is present when it should be increased. The hydrolysis mixture must be kept at 100°C for 1 h in an open tube. Perchloric acid cannot be used if hydroxymethylcytosine is present as this base is largely destroyed. When formic acid is used 0·5 ml of 88% should be allowed for 700 μg of DNA and the temperature should be maintained at 175°C for 30 min. Hydrolysis with HCl (6N) should be performed at 100°C for 3 h. With HCl and formic acid the hydrolysis mixture should be sealed in a Pyrex glass tube and in order to minimize the loss of bases the volume of air in the tube should be as small as possible or it should be replaced by CO_2. After hydrolysis the tube should be opened with care as a pressure is sometimes developed. If the tube is drawn down to a capillary before sealing this can be broken at a diamond scratch in order to release the pressure. To open the Pyrex tube a deep diamond scratch should be made and touched with a small very hot (oxygen flame) Pyrex rod.

The hydrolysate is then evaporated to dryness *in vacuo*, dissolved in a little dilute HCl and subjected to chromatography. Many solvent mixtures have been described for the separation of the purine and pyrimidine bases of nucleic acids (see Fink and Adams, 1966) but a very suitable one for paper chromatography is the isopropanol-HCl mixture of Wyatt (1951) (isopropanol, 65 ml +HCl, 0·2 g mole + water to 100 ml). This does not resolve cytosine and HMC but these can be separated in isopropanol-NH_3.

Hattmann (1970) hydrolysed T-even phage DNA in N HCl at 95°C for 60 min, removed the HCl at 37°C, dissolved the residue in 10% acetic acid and 10% isopropanol and chromatographed it on Whatman No. 1 paper in butanol : water, 86 : 14 in ammonia vapour. 6-methyl amino purine was found in T2 and T4 but not in T6. This compound was first found (0·46 mole/100 moles of adenine) by Dunn and Smith (1958).

4. *The nucleotides of DNA*

The four nucleotides present in the DNA of coliphage T4 have been prepared by enzymic digestion of the nucleic acid and separated by column chromatography (Kutter and Wiberg, 1969). The phage (actually amber mutant) was purified by low and high speed differential centrifugation and was resuspended in 0·1M NaCl and 0·01M Tris, pH 7·5 at 10^{12} particles per ml. The DNA was extracted by the method of Mandell and Hershey (1960) which is described on p. 290. After concentration and dialysis in the cold against 0·01M Tris, pH 7·5 (the optical density at 260 nm of the product was 19–25) the DNA was hydrolysed by the method of Lehman and Pratt (1960). The reaction mixture consisted of 130 μmoles of Tris buffer pH 7·5, 13 μmoles of MgCl$_2$, 1·3 mg of bovine plasma albumin, 0·4 μg of pancreatic DNase and the DNA (70 μmoles of phosphorus) in a volume of 13 ml. After incubation for 30 min at 37°C the mixture was heated for 10 min at 80°C. The pH was then adjusted to about 9 with N KOH and 1 mmole of glycine buffer, pH 9·2; 100 μmoles of MgCl$_2$ and 2000 units of *Escherichia coli* phosphodiesterase (DEAE fraction, Lehman, 1960) were added. The final volume was 16 ml and the mixture was incubated at 37°C for 6 h. The reaction mixture was heated at 100°C for 5 min and the precipitated protein was removed by centrifugation. After adjustment of the pH to 9·5 by the addition of N NaOH the digest was applied to a column, $20 \times 0·8$ cm packed with Dowex 1×8 formate, 200–400 mesh together with markers of dCMP, dTMP, dUMP, dGMP and dHMP (see p. 263). After washing the column with water the nucleotides were eluted with a steep gradient of ammonium formate pH 4·3, at 0·025M, 0·05M, 0·15M and 0·30M, 400 ml of each. All the nucleotides were separated from one another except dTMP and dUMP which overlapped. The eluate containing these was adjusted to pH 10 with NH$_4$OH, applied to a Dowex formate column and the dTMP and dUMP were separated by elution with 0·175M NH$_4$HCO$_3$. The nucleotides were identified by their spectra and assayed for ^{32}P.

The dHMP nucleotides of the T-even phages are characteristically glucosylated at the 5-hydroxymethyl group. In T4 all the HMC is singly glucosylated, in T2 70% is mono-glucosylated, 24% is non-glucosylated and 6% is di-glucosylated and in T6, 34% is mono-glucosylated, 72% di-glucosylated and 25% is non-glucosylated.

The various glucosylated HMC nucleotides can be separated by the chromatographic procedure described above and the nature of the glycosidic links between the 5-hydroxymethyl group and the sugar to which it is attached has been investigated by the use of α and β glucosidases. In the case of the monoglucosylated dHMP from T2 no action of either enzyme took place until the nucleotide had been dephosphorylated by the action of human semen monoesterase when the glucose could be quantitatively released by the α glucosidase but not the β enzyme.

The T4 DNA contains two distinct mono-glucosylated HMC nucleotides of which one (67%) is bound in an α glycosidic linkage while in the other the linkage is in the β configuration.

The diglucosyl unit of diglucosyl dHMP from T6 is a disaccharide in which the two glucose residues are linked to each other in a β linkage and to the hydroxy methyl group by an α linkage. The position of the di-saccharide linkage was not established.

Lehman and Pratt (1960) determined specifically the glucose released after glucosidase treatment by the coupled hexokinase–Zwischenferment assay of Kornberg (1950). Glucose was also determined after hydrolysis of the nucleotides with N HCl at 100°C for 30 min by the anthrone method (Morris, 1948). The reagent consists of anthrone (2 g) dissolved in 95% H_2SO_4 (1 litre). The specimen, 4 or 5 ml, is mixed with 8–10 ml of the reagent and allowed to stand for 10 min. The mixture becomes hot and a colour is developed. This is read at 620 nm against a blank and glucose standards. The range is 8–200 μg glucose.

Hattmann and Fukasawa (1963) released glucose from phage DNA by hydrolysis with N HCl at 105°C for 2 h in a sealed tube.

5. The bases and nucleotides of RNA

It is not possible to hydrolyse RNA to the free bases without destroying a large proportion of them. It is possible to break down RNA to the free purines and the pyrimidine nucleotides by treatment with 1N HCl at 100°C for 1 h (Smith and Markham, 1950) or to the nucleotides by alkaline hydrolysis in 0·3N KOH at 37°C for 18 h (Marrian et al., 1951; Strauss and Sinsheimer, 1963).

The acid hydrolysate was separated by descending paper chromatography in the MeOH-EtOH-HCl-water (50 : 25 : 6 : 19) solvent of Kirby (1955). The mixture of nucleotides from the alkaline hydrolysis was passed through a Dowex 50W–XI column in the ammonium form to remove potassium and the effluent was lyophilized. After dissolving in 0·04M citrate, pH 3·5, the nucleotides were separated by paper electrophoresis in the same buffer at 40 V/cm. The spots were eluted into 0·01N HCl and the bases and nucleo-tides were determined spectrophotometrically using the extinction coeffi-cients given by Beavan, Holiday and Johnson (1955).

6. The nucleotide sequences of phage RNA

The small RNA-containing phages (R17, MS2, Qβ) are of special signi-ficance at the present time because they are providing the means whereby the nucleotide sequence in messenger RNA can be related to the amino-acid sequence in the protein for which it codes. The RNA of these phages is not only the genome of the phage but it acts also as the messenger which directs the synthesis of three virus specific proteins. The number of proteins in the phage particles is two, the main coat protein (B protein) and the maturation protein (A protein). One further protein is required, an enzyme to replicate the RNA, but this is not incorporated into the complete phage particle. From genetic complementation studies the phage RNA contains three cistrons but it appears that there are regions of nucleotide sequences outside the cistrons (see e.g. Nichols, 1970) whose functions are not as yet clear.

The technique for determining RNA nucleotide sequences is too complex to discuss fully in this Chapter but, in essentials, it consists of a series of partial hydrolyses and separations of the products until small nucleotides whose sequence can be recognized are reached. The procedure used by Nichols (1970) begins with a partial hydrolysis of the phage RNA by ribonuclease T_1 under special conditions of enzyme to substrate ratio, ionic composition of the buffer, time and temperature. The products of the hydrolysis were fractionated by polyacrylamide gel electrophoresis which revealed some 40 bands. One of these was isolated and after further hydrolysis with ribonuclease yielded a number of oligonucleotides which were separated by two-dimensional chromatography. These were subjected to sequence analysis by the methods developed by Sanger (see Adams *et al.*, 1969) by which short fragments two to seven nucleotides long whose sequences are known can be isolated. From these sequences longer sequences can be determined and, by comparison with the already known amino-acid sequences of the phage coat protein and the synthetase protein, the triplet code for which is also known, the partial sequence of the nucleotides, the order of the cistrons in the genome and the sequences within the extracistronic regions have been established.

B. Proteins

The amino-acid compositions of several phages have been determined but with the realization that most phages consist of several different proteins it has become clear that the gross amino-acid composition of whole phage particles is not very meaningful. Work is now in progress to determine the amino-acid composition and sequence of isolated purified phage components.

The small phages either of the isometric RNA group of the filamentous DNA-containing group have been intensively studied and the amino-acid sequences of their major proteins have been determined.

The filamentous phage fd has a coat consisting of 2900 identical protein subunits each of which has a molecular weight of 5169 and contains only 49 amino-acid residues.

The procedure used to determine the amino-acid sequence is too complex to give in detail but it depends on the digestion of the coat protein into polypeptides by the action of various enzymes such as trypsin, pepsin and subtilysin A and by hydrochloric acid. The polypeptides are separated by chromatography and their amino-acid compositions determined after further hydrolysis. The full details and a large number of references are given by Asbeck *et al.* (1969).

Only 15 different amino-acids are represented in the coat protein of fd. Cysteine, arginine and histidine are not present though it is clear that they are present in the minor A protein of the filamentous phage (Rossomando and Zinder, 1968). The sequence from the N-terminal end is as follows; Acidic-hydrophilic part, (1) Ala-Glu-Gly-Asp-(5)-Asp-Pro-Ala-Lys-Ala-(10)Ala-Phe-Asp-Ser-Leu-(15)Glu-Ala-Ser-Ala-Thr-(20)Glu- Neutral hydrophobic part, Tyr-Ile-Gly-Tyr-(25)Ala-Trp-Met-Val-Val-(30)Val-Ile-Val-Gly-Ala-(35)Thr-Ile- Basic hydrophilic part, Lys-(40)Leu-Phe-Lys-Lys-Phe-(45)Thr-Ser-Lys-Ala-(49)Ser.

In the filamentous phage ZJ/2 there is one less threonine residue and one more alanine residue but the positions of these residues is not known.

C. Lipids

Until recently no phage was known to possess any lipid component. Small amounts of lipid could be found in most preparations but these were due to impurities derived from the lysates.

Espejo and Canalo (1968) isolated from sea water a phage active on an unidentified pseudomonad. The particle is 60 nm across, is isometric in shape and possesses spikes at its apices. Unlike other phages, this phage is inactivated by shaking with chloroform or ether. This behaviour, which is similar to that of some animal viruses which have a membrane around the nucleocapsid, suggested that there might be a lipid component.

It was possible to extract 10·5% of the dry weight of the virus into chloroform-methanol and after analysis on thin layer chromatograms this was shown to consist of several phospholipids, of which phosphatidylethanol amine was the main component. The DNA accounted for only 80% of the phosphorus content of the phage.

The virus density was 1·28 g/cm³ and the sedimentation coefficient was 230 in M NaCl. The DNA was double-stranded and its G + C content was 43% as determined from its melting temperature of 87·5 and its buoyant density of 1·702.

D. Acid soluble components of phage

When certain phage preparations are extracted with trichloroacetic acid some material remains in solution. Amongst the materials extracted there have been found small peptides, polyamines and inorganic cations.

Hershey (1957) reported that a peptide could be obtained from phage T2H. Later, Eddleman and Champe (1966) observed that three acid-soluble polypeptides are synthesized in cells of *E. coli* B infected with phage T4D and that two of these become incorporated into mature phage particles. They appear to correspond to the acid soluble peptide fraction described by Hershey. The three polypeptides are not formed in *E. coli* B infected with amber mutants of T4 which are deficient in phage head formation but are formed by mutants which are blocked in other assembly functions. Eddleman and Champe suggest that the polypeptides are associated with the formation of the phage head.

The peptides were obtained from cells 30 min after infection by adding 0·5 ml of cold 10% TCA to the cells which had been pelleted at 11,000 g for 5 min and resuspended in 0·5 ml water. After standing for 30 min at 4°C the precipitate was removed by centrifugation and the supernatant was fractionated by column chromatography. It was also shown that the peptides could be extracted from phage by the same procedure and that they could be released by osmotic shock (rapid dilution of the phage made up in 4M NaCl into water) and so were not produced by the action of the TCA.

Ames, Dubin and Rosenthal (1958) showed that phages T2 and T4 contain the polyamines putrescine and spermidine and that these cations were present in sufficient amount to neutralize about half of the viral DNA. Further investigation (Ames and Dubin, 1960) showed that several other viruses did not contain these polyamines (*E. coli* phages T3, T5 and P22; tobacco mosaic virus, tomato bushy stunt virus and poliomyelitis virus) and that this absence was related to the permeability of the virus particles to cations. This became evident when it was found that the osmotic shock resistant mutant $T4_0$ had only a trace of polyamine after it had been washed in magnesium-containing buffer. The virus remained infective when the polyamines normally present in it were replaced by magnesium indicating that they are not essential for viral activity. It was concluded that the role of the polyamines is that of a non-specific cation involved in the neutralization and stabilization of the DNA.

The polyamines can be extracted from the phage by treatment with 0·3N TCA at 25°C for 10 min. After removal of the protein and nucleic acid by centrifugation the supernatant was shaken with ether to remove the TCA and analysed for polyamines on a Dowex 50 column or by paper chromatography. The solvents used for the latter were n-butanol-acetic acid-pyridine-water, 4 : 1 : 1 : 2 or n-propanol-HCl-water, 3 : 1 : 1 or n-propanol-triethylamine-water, 85 : 3 : 15. The positions of the spots were detected with ninhydrin.

The following cations were found in phage T4, expressed as meq/eq

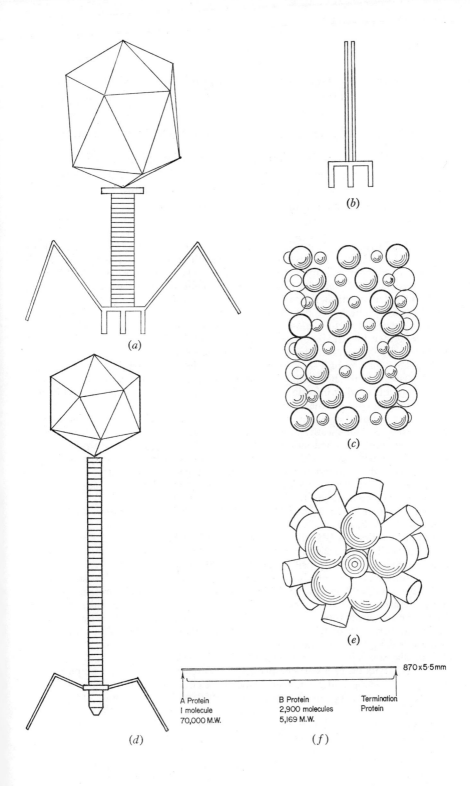

(a)

(b)

(c)

(d)

(e)

870 x 5·5mm

A Protein
I molecule
70,000 M.W.

B Protein
2,900 molecules
5,169 M.W.

Termination
Protein

(f)

of phosphorus, putrescine $^{2+}$, 250; spermidine $^{3+}$, 75; Ca^{2+}, < 2; Mg^{2+}, 340; Na^+, 90; K^+, 60.

IV. MACROMOLECULAR COMPONENTS OF PHAGE

In Section III the isolation and determination of the small molecules of which phage particles are composed was discussed. In the present Section methods for isolating and studying the structure and function of the macromolecular components will be examined.

FIG. 1a. Particle of T-even *E. coliphage* (T2, 4, 6). The head is a prolate icosahedron 115 × 85 nm. The contractile tail-sheath (shown extended) 95 × 18 nm, consists of protein subunits arranged as 24 stacked annuli each containing six large and six small subunits (see 1c). Between the tail and the head is a collar. Within the tail-sheath is the tail core (1b) itself composed of subunits arranged in the form of a tube 95 × 8 nm. The core is terminated by a hexagonal base plate bearing six spikes and six tail fibres, 140 × 2 nm. The fibres which are kinked half-way along their length are normally furled around the sheath but become extended under conditions necessary for adsorption to the host bacteria.

FIG. 1b. Tail core of T-even phage showing axial hole through which the phage DNA passes into the host cell. The core is attached to the base plate which carries six tail spikes. During infection the core is driven through the cell wall while the base plate and spikes remain on the surface.

FIG. 1c. Diagram showing one third of the extended tail-sheath of the T-even phage particle. The sheath is a stacked annular disc structure. Each disc consists of six large and six small subunits alternating and is slightly rotated relative to each neighbouring disc with the result that the sheath shows a coarse helical appearance. On contraction each small subunit pairs with a large one and all undergo a rearrangement which results in a new helical structure in which the diameter has increased and the length diminished by half.

Diagrams in Figs 1a, b, c are based on the work of Kellenberger *et al.* (1965) and Moody (1965, 1967b).

FIG. 1d. Coliphage T5. This has a regular icosahedral head 75 nm across, a non-contractile tail consisting of about 40 annular discs and near the tip a base-plate bearing a number, possibly 4, of kinked fibres.

FIG. 1e. A diagram showing the arrangement of the morphological subunits in coliphage ØX174. The spheres (20 in all) represent groups of six protein subunits. They are arranged in the shape of an icosahedron from which the apical subunits have been removed. Into the holes are fitted short spikes represented by cylinders, 12 in number, each of which probably has five-fold symmetry. The icosahedron is thereby completed and stabilized.

This diagram is based on data given by Edgell *et al.* (1969).

FIG. 1f. Diagram of a particle of filamentous phage such as fd. The particle is about 870 nm long and 5·5 nm in diameter. A circle of single-stranded DNA is enclosed in a protein capsid consisting of 2900 molecules of the "B" protein, MW 5169. One end of the particle is terminated by a single molecule of "A" protein of MW 70,000. There may be a third protein of low MW in the particle, possibly terminating the other end.

The macromolecular constituents of phage are its nucleic acid, which composes the genome and the protein aggregates which compose the capsid which together with certain appendages surrounds, protects and may act to secure the injection of the genome into the susceptible host cell. In all cases so far examined the phage genome consists of one molecule of DNA or RNA but the capsid and its appendages are composed of many thousands of protein molecules grouped together to form the structural and functional parts of the phage particle. Diagrams showing idealized phage particles are shown in Fig. 1.

All methods of disaggregating and separating the macromolecular components of phage are likely to denature them. The ideal procedure would cause no damage but in practice some denaturation has to be accepted. It has been found however that both the nucleic acids and the protein components, if properly prepared, still show some biological activity and this can be taken to show that they have not been seriously damaged.

Under suitable conditions it is possible to show that isolated RNA and DNA possess biological activity. This is done by some form of assay using protoplasts (see this Volume, Chapter V) into which the nucleic acid can enter and which can support its replication. Only a small fraction of the initial phage titre can be recovered in the free nucleic acid. The DNA from the larger phages such as the *E. coli* T-evens, has not yet been obtained in a form which can infect protoplasts and give rise directly to progeny phage. Failure to show a high infectivity need not necessarily mean that the nucleic acid has been damaged as the protoplast assay itself may be very inefficient.

In addition to examining the biological activity of the isolated nucleic acid it is possible to study the integrity of the molecule by determining its topology by electron microscopy, ultracentrifugation and light scattering studies. All these methods point to there being only one piece of nucleic acid in each phage particle but, depending on the phage, it can be double-stranded linear (as in the T-evens, T5, T3) or single-stranded and circular as in ØX174 and the filamentous phages. The RNA in the small isometric phages MS2, R17, etc., is single-stranded linear.

The isolation of the intact genome from any phage involves the removal of the protein capsid without causing any breaks in the nucleic acid strand. The principal causes of breakage are mechanical shear and attack by nucleases. Methods for avoiding these will be discussed.

It appears that the larger and more complex a phage particle is the more numerous are the protein species from which it is constructed. Methods have been developed to isolate the protein components from phage particles and to study their structure and their physical and chemical properties. As with the nucleic acids some biological activity can be demonstrated in the isolated phage components. This takes the form of spontaneous reassembly into recognizable substructures or even into whole infective phage. Some aspects of the reassembly of phage components is given in this Volume, Chapter V, and this is a good indication that the components have been isolated without damage.

A. Phage deoxyribonucleic acid

1. *Precautions to avoid breakage of nucleic acid strands*

To avoid damage by nucleases Richardson (1966) recommends (1) that sterile distilled water, reagents glassware and techniques be used, (2) that all dialysis tubing be boiled in 10% Na bicarbonate, washed in sterile water, stored in 50% ethanol and washed in sterile water before use and that (3) sterile surgical gloves be used when dialysis tubing is being handled.

Roberts and Steitz (1967) cleaned dialysis tubing by boiling in 2% Na_2CO_3, distilled water, 0·002M EDTA and water again.

The breakage of nucleic acid strands by shear is particularly likely with the very long molecules which are obtained from the large phages, like the T-evens. This has been studied by Hershey and Burgi (1960, 1962). Richardson (1966) avoided shear breakage by using pipettes with a wide bore of 0·4 cm. In general all procedures should be carried out with the minimum of force. Shaking should be avoided and mixing done by gentle rocking. Liquids should be poured instead of being pipetted wherever possible.

2. *Isolation of intact molecules*

The most frequently used procedure for preparing phage nucleic acid DNA and RNA, is the phenol method of Mandell and Hershey (1960). This is based on the original observations of Gierer and Schramm (1956) and Kirby (1955).

Coliphages T2 and T4 were concentrated and purified by filtration through Celite and differential centrifugation. Acid precipitation was not used to concentrate the phage as it caused some denaturation of the DNA. The phage was resuspended in 0·1M NaCl and 0·1M phosphate buffer (pH 7·1) at a concentration of 2×10^{12} phage particles/ml, chilled and shaken for 2 min with an equal volume of recently distilled, water saturated phenol. The shaking was performed mechanically on a machine which gave 240 excursions of 9·2 cm amplitude per min. It was important that the phage concentration be kept high because then breakage of the DNA strands was negligible. At lower concentrations it was rapid.

After centrifugation to separate the layers the lower one was removed by pipette and discarded. It was usually unnecessary to repeat the phenol treatment. The upper layer which contained almost all the DNA of the phage was freed from phenol by manually shaking with three to five changes of ethyl ether which had been purified by distillation over ferrous sulphate and stored in the cold with water and a trace of ethanol added. The ether was removed from the solution by bubbling air through it. The DNA content of the solution was 0·4 mg/ml and contained 1% of protein which could not be reduced below 0·1% by repeated phenol treatment.

At this concentration it was possible to transfer the DNA without breakage of the strands by pipette but at lower concentrations the solution had to be poured to avoid shear. The DNA was fractionated on columns packed with kieselguhr coated with methylated albumin (MAK) and it was shown that the nucleic acid which had been damaged by shear was retained less strongly than that which had been prepared with special precautions to avoid shear.

Richardson (1966) used the phenol method to isolate the DNA from coliphage T7. The phage at 1–1·5 mg/ml which had been prepared by the procedure of Davison and Freifelder (1962), was dialysed overnight against 0·01M potassium phosphate buffer (pH 7·0) containing 0·001M $MgCl_2$. It was then mixed with an equal volume of water-saturated redistilled phenol that had been neutralized with KOH just before use. After rocking gently for 10 min the mixture was centrifuged at 10,000 g for 10 min and the upper layer was carefully removed with a wide bore pipette (0·4 cm) to avoid shearing the DNA. This layer was treated with half a volume of phenol and dialysed extensively against several changes of 0·01M Tris buffer (pH 7·9) containing 0·5mM EDTA. The DNA was stored at 2°C. Electron micrographs of this DNA were obtained by Hall and Slayter (1966).

Marvin and Schaller (1966) found it necessary to use hot phenol to dissociate filamentous phage DNA from its protein. The phage (fd) was purified by differential centrifugation after treatment with DNase and RNase in the presence of 0·01M $MgCl_2$. It was resuspended in 0·08M $Na_2B_4O_7$ buffer (pH 9·4), heated at 60°C and mixed with an equal volume of phenol saturated at room temperature with the same borate buffer, also heated to 60°C. After shaking for 30 sec the mixture was centrifuged for 10–15 min at 1000 g at room temperature. The top aqueous layer was pipetted off and treated three successive times with half a volume of phenol-saturated buffer at room temperature. The phenol phases of the four extractions were serially re-extracted with half a volume of borate buffer and all aqueous extracts were combined. The phenol was removed by shaking with 3–4 volumes of peroxide-free ether, pipetting off the ether layer together with the cloudy middle layer and re-extracting with ether four or five times. The ether was removed by blowing nitrogen over the surface of the solution which was finally dialysed against 100–200 volumes of a solution containing 0·05M NaCl, 0·005M MgCl$_2$ and 0·002M Tris (pH 7·5). The nucleic acid prepared in this way was active in a proto-plast assay and was used in studies on the topology of the molecule (see p. 294).

The DNA from filamentous phage particles has also been isolated by the use of alkali. Day (1969) dissociated phage fd by treatment with 0·1N NaOH for 10 min at 20°C followed by neutralization and banding in a CsCl gradient of initial density 1·7 g/ml for 14 h at 45,000 rpm in a Spinco SW50 rotor. The DNA was thoroughly dialysed against 10^{-3}M EDTA. It was infective in a protoplast assay and had the physical properties described on p. 309.

Rossomando and Zinder (1968) also used alkali to dissociate filamentous phage. They diluted a concentrated suspension of phage f1 into an alkaline solution at pH 13. The solution was prepared as needed by dilution of a saturated NaOH solution with 0·1M NaCl and the pH was measured with an electrode specially made to cope with the high pH. After 1 h at room temperature the solution was neutralized with 1·0M Na$_2$HPO$_4$. A non-specific aggregation of DNA and protein took place but these components were separated by adding CsCl to a density of 1·3 g/ml and centrifuging at 100,000 g for 18 h. The protein banded at a density of 1·27 g/ml and the DNA which had a density of 1·73 g/ml was found pelleted at the bottom of the tube.

The DNA had a 260/230 nm ratio of 2·1 in agreement with that found by Marvin and Schaller (1966) for DNA prepared by phenol extraction.

3. *Determination of length of DNA strands by electron microscopy*

The lengths of individual molecules of DNA can be determined in the electron microscope by the method of Kleinschmidt *et al.* (1962) in which the DNA is caused to spread out in a monolayer of protein (cytochrome *c* is most frequently used) on the surface of a solution of a volatile salt such as ammonium acetate known as the hypophase. The method works best with double-stranded DNA but by the use of such agents as formaldehyde and alkali single-stranded nucleic acids can be examined (see Bujard, 1970). After the nucleic acid molecules have been allowed to spread and uncoil on the surface of the fluid they are picked up on EM grids which have been coated with a film of plastic backed with a layer of evaporated carbon. In order to render them easily visible in the electron microscope the grids have to be shadowed with a heavy metal such as uranium or platinum.

In the micrographs the nucleic acid strands are very much thickened as they are coated first with a layer of positively charged protein and then by a layer of metal. This is of no concern because these layers do not prevent the measurement of the contour length of the molecules. This is usually done with a map measurer on micrographs which have been prepared at accurately known magnifications.

Several attempts to determine the validity and reliability of this method of determining DNA length have been published. Inman (1965) showed that if a mixture of whole phage DNA and sheared DNA is examined the length distribution corresponds quite well to the concentration of the two species of DNA and that there is no preferential selection for either the short or the long molecules during preparation for electron microscopy.

The measured lengths are however affected by the composition of the hypophase. Inman (1967) studied the effect of concentrations of different salts in the hypophase and in the DNA-cytochrome mixture on the observed lengths of phage λ DNA. When the DNA was spread on to water the length was 17·2 μm but this was reduced to 13·6 μm on a hypophase of 0·1M ammonium acetate and to 10·8 μm on sodium chloride. The effect was much less when the hypophase contained 0·5% formaldehyde. No explanation could be offered for these effects but they could be invoked to account for differences in the published values for the same nucleic acids. For example ØX174 RF DNA was found to be 1·64 ± 0·04 μm by Kleinschmidt *et al.* (1963) using 0·1M ammonium acetate and 1·89 ± 0·04 μm by Chandler *et al.* (1964) using a hypophase of water. Bujard (1970) studied the effect of ionic changes on the length of phage fd DNA.

A fairly recent example of the use of the Kleinschmidt method is that of Rhoades *et al.* (1968) who studied the DNA from phage P22 which is lysogenic for *Salmonella typhimurium*.

After purification of the phage by differential centrifugation it was subjected to zone centrifugation through a 5–20% sucrose gradient containing 0·1M NaCl and 0·01M Tris (pH 8·0). The phage was mixed with an equal volume of water-saturated phenol and gently shaken at room temperature. The phenol was freshly distilled immediately before use and was neutralized with one tenth of a volume of M Tris-HCl buffer at pH 8·0. The denser phenol layer was separated by brief centrifugation and removed by pipette. Fresh phenol was added and the extraction repeated once or twice. The aqueous layer was freed of phenol by dialysis against four changes of 0·5M NaCl and 0·01M Tris (pH 8·0). The dialysis tubing was prepared as described on p. 290.

The DNA was prepared for electron microscopy by the modification of the Kleinschmidt method described by Ritchie *et al.* (1967) see below. All the molecules were found to be linear and had a mean contour length of

13·7 μm which corresponds to a MW of $26·3 \times 10^6$ daltons using the mass per unit length of the B form of DNA of 192 daltons per Å.

Ritchie *et al.* (1967) examined the DNA from *E. coli* phages T3 and T7. It was dissolved in 0·03 ml of 0·05M NaCl and 0·01M Tris-HCl (pH 8) at a concentration of 1·15 μg/ml, mixed with an equal volume of 0·04% cytochrome *c* (type III) in 4·0M NaCl and spread on to the surface of quartz distilled water (60 cm²) by running down a flame cleaned steel blade. After 5–10 min the surface film was picked up on a grid covered with a carbon plastic filmed grid and shadowed.

4. *The structure of filamentous phage DNA*

The DNA of all the filamentous phages which have been examined in detail is both single-stranded and circular. The DNA of ØX174 is also circular and it was with this phage that the first evidence for circularity in phage DNA was obtained (Fiers and Sinsheimer, 1962c).

The first indication that the filamentous phage DNA could not be linear came from the base ratios (Marvin and Hoffman-Berling, 1963; Hoffman-Berling, Marvin and Durwald, 1963). Later Salivar *et al.* (1964) showed that in the case of M13 thymine accounted for one third of the total bases and that the ratios A : T and G : C were so different from unity that they were incompatible with the Watson–Crick requirement for double-stranded DNA. A second piece of evidence against the DNA being double-stranded came from the melting curve in which the change of optical density at 260 nm is measured as the temperature is raised. There was a continuous increase in the density in the range from 25°C to 65°C which is quite contrary to the picture given by double-stranded DNA where there is little change until 80°C is reached. It was also found that the buoyant density of the DNA did not change after heating to 99°C and rapidly cooling.

Evidence for the filamentous phage DNA being in the form of a ring was given by Marvin and Schaller (1966) using methods based on those of Fiers and Sinsheimer (1962a, b, c) for ØX174. The phage was prepared and the DNA isolated as described on p. 291. When it was subjected to the action of exonuclease I, which degrades single-stranded DNA from the 3′-OH end, the biological activity of the fd DNA as measured by spheroplast assay was almost unaffected. A slight attack by the exonuclease was found after treatment with alkaline phosphatase (to remove any possible terminal phosphates) but this was ascribed to endonuclease contamination of the alkaline phosphatase. Spleen phosphodiesterase also had no effect on fd DNA and it was concluded that there was no free 5′-OH end in the DNA.

When the DNA was treated with the endonuclease pancreatic DNase, the biological activity was lost and at the same time the viscosity of the DNA increased to a maximum at the time when, on average, each molecule had been broken at one place. Thereafter the viscosity declined. It was shown that in a solvent where the DNA molecules were extended their sedimentation coefficient was less after enzyme treatment than before.

These observations can be explained if the molecule of DNA, as isolated, was in the form of a ring so that after one hit a linear molecule of the same MW was formed. This would result in an increase in the viscosity of the solution but a decrease in the sedimentation coefficient. Later Bujard (1970) showed by electron microscopy that the DNA is clearly circular.

B. Phage ribonucleic acid

The phenol method has been used by Strauss and Sinsheimer (1963) to extract the RNA from phage MS2 and by Gesteland and Bodtker (1964) for phage R17. The former authors took a cold suspension of purified MS2 (see p. 275) at about 25 mg/ml in 0·1M Tris (pH 7·0), and added an equal volume of cold redistilled phenol saturated with the same buffer. The mixture was shaken for 1 min on a Vortex mixer and the emulsion was broken by centrifugation at 6000 *g* for 10 min. The aqueous layer was removed and added to an equal volume of phenol and the extraction process was repeated. It was found that the yield of MS2 RNA could be improved if a volume of Tris buffer equal to the original volume of the phage suspension was added to the phenol layer from the first extraction, shaken and spun as before. The aqueous layer was then used to extract the phenol layer from the first extraction. This aqueous layer was combined with the initial aqueous layer and the RNA precipitated by the addition of two volumes of cold ethanol. After several hours the precipitate was spun down at 6000 *g* for 15 min. The supernatant solution was discarded and the precipitate was taken up in 0·1M Tris (pH 7·0). The RNA was precipitated twice more and then taken up in one half to one third of the initial volume of the phage suspension and clarified by spinning at 27,000 *g* for 30 min. The residual phenol was removed by dialysis for short times against several large volumes of Tris buffer. The final product which represented 80–90% of the phage RNA was stored at −70°C. The physical properties of the RNA are given in Table I.

Gesteland and Bodtker (1964) isolated the RNA from phage R17 by a variation of the phenol method. Five ml of a 1% suspension of the phage in SSC (0·15M NaCl plus 0·015M Na citrate, pH 7) was treated with 2% Na dodecyl sulphate for 15 min at room temperature. The solution was then chilled and all subsequent operations were carried out at 4°C. After adding 50 mg of bentonite (fractionated according to Frankel-Conrat *et al.*, 1961) the RNA was purified by shaking with an equal volume of SCC-saturated distilled phenol for 10 min. The two layers were separated by centrifugation, the aqueous layer pipetted off and the phenol layer was again extracted with 1 ml of SSC. The combined aqueous layers were shaken twice more with 0·5 and 0·25 volumes of phenol for 5 and 3 min respectively. The RNA was then precipitated from the aqueous phase by adding two volumes of ethanol and resuspended in 0·1mM EDTA at pH 8·0. The solution was made 0·5% with potassium acetate and the RNA reprecipitated with two volumes of ethanol. After a third precipitation the RNA was dissolved in 0·1mM EDTA, dialysed against 10mM EDTA for 12 h against 0·1mM EDTA for 24 h and stored at −20°C.

C. Phage proteins and components composed of protein

When phage particles are assembled inside the infected host cells the protein molecules which form the various parts such as the capsid, tails, fibres, etc., become bound specifically together by comparatively weak bonds of the hydrophilic and hydrophobic variety. No covalent bonds are formed. It should therefore be possible by choosing suitable bond weakening reagents to separate the parts of the phage particles without destroying the protein molecules of which they are constructed.

Numerous studies have been directed towards this end and it has become clear that some parts of the phages are held together much more strongly than others. For example Poglazov and Nikolskaya (1969) showed that under controlled alkaline conditions T2 is split up into the substructures, tail sheaths, cores, fibres and base plates but the capsid is dissociated into its capsomeres.

In this Section the methods used for dissociating and separating the substructures and proteins of several phages will be discussed under the headings of the particular phages.

1. *The T-even Coliphages*

Brenner *et al.* (1959) studied the dissociation of some of the T-even phages at low pH. They found that T2L could be broken down into tail sheaths, cores and fibres at pH 2 but that T2H, T2B and T6 required more acid conditions (half a volume of N H_2SO_4) to dissociate the sheaths but at the same time the cores and fibres were lost. They therefore concentrated their work on T2L and devised the following scheme for the isolation of contracted tail sheaths and tail fibres in pure form. The heads were digested to small polypeptides by this procedure.

To purified phage in 0·1M NaCl at about 2×10^{13} ml an equal volume of 0·2M glycine-HCl buffer (pH 2) containing 0·1M NaCl was added and the pH readjusted to 2. After centrifugation at low speed the supernatant was discarded and the precipitate was taken up in 0·1M phosphate buffer (pH 7·0) and 5×10^{-3} $MgSO_4$. DNase (10 $\mu g/ml$) was then added to digest the released DNA. After centrifugation at low speed the supernatant was discarded and the sediment was washed once with water and then three to five times with 2% ammonium bicarbonate until negligible DNA remained. The material was then treated with 50 μg of trypsin per ml for 40 min at 37°C and with 50 μg of chymotrypsin per ml for 40 min. The pH was about 8. After low speed centrifugation the supernatant was spun at 100,000 g for 60 min. The pellet which contained the sheaths was resuspended in 1% ammonium acetate pH 7·0 and spun at 10,000 g for 10 min. The sediment was discarded and the supernatant again spun at 100,000 g for 60 min. The sedimented sheaths were taken up in 1% ammonium acetate at pH 7·0.

The supernatant from the first high speed centrifugation contained the tail fibres. It was dialysed against 0·01M phosphate buffer (pH 6·8) and spun at 10,000 g for 10 min. The pellet was discarded and the supernatant was applied to a hydroxyapatite column equilibrated with 0·01M phosphate buffer (pH 6·8). The column was prepared by the procedure of Tiselius et al. (1956). It was washed with 0·01M phosphate until no more protein was eluted (this consisted of peptides derived from the phage heads). The buffer strength was raised stepwise, 0·04, 0·06, 0·08, 0·1 and 0·12M and three column volumes were run through. The fibres were found mainly in the 0·08 and 0·1M phosphate fractions.

The sheaths, which were in the contracted state, had a sedimentation coefficient of 114 S and a particle weight of 12×10^6. They resisted attack by boiling N H_2SO_4 or 0·2N NaOH for 20 min and 8M urea, 8M guanidine-HCl or 1% SDS at pH 10·5 for 24 h. They were disaggregated into their subunits by 66% acetic acid.

In the electron microscope the sheaths were hollow cylinders 350 Å long and 250 Å in diameter with a central hole 120 Å across. The fibres were 1300 Å long and 20 Å across. When attached to the phage particle they showed a kink halfway along but during purification they generally broke at the kink. Tail cores were also found. They were 800 Å long, 70 Å wide and possessed a central hole 25 Å across.

Brenner et al. (1959) also discussed the mechanism of the contraction of the tail sheath. In the extended form, which is only found on the intact phage particle, the sheath is 800 Å long and shows 24 equispaced parallel bands. After contraction the sheath is only 350 Å long but has increased in width. The volume is conserved and so it was concluded that the protein subunits of the sheath became rearranged during contraction. The sheath consists of 200 protein subunits of MW 50,000. Sometimes the contracted sheaths could be seen in end view when they showed a cog-wheel appearance with 15 peripheral teeth.

The significance of these structural changes is discussed further on p. 308.

Poglazov *et al.* (1965) showed that the sheaths of phage T2 could be isolated by alkaline treatment.

To a purified suspension of T2 in 0·1M NaCl was added concentrated KOH until the pH was 12·2. The resultant gel was slowly diluted five to six times with 0·1M borate buffer (pH 8·5) so that the phage DNA remained in solution. MgCl$_2$ (0·005M) and DNase 15 μg/ml were then added and after incubation at 37°C for 1 h the tail sheaths were separated by three cycles of low and high speed centrifugation at 10,000 g for 15 min and 105,000 g for 1 h. Further purification was made by precipitation of the sheaths at pH 3·3 when they could be easily collected by centrifugation at 3000 rpm followed by resuspension at pH 9·5.

The sedimentation properties of the sheaths were examined in the ultra-centrifuge and found to be closely dependent on the pH. At pH 9·5 or higher only one peak with a sedimentation coefficient of 107 S was observed but as the pH was lowered a second peak of 155 S appeared until at pH 6·0 to 5·0 it comprised the whole of the material. It was confirmed by electron microscopy that the 107 S component was composed of intact sheath monomers and that the 155 S component was an end to end dimer. Further lowering of the pH caused increasing degrees of aggregation.

Further studies by Poglazov and Nikolskaya (1969) showed that at pH 12·2 the head of phage T2 was dissociated into its capsomeres but that the tail separated into its constituent elements, sheaths, cores, fibres and base plates. After neutralization to pH 7·2 and removal of DNA by DNase (40 mg/ml for 2 h at 37°C) the solution was again made alkaline to pH 11·0 and the tail elements were sedimented at 50,000 rpm for 12 h. The supernatant fluid was discarded. The sediment was resuspended in 0·1M Tris-NaCl buffer (pH 10·3) containing 0·001M EDTA. The tail elements in this suspension were separated by centrifugation through a 10–60% linear sucrose density gradient made in the same Tris-NaCl-EDTA buffer. After 1 h at 39,000 rpm three layers were found. The upper layer contained the tail cores and fibres, the middle layer contained mostly sheaths while the bottom layer contained mainly large protein aggregates. The upper layer was centrifuged again through a sucrose gradient and gave two bands. The upper layer was fibres and the lower cores and some fibres. The fibres had a sedimentation coefficient of 13 S and the cores 31 S. The cores averaged 800 Å in length and 70 Å in diameter. They showed a periodicity of 35–40 Å along their length.

The subunits of the cores became dissociated at high pH (12·5–12·6). Their sedimentation coefficient was 1·2 S. Structures resembling cores could be reconstituted by neutralization but their length was variable.

Attempts to prepare phage capsids free from tail elements have not been successful because the capsids are more labile than the tails and become broken down during procedures necessary to remove the latter. It is possible to overcome this difficulty by the use of amber mutants. Kellenberger (1968) made use of an amber mutant of T4 defective in gene 10, which when grown on the non-permissive host gives rise to tailless heads, that is phage capsids to which the tail elements have never been attached.

A culture of *E. coli* B was grown to 2–4×10^8 cells/ml in a medium containing 0.7% Na_2HPO_4, 0.3% KH_2PO_4, 0.05% NaCl, 0.1% NH_4Cl, 0.4% glucose, $10^{-3}M$ $MgSO_4$, $10^{-4}M$ $CaCl_2$, $2 \times 10^{-6}M$ Fe citrate and 0.5% Difco Casamino acids. The cells were infected with four to six phage particles per cell and 5–8 min later the culture was superinfected with the same multiplicity of phage. The cells became completely lysis inhibited. After 90–120 min the cells were collected by centrifugation, frozen, and after thawing, taken up in a very small amount of $10^{-3}M$ $MgSO_4$ containing RNase and DNase and lysed by the addition of chloroform. The heads were very fragile and released their DNA during this treatment. After centrifugation at 3200 rpm the supernatant was removed, the sediment washed in water and the supernatant after a further spin at 3200 rpm was added to the first. Celite and more chloroform were added and after a further centrifugation an almost pure suspension of capsids was obtained. A little DNA still left in the capsids was removed by pelleting them at 24,000 rpm for 2 h, resuspending in water and treating with DNase. The purity was still further improved by equilibrium density gradient centrifugation in CsCl. The capsid suspension (0.5 ml) in water or Tris buffer was layered on to 4.5 ml of a solution of 16.65 g CsCl in 50 ml water. After 12–24 h at 28,000 rpm the capsids had formed a single band, or infrequently a doublet both parts of which appeared to be similar when analysed electrophoretically.

The capsids were degraded to subunits by the following three methods.

(a) *Acid degradation.* When the capsids were treated with two volumes of glacial acetic acid, a method devised by Frankel-Conrat (1957) for degrading TMV, they dissolved. After removal of the acid by dialysis the protein precipitates but can be redissolved by the addition of a little 12M urea followed by dialysis against 8M urea. This solution was subjected to polyacrylamide gel electrophoresis either directly, after adjustment of the pH to 7–8 or after treatment with Cleland's reagent or with mercaptoethanol. Oxygen was removed by bubbling nitrogen through the suspension and the solid reagent (0.2M Cleland's or 0.1M mercaptoethanol) was added and dissolved by bubbling nitrogen through. The tube was sealed with Parafilm and heated at 45°C for 20 min.

(b) *Alkaline degradation.* The capsids in distilled water were diluted 1 : 10 with 9M urea and then 20% NaOH was added to raise the pH to above 12·8. After warming to 45°C for 20 min the material was treated with Cleland's reagent as described above for another 20 min at 45°C. The pH was reduced to 7·2–7·8 with conc. HCl.

(c) *Guanidine hydrochloride degradation.* The capsids were suspended in 6M guanidine hydrochloride and kept at 45°C for 30 min. They were then dialysed against 8M urea and treated with reducing reagents for 20 min at 45°C.

All three methods gave completely denatured polypeptides. The observations made on these degraded capsid preparations are discussed on p. 306.

2. *Coliphage* ØX174

The particles of this small phage are about 250 Å across (Hall *et al.*, 1959). They are icosahedral in shape and show projections at the vertices (Tromans and Horne, 1961). There is no tail. Preparations of this phage usually contain two sorts of particles; infective particles with a sedimentation coefficient of 114 S and another particle of similar size but a reduced amount of DNA and no infectivity of 70 S. Bleichrodt and Knizenburg (1969) believe that the 70 S particles are produced from the complete 114 S particles by interaction between them and cell wall debris. They found that if sucrose was added to a culture of *E. coli* infected with ØX174 to inhibit lysis and the infected cells collected and caused to lyse under conditions where adsorption to cell debris is a minimum then the amount of the 70 S component is very small (Bleichrodt and van Abkoude, 1967).

Carusi and Sinsheimer (1963) separated the 70 S component of ØX174 and used it to prepare the protein of the phage. To 3 ml of the 70 S particles in 0·01M borate buffer (pH 9·1) containing 5 mg of phage protein per ml were added 0·4 ml of 10% recrystallized SDS in water and 0·6 ml of 0·1M borate buffer (pH 10·5). The pH was adjusted to 10·5 with 0·1N NaOH and the mixture kept at 40°C for 20 h. After dilution with 3 ml of 0·01M borate buffer (pH 10·5) and the addition of a drop of saturated KCl a precipitate of potassium dodecyl sulphate was formed and this was sedimented in the cold at 12,000 *g* for 20 min. The clear supernatant kept cold in ice was treated with 1·5 ml of cold saturated ammonium sulphate. The protein precipitate was allowed to flocculate for 30 min and collected by centrifugation. It was dissolved in 7 ml of 0·01M borate (pH 10·5) and reprecipitated twice. It was finally dissolved in the particular solvent needed for the subsequent experiments.

The sedimentation coefficient was 2·9 S but was affected by the SDS adsorbed to the protein. Methods for correcting for this are given by Carusi and Sinsheimer (1963) and Knippers and Hoffman-Berling (1966), see p. 302. The MW of the protein, based on the least abundant amino acid, was 25,500.

Edgell *et al.* (1969) showed that if ØX174 was treated with 4M urea the spikes at the vertices of the phage particle could be removed. The urea was removed by dialysis and the spike material was separated from the remaining capsids by sucrose gradient centrifugation. In this context the term capsid refers to the phage coat structure less the spikes. The spike material and the capsid material could be dissociated by treatment with 9M urea and 5–10% mercaptoethanol for 3 h at 30°C. Polyacrylamide gel electrophoresis revealed that the spike material contained three electrophoretically different proteins one of which is found as a minor component of the capsid. The latter consists almost entirely of one homogeneous protein.

The significance of these findings for the structure of the ØX174 particle is discussed on p. 309.

3. The male-specific filamentous coliphages

The coat protein of the filamentous phage f1 has been studied by Knippers and Hoffman–Berling (1966). This protein very readily aggregates and it is only possible to prepare it in monomeric form by the use of strongly denaturing solvents.

Protein free from detectable amounts of phosphate was obtained from phage disintegrated with phenol. Purified phage (100 mg) was suspended in 20 ml of borate buffer (0·01M Na tetraborate, pH 8·2) and shaken for 8 min with one volume of redistilled phenol saturated with the same buffer. After centrifugation for 10 min at 3200 *g* the aqueous layer was aspirated and the phenolic layer was re-extracted with one volume of buffer four times. DNA could be obtained from the first and second aqueous extracts. The phenolic layer was diluted with two volumes of methanol which improved the solubility of the final product and was dialysed successively against the following solutions; 1 : 1 methanol borate buffer, borate buffer and distilled water for 12 h each. The protein precipitated. It was stored dry in a refrigerator. All extractions were done in the cold room.

Only in 1% SDS did the protein show a very small sedimentation coefficient, 1·28 S, which corresponded to a molecular weight of 10,300 after correction for bound SDS. The chemical monomeric weight was believed at the time to be 9000 but this has now been corrected to 5169 (Asbeck *et al.*, 1969) so it is clear that Knippers and Hoffman-Berling were dealing with a dimeric form of the phage coat protein. If the SDS concentration were reduced to 0·2% the sedimentation coefficient rose to the 5 S range.

Correction for the bound SDS was made as follows. Phage protein was dissolved in 0·01M Tris-HCl (pH 7·0) containing SDS at the desired concentration. The solution was dialysed against 200 volumes of a solution of the same buffer containing SDS for 24 h at 20°C. The SDS concentration inside and outside the bag was determined by the colorimetric method of Karush and Sonenberg (1950). Subtraction of the SDS concentration outside the bag from that inside gave the concentration of the SDS bound to the protein. In 1% SDS 0·35 g were bound per g of protein. The partial specific volume of the protein–SDS complex, $\bar{v}_c$, is given by

$$\frac{\bar{v}_p + x\bar{v}_{SDS}}{1 + x}$$

where x is the weight fraction of bound SDS, $\bar{v}_{SDS}$ is taken to be 0·855 ml/g and subscript p refers to protein. $\bar{v}_p$ was found to be 0·74 by pycnometry of a solution in 0·1N NaOH or a neutral solution prepared by dialysis of a solution in 8M urea and 0·01M Tris against Tris.

The protein of phage f1 has also been examined by Rossomando and Zinder (1968). It was isolated by a procedure which has already been described on p. 301. It was dissolved by adjusting the pH to 13 and then neutralized by dialysis against the desired buffer and salt system. The 280 : 260 nm ratio was 1·5 but the sedimentation coefficient was 5–7 S which indicated that the preparation was not in monomeric form (see above).

It was shown spectrophotometrically that the tyrosine groups of the phage protein could be titrated with alkali but that the viability of the particle was not immediately lost. Prolonged treatment with alkali caused disassembly and inactivity of the phage. When an amber mutant of f1, bearing a mutation in gene 3, was examined it showed an increased sensitivity to alkali treatment. It was shown that this gene does not control the synthesis of the major coat protein but is responsible for a minor protein (A protein) in the structure of the particle. The protein is believed to be located at one end of the particle. It is known that the main coat protein does not contain histidine or arginine (Asbeck *et al.*, 1969) so if the phage were to become labelled with radioactive histidine then there would be evidence for the existence of the minor protein. Rossomando and Zinder were able to demonstrate a radioactively labelled protein component of f1 after growing the phage on labelled histidine in addition to the main protein which did not become labelled with the histidine.

4. The male-specific RNA-containing coliphages

Two of these phages, R17 and M12, which are very similar but were isolated in different hemispheres, were examined by Enger and Kaesberg (1965). The proteins were dissociated in 67% acetic acid and purified. The amino-acids were released by hydrolysis in 6N HCl and peptides were obtained by tryptic digestion. There were 11 identical peptides and two very similar ones. R17 was found to have one more lysyl peptide than M12. It contained one more mole of lysine residues and one less mole of glutamic acid or glutamine residues than M12 per 14.2×10^3 g of protein. The MW of the chemical subunit of the two coat proteins was 14.2×10^3.

Sugiyama *et al.* (1967) also used the acetic acid to dissociate MS2. One volume of ice cold MS2 (1–2%) in 0·1M Tris-HCl (pH 7·0) was treated with two volumes of glacial acetic acid which had been chilled but not frozen. The mixture was stood in ice for 1 h with occasional stirring. After removal of RNA by centrifugation at 8000 rpm in the cold the clear protein-containing supernatant was diluted to not more than 3 mg/ml and dialysed overnight against three or four changes of 0·001M acetic acid at ice temperature. Loss of acid by evaporation was avoided as much as possible and the pH was kept at about 3·2. Any remaining virus was removed by spinning at 40,000 rpm for 3 h. The MW of the phage coat protein was estimated at 17,000.

In addition to the main coat protein phage R17 and probably all the other similar phages, contains a maturation protein (A protein). Its MW is about 40,000 and it contains five histidine residues. As this is the total amount of histidine in the phage there can be only one molecule of A protein in each particle (Steitz, 1968). The A protein was isolated from a specimen which had been purified by two bandings in CsCl at a concentration not exceeding 70 mg/14 ml tube. The phage (300 mg) in SSC (0·15M NaCl, 0·015M Na citrate, pH 7·0) with a small amount of [³H]histidine labelled phage was made 6·0M with guanidine-HCl in 0·1M Tris-HCl (pH 8·5). The mixture was incubated at 46°C for 4·5 h, transferred to a dialysis sac and dialysed for 18 h at room temperature against three changes of urea-Tris (8M urea, 0·05M Tris-HCl, pH 8·4). The dissociated phage components were transferred to a column of phosphocellulose (Whatman P11) equilibrated with urea-Tris made 0·04M in NaCl. The A protein was eluted in urea-Tris (pH 8·7) with a linear NaCl gradient 0·04–0·4M. After locating the histidine peak the pooled fractions were freed from urea on a column of Sephadex G-25 in aqueous ammonia at pH 11. The fractions containing the A protein were pooled and 1·5 ml of a solution containing 0·1% SDS and 5×10^{-3}M Cleland's reagent were added. After lyophilization the protein was dissolved in 1·5 ml of water containing 5×10^{-3}M Cleland's reagent and heated to 46°C for 1 h and 65°C for 30 min to dissolve the protein. Final purification was effected by chromatography on Agarose A5–M (Biogel, 100–200 mesh) at room temperature in the presence of 0·1% recrystallized SDS, 0·1M NH_4HCO_3 and 5×10^{-3}M Cleland's reagent at pH 8·5. The purity of the material was checked by polyacrylamide gel electrophoresis in the system described by Vinuela et al. (1967).

5. The blue-green alga phage LPP–1

Phage LPP–1 has been dissociated into its structural components by treatment with EDTA (Luftig and Haselkorn, 1968). A phage preparation (45–60 absorption units) which had been purified by the two phage extraction procedures described on p. 276 was pelleted by centrifugation at 22,000 rpm for 90 min and then resuspended overnight at 4°C in 0·7 ml of TM buffer (Tris, 0·01M, pH 7·5 and 0·01M Mg^{2+}). EDTA (0·35M) was then added to give a final concentration of 100mM. The suspension, which immediately became viscous, was kept at room temperature for 15 min. The Mg^{2+} was added to give 120–130mM and DNase (20–40 μg) to digest the released DNA. After 45 min at 37°C the mixture was dialysed first against M NaCl and 10^{-2} Tris and then against 10^{-3}M EDTA, pH 7·5. This preparation was fractionated into tail components and empty head capsids by zonal centrifugation through 5–20% sucrose at 35,000 rpm for 60 min.

The head components were dissociated into subunits by dialysis against 10^{-3}M EDTA (pH 7·5) followed by dialysis against 6M urea in 10^{-2}M Tris. The head proteins eluted as a single peak from a Sephadex G-100 column which had been previously equilibriated against 6M urea. Its MW was estimated at 17,500 by comparison with RNase A, trypsin, lysozyme and the half haemoglobin molecule.

V. THE STRUCTURE OF PHAGE PARTICLES

The components and substances from which bacteriophage particles are constructed have been described in the preceding Sections and it is now proposed to discuss the complete virus particles or virions. It is clear from studies on the infection of susceptible bacteria that these virions are highly efficient at causing successful infections and that with a few exceptions they are also very efficient in safeguarding the integrity of the viral genome during the extracellular period of their existence. It is also remarkable that the virion, after remaining passive for an indefinite period, is instantly capable of transferring the genome to a host cell should one which exhibits the appropriate receptor sites approach sufficiently close for a collision to occur.

Our knowledge of the structure of the complete phage particle is derived from two main sources. The most illuminating information has been obtained by electron microscopy but it should not be overlooked that this instrument can only be used on material that is totally desiccated and flattened out on the surface of a thin film of either an organic plastic or of graphitic carbon. Neither of these circumstances resemble remotely the aqueous environment in which the phage particle expresses its viral function. The information obtained from electron micrographs should, where possible, be compared with that obtained from analytical ultracentrifugation, light scattering, X-ray diffraction, ultraviolet absorption spectroscopy and other techniques where the particles remain in aqueous suspension.

There is no reason to believe however, that the detailed picture of the structure of phage particles built up from electron micrographs differs markedly from the true structure as it exists in aqueous suspension. The differences that have been encountered concern the actual dimensions of the particles and this is probably due to their degree of hydration.

An example of this is given by the two RNA phages MS2 and R17 which are identical in the electron microscope. Strauss and Sinsheimer (1963) found that the particle of MS2 had a diameter of 26 nm in the electron microscope but that it had a bouyant density of 1·46 in CsCl. If the particle had a uniform density of 1·46 it would have a MW of $8·0 \times 10^6$ but from the sedimentation coefficient (81 S in 0·1M NaCl and 0·01M Tris, pH 7·6) the MW should be $3·8 \times 10^6$. A figure of $3·6 \times 10^6$ is given for the MW derived from light scattering measurements. Strauss and Sinsheimer concluded that the virus particle was probably hollow and permeable to CsCl.

Fischbach et al. (1965) examined phage R17 by X-ray scattering and calculated a radius of gyration of 128 ± 3 Å after extrapolation to zero concentration. A curve of the scattering intensity against scattering angle gave the radial density distribution. This showed that the particle had a mean outer radius of 133 Å and an outer shell of 30–40 Å in thickness. Within this was a region of somewhat lower electron density and at the centre a hollow region of about 15 Å radius. The volume of a sphere of 133 Å radius is greater than the dry volume of R17 obtained by multiplying the MW ($3·6 \times 10^6$; Gesteland and Bodtker, 1964) by the partial specific volume of the virus. To explain this Fischbach et al. suggest that there is about 1 g of water associated with each g of virus and that the central hollow contains only solvent. These results are largely in agreement with those of Strauss and Sinsheimer (1963) and show that without the data from the physical methods the picture of the virus obtained from electron microscopy would be far from complete.

The arrangement of the nucleic acid within the phage capsid has not yet been ascertained nor will this be possible until the full nucleotide sequence of the RNA has been found and the extent of the base paired double-stranded regions has been revealed. Two regions of this sort have been identified by Nichols (1970).

The structural details (dimensions, sedimentation coefficients, etc.) of representative phages are given in Fig. 1 and Table I and it is not proposed to describe them minutely in the text.

The large coliphage T4 is probably the most intensively studied virus but there are still many details about its structure which are unknown. Unlike the many viruses in the plant and animal kingdoms this particle is neither isometric nor can the subunits of its capsid be resolved in the electron microscope. Chemical studies have shown that the major component of the capsid is a protein of about 50,000 MW and genetic studies with amber mutants have shown that this is the product of gene 23 (Kellenberger, 1968). There are at least two minor components in the capsid but the genes for these have not yet been identified. In the isometric RNA phages the capsid protein is capable of spontaneous self assembly into complete capsids. This is not so in the case of T4 where the initial product of gene 23 must be acted upon by the products of at least seven other genes (Laemmli et al., 1970). It is unlikely that the products of these genes become part of the final structure of the capsid, they merely act as form determining agents or modifiers. It appears that the product of gene 23 has a MW of 58,000 when synthesized but is cleaved during head formation and found in the complete heads with a MW of 47,000. It may be that the product of one of the head genes is a proteolytic enzyme. So far the head gene mutants have not given rise to intermediate structures but to aberrant forms such as multilayered and single layered polyheads which are tubular forms usually open at the ends, isometric and elongated τ particles which are closed shells but which lack the angularity of the icosahedral capsids or irregular aggregates or lumps of protein. In the absence of identifiable intermediate structures on the way to head formation it is not possible to describe a precise pathway for head assembly nor is it likely that a complete description of the arrangement of the protein molecules in the head can be made.

The shape of the head of T4 is now believed to be an elongated or prolate icosahedron (Bradley, 1965b; Moody, 1965). It generally shows a regular angular outline in electron micrographs but, as the individual subunits cannot be seen the true three-dimensional shape cannot be known with certainty. The prolate icosahedron was the shape selected out of four possible ones by Moody on the grounds that it would show the greatest number of hexagonal outlines when allowed to fall at random upon a flat surface. This has a 5 : 2 symmetry as opposed to the 5 : 3 : 2

symmetry of the perfect icosahedron both of which present difficulties in matching the six-fold symmetry of the tail sheath with the five-fold symmetry of the head vertex to which it is attached. Also attached to the head is the tail core the symmetry of which is unknown and attached to this at the opposite end to the head is the base plate. This plate is clearly hexagonal. Moody (1965) has suggested that the symmetry of the base plate is necessary for it to fit precisely with the components of the cell wall which frequently (but not as yet in *E. coli*) show a hexagonal packing. He also believed that there would be no serious difficulty in understanding the interaction between the tail core and the head even if these did not have a compatible rotational symmetry since asymmetric interactions between proteins do commonly occur.

The arrangement of the DNA within the phage head is not well understood. All information points to a non-uniform packing with an area in the centre which is free of nucleic acid. Cummings and Wanko (1963) fixed T2 in phosphate buffered OsO_4 at pH 5·7 for 10 min at room temperature, centrifuged the phage down and embedded the pellet in methacrylate. Sections showed a light region close to the centre of the heads about 150×70 Å with its long axis parallel with the long axis of the head. Cole and Langley (1963) inferred that there was a central DNA-free region in the heads of T2 from inactivation studies using slow electrons.

All three of the T-even phages possess tail fibres, six in number, but only T4 requires the presence of tryptophan in order to extend the fibres. Normally the fibres at least in the case of T4 are carried furled around the tail sheath and they must be extended in order for adsorption to the host cell to occur. Cummings *et al.* (1969) found that the sedimentation coefficient of T4 was reduced from 1000 S to 900 S when the fibres were extended but that when the ionic strength of the suspending fluid was increased the sedimentation coefficient fell even more to 700 S. Phage T6, which does not require tryptophan, showed a reduction from 1000 S to 800 S when that amino-acid was added. In the case of T2 increasing the pH or reducing the ionic strength reduced the sedimentation coefficient from 1000 S to 700 S and caused the extension of the fibres.

Cummings *et al.* believe that the changes in sedimentation properties cannot all be ascribed to the rearrangement of the tail fibres and have shown that there is an increase in the size of the heads as seen in the electron microscope under conditions where the sedimentation coefficient is reduced. They suggest that the actual dimensions of the head in solution may not be accurately maintained when the particles are prepared for electron microscopy by a process which necessarily involves drying.

The contractile tail sheath which is such a distinguishing feature of the T-even phages is also found in a wide variety of other phages (see Bradley,

1967) but only in the T-even phages has the structure of the sheath been intensively studied. The complete tail is a complex structure consisting of the tubular sheath surrounding a narrower tube called the tail core. At one end of the core the head is attached and at the other there is the six-sided base plate to which the six tail fibres are attached (Fig. 1). The sheath on the intact phage is in the extended state but it can be caused to contract, either when the base plate contacts a receptive bacterium or spontaneously. In both cases the sheath contracts to about half its length with a measureable increase in diameter. Its volume is conserved and no material is lost.

In negatively stained preparations the sheaths show a series of bands perpendicular to the long axis giving the impression that they are constructed of a set of stacked discs. There are 24 discs in each sheath. On closer examination each disc is seen to consist of alternating large and small light dots. These are the protein subunits from which the discs are constructed. Each disc is slightly rotated relative to its neighbour so that the large subunits are arranged on a coarse helix. The small subunits lie between the larger ones and fill the space between the large helical coils.

The sheaths have been studied extensively by Bradley (1963, 1965a) and Moody (1967a, b). A structure consisting of alternating large and small subunits, six of each in every annulus, has been proposed (Fig. 1c). The six-fold symmetry of this structure agrees with that of the base plate.

When the sheath has contracted it is sometimes possible to observe a different set of helices and to explain this, Moody (1967b), has suggested that there is a rearrangement of the pairs of large and small subunits in such a way that the six-fold symmetry is preserved but that the material in the sheath is redistributed to give a cylinder of about the same internal radius a larger outer radius and a length about half that of the extended sheath (Fig. 1c). A consequence of this is that the tail core would enter the cell by right-handed long-pitched corkscrew motion.

The structure of the contracted tail sheath has been found to be very similar to that of polysheath which is a product of certain amber mutants of phage T4 (Epstein et al., 1963). That this might be so was suggested by Kellenberger and Boy de la Tour (1964) and Moody (1967a) has provided a detailed study by optical diffraction of electron micrographs to support the suggestion. A feature of the preparations of phage T4D used by Moody was the presence of free contracted tail sheaths which occasionally were found standing on end on the specimen grids. These became stained in such a manner that a set of 12 spiral grooves were revealed on their surfaces. This was strong evidence that the long pitch helical grooves seen on the sides of the contracted sheath were 12 in number. The polysheath, which is formed in lengths much greater than contracted tail sheath, was more amenable to optical diffraction studies but the number of grooves could not be determined with accuracy. It was believed to be between 10 and 14; considering the data from the contracted sheath 12 was thought to be the most likely number.

A combination of biophysical, biochemical and electron microscopical techniques has enabled Edgell *et al.* (1969) to propose a model for the coat of phage ØX174. As already described (p. 300) the apical spikes observed by Tromans and Horne (1961) can be removed by treatment with urea leaving a capsid composed of mainly a single protein. It was estimated that this has a MW of 25,000 and that there are 116 molecules in each capsid. It is not possible to construct an icosahedral shell of the type described by Caspar and Klug (1962) from this number of subunits. However if a modified Caspar and Klug shell is built of 120 identical structure units (20 hexamers) in which there are 12 holes at the vertices then a structurally complex spike could be fitted into each one to complete the icosahedron. The spikes may have five-fold symmetry. Edgell *et al.* noted that of the seven known cistrons in ØX174 four determine the properties of the phage coat and that four proteins are present in the complete coat.

In the case of T2, although reasonably precise information is available concerning the external shape and size of the capsid (see p. 306) the internal dimensions are in doubt. Klimenko *et al.* (1967) considered three possible thicknesses for the wall of the capsid, 35, 50 and 75 Å and arrived at three different internal volumes for each of two likely external dimensions. Even so the volume available was insufficient to accommodate the phage DNA (62 μm, 130×10^6 daltons) if it were packed hexagonally with 24 Å between the double-helical strands. They assumed that the DNA must be packed more tightly than this and that the secondary structure of the DNA must be to some extent disrupted.

The conformation of the DNA in the filamentous phages has been investigated by Marvin (1966), Marvin and Schaller (1966), and Day (1969). The DNA is single-stranded and exists as a closed loop (see p. 294). The proportions of thymine (35%) and adenine (24%) preclude the Watson–Crick type of base pairing and make double helical structure unlikely. Marvin gives evidence that the DNA lies like a tightly stretched loop of string extending from one end of the phage particle to the other. He believes that the two adjacent strands do not touch each other but are individually coated with protein.

Day (1969) by studying the ultraviolet absorption of the intact phage, its isolated DNA and protein has shown that the DNA both within the phage particle and in the free state exhibits marked hypochromism. That is the molar extinction of the intact DNA does not equal the sum of the molar extinctions of the equivalent amounts of the free nucleotides. This observation together with the fact that the axial separation of the bases is only 2.7 ± 0.2 Å (length of phage particle is 8700 ± 200 Å, MW of DNA is $2.0–2.1 \times 10^6$) has led Day to propose that the single strand of DNA in the virus particle is subjected to extensive base stacking and base tilt similar to that found in double stranded DNA in the "A" form.

REFERENCES

Adams, J. M., Jeppesen, P. G. N., Sanger, F., and Burrell, B. G. (1969). *Nature, Lond.*, **223**, 1009–1014.

Ames, B. N., and Dubin, D. T. (1960). *J. biol. Chem.*, **235**, 769–775.

Ames, B. N., Dubin, D. T., and Rosenthal, S. M. (1958). *Science*, **127**, 814–815.

Arber, W., and Linn, S. (1969). *A. Rev. Biochem.*, **38**, 467–500.

Asbeck, F., Bayreuther, K., Kohler, H., von Wettstein, G., and Braunitzer, G. (1969). *Hoppe-Seyler's Z. physiol. Chem.*, **350**, 1047–1066.

Beavan, G. H., Holliday, E. R., and Johnson, E. A. (1955). *In* "The Nucleic Acids" (Eds E. Chargaff and J. N. Davidson), Vol. 1, Ch.14. Academic Press, New York.

Bendet, I., Schachter, E., and Lauffer, M. A. (1962). *J. molec. Biol.*, **5**, 76–79.

Berenblum, I., and Chain, E. (1938). *Biochem. J.*, **32**, 295–298.

Bleichrodt, J. F., and van Abkoude, E. R. (1967). *Virology*, **32**, 93–102.

Bleichrodt, J. F., and Knizenburg, C. M. (1969). *Virology*, **37**, 132–134.

Bradley, D. E. (1963). *J. gen. Microbiol.*, **31**, 435–445.

Bradley, D. F. (1965a). *Jl R. microsc. Soc.*, **84**, 257–316.

Bradley, D. F. (1965b). *J. gen. Microbiol.*, **38**, 395–408.

Bradley, D. E. (1967). *Bact. Rev.*, **31**, 230–314.

Bradley, D. E., and Kay, D. (1960). *J. gen. Microbiol.*, **23**, 553–563.

Brenner, S., Streisinger, G., Horne, R. W., Champe, S. P., Barnett, L., Benzer, S., and Rees, H. W. (1959). *J. molec. Biol.*, **1**, 281–292.

Buchwald, M., Steed-Glaister, P., and Siminovitch, L. (1970). *Virology*, **42**, 375–389.

Bujard, H. (1970). *J. molec. Biol.*, **49**, 125–137.

Burgi, E., and Hershey, A. D. (1963). *Biophys. J.*, **3**, 309–322.

Burton, K. (1956). *Biochem. J.*, **62**, 315–323.

Carusi, E. A., and Sinsheimer, R. L. (1963). *J. molec. Biol.*, **7**, 388–400.

Caspar, D. L. D., and Klug, A. (1962). *Cold Spring Harb. Symp. on quant. Biol.*, **27**, 1–27.

Chandler, B., Hayashi, M., Hayashi, M. N., and Spiegelman, S. (1964). *Science*, **143**, 47–49.

Cole, A., and Langley, R. (1963). *Biophys. J.*, **3**, 189–197.

Cummings, D. J., Chapman, V. A., and DeLong, S. S. (1969). *Virology*, **37**, 94–108.

Cummings, D. J., and Wanko, T. (1963). *J. molec. Biol.*, **7**, 658–661.

Davison, P. F., and Freifelder, D. (1962). *J. molec. Biol.*, **5**, 635–642.

Day, L. A. (1969). *J. molec. Biol.*, **39**, 265–267.

Dische, Z. (1953). *J. biol. Chem.*, **204**, 983–987.

Dunn, D. B., and Smith, J. D. (1958). *Biochem. J.*, **68**, 627–636.

Eddleman, H. L., and Champe, S. P. (1966). *Virology*, **30**, 471–481.

Edgell, M. H., Hutchinson, C. A., and Sinsheimer, R. L. (1969). *J. molec. Biol.*, **42**, 547–557.

Enger, M. D., and Kaesberg, P. (1965). *J. molec. Biol.*, **13**, 260–268.

Epstein, R. H., Bolle, A., Steinberg, C. M., Kellenberger, E., Boy de la Tour, E., Chevalley, R., Edgar, R. S., Susman, M., Denhardt, G. H., and Leilausis, A. (1963). *Cold Spring Harb. Symp. on quant. Biol.*, **28**, 375–394.

Espejo, R. T., and Canalo, E. S. (1968). *Virology*, **34**, 738–747.

Fiers, W., and Sinsheimer, R. L. (1962a). *J. molec. Biol.*, **5**, 408–419.

Fiers, W., and Sinsheimer, R. L. (1962b). *J. molec. Biol.*, **5**, 420–423.

Fiers, W., and Sinsheimer, R. L. (1962c). *J. molec. Biol.*, **5**, 424–434.

Fink, K., and Adams, W. S. (1966). *J. Chromat.*, **22**, 118–129.

Fischbach, F. A., Harrison, P. M. and Anderegg, J. W. (1965). *J. molec. Biol.*, **13**, 638–645.

Fisk, C. H., and SubbaRow, Y. (1925). *J. biol. Chem.*, **66**, 375–400.

Frankel-Conrat, H. (1957). *Virology*, **4**, 1–4.

Frankel-Conrat, H., Singer, B., and Tsugita, A. (1961). *Virology*, **14**, 54–58.

Gefter, M., Hausmann, R., Gold, M., and Hurwitz, J. (1966). *J. biol. Chem.*, **241**, 1995–2006.

Gesteland, R. S., and Boedtker, H. (1964). *J. molec. Biol.*, **8**, 496–507.

Gierer, A., and Schramm, G. (1956). *Nature, Lond.*, **177**, 702–703.

Hall, H. S., and Slayter, E. C. (1966). *J. molec. Biol.*, **21**, 113–114.

Hall, J. B., and Sinsheimer, R. L. (1963). *J. molec. Biol.*, **6**, 115–127.

Hall, C. E., Maclean, E. C., and Tessman, I. (1959). *J. molec. Biol.*, **1**, 192–194.

Hattmann, S. (1970). *Virology*, **42**, 359–367.

Hattmann, S., and Fukasawa, T. (1963). *Proc. natn. Acad. Sci. Wash.*, **50**, 297–300.

Herriott, R. M., and Barlow, J. L. (1952). *J. gen. Physiol.*, **36**, 17–28.

Hershey, A. D. (1957). *Virology*, **4**, 237–264.

Hershey, A. D., and Burgi, E. (1960). *J. molec. Biol.*, **2**, 143–153.

Hershey, A. D., and Burgi, E. (1962). *J. molec. Biol.*, **4**, 313–315.

Hershey, A. D., Dixon, J., and Chase, M. (1953). *J. gen. Physiol.*, **36**, 777–789.

Hoffman-Berling, H., Marvin, D. A., and Durwald, H. (1963). *Z. Naturf.*, **18b**, 876–883.

Inman, R. B. (1965). *J. molec. Biol.*, **13**, 947–948.

Inman, R. B. (1967). *J. molec. Biol.*, **25**, 209–216.

Kay, D. (1963). Seventeenth Annual Symposium on Fundamental Cancer Research, Univ. of Texas, M. D. Anderson Hospital. Williams and Wilkins, Baltimore.

Karush, F., and Sonenburg, M. (1950). *Analyt. Chem.*, **22**, 175–177.

Kellenberger, E. (1968). *Virology*, **34**, 549–561.

Kellenberger, E., and Boy de la Tour, E. (1964). *J. Ultrastruct. Res.*, **11**, 545–563.

Kellenberger, E., Bolle, A., Boy de la Tour, E., Epstein, R. H., Franklin, R. H., Jerne, N. K., Reale-Scafati, A., Sechaud, J., Bendet, I., Goldstein, D., and Lauffer, M. A. (1965). *Virology*, **26**, 419–440.

Kirby, K. S. (1955). *Biochim. biophys. Acta*, **18**, 575–576.

Kleinschmidt, A. K., Burton, A., and Sinsheimer, R. L. (1963). *Science*, **42**, 961.

Kleinschmidt, A. K., Lang, D., Jacherts, D., and Zahn, R. K. (1962). *Biochim. biophys. Acta*, **61**, 857–864.

Klimenko, S. M., Tikchonenko, T. I., and Andreev, V. M. (1967). *J. molec. Biol.*, **23**, 523–533.

Knippers, R., and Hoffman-Berling, H. (1966). *J. molec. Biol.*, **21**, 281–292.

Kornberg, A. (1950). *J. biol. Chem.*, **182**, 805–813.

Kornberg, A., Zimmerman, S. B., Kornberg, S. R., and Josse, J. (1959). *Proc. natn. Acad. Sci. Wash.*, **45**, 772–785.

Kutter, E. M., and Wiberg, J. S. (1969). *J. Virology*, **4**, 439–453.

Laemmli, U. K., Molbert, E., Showe, M., and Kellenberger, E. (1970). *J. molec. Biol.*, **49**, 99–113.

Lang, D., and Coates, P. (1968). *J. molec. Biol.*, **36**, 137–151.

Lehman, I. R. (1960). *J. biol. Chem.*, **235**, 1479–1487.

Lehman, I. R., and Pratt, E. A. (1960). *J. biol. Chem.*, **235**, 3254–3259.

Loeb, T., and Zinder, N. D. (1961). *Proc. natn. Acad. Sci. Wash.*, **47**, 282–289.

Luftig, R., and Haselkorn, R. (1968). *Virology*, **34**, 664–674.

Mandell, J. D., and Hershey, A. D. (1960). *Analyt. Biochem.*, **1**, 66–67.

Marrian, D. H., Spicer, V. L., Balis, M. E., and Brown, G. B. (1951). *J. biol. Chem.*, **189**, 533–451.

Marvin, D. (1966). *J. molec. Biol.*, **15**, 8–15.

Marvin, D., and Hoffman-Berling, H. (1963). *Nature, Lond.*, **197**, 517–518.

Marvin, D., and Hohn, B. (1969). *Bact. Rev.*, **33**, 172–209.

Moody, M. F. (1965). *Virology*, **26**, 567–576.

Moody, M. F. (1967a). *J. molec. Biol.*, **25**, 167–200.

Moody, M. F. (1967b). *J. molec. Biol.*, **25**, 201–208.

Morris, D. L. (1948). *Science*, **107**, 254–255.

Nichols, J. L. (1970). *Nature, Lond.*, **255**, 147–151.

Ogur, M., and Rosen, G. (1950). *Archs Biochem.*, **25**, 262–276.

Poglazov, B. F., and Nikolskaya, T. I. (1969). *J. molec. Biol.*, **43**, 231–233.

Poglazov, B. F., Borhsenius, S. W., and Belavtseva, E. M. (1965). *Virology*, **26**, 650–658.

Rhoades, R. R., MacHattie, L. A., and Thomas, C. A. (1968). *J. molec. Biol.*, **37**, 21–40.

Richardson, C. C. (1966). *J. molec. Biol.*, **15**, 49–61.

Richardson, J. P. (1966). *J. molec. Biol.*, **21**, 83–114.

Ritchie, D. A., Thomas, C. A., MacHattie, L. A., and Wensinck, P. C. (1967). *J. molec. Biol.*, **23**, 365–376.

Roberts, J. W., and Steitz, J. A. (1967). *Proc. natn. Acad. Sci. Wash.*, **58**, 1416–1421.

Rossomando, E. F., and Zinder, N. D. (1968). *J. molec. Biol.*, **36**, 387–399.

Rueckert, R. R., Zillig, W., and Huber, K. (1962). *Virology*, **17**, 204–207.

Salivar, W. O., Tzagoloff, H., and Pratt, D. (1964). *Virology*, **24**, 359–371.

Schachman, H. K. (1959). "Ultracentrifugation in Biochemistry". Academic Press, New York.

Schildkraut, C. L., Marmur, J., and Doty, P. (1962). *J. molec. Biol.*, **4**, 430–443.

Sinsheimer, R. L. (1959). *J. molec. Biol.*, **1**, 37–42.

Sinsheimer, R. L. (1968). "Progress in Nucleic Acid Research" (Eds J. N. Davidson and W. E. Cohn), **8**, 115–169. Academic Press, New York.

Smith, J. D., and Markham, R. (1950). *Biochem. J.*, 509–517.

Steitz, J. A. (1968). *J. molec. Biol.*, **33**, 937–945.

Stent, G. S. (1963). "Molecular Biology of Bacterial Viruses". W. H. Freeman and Co., San Francisco and London.

Strauss, J. H., and Sinsheimer, R. L. (1963). *J. molec. Biol.*, **7**, 43–54.

Sugiyama, T., Hebert, R. R., and Hartman, K. A. (1967). *J. molec. Biol.*, **25**, 455–463.

Svedberg, T., and Pedersen, K. O. (1940). "The Ultracentrifuge". University Press, Oxford.

Szybalski, W. (1968). "Methods in Enzymology", 12, Part B, 330–360. Academic Press, New York.

Tiselius, A., Hjerten, S., and Levin, O. (1956). *Archs Biochem. Biophys.*, **65**, 132–155.

Tromans, W. J., and Horne, R. W. (1961). *Virology*, **15**, 1–7.

Twort, F. W. (1915). *Lancet*, ii, 1241–1243.

Vinuela, E., Algranati, I. D., and Ochoa, S. (1967). *Europ. J. Biochem.*, **1**, 3–11.

Wyatt, G. R. (1951). *Biochem. J.*, **48**, 584–590.

Wyatt, G. R. (1952). *J. gen. Physiol.*, **36**, 201–205.

Wyatt, G. R., and Cohen, S. S. (1952). *Nature, Lond.*, **170**, 1072–1074.

Wyatt, G. R., and Cohen, S. S. (1953). *Biochem. J.*, **55**, 774–782.

Zinder, N. D., Valentine, R. C., Roger, N., and Stoeckenius, W. (1963). *Virology*, **20**, 638–640.

CHAPTER VII

Methods for Studying Bacteriocins

Anna Mayr-Harting, A. J. Hedges and R. C. W. Berkeley

Department of Bacteriology, The Medical School,
University of Bristol, BS8 1TD, U.K.

The bulk of this article was written in 1967. Publication delays led to a need for limited revision of the content to take account of developments in the field which occurred before the proof stage (April 1971). A number of important developments occurred during that time, which the authors could not properly accommodate without substantial revision of the article. Revision has been confined to essential corrections to the text and the inclusion of a number of modifying footnotes.

I. INTRODUCTION

The study of bacteriocins began with the discovery by Gratia in 1925 of a highly specific antibiotic (*principe V*) produced by one strain of *Escherichia coli* and active against another strain of the same species. This first paper described many of the basic features of what was later realized to be a group of similar antibiotics produced by various members of the Enterobacteriaceae and for which the generic name "colicine" was proposed by Gratia and Fredericq (1946). With the discovery that the production of apparently similar agents is not limited to coliform organisms, Jacob *et al.* (1953) proposed the more general term "bacteriocine" for highly specific antibacterial proteins, produced by certain strains of bacteria and active mainly against some other strains of the same species. As was pointed out by Holland (1967a), this definition still holds good today; although both "colicine" and "bacteriocine" are now spelt without the final "e".

It is possible roughly to distinguish three overlapping periods in the history of study, and hence methodology, of bacteriocins. The first, largely descriptive, period may be considered to have ended with the publication of a substantial review by Fredericq in 1948 (1948a). By that time most of the basic methods of detection, assay, and the bacteriocin-typing of bacterial strains had been established, as had some methods for the study of specificity and number of bacteriocin receptors on sensitive cells.

The second period—the genetical study of colicinogeny—was inaugurated in 1953 when Fredericq and Betz-Bareau described the transfer of colicinogeny between donor and recipient cells. These studies, and those which followed, emphasized the striking resemblances between bacteriocins (in particular, colicins) and bacteriophage that had been noted by previous authors. Indeed, one of the earliest technical problems was to make the distinction between these two antibacterial agents—a task often made more difficult by the production of both in different cells of the same bacterial strain.

Nomura (1967b) summarized the chief points of resemblance between colicin and bacteriophage:

(i) Both require an initial adsorption to specific receptors on the surface of the sensitive cell; some colicins may actually share bacteriophage receptors.

(ii) The Col factor resembles prophage in lysogenic cells (Billing, this Series, Vol. 3B); inducers for phage also induce colicin production; both prophage development and colicin production are lethal biosyntheses; Col$^+$ cells are immune to their homologous colicin just as prophage carriers are immune to their corresponding phage.

The chief dissimilarity is that cells attacked by bacteriocins are not stimulated to replicate more of the same agent, i.e. the bacteriocin "lethal particle" does not contain its own genetic information. More recent studies have indicated similarities between the Col factor and other transfer factors, e.g. the F-factor. The question of the relation of bacteriocins and their genetic factors with other known systems has been widely discussed from an evolutionary standpoint by Reeves (1965a).

It is clear that the "genetic period" is far from ending and, indeed, it has merged into the third field of study—a suitable term for which might be "the molecular biology of bacteriocins". Under this heading are grouped two complementary areas of investigation:

(i) the chemical nature and "architecture" of the bacteriocin "particle", and studies of its biosynthesis and liberation;

(ii) the mode of action of bacteriocins on sensitive cells—studied down to the molecular level.

Studies carried out in the first of these areas have demonstrated that, although the activity of those agents currently classed as bacteriocins seems always to reside in protein molecules, the range of complexity of structure is very wide. At one extreme might be put megacin A, which has recently been shown to be an enzyme molecule (phospholipase A: Ozaki *et al.*, 1966). At the other extreme are those bacteriocin "particles" (e.g. many pyocins) that resemble incomplete bacteriophage and show a very definite organization (see Bradley, 1967).

Perhaps occupying an intermediate position are the much-studied coli-cins and their relatives. These have been found to occur either as "simple" proteins, or as proteins associated with lipopolysaccharide in a manner similar to, or identical with, the O-antigens of Enterobacteriaceae (Oakley, this Series, Vol. 5A). Only rarely has the electron microscope revealed phage-like structures among these bacteriocins (except when phage was also produced by the same strain).

Reeves (1965a) listed 16 classes of bacteriocin named on the basis of the species that produce them. With further study it may become possible to answer questions about the homology of these various agents and to decide whether all of them should continue to be grouped under the single name "bacteriocin"; there are already suggestions that perhaps megacin A should be excluded. Even at the present level of knowledge it may not be prema-ture to attempt a more standardized system of nomenclature with respect both to the name of the class of bacteriocin (e.g. colicin, vibriocin, entero-coccin: each of these is formed on a different *sort* of epithet); and to the individual bacteriocin types within a class. Excellent suggestions for the naming of individual colicins have appeared in reviews by Reeves (1965a) and Nomura (1967a).

Studies in the second area of "molecular biology", viz. the mode of action of bacteriocins, have led to interesting speculations about their possible effects on the bacterial cell membrane and on regulatory control mechan-isms. It may come about that these studies will lead to the future use of bacteriocins as "biochemical tools" in more general investigations of cellular physiology.

II. DETECTION AND ISOLATION OF BACTERIOCINOGENIC STRAINS

The detection and isolation of freely diffusing bacteriocins presents few problems. The methods worked out for colicin producers by Gratia, Fredericq and their collaborators are simple and effective, and little need for their modification and improvement has arisen. Other bacteriocins, differing from colicins in their physical and chemical properties, require more elaborate methods for their detection; and it must be admitted that this problem has not been solved satisfactorily for the producers of some bacteriocins. The main difficulty which has beset the detection of bacterio-cin producers has been the close relationship between the phenomena of bacteriocinogeny and lysogeny.

A. Detection of freely produced bacteriocins

The simplest methods for the detection of bacteriocinogeny are (1) the spotting of the culture under test, or of its supernatant, on a plate carpeted with an indicator strain, and (2) streaking of the culture across a plate and cross-streaking with potential indicator organisms. For details of these methods see Sections III.B, 1 and X.B, respectively.

The most commonly used method for detecting producers of bacteriocin is the double- or triple-layer method developed by Gratia, Fredericq and their collaborators, and modified in various ways by a number of workers. The method used by Hamon (1956a) is given here in full:

One-ml volumes of 10^{-5}, 10^{-6} and 10^{-7} dilutions of an overnight broth culture of the test strain are mixed with equal volumes of nutrient agar which has been melted and kept at 50°C. Each of the mixtures is quickly poured over a peptone water agar base.† When this layer is set and really dry, 10 ml of peptone water agar are poured on top. The plates are incubated for 48 h at 37°C. The surface is then carpeted with the sensitive indicator strain and the plates are incubated for another day.

Colonies in the middle layer which have produced bacteriocin show a halo of inhibition in the surface growth and can easily be retrieved from the depth of the agar.

This basic method finds many applications. Fredericq et al. (1949) used it to detect colicin producers in faeces. Before the introduction of this method a sample of faeces had to be plated, a number of colonies from this plate had to be grown into pure cultures in broth and each of these tested separately for colicin production. Using the layer plate method, the faeces are inoculated into peptone water and incubated overnight. The mixed culture is then diluted 10^{-7}, and 1 ml of this dilution spread over the surface of a peptone water agar plate. When it has been absorbed and the surface is quite dry, another layer of agar is poured on top and the plate is incubated for 48 h at 37°C. The surface of the top layer is then carpeted with the indicator strain by means of a filter paper disc and incubation is continued for another 24 h.

This method can also be used to search for non-producing mutants in a bacteriocin-producing culture. Its most important application is, however, in genetical studies where it is used to reveal the transfer of bacteriocinogenic factors (see Section IX).

This method is satisfactory only if the producer strain grows and produces bacteriocin in the semi-anaerobic conditions of the sandwich culture, and if the bacteriocin can diffuse through the thickness of the top layer.

If this is not the case, organisms tested for production are applied to the surface of an agar plate, usually by stab inoculation, and grown into

† For the usual, 9 cm, Petri dishes a volume of 2 ml is uncomfortably small and 3 or even 4 ml much easier to handle. Moreover, provided each dilution is poured immediately after mixing with agar, a much better and smoother layer is obtained if the agar has been kept at 56°C.

macrocolonies. The indicator culture may be applied in a variety of ways, e.g. by a filter paper disc soaked in it and then placed for a few moments on the surface of the plate with the test culture (Gratia and Weerts, 1946) or by putting a dry filter paper disc on the plate and pipetting a few drops of the indicator culture on to it; the culture spreads through the disc, and hence on to the plate, by capillary action (Fredericq and Levine, 1947).

In this laboratory, replica plating is used for the detection of staphylocinogenic cocci (R. Taylor, unpublished).† The culture under test is diluted to give 30 to 60 colonies on the surface of a plate. After the colonies have grown to a suitable size, usually after 30–40 h incubation, they are replicated on a lawn of the indicator organisms. The lawn is prepared by diluting 0·025 ml of an overnight shaken culture in 10 ml of nutrient broth. This is poured over a plate and the surplus drained off. The plate must be dried thoroughly. It is best to use it at once, but it may be kept in the refrigerator overnight.

The medium used should, of course, be suited to the organism under investigation. Even where differences in the composition of the medium may not much affect the growth, they may affect the amount of bacteriocin produced or the amount released into the medium (see Section IV.A).

Some bacteriocins, notably staphylocin, are not released in a diffusible form unless the producers are grown in Tryptose Soy broth or, better still, in any kind of Yeast Extract broth.

A method which has been described recently (Kekessy and Piguet, 1970) may be useful, because it dispenses with the preparation of multiple layer plates or the killing of the producer inoculum by chloroform. The producer is inoculated on the surface of a plate in any suitable way. After incubation, the agar disc is detached from the dish and made to fall into the lid with the inoculated surface down. The indicator is then put on the sterile new surface, the agar separating the producer and indicator inocula. Obviously, only bacteriocins which are produced and diffuse freely can be detected in this way.

B. Detection of bacteriocins that are not produced, or do not diffuse, freely

Hamon and his collaborators have searched for bacteriocins in a great variety of micro-organisms, and recommend various methods for the more difficult ones. The most valuable of these are based on the induction of colicin production by u.v. as described by Jacob et al. (1952) (see Section

† We have recently tested this method with organisms other than staphylococci. It is moderately successful for the detection of pyocins, and very satisfactory indeed for work with colicins.

IV.C). Hamon made use of u.v. induction in a variety of ways, adjusting the method to the circumstances.

Successful u.v. induction can be demonstrated either by an increase of bacteriocin titre in the culture or by an increase in the number of bacteriocin-producing individuals in the culture; this latter is possible by making use of the Lacuna Count Method (Ozeki *et al.*, 1959; see Section III.D).

In marginal cases, u.v. induction will reveal as a bacteriocin producer a strain which would otherwise be regarded as negative. The number of organisms recognized as bacteriocin producers and also the activity spectrum of known bacteriocin producers is considerably increased and enlarged after irradiation.

Hamon and Péron (1961) and Hamon *et al.* (1961) found u.v. irradiation useful for the detection of bacteriocinogeny in various kinds of organisms, particularly *Serratia*—where the number of bacteriocinogenic strains was more than doubled by this method—and *Pseudomonas*. Hamon and Péron (1962b) emphasized that there are different types of bacteriocin liberation after induction: type (a) where the liberation of bacteriocin starts a few minutes after irradiation and continues for ca. 3 h, accompanied by a slowing down of the bacterial growth rate; type (b) where the titre of the bacteriocin does not rise for 60–150 min after irradiation and then increases suddenly 10–20 times.

Organisms of the genus *Listeria* belong to type (a) and are very sensitive to u.v. induction, but are peculiar in so far as the free monocin in the culture medium may begin to decrease after 2 h owing to its adsorption to bacteria. The test for bacteriocin production must therefore be carried out with material within 2 h of irradiation (Hamon and Péron, 1962c). Although, generally, Hamon and his colleagues preferred the Lacuna Count Method for testing the result of irradiation, this method is not applicable for Listeriae where formation of lacunae has never been observed.

When it is not known if the induction pattern corresponds to type (a) or to type (b) the irradiated culture should be tested for bacteriocin at intervals over a suitably long period following induction.

Generally, the irradiation of the cultures tested for bacteriocin production has been carried out in shallow layers of peptone water. A different method of detecting bacteriocin producers by induction was used by Ivánovics and Nagy (1958) who spotted the culture of *Bacillus megaterium* examined for production of megacin on the surface of a plate inoculated with the indicator, and irradiated the surface of the plate before incubating it. Kuttner (1966), in work with the bacteriocins of group A streptococci, however, concluded that the effect of this method was due not so much to induction by irradiation as to the thinning out of the indicator inoculum, and that irradiation could entirely be replaced by dilution of the indicator carpet.

It is likely that far too little attention has been paid to this aspect. The inhibition zones of known colicin producers can be increased very considerably by diluting the indicator inoculum, and one might in this way detect bacteriocin production in strains that appear to be negative when tested with the ordinary dense indicator inoculum. It is also possible that by using inducers other than ultraviolet light more bacteriocinogenic strains might be detected. In our laboratory *B. megaterium* strains not inducible by ultraviolet light have been induced with mitomycin C (Seed, 1970).

Nicholle and Prunet (1964) have described a rather unusual method for the detection of bacteriocins produced by *Salmonella typhi*. The majority of these strains produce their bacteriocin, which is not inducible, only on solid medium. Their method is rather laborious, but as they have used it very successfully perhaps it may find other enthusiasts. Slopes of nutrient agar are prepared from which all condensation water must be carefully removed. About half-way up the slope the agar is cut through with a scraper and the top of the slope removed. The slope is then inoculated by stabbing a straight wire into the agar underneath. The wire is guided by a copper half cylinder fixed to the wire holder, the copper gliding with its convex surface along the inner surface of the glass tube. After 48 h incubation the surface of the slope is inoculated with the indicator strain (*E. coli* K 12 S), taking care to leave about 5 mm below the cut edge of the slope uninoculated so as to avoid contamination of the indicator strain with the strain under test. After overnight incubation, the results can be read.

C. Distinction between lysogeny and bacteriocinogeny

As has been remarked in the Introduction, this distinction may be difficult to make owing to a variety of causes. Apart from the similarity of their manifestation, an indicator strain may be sensitive to lysogenic phage as well as to bacteriocin liberated by the same producer strain. The choice of indicator is therefore of great importance. Moreover, the presence of lysogenic phage may mask the presence of bacteriocin and the degree of masking may change with age of culture.

The oldest method of distinguishing between phage and bacteriocin was devised by Gratia (1932), and it is still generally used. Gratia spotted a series of dilutions of the supernatant under test on a plate carpeted with an indicator strain. The spot of the undiluted supernatant might show a confluent clear area of inhibition whether it contained a phage or a bacteriocin. In the case of a phage, the dilutions would show a decreasing number of discrete phage plaques; a bacteriocin, on the other hand, would show a diffuse thinning of growth getting less marked with increasing dilution of the supernatant. This method is useful and reliable in cases where the growth of the indicator strain is smooth and not altered by metabolic products other than bacteriocin diffusing out from the test supernatant.

Gratia and his collaborators thought that, in general, no bacteriocin activity was detectable in dilutions beyond 10^{-3}, whereas phage activity was still present at much higher dilutions. This may be so for colicins but it certainly does not hold for pyocins. A. R. Thom (personal communication) has shown that a pyocin producer whose pyocin activity could be demonstrated up to a dilution of 10^{-2} showed clear-cut phage holes only when used neat on a pyocin-resistant indicator. There is no *fixed* quantitative relationship between the yield of phage and bacteriocin produced by any particular strain.

Reports on the optimal dose for u.v. induction of phage and bacteriocin are contradictory. Šmarda (1961) and Šmarda and Čermák (1964) found clear-cut differences in the latent period before liberation of phage or bacteriocin. Both these factors, however, must be regarded as differing from bacteriocin to bacteriocin, and from prophage to prophage. Differential induction, therefore, can hardly be used for the detection of bacteriocin in a strain containing also an inducible prophage, but is suitable only for the separation of phage and bacteriocin in a system with which one is already well acquainted.

A species in which the detection of bacteriocin production and its distinction from lysogeny and from other unexplained phenomena is particularly difficult is *Pseudomonas aeruginosa*. In brief the difficulties are: (a) the poor diffusibility of pyocins; (b) the fact that almost all strains possess one or more phages of various degrees of defectiveness; (c) the majority of strains of *Ps. aeruginosa* exhibit autolytic phenomena which, even if distinguishable from phage effects, may make the growth on a plate so uneven that it is very difficult to interpret any localized defects in the bacterial carpet; finally (d) the supernatants of many cultures contain diffusible substances which affect the autolytic processes of the indicator strain to such a degree that they may imitate a very diffusible pyocin. These difficulties were commented on by Papavassiliou (1961) and were well known to Hamon *et al.* (1961) who only partially overcame them by employing two modifications. These were (a) the use of very soft agar in order to improve the diffusibility of pyocin; (b) growing the test strain in mixed culture with a "universal" phage indicator strain to reveal the presence of phage.

A. R. Thom (personal communication) and J. Govan (personal communication) have tried to separate phage and pyocin by spinning the supernatant of a producer culture in the ultracentrifuge at various speeds. Both found that the pyocin activity was entirely or almost entirely in the sediment, as was the phage activity. In view of the electron micrographs of pyocins which have been published in recent years (Kageyama, 1964; Higerd et al., 1967; Bradley, 1967) showing them to consist of well-developed phage components, this is perhaps not surprising.

There seems to be one promising method for getting rid of phage from a supernatant which may contain both bacteriocin and phage, induced or uninduced. Once again, we owe this method to Hamon (1956a) who used it for the isolation of bacteriocins. It is based on the fact that phages are far more sensitive to irradiation with u.v. than are bacteriocins. Hamon used the method to obtain phage-free preparations of pyocin: after 2 h irradiation he had inactivated more than 99% of phage, whereas the pyocin had not detectably lost its activity. One would still have to consider whether the phage, though no longer able to multiply, might not still be able to kill on being adsorbed thereby giving an imitation of bacteriocin action. Moreover, it does not seem to have been established whether this relative u.v. resistance of pyocin compared with phage is general, and also whether it is in any way affected by protecting, or sensitizing, components of the medium.

For the reverse procedure, i.e. getting rid of the bacteriocin in order to separate out the phage, Hamon has advocated the use of antiserum against the bacteriocin. The effectiveness of this method would, obviously, depend on using for the preparation of antiserum a liquid guaranteed free of phage or phage components. How to achieve this seems as much a problem as the one it is meant to solve.

III. ASSAY

In the absence of a sufficiently specific chemical or physical reaction for detecting bacteriocins, the available methods of estimation are microbiological assays. As such they share both the merits and disadvantages of this class of assay.

Their principal merits are high specificity and high sensitivity. However, these advantages may be entirely lost unless great care is taken in order to prevent interference (either inhibitory or stimulatory) by substances other than bacteriocin in the assay sample. This precaution is especially necessary with much of the current work, which is concerned with the comparison of yields produced under different conditions (see Section IV.A) or at various stages of a purification procedure (see Section V).

Perhaps of the chief disadvantages of biological assays the first is their generally low precision, a feature that necessitates the setting up of many replicate determinations in a statistically controlled design when the highest precision is required. Fortunately, in many instances the experimenter wishes to know his result only in rough, comparative terms and may dispense with these refinements. The second of these disadvantages is largely unavoidable, i.e. the necessity of allowing sufficient incubation time for the sensitive indicator strain to develop its response. Although this usually entails a period of 6–18 h between setting up the assay and reading the responses, the price paid for the relatively high precision of the Diffusion Zone method (see B, 3, below) is a wait of perhaps 3 or 4 days before having the final results. There have been some interesting attempts to shorten this waiting period, two of which are outlined in B, 4 (a), below.

A further problem is exemplified by attempts to compare yields of, say, colicins of different types. Papavassiliou (1963) has discussed the use of a single "universal" indicator strain, as opposed to separate indicator strains each suited to a particular colicin. He decided in favour of the latter in view of the variable number of cells to be found in populations of the "universal" indicator that are resistant to the different colicins. In fact, this sort of comparison is of doubtful validity. Not only may the "Lethal Units" of the various colicins differ in magnitude (see C, below), but so may their mode of action (see Section VIII. D) and one may be attempting to compare the incomparable.

A. Preparation of samples for assay

Where qualitative detection rather than quantitative estimation is the object of the assay it is often possible to use samples without any special preparation. For example, a drop of crude culture fluid may be tested for activity directly by the Critical Dilution Method (described in B, 1, below) provided that checks for interfering substances are carried out. In most instances, however, the experimenter wishes to estimate the *concentration* of bacteriocin present in a sample at a particular moment of time. It is therefore necessary either to remove all producer cells from the preparation or, less satisfactorily, to kill them.

When working with purified preparations this object will have been achieved but in work with crude material some preparative procedure must be adopted.

The best method would seem to be low-speed centrifugation (clarification) followed by filtration through a bacterial filter (Mulvany, this Series, Vol. 1). Many bacteriocins are retained by Chamberland and Seitz filters (Fredericq, 1948a) but may pass through collodion membrane filters (e.g. Šmarda and Šmarda, 1965). E. van Horn (1961) succeeded in sterilizing crude E2-P9(O) colicin by filtration through a cellulose nitrate membrane (Membranfiltergesellschaft) of 0·45 μm Average Pore Diameter without detectable loss of activity. Unfortunately, subsequent experience in this laboratory has shown that under some conditions most of the activity of colicin preparations may be lost by membrane filtration. This problem, which is most acute when filtering cultures grown in defined media, is worthy of further investigation.

In view of the uncertainty of success that attends filtration, it is not surprising that most experimenters have settled for the rather easier task of killing the residual producer cells. This may often be less satisfactory than their removal because some cells may release additional bacteriocin after death (van Horn, 1961; and see Section D).

A number of authors have used chloroform as a killing agent (Fredericq, 1948, 1957; Goebel et al., 1956). Thus, de Witt and Helinski (1965) added 2 drops per ml to a sample of culture fluid with thorough mixing on a Vortex Junior blender. The chloroform was then allowed to settle out, or was centrifuged down (Barry et al., 1965), and the assay sample was carfully pipetted from the top. Other workers seem to have relied on volatility (e.g. by bubbling air through the preparation), to get rid of residual chloroform which would otherwise interfere in the assay.

Unfortunately, chloroform may have its disadvantages; for instance van Horn (1961) was able to recover viable colicin producer cells after $5\frac{1}{2}$ h contact with chloroform (ca. 2 drops per ml) at room temperature. It seems possible that hand-shaking was inadequate to ensure intimate contact with all cells. A second disadvantage is the possibility that chloroform may inactivate some bacteriocins (Fredericq, 1957a) and this may be true also for ether and ethanol (Papavassiliou, 1963). For this reason some experimenters prefer to use streptomycin, e.g. Papavassiliou (1963). Since this antibiotic is more difficult to remove from the sample fluid than is chloroform it is necessary to use a streptomycin-resistant indicator strain in the assay method. However, selection of streptomycin-resistant strains from colicin-sensitive cultures sometimes selects also for resistance to one or more colicins (Moutousis et al., 1960)—a feature which may make the process somewhat tedious.

In some cases the experimenter is favoured with a situation in which the bacteriocin is sufficiently thermostable to withstand temperatures that kill the producer cells (see Section VI.C). Thus, by heating 48 h nutrient broth cultures of Shigella sonnei P9 at 65°C for 20 min, van Horn (1961) achieved the dual objective of (i) killing the producer cells and (ii) inactivating a thermolabile colicin component produced by this strain. By centrifugation of the heated cultures in a bench centrifuge at 2500 rpm for 40 min, she obtained a clear solution of the thermostable E2 (which contained ca. 10^6 dead producer cells per ml). Occasionally, autoclaving (Heatley and Florey, 1946) or prolonged exposure to u.v. light have been successfully employed.

It is clear that for the most rigorous assay of crude preparations (should this ever be required) recourse may have to be made to high-speed centrifugation (Sykes, this Series, Vol. 5B), while remembering that the particulate bacteriocins, e.g. pyocins, may be removed from suspension by this method.

B. Methods of assay

1. *Critical Dilution Method*

This method was developed for the assay of colicins and pyocins by Jacob and his colleagues (Jacob *et al.*, 1952; Jacob, 1954) from the commonly used method for titration of bacteriophage (Billing, this Series, Vol. 3B). It has since become the most generally applied method for both qualitative detection (eg Bradley and Dewar, 1966; Ivánovics and Nagy, 1958) and for quantitative assay of a variety of bacteriocins, e.g. colicins (Goebel *et al.*, 1956; Papavassiliou, 1963; de Witt and Helinski, 1965); pyocins (Kageyama and Egami, 1962; Higerd *et al.*, 1967) and megacins (Ivánovics and Alföldi, 1957; Holland, 1961; Marjai and Ivánovics, 1962).

The basis of the method is simple and consists of:

(a) preparation of a series of dilutions of the sample (usually a two-fold series has been used);
(b) deposition of uniform drops from each dilution on to the surface of a plate of nutrient medium that has been seeded with a uniform and standard inoculum of the sensitive indicator strain (a double-layer plate has often been used);
(c) after a standardized period of incubation, examination of the degree of inhibition due to each drop, and the choice of an arbitrary end-point (usually the last dilution showing *complete* inhibition of the indicator strain).

An example of the method as often applied is given by Goebel *et al.* (1956) for colicin K:

Plates marked in eight equal segments and containing 18 ml of 2% nutrient agar were over-layered with 2·5 ml of soft (0·5%) nutrient agar which contained 5×10^7 cells of the indicator strain (*E. coli* B). Doubling dilutions of the colicin sample were made in nutrient broth, and 0·02 ml of each dilution was placed on the surface of the plate (one dilution per segment) by means of a standard nichrome loop of 5 mm diameter. After standing at room temperature for 1 h the drops had dried into the plate, which was then incubated at 37°C for 6 h.

This short incubation period was sufficient to detect clear responses, but see remarks at the end of this Section. The end-point was chosen as in (c) above.

If a reference, or standard, sample is titrated in parallel with the "unknown" sample, the method may clearly be used as a true comparative assay (e.g. Ivánovics and Alföldi, 1957). Thus, if the "unknown" sample produces the same response at a dilution of 1/1000 that the reference sample does at 1/2000 then the unknown is half as potent as the standard, whose strength is known—always provided that the two preparations are strictly comparable and that there are no interfering effects.

However, most authors have preferred to use the method as an "absolute" assay without reference to a standard preparation, although some have included one as a check on the reproducibility of the method (Ivánovics et al., 1959a; Holland, 1961). The usual procedure has been to define an Arbitrary Unit (A.U.) such that if the end-point is given by a dilution of, say, 1/250 then the sample is deemed to contain 250 A.U. per ml.

The obvious limitation of the Critical Dilution Method is the inherent uncertainty as to the exact position of the end-point between subsequent steps of a (usually geometric) dilution series. Another, and perhaps more serious, objection is that it gives no information on the comparability of the samples tested, and the need for adequate controls for non-bacteriocin effects has already been stressed. However, this objection applies equally to the method next to be described (B, 2), and the extreme simplicity of the Critical Dilution Method makes it the obvious choice of assay where these objections can be shown to be of no consequence. Goebel et al. (1956) state "This method is remarkably reproducible provided that the number of test (indicator) organisms per plate is kept reasonably constant and the incubation time is always the same".

2. Survivor Count Method

In cases where it is desired to express bacteriocin concentration in Lethal Units (L.U.) per ml (to be discussed more fully in Section III.C), some form of Survivor Count Method is necessary. The rationale of this approach is based on results obtained from studies of the kinetics of adsorption and lethal action of bacteriocins (see Section VIII). With the exception of megacin A, which now appears to be a phospholipase (Ozaki et al., 1966), most bacteriocins yet studied show the following relevant properties (see reviews by Reeves, 1965a; Nomura, 1967a):

(i) bacteriocin is adsorbed to specific receptors on the bacterial "surface";
(ii) this adsorption is irreversible under the usual experimental conditions;
(iii) the average cell of the sensitive indicator organism has more than one receptor, usually more than 10;
(iv) the kinetics of adsorption of a lethal dose of bacteriocin corresponds to a "single-hit" process.

Suppose that a sample of bacteriocin is allowed to react with a large excess of sensitive indicator cells under idealized conditions such that:

(i) the adsorption period is infinitely long;
(ii) the multiplication of unaffected cells is prohibited;
(iii) each sensitive cell has an infinitely large number of receptors;
(iv) the cells of the sensitive population are uniformly viable and sensitive to bacteriocin.

At the end of this period the "particles"[†] of bacteriocin may be supposed to be distributed among the sensitive cells according to the well-known **Poisson Distribution.** Only those cells that have escaped adsorbing a single "particle" will remain viable. Thus by estimating the fraction of the original population that remains viable, it should be possible to estimate the concentration of L.U. per ml of the original sample:

$$N_\infty/N_0 = \exp(-L_0/N_0); \quad L_0 = -N_0 (\ln (N_\infty/N_0))$$

where L_0 = L.U. per ml of sample; N_0 = viable cells per ml at time of mixing; N_∞ = viable cells per ml at end of experiment.

How far may these idealized conditions be approached in practice? Good descriptions of experimental techniques have been given for colicin K by Goebel *et al.* (1956) and for megacin by Holland (1962). The method has also been used for colicins and pyocins in this laboratory (Mayr-Harting, unpublished experiments). Let us consider the various stages of the technique.

(1) The suspension of sensitive indicator cells should be as physiologically uniform as possible and should approach 100% viability. Moreover, the cells should be free from tendencies to chain formation or clumping so that methods of viable counting (Postgate, this Series, Vol. 1) can give accurate estimates of N_0 and N_∞. Perhaps the best method would be to use cells grown in continuous culture using a chemostat or turbidostat (Tempest, this Series, Vol. 2), but the published methods have used batch culture techniques. Holland (1962) used a broth culture of *B. megaterium* that had been grown with shaking at 30°C and had just reached the end of exponential growth. This culture was then washed and resuspended to a standardized density as determined with a spectrophotometer. Mayr-Harting (1964, and unpublished experiments), who worked with heavier inocula and concentrated bacteriocin, used cells scraped from the surface of a 12-h culture on a 12 in. square dish of nutrient agar. The cells were then resuspended to a standardized density. Under these conditions she has found a high degree of viability.

† The word "particle" is used in order to generalize the statements. A "particle" may be a single molecule (see Section VIII.B, 2).

(2) The next step involves equilibration of the indicator suspension at the temperature of reaction (usually 35°C or 37°C) and the withdrawal of a sample for viable counting to give the estimate of N_0.

(3) A non-saturating solution (or suspension) of the bacteriocin (also equilibrated) is now immediately added in known proportion to the cell suspension and thoroughly mixed. If possible, it is best to arrange concentrations so that the proportion of survivors is about 50% of the original inoculum. In practice the "infinitely long" adsorption period can be drastically curtailed. Fredericq (1952) found that colicin adsorption was virtually completed within the first 10 min of reaction and this rapid adsorption seems to be generally true (see Maeda and Nomura, 1966). Holland (1962) used a reaction period of 20 min at 37°C; Mayr-Harting (1964, and unpublished experiments) preferred a period of 45 min at 36°C followed by 1–2 h in the refrigerator; Maeda and Nomura (1966) used 45 min at 37°C or 2 h at 0°C. A point to be borne in mind is that if the adsorption period is greatly prolonged at incubation temperature further growth of surviving cells may take place and so upset the estimation of N_∞.

(4) At the end of the adsorption period a sample is taken to allow estimation of N_∞ by a convenient method of viable count.

When counts are made with a sufficient degree of replication this method is capable of reasonable precision and high sensitivity. The assumptions made in this method are further discussed in Section III.C below.

3. *Diffusion Zone Method*

Apart from the more grossly particulate species, most bacteriocins appear to be diffusible, albeit slowly, through agar gels. It was therefore natural that attempts should be made to assay them by means of the inhibition zone assay methods commonly used for antibiotics. Early attempts were abandoned (Heatley and Florey, 1946; Halbert and Magnuson, 1948) owing largely to the shallowness of regression of zone diameter on log (bacteriocin concentration). This made it impossible to estimate unknown concentrations with any degree of confidence.

The shallowness of regression is a consequence of the slow diffusion of bacteriocins, whose molecular size is considerably larger than that of the common therapeutic antibiotics. This difficulty was overcome by van Horn (1961) who simultaneously increased the sensitivity and discrimination of a Diffusion Zone assay method for colicins by means of the technique of "prediffusion". Prediffusion involves allowing the bacteriocin to diffuse from its reservoirs into the agar gel under conditions which prevent the growth of the indicator strain. On subsequent incubation the individual zones are increased in size and the regression is much steeper.

The form of assay developed by van Horn (1961) allowed, on a single assay plate, the comparison of three "unknown" solutions of colicin (E2–P9) with a "standard" preparation; each of the four samples being applied at two levels (i.e. "neat" and "neat/2") with eight-fold replication. The experimental design was a true 8×8 Latin Square since one advantage of the slow diffusion of bacteriocins is that the time normally taken to charge the reservoirs (i.e. "order of filling") has no measurable effect on zone size. One further general comment should be made at this point, viz. the regression of zone diameter on log (colicin concentration) is not homogeneously linear over the entire possible range of response. Rather can the regression best be represented by two separate linear regions which intersect (see Fig. 1). For this reason, as well as for the usual statistical arguments (see Finney, 1952), it is necessary to equalize the potencies of the four samples to be compared as far as possible before assay if the highest precision is required. Obviously this may entail the execution of a rough preliminary assay so that the so-called "Neat" preparations of each of the four samples may be brought by dilution to nearly equal potency. When these precautions are taken the method conforms to the requirements of linearity of regression and homoscedasticity of response (see Finney, 1952) required for a valid assay (van Horn, 1961).

A brief description of the method† follows:

The assay plate is a 12 in. × 12 in. × 1 in. desiccating dish (Jencons Ltd., Hemel Hempstead) to which a sheet aluminium lid has been fitted. These plates are wrapped and sterilized by autoclaving at 15 lb/in.² for 20 min. For use, the plate is set on a specially levelled surface and 300 ml of molten (sterile) nutrient agar is poured into it and allowed to gel. Surface moisture is dried off by a short period of incubation. Next a further layer is poured which consists of 100 ml of nutrient agar seeded with an inoculum of the sensitive indicator strain. (In the experiments of Miss van Horn this entailed the addition of 1·0 ml of an overnight broth culture of *E. coli* C6 resulting in a final concentration of about 10^6 cells/ml.)

When the inoculum layer has set the plate is put at +4°C for 1–2 h. This serves the two-fold purpose of (a) arresting growth of the indicator cells; (b) causing the gel to harden, which facilitates the subsequent cutting of reservoirs.

Sixty-four (8 × 8) reservoirs are then punched in the medium by means of a sterile No. 5 cork-borer (dia = 8 mm) and the plugs removed with a sterile lancet-headed needle. Positioning is facilitated by placing under the

---

† A modification of this method has since been published (Richardson *et al.*, 1968). The newer method uses a single, thin seeded layer of medium, and replaces the punch-holes by "fish-spine" insulator beads used as reservoirs.

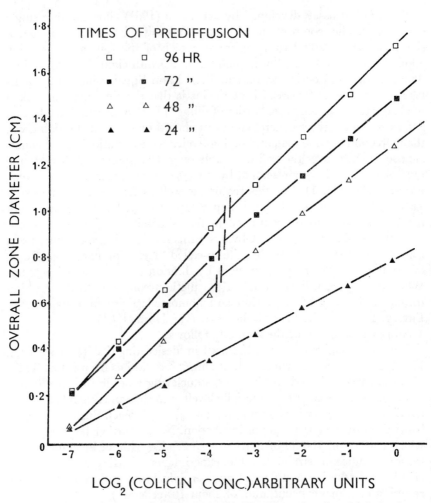

FIG. 1. Diffusion zone assay of colicin E2–P9: effect of various periods of pre-diffusion on the regression of zone-diameter on log (colicin concentration). The double vertical lines indicate the points of intersection of the two linear regions. (Data from van Horn, 1961.)

plate a template which can be seen through the transparent medium. This is in the form of an 8×8 grid that has 27 mm between its intersections.

The same template bears also the letters A to H arranged on the intersections in the form of a randomized Latin Square. Eight treatments (four samples, each at two levels) are randomly allotted to the letters A to H and then applied in alphabetical order, the eight replicates of a single treatment being completed before moving to the next. Charging is accomplished by means of an automatic pipette (East & Co., Oxford) set to deliver 0·45 ml.

The plate is then allowed to stand at +4°C for a period of prediffusion the length of which depends on the bacteriocin to be assayed; with colicin E2–P9 the period is usually 48 h. The plate is thereafter incubated at 37°C for 14–16 h.

Some trouble is sometimes experienced from water which condenses on the aluminium lid and may drop off and blur the outline of inhibition zones. E. van Horn found that this trouble was minimized if (a) the lid was occasionally wiped dry during the prediffusion period, and (b) the first few hours of incubation were carried out with the lid removed. The same problem might be solved by pouring a third, sterile nutrient agar layer on top of the inoculum layer (see Hedges, 1960).

After incubation the inhibition zones are measured, with vernier callipers fitted with needle points, to the nearest 0·1 mm (overall diameter), and the computation of potencies and analysis of assay validity is executed exactly as described by Hedges (1960) for a similar parallel-line assay.

This method has been found capable of good reproducibility and quite high precision. With the techniques as described above, and with properly equalized samples, van Horn (1961) found that the 95% confidence limits were about ±8% of the estimated relative potency. Its sensitivity, as might be expected, is rather less than that of the Survivor Count Method. Using colicin E2–P9 it was found that the latter method would detect colicin of one-third the minimum potency measurable by the Diffusion Zone Method. Moreover, the Diffusion Zone Method obviously cannot be used with the bacteriocins that do not diffuse through agar gels, e.g. some pyocins.

However, the method has, in common with other parallel-line assays, the additional advantage that different molecular species of bacteriocin as well as non-bacteriocin inhibitors may be shown up as incomparable by virtue of their different regression parameters (i.e. deviations from parallelism with the standard preparation): a feature not possessed by the previously described methods.

4. Other methods

(a) *Modified survivor count assays.* A logical development in the attempt to increase the rapidity of the bio-assay of bacteriocins is the substitution of measurement of the light-absorbing properties of bacterial suspensions for direct methods of viable counting in the Survivor Count Method. Thus, under standardized conditions, a suspension of indicator cells may receive a dose of bacteriocin preparation while another comparable suspension receives a "blank" treatment. If, after a suitable adsorption period, these suspensions are incubated a difference in their optical densities should appear due to the reduction of viable cells in the bacteriocin tube.

Not only is the rapidity of measurement increased by this approach, but most of the sources of imprecision associated with the classical Survivor Count Method are removed or decreased, viz. sampling errors, dilution errors, effects of diluent on viability.

Reeves (1965b) described an assay for colicin E2–CA42, based on this principle, which is both sensitive and reproducible provided that the experimental conditions are kept constant. The essential features were as follows: colicin was diluted in a two-fold (or 1·5-fold) series in 4 ml of medium at 10°C. A log-phase culture of the sensitive strain was grown until it reached an Optical Density (0·6 at 650 nm) corresponding to a viable count of 5×10^8 cells per ml and was then placed at 10°C for 10 min to equilibrate. One-ml portions were then added to each colicin dilution and 12 min afterwards (the time taken for the operations) the rack of bottles was placed at 37°C and shaken for 1·5 h. The tubes were thereafter cooled to arrest growth and the O.D. was read at 650 nm. The assay assumed that the killing effect of colicin was immediate and that the rise in O.D. during the 1·5 h incubation period was proportional to the percentage of survivors. A control tube without colicin allowed measurement of the O.D. corresponding to 100% survival. When the percentage of bacteria killed, worked out on the above assumptions, was plotted on probability paper against $\log_2$ (colicin dilution) a linear relation was obtained over the range between 20% and 80% killing. This straight line was used to read off the dilution corresponding to 50% killing and its reciprocal was taken to be the titre in "Probit Units" per ml.

One possible snag in the optical density method is that the "test" tube contains, at the time of measurement, not only cells that have survived admixture with bacteriocin (or their progeny), but also the corpses of the cells that were killed. These latter contribute to the light-absorbency of the suspension and so make the difference between "test" and control tubes less than would be so if only the viable cells were compared.

It was for this reason that a method was developed for colicin E2–P9 in this laboratory by R. J. Gardner-Hopkins (personal communication, 1965) and by Shannon and Hedges (1970). This method involves the use of the redox indicator 2,3,5-triphenyl tetrazolium chloride (TTC), which has been otherwise used in microbiology. The essence of the method is that the tetrazolium salt is reduced to its red-coloured formazan *intracellularly* by viable cells. If light-absorbency is measured in the appropriate waveband this method should allow a more sensitive detection of the difference between the "test" and "control" tubes since the killed cells contribute little to the absorption. In fact, it has been found possible to compare a large number of samples with sensitivity comparable to that of the Survivor Count Method and precision similar to that of the Diffusion Zone Method, all within a 4·5 h period of which the actual assay takes ca. 1·5 h.

The approach described by Shannon and Hedges employs a four-point, parallel-line type of assay, which necessitates the usual preliminary "equalization" of sample potencies (as described in Section B, 3, and for similar reasons). When the potencies are completely unknown a series of eight four-fold dilutions is set up for each sample. After the final measurements have been made adjacent pairs of dilutions are selected so that they fall within the same linear region of the response curve (a typical response curve is shown in Fig. 2).

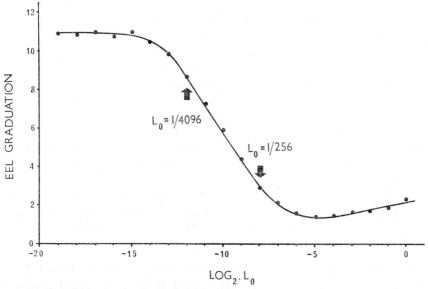

FIG. 2. Tetrazolium assay of colicin E2–P9: regression of O.D. on $\log_2 L_0$, where L_0 = degree of dilution of producer culture supernatant. The region between the arrows is considered to be linear and is that used in the assay proper. (Data from R. Shannon, 1968—personal communication.)

The indicator strain (*E. coli* C6) is grown in a standard broth medium (GLB: glucose-Lemco-peptone-salt) overnight at 37°C. One ml of this culture is inoculated into 50 ml of fresh GLB at 37°C and is further incubated at 37°C. After 2 h the culture is tested for TTC reducing activity at short intervals as follows:

To a tube containing two drops (0·04 ml) of 2% TTC at 37°C is added 0·5 ml of the culture. After 15 min at 37°C the tube is transferred to an ice bath, and two drops of formalin plus 1 ml GLB are added. The chilling and the formalin arrest further development of colour; the addition of GLB adjusts the concentrations to be comparable with those in the assay proper. The colour intensity is then read in an EEL portable colorimeter using the green (No. 624) filter and a GLB blank. The culture is used for assay when the colour intensity has reached the instrument graduation of 2·0.

For assay, 1 ml portions of the colicin (E2–P9) dilutions, both test and standard, are delivered in duplicate to 2 in. × ½ in. tubes. The diluent is GLB,† two sterile tubes of which are always included as controls. After equilibration at 37°C each tube receives 0·5 ml of the indicator culture. Delivery is as rapid as possible and in reverse order for the duplicate set in order to minimize time effects. After thorough mixing the tubes are incubated for 50 min for optimum differentiation to occur.

TTC (0·5 ml of 0·16% solution) is then added to each tube in the same order as for addition of the indicator strain to give a final concentration of TTC = ca. 0·04% (w/v). After thorough mixing, the tubes are incubated at 37°C for a further 15 min in order to allow reduction of the TTC. They are thereafter transferred to an ice bath and each tube receives two drops of formalin to arrest reaction. Colorimetric readings are then made as described above, using diluted samples if necessary, and the appropriate pairs of results are used to compute the relative potencies on the basis of the parallel-line assay technique similar to that applicable to the Diffusion Zone Method.

It should, perhaps, be stressed that the form of assay just described is a *comparative* assay necessitating the inclusion of some form of reference preparation in contradistinction to the Survivor Count Method (B, 2) on which it is based.

(b) *Miscellaneous variants.* A variant of the Critical Dilution Method (B, 1) was used by Litkenhous and Liu (1967) for the assay of bacteriocin from *Bordetella pertussis.* Instead of depositing drops on a seeded plate, these authors filled reservoirs cut into the agar as for the Diffusion Zone Method. An inhibition zone of a certain size was arbitrarily selected as end-point and the number of Arbitrary Units per ml of the test preparation was taken as the reciprocal of the bacteriocin dilution that produced this effect. The method cannot, of course, be used for non-diffusible bacteriocins.

A novel method for assaying pyocins was suggested by Kageyama *et al.* (1964) who observed that the release from sensitive indicator cells of material specifically absorbing light in the ultraviolet region (260 nm) was

† GLB may be unsuitable as a growth and dilution medium for certain bacteriocins (e.g. colicin D—Timmis, 1970).

proportional to pyocin concentration under defined conditions with indicator cells in excess. One ml samples of pyocin preparations were added to 20 ml amounts of cultures of the sensitive strain, and the mixtures were incubated for a set time (2 h) at 37°C. After centrifugation the Optical Density of the supernatant fluid was measured at 260 nm and was plotted against pyocin concentration (expressed as Optical Density at 280 nm).

(c) *Unsuccessful methods.* It seems worthwhile to record that certain methods that have been used for assay of the therapeutic antibiotics have proved unsuitable for measurement of bacteriocin activity. Thus, the tube dilution method classically employed to determine the Minimum Inhibitory Concentration (MIC) of antibiotics is generally unsuitable for colicins owing to the frequency of occurrence of resistant cells in populations of the indicator strain (Papavassiliou, 1963).

Furthermore, the use of narrow tubes in the Diffusion Zone Method (Mitchison and Spicer, 1949) is not suitable for colicins according to van Horn (1961), who found that the zone edges were insufficiently distinct for accurate measurement.

C. The unit of bacteriocin activity

Whereas for the classical antibiotics we are in the desirable position of being able to define an Absolute Unit of activity in terms of the weight of a pure, fully active preparation of known molecular structure, with bacteriocins this is not yet so. Instead many authors have used their own Arbitrary Units, defined either in terms of a standardized assay method (e.g. see B, 1) or in terms of a reference preparation (e.g. see B, 3). Unfortunately, a technical method may exhibit day-to-day variations that are too great for precise estimations, and the potency of a standard preparation may decrease on long storage (see Section VI.C). Indeed in the absence of an Absolute Unit it is difficult to measure and assess these actual variations, and the comparison of results between different experimenters is made more difficult.

Between the extremes of Absolute and Arbitrary Unit, there is the quasi-absolute "Lethal Unit", which has been used by various authors. This unit is able to serve the purpose of substituting for an Absolute Unit in making some, but not all, of the comparisons mentioned above. It is felt necessary, however, to add this cautionary note in view of the difficulties of both its measurement and its interpretation.

The basis of the Lethal Unit is simple enough: it is the *minimum* amount of bacteriocin that will kill a single sensitive indicator cell. The assumptions upon which the measurement of Lethal Units is based were set out in Section III.B, 2 and will be discussed further in Section VIII.B. Clearly, the simplest case would be that where a single bacteriocin molecule corresponded to the Lethal Unit (L.U.). Evidence that this may be so for at least one colicin-indicator system was presented by Reeves (1965b; but see Section VIII.B, 2). On the other hand, the results of Maeda and Nomura (1966) for a similar colicin suggest that 1 L.U. corresponds to about 100 molecules. The problem of reconciliation of this last finding, which is similar to that of Holland (1961) for megacin, with the single-hit kinetic data has been discussed by several authors (see Reeves, 1965a; Nomura, 1967a). One possibility is that not all receptors that specifically bind bacteriocin are equally likely to lead to death of the cell. It may be that in some cells only 1% of specific receptors is able to produce the lethal effect following bacteriocin adsorption.

If this is so then should the L.U. still correspond to the adsorption of one molecule of bacteriocin per cell by the "effective" receptors, or should it correspond to the 100 molecules that may have to be bound in order to be reasonably certain of occupying a "lethal" receptor? In fact, the method of assay, as set out in B, 2, gives the second answer since a cell that had adsorbed, say, 50 molecules of bacteriocin none of which was fixed by a "lethal" receptor would be counted as a "survivor", i.e. a cell that had adsorbed no part of an L.U. (see Hedges, 1966: appendix D).

One thing seems certain, viz. the L.U. is a function not only of the particular bacteriocin but also of the indicator strain used for its assay. Quite apart from the difficulties mentioned above, other factors that could upset the assay of L.U. concentration are:

(i) the presence of dead cells, which may adsorb bacteriocin, in the inoculum of the indicator strain (Mayr-Harting and Shimeld, 1965);

(ii) the presence of mutants that adsorb bacteriocin but are "resistant" to it, e.g. tolerant mutants (see Nomura, 1967a; and Section IX.E);

(iii) the presence of genotypically or phenotypically "resistant" cells, whether or not they adsorb bacteriocin;

(iv) non-specific adsorption of bacteriocin by the indicator cells (see Šmarda, 1965a; Šmarda and Šmarda, 1965), or non-lethal adsorption (see Section VIII.B, 3);

(v) the marked variation in receptor distribution (and, perhaps, efficiency) that occurs between different indicator strains and between cultures of the same strain grown in different media (Mayr-Harting and Shimeld, 1965); and even at different culture-ages of the same organism (Shimeld, 1966);

(vi) the assumption of a 1 : 1 correspondence between the number of cells killed and the number of L.U. per ml. This assumption has been made not infrequently in the literature in spite of the fact that, as was shown by Dulbecco *et al.* (1956) in another context, calculations based on the Poisson Distribution hold down to as few as eight receptors per cell (in place of the infinitely large number demanded by theory). The extent to which Poissonian expectations are realized in practice is further discussed in Section VIII.B, 2.

In conclusion it should be remarked that unless the possibilities mentioned above are borne in mind quite spurious comparisons and calculations may result.

D. The Lacuna Count Method

Although not strictly an assay method for bacteriocins, it is convenient to describe in this Section the Lacuna Count Method of Ozeki *et al.* (1959). This is a method of assaying the proportion of cells of a bacteriocin producer population that are actively liberating the lethal principle under various conditions. It is therefore of relevance to Detection (Section II), Production (Section IV), and Genetics of Bacteriocins (Section IX).

The technique is a modification of the soft agar layer method used in bacteriophage studies (Billing, this Series, Vol. 3B) and the procedure described by Ozeki and his colleagues is as follows:

Three ml of soft (0·35%) nutrient agar was seeded with ca. 10^8 cells of the indicator strain plus ca. 10^4 cells of a young broth culture of the producer strain. This mixture was poured on to a sterile nutrient agar base layer in a Petri dish.

After 5 h incubation at 37°C the plate was examined when ca. 100 small clear spots, 0·2 to 0·8 mm in dia., were visible in the otherwise confluent growth of the indicator strain. Each spot was assumed to be due to the diffusion of bacteriocin from a single cell (which was killed in its liberation) thus producing the small inhibition zone which the authors named a "Lacuna".

The method was extended by using an antibiotic-resistant indicator strain in the presence of an inhibitory level of the antibiotic (streptomycin or chloramphenicol). It was found that the number of lacunae in the absence of streptomycin was 10- to 100-fold greater than in its presence. The authors concluded that most lacunae are due to the actual production and liberation of bacteriocin during the growth of the producer cells on the plate, whereas a few cells (1–10%) contain sufficient, but as yet unliberated, bacteriocin at the time of inoculation. The relevance of this last point to the preparation of bacteriocin samples for quantitative assay has been referred to in Section A.

IV. CONDITIONS FOR PRODUCTION AND BIOSYNTHESIS

Reeves (1965a) wrote: "Bacteriocinogenic strains although they possess the stable genetic ability to produce a bacteriocin, do not do so all the time or under all conditions. The factors controlling the synthesis are only incompletely understood." This still holds true and only a few workers have systematically studied the cultural conditions for production of these substances although rather more attention has been paid to some of the conditions necessary for biosynthesis of bacteriocins following the discovery of Jacob *et al.* (1952) that colicin synthesis could be induced by u.v. light.

It now seems unlikely that systematic studies of cultural conditions will prove to be as fruitful in achieving the high titres required for most sorts of investigation as will the careful choice of a producer strain. Characteristics which may influence yield are:

(1) the possession of receptors for homologous bacteriocin (which may be important when the yields are relatively low, e.g. colicin I (Monk and Clowes, 1964a));
(2) the marked strain-to-strain variation in the maximum yields of a particular bacteriocin, e.g. colicin D (Timmis, 1970);
(3) the frequent occurrence of multiple bacteriocinogeny;
(4) the production in the medium of inhibitors or inactivators (Section IV.D).

Transfer of the relevant bacteriocinogenic factor to a suitable recipient may overcome one or more of these problems (Sections IX.A and IX.B).

A. Conditions of culture

Bacteriocins are produced on solid media and this is of use in detection of bacteriocinogenic strains† and in typing (see Sections II and X.B, respectively). Also, Smith (1965) used plugs cut from nutrient agar which contained colicin as her original material in electrophoresis studies and Fredericq (1950) used a peptone agar medium in experiments on the penetration of a cellophane membrane by colicins E, K, and V. However, preparations of bacteriocins in solid media are of restricted use in studying the properties of these substances and solutions, which are also essential for purification, and are now almost invariably used for this purpose. In some instances either no bacteriocin is produced in liquid medium or the yield obtained from production on a solid medium is greater than in a liquid one and bacteriocin solutions are therefore obtained from processing solid

---

† Bacteriocin production is not always spontaneous and the culture may have to be induced to produce its bacteriocin(s).

media after growth. *Salmonella typhi*, for example, produces no colicin B in liquid media (Nicholle and Prunet, 1965) and Litkenhous and Liu (1967) found that more *Bordetella pertussis* bacteriocin was produced on dialysed brain heart infusion (BHI) agar than in liquid BHI aerated on a shaker. In such cases bacteriocin solutions can be obtained by extraction of the agar (see Section V.A).

A less commonly used method of preparing bacteriocin solutions from organisms grown on solid surfaces is that described by Heatley and Florey (1946), who suspended a cellophane sac, filled with a liquid medium, in a plugged outer tube and after sterilization inoculated the outer surface of the sac with *E. coli* CF1. The apparatus was then incubated for 24 h at 37°C after which the colicin solution was recovered from the inside of the bag. It was shown that the ability of strain CF1 to produce its colicin, apparently identical to colicin V, under these conditions but not in liquid culture was due to inadequate aeration in the latter, and when such cultures were vigorously aerated high yields were obtained. However, the cellophane sac method is unique in that it does permit the direct collection of sterile bacteriocin preparations.

Gratia (1944) described another method of preparing bacteriocin solutions from organisms grown on solid media but in this instance producing antibiotic molecules too large to pass through cellophane. The producer organisms are grown on a sheet of cellophane laid over a solid medium in a Petri dish. After incubation the sheet is removed and the bacteriocin, which accumulates among the producer cells, is washed off with these cells in a minimum of liquid and the bacteria are then removed by centrifugation.

Acceptable yields of bacteriocin obtained in a liquid medium enables the avoidance of such techniques and is a desirable aim. Fluid media used for bacteriocin production are often of the digest or enriched type and their use involves the acceptance of two disadvantages. First, many of these media contain quantities of high molecular weight material of a similar nature to bacteriocins thus rendering subsequent purification more difficult. It should be noted here that frequently no attempt is made to purify bacteriocin prepared in such media beyond removing the killed cells by centrifugation.

Secondly, it is found in this laboratory that large fluctuations in colicin yield occur in uninduced cultures with different batches of these types of media. Papavassiliou (1963) and Farkas-Himsley and Seyfried (1963) also found this kind of variation with different batches of nutrient broth with colicin and *Vibrio comma* bacteriocin, although Papavassiliou suggests that the variation in his yields may have been due to the sterilization technique used. In view of the work by Goebel and his school, some of which is described below, which shows that only very small alterations in medium constitution and conditions of culture cause substantial changes in bacteriocin yield, it seems not improbable that most other workers have also found similar irregularity of yields in media which are impossible to standardize to the extent that is possible with a chemically defined medium and, indeed, unless rigorous control is exercised in its making, in this type of medium too. However, Ivánovics and Alföldi (1955) reported "invariably reproducible results" with three media prepared with yeast extract and acid hydrolysed casein which they produced themselves.

Offsetting the disadvantages associated with complex media is the finding that, in general, these support larger bacteriocin yields (Fredericq, 1963) than do simple media. Goebel et al. (1956), for example, have shown that no variant of E. coli K 235 produces significant quantities of colicin K in a synthetic medium and, although addition of 0·1% dialysed meat or yeast extract enhanced the yield, it was never as great as when the organisms were grown in a Casamino acids medium. Most workers have therefore concentrated on obtaining high yields in complex media rather than on developing simple media giving satisfactory titres. However, no attempt can be made to generalize either as to the sort of complex medium or the conditions of culture best suited to producing bacteriocin in high concentrations since a nutrient important for bacteriocinogenesis by one organism may inhibit this process in another. Similarly, antithetical conditions of culture may be required by different organisms.

Some of the nutritional factors and cultural conditions which affect bacteriocin yields in complex media are illustrated by the results of the investigations of Goebel's group and by Farkas-Himsley and Seyfried with colicin K and V. comma bacteriocin, respectively. Goebel et al. (1955) found that in medium containing 1% Difco Casamino acids, 1·5% glucose, 0·15% dialysed Difco yeast extract, 0·12% Na_2HPO_4 and 0·05% KH_2PO_4, it was essential that E. coli K 235 L^+O cultures be maintained at pH 7·0 for maximal colicin K production. Matsushita et al. (1960), using a tryptophan-dependent variant of this strain, E. coli K 235 Tr^-–3, later showed that, in the following medium: 0·02M ammonium salt, 0·2 g $MgSO_4$, 0·2% Casamino acids, 100 μg phosphorus per litre, 100 μg L-tryptophan per litre at pH 6·8, the nature of the anion of the ammonium salt used and of the primary carbon source markedly affected the production of colicin K. As can be seen in Table I, acetate and citrate have strong inhibitory action on colicin production in lactate medium but chloride and acetate have a similar effect in the glycerol medium.

After other experiments at a constant pH of 7·0 in a similar medium containing either glucose or lactate these authors concluded that glucose inactivated colicin K or inhibited its synthesis.

TABLE I
(Reproduced with permission from Matsushita et al., 1960)

**Effect of acetate and citrate upon colicin K production by
E. coli K 235 Tr⁻—3**

Carbon source (%)	Buffer	0·02M ammonium salt	Turbidity of culture	Colonies in culture (per ml)	Colicine K in supernate (units per ml)	Final pH of culture
0·2 glucose	0·05M maleate	Chloride	2700	$6·8 \times 10^9$	<2	6·79
		Acetate	2520	$5·6 \times 10^9$	<2	7·92
		Citrate	2640	$5·9 \times 10^9$	<2	6·76
0·5 glycerol	0·05M maleate	Chloride	3000	$6·1 \times 10^9$	8	5·92
		Acetate	3280	$6·6 \times 10^9$	8	5·90
		Citrate	2700	$5·6 \times 10^9$	64	6·17
0·9 lactate	0·05M tris	Chloride	4920	$6·5 \times 10^9$	1024	8·33
		Acetate	5670	$6·2 \times 10^9$	32	8·13
		Citrate	4680	$4·8 \times 10^9$	32	8·29

Farkas-Himsley and Seyfried (1963) studied the conditions affecting the production of *V. comma* bacteriocin in Oxoid nutrient broth and showed that this antibiotic was produced only if cultures in the logarithmic phase of growth, and containing between $7–9 \times 10^7$ and 2×10^8 bacteria per ml, were induced. No production occurred when early logarithmic or stationary phase cultures were used and the redox potential of the medium had to lie below -78 mV for any production at all to occur: optimal conditions were between -265 and -270 mV.

In a few instances chemically defined media have been developed which give yields as good as the complex media used initially. Ben-Gurion and Hartman (1958) used originally a proteose-peptone broth for pesticin production by *Pasteurella pestis* but later Hartman and Ben-Gurion (1958) showed that casein hydrolysate medium was equally good. They went on to substitute a chemically defined medium containing 18 amino-acids but finally eliminated all but eight of these; methionine, phenylalanine, valine, glycine, leucine, isoleucine, lysine and arginine, when incubated at 37°C. Arginine could be omitted when the incubation temperature was 27°C. This medium gave yields as high as those obtained in the proteose-peptone broth originally used. Alföldi (1958) has demonstrated that the requirement of a complex medium by *B. megaterium* 216 for post-induction megacin synthesis can be satisfied by a mineral salts medium containing glutamate and a sufficiently high level of manganese ions.

So far all the media mentioned in this Section have contained an organic source of nitrogen but media containing only an inorganic nitrogen source have been used, for example colicin 15 is produced by *E. coli* WT 15 in a glucose-ammonium salts basal medium (Sandoval *et al.*, 1965).†

Thus, the not altogether surprising conclusion emerges that the medium most suitable for production of a particular bacteriocin by a particular strain must be determined empirically. The need to determine the best conditions for production of bacteriocin in each instance is emphasized by some results in the recent publication of Herschman and Helinski (1967a) These authors found that two derivatives of *E. coli* W 3110, one colicinogenic for E2 and the other for E3, gave highest colicin yields under very different conditions. W 3110 (Col E2) was grown in a 100 litre fermenter to about 5×10^8 cells/ml and at this point 0·2 μg/ml mitomycin C was added and aeration was discontinued. Two hours later the culture was harvested and yielded a preparation having a titre of 23,000 arbitrary units per ml. If W 3110 (Col E3) was treated similarly it was found that the shift to anaerobic conditions after addition of mitomycin C resulted in an inhibition of colicin production. It was also found that cell lysis began about 1 h after addition of the inducer. Thus aeration was continued after mitomycin C addition and the cells harvested 50 min later; the activity of the culture being 50,000 arbitrary units per ml.

It is sometimes expedient to use complex media rich in organic nitrogen and increased yields may result from alteration of such factors as the nature and concentration of the carbon source, the form in which nitrogen is supplied, the concentration of certain ions and the conditions of pH, Eh and temperature. A paper by Mindich (1966) lists, but does not give details of, several factors affecting the production and action of pneumocin, namely: ionic strength, pH, temperature, presence of particular peptides and miscellaneous substances such as formate, carbonate, and tertiary and quaternary amines. However, in a number of instances relatively simple media have been devised which give satisfactory yields and render the task of purification easier.

In induced cultures the conditions giving best growth may lead to the best bacteriocin yields.

B. Production with time

Papavassiliou (1963) reported that colicin production does not seem to be dependent on the time of incubation of the culture of a colicinogenic strain since *E. coli* CA 38 and K 235 grown in Difco nutrient broth at 37°C

† Colicin 15 may be a "defective phage".

contained essentially the same colicin levels after 6, 8, 9 and 24 h and 7 days incubation, and Farkas-Himsley and Seyfried (1963) have also noted that *V. comma* bacteriocin levels were the same after 4, 12, and 24 h. However, Halbert and Magnuson (1948) found that, in solid synthetic medium containing succinate, the highest yield of colicin produced by *E. coli* 438 and extracted by the freeze–thaw method, occurred at 72 h whereas in a similar medium containing glutamate and succinate the maximum level was at 48 h. Moreover, Mayr-Harting and van Horn (1961) showed that, at the end of the logarithmic phase of growth of a culture in nutrient broth originally inoculated with about 100 organisms per ml, *E. coli* P9 (O) had produced only 2·5% of the total colicin found in a 48 h culture. At 16 h the level was about 35% and only at 32 h did the titre cease to increase. They have also shown that the inoculum size affects the time and level of maximum yield.

Thus the timing of bacteriocin harvest must also be determined empirically for each different organism, method, and set of conditions. The time needed to achieve the maximum yield is usually much reduced if the culture is induced.

C. Induction

Bacteriocin yields may often be increased from several to a thousand-fold by induction with u.v. light; by treatment with, or deprivation of, certain chemicals and by exposure to certain other physical conditions.

The process of induction is of great practical importance because of enhanced bacteriocin yield which is more reproducible than that of uninduced cultures. It is also advantageous in that the product may be harvested after only a few hours as opposed to a day or more in an uninduced culture. This gives a better preparation as little or no cell autolysis liberating contaminating polymeric material has occurred, the concentration of inhibitors is lower, and inactivators have had less time to act on the bacteriocin molecule.

1. *Ultraviolet light*

The effect of u.v. light in inducing colicin production was discovered by Jacob *et al.* (1951) using *E. coli* ML. These workers irradiated cultures in a chemically defined medium for 48 sec using a low pressure, high tension mercury vapour lamp giving an energy of 500 ergs/mm² at 2537 Å at a distance of 100 cm. After 150 min post-irradiation incubation, the level of colicin in the medium reached a maximum which, in this instance, coincided with a levelling-off of the sharp decrease in optical density of the culture (Jacob *et al.*, 1952). Such a decrease is not a feature of colicin production by all strains, most of which merely cease to divide with little or no decrease in optical density while colicin liberation continues at a relatively slow rate (Hamon, 1964). The difference between these two types of behaviour can be accounted for by the presence of inducible bacteriophage in the first type. Megacin A, on the other hand, is also produced with concomitant lysis of producer organisms after induction but bacteriophage lysis is not implicated.

The technique usually adopted for u.v. induction is exemplified by that of Holland (1961) who irradiated exponentially growing *B. megaterium* 216 cells in a tryptone–yeast extract–Lemco medium in a 2 mm layer in a dish which was rocked during the 60-sec irradiation period. The culture was reincubated for a further 90 min after induction. The lamp used was a Hanovia Chromatalite without a filter at a distance of 50 cm above the suspension, the energy supplied being nominally 1.5×10^3 ergs/cm^2, at least 75% of which was at 2537 Å. Some workers (e.g. Amati, 1964) suspend the cells to be induced in another medium that does not absorb u.v. light prior to induction and then transfer them to a further aliquot of growth medium for the post-induction incubation period. However, this is not mandatory and very large increases in titre have been obtained with short irradiation times in broth. Higerd *et al.* (1967), for example, irradiated 50 ml samples in a square dish (20.5×34.0 cm) of *Ps. aeruginosa* W9 growing in a 2% tryptone broth for 40 sec at a distance of 30 cm from a Westinghouse Steri-lamp 782L–20 and, after further incubation at 37°C for 3 h in the dark, obtained titres from 50 to 1000 times higher than those obtained in uninduced cultures.

Examples of the irradiation times and distances used with various lamps have been given here not with the intention that they should be regarded as typical, but to give some indication of the orders of magnitude of the variables in this method. We have found, when trying to repeat others' work, that it is usually impossible to translate the emission data in the literature into meaningful equivalents for our lamp owing to uncertainty as to the method used to measure the radiation. However, it is useful to measure the output of a lamp in some way to provide a check as to its performance. This is particularly important where ultraviolet filters are used, some of which increase in density with use.

It is therefore necessary to determine the optimal conditions for each system. Of these conditions the most critical is the duration of irradiation, for example see Reeves (1963).

Ozeki *et al.* (1959) have shown by using Lacuna Counts (see Section III.D) that the effect of u.v. light on a *S. typhimurium* LT2 derivative colicinogenic for E2 is to increase the number of producers from about 1% to over 50% of the population surviving irradiation.

2. Chemical induction

This method of induction is now widely used. It is much more convenient than the ultraviolet method since it usually only involves addition of the substance at a suitable level to the growing culture.

The most commonly used compound is mitomycin C, which is usually added to cultures in the logarithmic phase of growth to give a final concentration of 1 μg/ml.† After addition, cultures are reincubated for about 2 h before being harvested (e.g. de Witt and Helinski, 1965). However, both higher and lower concentrations are used; for example, Amati (1964) used 5 μg/ml for induction of *E. coli* C600, and Herschman and Helinski (1967a) used 0·2 μg/ml for induction of *E. coli* W3110. In one instance where the induction brought about by this compound and u.v. irradiation has been compared it was shown that the antibiotic produced a 200-fold increase in *Neisseria meningitidis* bacteriocin titre whereas u.v. light increased the yield only four-fold (Kingsbury, 1966).

Marjai and Ivánovics (1964) have surveyed a range of substances for the ability to induce megacin production by *B. megaterium* 216. The method they adopted was as follows: 100 ml Ehrlenmeyer flasks containing 10 ml aliquots of a synthetic medium were inoculated with 0·2 ml of an overnight culture in the same medium, and were then incubated at 37°C with gentle shaking. When the exponentially growing cultures had reached an optical density of 0·2, which corresponds to about 10^7 colony-forming organisms/ml, the chemicals were added to the cultures, which were then reincubated. It was found that of 20 compounds tested nitrogen-mustard, two ethylimines, mitomycin C and carcinophilin, hydrogen peroxide, and N-methyl-N'-Nitro-N-Nitrosoguanidine caused induction with lysis 1–3 h after their addition to the culture. Each compound was added at its bacteriostatic level which was determined in a preliminary experiment and which varied between 0·5 and 10,000 μg/ml.

Several dyes have also been used to induce colicin production. Use of Acridine orange in combination with exposure to white light by Šmarda et al. (1964) produced only a two-fold increase in colicin yield. Gentian violet similarly induced an eight-fold increase in titre in meat-peptone broth whereas in a salt medium no increase in colicin level occurred (Borunova and Girdo, 1966). Girdo later studied the effects of some other triphenylmethane dyes, and in addition to these chloramphenicol (CM) and 12 colicins, all of which were found to act as inducing agents. Of the dyes Crystal violet was the most effective inducer, and CM induced *E. coli* P678 (Col E1) and P678 (Col E2) after 2 h exposure; the optimal CM level for induction being 10–100 μg/ml. After induction CM must be

† Rather lower final concentrations, 0·1–0·4 μg/ml, are now commonly employed.

removed from the medium otherwise repression of the induced synthesis occurs. Girdo has also shown that certain combinations of these agents can increase the inducing effect. For example, Crystal violet increases induction with suboptimal doses of u.v. light but represses induction with optimal doses. It also increases the induction due to mitomycin.

The practical importance of these results is small but such methods do allow some insight into the mechanism of induction and it may be that in this respect they will prove valuable.

3. Deprivation induction

Certain colicinogenic thymineless *E. coli* strains can be induced by deprivation of thymine. Sicard and Devoret (1962) grew *E. coli* 15 T^- at 37°C in a minimal medium deficient in thymine for 90 min and then, after incubation in the presence of thymine for a further 90 min, demonstrated that colicin was detectable whereas it was not found in cultures grown in a normal medium. Luzzati and Chevalier (1964) have published fuller results of an investigation into induction of thymine deprivation using two derivatives of *E. coli* E118 a thymine-requiring mutant of *E. coli* K12 into one of which had been transferred Col factors E and V, and into the other E2. Other strains used were *E. coli* 15 T^- (Col$^+$) Col s, *E. coli* 15 T^- Pro$^-$ Try$^-$ (Col$^+$) Col r and *E. coli* 15 T^- h^- (Col$^+$) Col r. These authors confirmed that for colicin production it is essential that after a period of thymine deprivation the culture is incubated in a medium supplying thymine. The amount of colicin produced is a function of both the duration of thymine deficiency and the post-incubation period in a thymine-containing medium. With *E. coli* E118 (Col E1) (Col V) cells that were grown in a minimal medium containing proline (50 μg/ml) and thymine (1×10^{-4}M), washed twice with 0·15M NaCl, resuspended in minimal medium containing proline but no thymine, and incubated at 37°C, the maximum colicin production, after a post-incubation period of 60 min in the presence of thymine occurred in cells incubated without thymine for 180 min. The colicin yield increased rapidly to this maximum and fell off equally rapidly after it had been reached. For the other strains the maximum yields were obtained after the following times: *E. coli* 15 T^- Pro$^-$ Try$^-$ (Col$^+$) Col r and 15 T^- (Col$^+$) Col s: 80 min; *E. coli* 15 T^- h^- (Col$^+$) Col r: 20 min; *E. coli* E118 (Col E2): 260 min.

4. Temperature induction

Another method of induction, which is more useful in that it provides a means of investigating the mechanism of this process, is that brought about by high temperature treatment of temperature-sensitive mutants which when treated in this way produce bacteriocin. Kohiyama and

Nomura (1965) isolated such mutants by treating *E. coli* K 12 strain 162 (Col E2) with N-methyl-N'-nitro-N-nitrosoguanidine (600 μg/ml at pH 5·0 for 2 h at 37°C), plating survivors on nutrient agar and incubating at 30°C. Duplicate "replica" plates were then prepared and incubated at 30°C and 37°C and mutants growing at 30°C but not at 37°C were selected. The temperature-sensitive mutants thus obtained were grown in broth at 30°C to a population of about 1×10^8 per ml and then induced by transference to broth at 41°C. About one-fifth of the mutants thus treated had produced 50 times more colicin at the end of 150 min at 41°C than they had produced at 30°C.

Cold-shock treatment has been shown by Farkas-Himsley and Seyfried (1963) to induce greater yields of *V. comma* bacteriocin from organisms grown under thioglycollate-produced anaerobic conditions. The cultures were grown in nutrient broth for $1\frac{1}{2}$–2 h at 37°C to give about 8×10^7 cells/ml and then thioglycollate was added to a final concentration of 0·15%. After a total of about $3\frac{1}{2}$ h incubation at 37°C the cultures were incubated at 8°C overnight and then reincubated at 37°C when lysis and bacteriocin liberation occurred.

D. Inactivators and inhibitors

In some instances the yield of bacteriocin has been shown to be adversely affected by an inactivator. For example, the *Serratia marcescens* bacteriocin is produced, under some conditions, in parallel with an inactivator that appears to be an extracellular protease. In this instance the inactivation can be avoided by altering the incubation temperature of the bacteriocinogenic culture to one at which the antibiotic but not the enzyme is produced (Foulds and Shemin, 1969).

A specific inhibitor of colicin B, probably a lipopolysaccharide, is released into growth media by some mutants of *E. coli* (Gutterman and Luria, 1969). It is possible that such agents liberated by producer strains under certain conditions could affect the apparent yield of a bacteriocin.

E. Biosynthesis

1. *Determination of biosynthesis of bacteriocin*

In order to distinguish between biosynthesis and liberation of bacteriocin it is necessary to measure the concentration of the antibiotic both in the culture medium and within the producer cell.

Jacob *et al.* (1952) measured the latter by centrifuging off the bacteria, grinding them with sand and, after resuspending them in the initial volume of fluid estimating the colicin concentration. Ultrasonic disintegration of the bacterial cells is an alternative and rather more satisfactory method of disrupting cells since it does not necessitate separation of the bacteria from the growth medium. This method has been used to break down cells of *Shigella sonnei* P9 (O) in this laboratory (R. J. Gardner-Hopkins, personal communication, 1965). Care must be exercised when using this method to ensure that bacteriocin is not affected by the heat generated (Hughes *et al.*, this Series, Vol. 5B).

Megacin synthesis in *B. megaterium* 216 has been followed by Alföldi (1958) using lysozyme to break down the producer cells. The enzyme was added to a final concentration of 50 μg/ml when 15 min incubation at 37°C sufficed to cause lysis.

Herschman and Helinski (1967b) used a similar method to lyse several *E. coli* strains. In this instance 1·8 ml water, 0·2 ml of 0·07M EDTA, and 0·08 ml of a 10 mg/ml solution of lysozyme were added to 20 ml of culture and incubated for 5 min at 0°C when 0·04 ml of a 25% solution of sodium dodecyl sulphate was added.†

2. Lethality of synthesis

It is generally held that the biosynthesis of bacteriocin is lethal to the producer cell; an assertion that was incorporated into the original definition of "bacteriocin" (Jacob *et al.*, 1953). Evidence for this statement obtains from observations that the Lacuna Count Method (see Section III.D) produces areas of inhibition not having a central colony of producer organisms and from direct experiments such as that of Ozeki and his co-workers. Ozeki *et al.* (1959), using drops of medium containing single cells of a *S. typhimurium* LT2 derivative colicinogenic for E2, demonstrated that cells producing colicin were not subsequently viable. However, Herschman and Helinski (1967b) showed that *E. coli* strains, colicinogenic for E1, E2, and E3, died in the presence of chloramphenicol after induction with 0·2 μg/ml mitomycin C. This, of course, indicates that the *synthesis* of the colicin is not lethal but that some other event induced by mitomycin C must be responsible for the death of the induced cells.

V. ISOLATION AND PURIFICATION
OF BACTERIOCINS‡

A. Isolation

Bacteriocin may be present in solution in liquid cultures, in solid growth media or within bacterial cells, and before purification is started must be

† Care should be taken that the bacteriocin is not affected by treatment with such agents.

‡ Many of the methods falling into Sections VI and VII are methods applicable to any protein. Almost invariably these have been dealt with at length elsewhere and the treatment in these Sections is mainly confined to reference to illustrative examples drawn chiefly from the recent literature.

isolated in solution. When produced in liquid growth media the antibiotic preparation will usually contain dead cells or cell debris, which may be removed by centrifugation. Large volumes of culture fluid may in some instances be conveniently clarified using a Sharples centrifuge with a continuous feed (e.g. Barry et al., 1965). However it should be noted that Herschman and Helinski (1967a) found that after induction over 90% of the activity of colicins E2 and E3 was associated with the cell pellet and they removed this activity from the surface of the cells without causing cell lysis by three successive washes in a Waring Blender at low speed with 1·0M NaCl in 0·01M pH 7·0 phosphate buffer.† Membrane filtration has also been used to separate cells from broth cultures. Šmarda and Šmarda (1965) removed *Shigella dispar* P14 cells from 24-h broth cultures with an ultra-filter of average porosity 0·3–0·5 μm. However, it is frequently found that loss of activity may occur when bacteria are removed from colicin preparations by this method (see Section III).

If the bacteriocin is incorporated in a solid medium it is usual to extract it by a "freeze–thaw" technique exemplified by the extraction of *Bordetella pertussis* bacteriocin from brain heart infusion agar. The Petri dishes in which the producer organism had been grown on 15-ml aliquots of agar were frozen at −20°C for 48 h, thawed at 37°C, and the fluid containing the bacteriocin was separated from the collapsed agar by centrifugation at 10,000 g for 50 min at 40°C (Litkenhous and Liu, 1967).

Bacteriocin may also have to be extracted from cells. One example of such an extraction is that carried out by Homma and Suzuki (1964) who used lysozyme and EDTA at 150 μg/ml and 5×10^{-3}M, respectively, to lyse *Ps. aeruginosa*; the resulting soluble fraction being used as the starting material for purification.

B. Purification

The methods applied to bacteriocin purification are those which are generally used in protein purification and have been dealt with earlier in this Series (Vol. 5B) and elsewhere (e.g. Morris and Morris, 1963; Dixon and Webb, 1964). In this Section, then, there is no detailed treatment of the methods which have been applied to bacteriocins. However, three of Dixon and Webb's four prerequisites to purification are given since they are as relevant to bacteriocin as to enzyme. The fourth, preparation of a solution, has been dealt with above.

† In the case of E2–P9, Timmis (1970) found that it was impossible to elute bound colicin with NaCl from the *E. coli* K12 W1485 cells in this way. The mitomycin-induced cells were therefore concentrated by centrifugation, which served also to concentrate the bacteriocin, and broken by ultrasonic treatment. After a further centrifugation to remove the cell debris, the supernatant became the starting material for a purification procedure.

1. *Prerequisites for purification*

The assay method used to follow purification needs to be rapid, simple, and not necessarily very accurate. Unfortunately, such methods are conspicuous by their absence. Simple, inaccurate methods exist but speed is difficult to achieve in a biological assay.

A rapid method for determining protein is also required so that specific activity (i.e. units bacteriocin per mg protein)—which gives a measure of purity—may be estimated. This need is fulfilled by the method of determining absorption at 280 nm with a spectrophotometer. Inaccuracies are introduced by the presence of nucleic acids but can be partially corrected for if measurements are taken at both 260 nm and 280 nm and a formula such as the one given below applied:

$$\text{Protein (mg/ml)} = 1\cdot45\,E_{280} - 0\cdot74\,E_{260}$$

Alternatively protein may be estimated by a colorimetric method using the Folin phenol reagent (Lowry *et al.*, 1951).

It is also useful to adopt the practice of drawing up a table indicating the progress of the purification, including information of the following type: volume (ml), concentration (units/ml), total activity (arbitrary units), protein (mg/ml), specific activity (units/mg), yield (%), and degree of purification.

Finally, a reproducible rich initial source of bacteriocin considerably eases the task of purification and time spent seeking optimal conditions for production is not wasted.

2. *Concentration and removal of small molecules*

Unfortunately, it is not always possible to obtain a sufficiently concentrated source of bacteriocin and hence large initial volumes of solution are required which means that a first concentration step is necessary. Generally speaking, during concentration and purification the temperature should be kept as low as possible and the pH carefully controlled. Reference should be made to other parts of this work (Vol. 5) for fuller treatment of this subject but the necessity for constancy in the nature of the starting material for successful repetition of a purification procedure must be emphasized.

Concentration alone of *Lactobacillus fermenti* bacteriocin in a rotary evaporater at 40°C was achieved by de Klerk and Smit (1967) and of colicin K by Goebel and Barry (1958) by distillation *in vacuo* at below 20°C. Lyophilization, used to concentrate colicin A (Barry *et al.*, 1965), similarly effects only concentration.

Ultrafiltration achieves concentration of large molecules but not small ones. However, if large volumes have to be dealt with this method is impractical as also may be a two stage process of dialysis and concentration by evaporation. A similar criticism may apply to the method of carbowax concentration used by Litkenhous and Liu (1967). These methods are very useful where they follow a concentration process such as ammonium sulphate precipitation or fractional absorption by which initial large volumes may be easily reduced. Ammonium sulphate precipitation is frequently used as a preliminary concentration step and achieves in addition some puri- fication (e.g. Reeves, 1963; Sandoval *et al.*, 1965; Keene, 1966).

Which of these methods is chosen will depend on the volume and nature of the starting material, the apparatus available, and the sequence of the purification procedures.

Following this initial step the impure material is subjected to a suitable combination of some of the purification methods given below. Again the best protocol has to be determined empirically but, generally speaking, better results are obtained by avoiding repetition of a single method.

3. *Fractional precipitation*

Ammonium sulphate is the reagent most frequently used to bring about precipitation and some examples where it has been used are cited above. The reason for the choice of ammonium sulphate is that it is highly soluble and the solubility does not vary much with temperature. It has, however, the disadvantage that concentrated solutions are acidic and hence the pH must be adjusted with either ammonium hydroxide or sulphuric acid if pH alteration during fractionation is to be avoided.

The effect of variation of pH on the solubility of proteins has been made use of by Holland (1961) who, having determined that the minimum solu- bility of megacin in crude lysates of *B. megaterium* 216 was at about pH 4, adjusted 50 litres of material at 8°C to this pH by addition, with stirring, of about 2 litres of normal hydrochloric acid, thus causing the bacteriocin to precipitate.

Precipitation may also be brought about by lowering the dielectric constant of the bacteriocin solvent by addition of organic solvents. Goebel and his group (Hinsdill and Goebel, 1964), for example, used ethanol precipitation in their purification of colicin K. It is essential to carry out precipitation by organic solvents at a low temperature since a considerable amount of heat is generated when solvents such as ethanol are added to water.

4. *Fractional adsorption*

Although this method is widely used in enzyme purification it has been applied to the purification of bacteriocins in relatively few instances. Mindich (1966), for example, purified the bacteriocin of *Diplococcus pneumoniae* by adding 100 mg of bentonite to 5 litres of culture supernatant.

He then separated the bentonite by centrifugation, washed it once with 12 ml of water, and extracted twice with 8 ml of 10% pyridine (pH 5·5). This method achieved a better purification than one involving an ammonium sulphate precipitation. Glass powder was used in a similar way by Nüske *et al.* (1957) in their purification of *E. coli* SG 710 bacteriocin.

5. *Column chromatography*

The methods used and falling under this heading are not homogeneous with respect to the physical principles involved and can be divided into two groups.

(a) *Ion exchange chromatography.* The most widely used material in this process is DEAE-cellulose. Kageyama and Egami (1962) used this method in a procedure for the purification of pyocin. Other bacteriocins purified by this technique are colicin K (Rüde and Goebel, 1962) and colicin F (Reeves, 1963). However Dandeu and Barbu (1967a, 1967b) have found that colicins E and K could not be eluted from DEAE-cellulose columns.

(b) *Molecular exclusion chromatography.* This method has been used only rarely.† De Klerk and Smit (1967) used the cross-linked dextran, Sephadex G-100, in their procedure for the purification of the bacteriocin of *Lactobacillus fermenti* by column chromatography and Dandeu and Barbu 1967b) used G-200 in their purification of colicin K.

6. *Fractional denaturation*

Differences in the relative stability of some bacteriocins enable partial purification to be achieved by heat treatment. For example, the minor contaminating fraction in the crude colicin produced by *Shigella sonnei* P9 (O) can be destroyed by pasteurization at 65°C for 20 min leaving it pure with respect to colicin E2.

7. *Centrifugation*

Where the bacteriocin is of very large molecular size it is possible to make good use of this process in a purification procedure. Bradley and Dewar (1966) removed the bacterial cells from crude preparations of bacteriocins by centrifugation at 2000 to 3000 *g* and then centrifuged the supernatant at 15,000 *g* for 3–4 h. The resulting pellet was resuspended in 0·1 ml of neutral 0·1M ammonium acetate and centrifuged again at 2000 to 3000 *g* for 20 min to remove any remaining bacteria. Repetition of this procedure may be needed to obtain a pure preparation. The resulting supernatant suspension was then examined with an electron microscope.

† But is now used frequently (see, e.g. Jesaitis (1970), Timmis (1970)).

8. *Electrophoresis*

In addition to the above methods the zonal methods of electrophoresis are available for purification purposes although since they have been more widely, but not exclusively, used for analytical purposes in bacteriocin research they are dealt with in the Section below.

9. *Isoelectric Focusing*

This method, referred to on page 356, is now used preparatively, e.g. for colicin D (Timmis, 1970). (See Vesterberg, this Series, Vol. 5B.)

C. Criteria of purity

It is essential that any purified bacteriocin preparation is tested for homogeneity using more than one criterion. The methods available for checking purity fall into two main categories: electrophoresis and ultra-centrifugal analysis. It is generally found that with proteins homogeneity after electrophoresis is better evidence than apparent homogeneity in the ultracentrifuge (Dixon and Webb, 1964) and a particular example of this in the bacteriocin field is the inability of Herschman and Helinski (1967a) to distinguish between colicins E2 and E3 in the ultracentrifuge, yet they were readily separable by electrophoretic methods.

1. *Electrophoresis*

Most of the many variants of this technique have been used at one time or another and these are fully described elsewhere (Sargeant, this Series, Vol. 5B). Hence in this Section only some examples will be given.

Holland (1961) has examined a purified megacin preparation using two frontal methods both of which gave results characteristic of single-component systems. The disadvantage of such methods is that recovery of the separated components is difficult hence preventing assessment of the activity of the fractions. Similarly, certain zonal methods have been developed in which recovery of fractions is impracticable and which are useful only for analytical purposes. Disc electrophoresis methods such as that described by Ornstein (1964) fall into this category. Herschman and Helinski (1967a) have used this method to examine purified colicin E2 and E3 but the entire gel is stained with a protein dye to locate the fractions, thus making distinction between active and non-active protein impossible. However, with larger gels such as that used in the apparatus described by Smithies (1959) and used by Reeves (1963) to examine colicin F, it is possible, after a run, to slice the gel lengthways, stain one strip and extract for examination of activity the bacteriocins from the remaining strips using a suitable solvent. For example, Reeves (1963) used 20% (w/v) ammonium sulphate; 1M ammonium chloride; 4M urea.

Goebel and Barry (1958) have also used a large volume of supporting medium, for zone electrophoresis of colicin K. These authors found that starch and cellulose were unsatisfactory and used polyvinyl chloride. After running, the medium was cut into strips across the length of the gel, the fluid sucked off, and the supporting medium washed in a sintered-glass funnel. The resulting filtrates were then analysed for protein, carbohydrate, and colicin K activity.

Electrophoresis using a fibrous support is another variant which has been used occasionally. Nüske et al. (1957), for example, examined the purity of a colicin preparation from E. coli SG 710 with the apparatus described by Turba and Enenkel (1950) using filter paper, and Dandeu and Barbu (1967b) used cellulose acetate as a supporting medium for electrophoretic examination of colicin K.

The recently developed technique of isoelectric density gradient fractionation† described by Vesterberg and Svensson (1966), (Vesterberg, this Series, Vol. 5B) has been used by Herschman and Helinski (1967a) to examine purified colicin E2 and E3 preparations. Colicin E2 was separated into two fractions by disc electrophoresis and the use of the isolectric fractionation technique has enabled these authors to suggest that there were two fractions which are conformers of a single protein rather than iso-colicins since, on re-running both fractions, significant conversion to the alternative form occurred.

2. *Large plate electrophoresis*

This method is used mainly to examine crude bacteriocin preparations and is a measure of purity only in a loose sense in that it reveals the number of components produced by a particular strain. The results have been used to group bacteriocinogenic strains, in some instances for epidemiological purposes (Chapple, 1962a; 1962b).

The method was developed from one described by Ludford and Lederer (1953), and subsequently used by Chapple (1959), which allowed the examination of two strains per electrophoretic run on an agar strip in a Petri dish. The large plate method which was later developed (Chapple, 1962b and J. M. Picken, unpublished) enabled the electrophoretic examination of nine or ten strains on a single plate. This method has been used in a modified form by Maré et al. (1964) and some alterations have been made in this laboratory. The method currently in use here has been described by Smith (1966) but is reproduced for the sake of accessibility.‡

† Now generally called *isoelectric focusing*.

‡ This method has now been superseded, although it was used extensively by Seed (1970) early in her investigation (in this laboratory) of megacins. Later she used a starch-gel block technique, slicing the gel horizontally after a run and over-layering the slices with nutrient agar seeded with an indicator organism in order to locate the bacteriocin.

An apparatus was designed such that electrophoresis could be carried out in parallel in two glass dishes 12 in. × 12 in × 1 in. deep, chosen because they are flat-bottomed. It consists essentially of two perspex base plates supported on an angle iron frame. Each perspex base plate carries two buffer trays, also made of perspex, measuring 23·7 × 8·5 × 1 cm. In each of these platinum electrodes run the length of the tray and are connected to a d.c. power supply (Fig. 3).

Fig. 3. Electrophoresis of colicins: apparatus set up for large-plate method with plates in position. (Reproduced with permission from Smith, 1966.)

1200 ml of buffered agar is required for each experiment. A sodium phosphate buffer is usually used and this is initially made up to twice the required concentration. Four per cent Difco-Bacto agar is made by adding 24 g of Difco agar to 600 ml distilled water and heating until the powder is dissolved. The solution is then cooled to 60°C and mixed with 600 ml of the double strength phosphate buffer at the same temperature. Two sterile plates are warmed to 37°C, levelled in a specially designed stand with screw feet (Fig. 4), and 100 ml of buffered agar at 60°C are poured carefully in to give a uniformly thick layer. The plates are then covered and allowed to stand for 24 h before use. The remaining 1 litre of buffer agar is poured into an aluminium tray 28 × 10 × 5 cm, allowed to set and kept until required for use as the material providing electrical contact between the buffer tray and the agar in the large plates. For this purpose it is cut into four blocks one of which is placed in each tray and the large plates, colicin

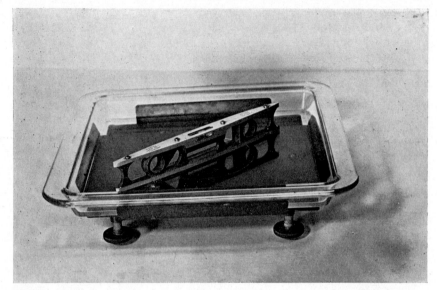

Fɪɢ. 4. Electrophoresis of colicins: levelling equipment for large plate method. (Reproduced with permission from Smith, 1966.)

having previously been added, are inverted on these blocks of agar, the inner edges of which are separated by 19 cm, and the current is applied.

Colicin is added to the agar, by one of two methods, at sites on the centre line of the large plate. The sites have previously been prepared by successive applications of three filter paper discs which are removed when saturated.

(a) Producer organisms are inoculated into Petri dishes of nutrient agar with a straight wire and incubated at 37°C for 48 h. Then plugs of agar containing colonies thus produced are cut out using a 9 mm cork borer and placed on the centre line of the agar in a large plate with the colony uppermost. The colicin is allowed to diffuse into the gel for 60 min at room temperature after which the agar plugs are removed.

(b) Producer organisms are grown in liquid culture and, after removal of the cells by centrifugation and sterilization of the supernatant by chloroform, drops are applied to the sites on the centre line and allowed to soak into the gel.

It is usual to apply two drops, from a 50 drops/ml Pasteur pipette, of a 15% (w/v) dextran C solution to each of two sites near the extremes of the centre line to give a measure of electro-osmotic flow and to check the uniformity of the electric field in the agar. The dextran spots, which move towards the cathode, can be seen after a separation as clear areas in the opalescent gel.

The usual duration of an electrophoretic separation is 6 h and at the end of this period the large plates are removed from the apparatus and inverted for about half an hour over chloroform to sterilize the surface of the agar. This sterilization procedure has been found unsatisfactory by Seed (1970) when working with megacin and she irradiates the surface of the gel with u.v. for 1 h using a Hanovia Chromatalite without a filter. After this the surface is dried in an incubator and each plate is over-layered with 75 ml amounts of 1% nutrient agar at 50°C to which has been added 1 ml of an overnight culture of the indicator strain. The plates are then refrigerated at 4°C for 12 h to allow diffusion of the colicin from the buffered agar into the seeded agar layer to take place. The plates are then incubated overnight at 37°C and examined for inhibition zones.

Smith (1966) has systematically studied the variables in the above method and has concluded that for the colicins examined a current of 37·5 mA, and a voltage of 75 V applied to a gel made up in Sørensen's phosphate buffer pH 7·6 for 6 h gives the best separation.

Several support-media alternative to Difco agar were tried. With agarose less resolution was obtained, and no movement of the bacteriocin was obtained in starch gels of suitable concentration. Polyacrylamide gels were prepared in specially made perspex trays rather smaller than the large plates but this support-medium did not allow confluent growth of the indicator strain and the non-specific method of staining with a solution of Naphthalene black 10B had to be adopted. Pevikon C-870 also proved unsatisfactory and the Difco agar support-medium is still used.

3. *Ultracentrifugal analysis*

Several workers have used this method (Sykes, this Series, Vol. 5B) to examine the homogeneity of purified bacteriocin preparations, for example, megacin by Holland (1961), colicins E2 and E3 by Herschman and Helinski (1967a) and pyocin by Homma and Suzuki (1964).

4. *Immunological methods*

Evidence of homogeneity may be obtained from precipitation lines; single lines formed after double diffusion indicating immunochemical homogeneity. Dandeu and Barbu (1967b) and Herschman and Helinski (1967a) have applied this criterion to colicins K, and E2 and E3 respectively. The homogeneity of colicin CA42–E2 has been tested by Reeves (1965a) by immunoelectrophoresis as has that of colicin K (Hinsdill and Goebel, 1964).

VI. PHYSICAL AND CHEMICAL PROPERTIES
OF BACTERIOCINS

The earliest evidence as to the nature of bacteriocins was obtained from experiments on the degradation of crude preparations of these antibiotics by proteolytic enzymes. Also, rough estimates of the molecular size were made from a consideration of the diffusibility of the substances through agar and through semi-permeable membranes. Such methods are still useful in initial studies on newly discovered bacteriocins as is exemplified by the description of colicin Q by Šmarda and Obdržálek (1966) but with the availability of increasing numbers of pure bacteriocin preparations several of these antibacterial agents have been described in terms of more precise chemical analyses and physical measurements.

A. Chemical properties

Evidence as to the gross chemical nature of a bacteriocin is easily obtained using enzymes. For example, Kingsbury (1966) has used pronase, trypsin, deoxyribonuclease and ribonuclease to determine the nature of the bacteriocin produced by *Neisseria meningitidis*. However it should be noted that although pyocin is regarded as a protein, Kageyama and Egami (1962) found that in its native form its activity was unaffected by trypsin, chymotrypsin, nagarase and pronase, but after heating this pyocin at 75°C for 10 min the bacteriocin was digested by nagarase (Kageyama, 1964). It is frequently found that bacteria which are proteolytic enzyme producers also produce bacteriocins resistant to these enzymes and conversely that bacteriocins produced by non-proteolytic bacteria are susceptible (Hamon, 1964). To test the sensitivity of these antibiotics they are usually incubated in solution at a pH and temperature appropriate to the particular enzyme but susceptibility to a proteolytic enzyme may also be demonstrated in solid media. The method used (Fredericq, 1948a) was to streak the producer organism across a plate of growth medium, cross-streak with a proteolytic enzyme producing organism and, after incubation and subsequent removal of the growth, the surface of the medium was seeded with an indicator organism. Where the bacteriocin was destroyed by the enzyme no inhibition zone was seen.

The chemical characteristics of purified bacteriocins have been investigated by two types of analysis. The first of these is an elementary analysis and is usually confined to estimation of nitrogen and phosphorus. Frequently analyses of the second type, for the main biological polymers or their constituents, are performed concurrently. A recent paper by de Klerk and Smit (1967) gives results of both these types of analysis on *L. fermenti* bacteriocin. Nitrogen was determined by a micro-Kjeldahl technique and phosphorus as total phosphate after treatment of the bacteriocin with 12N-perchloric acid. Carbohydrate and lipid were estimated after suitable hydrolysis of the bacteriocin, hexosamine being separated from interfering sugars and lipids by cation exchange chromatography and then estimated by a modified Elson–Morgan technique. Neutral sugars were eluted from a cation exchange column with water, concentrated by evaporation under reduced pressure at low temperature and separated by descending paper chromatography. After location of the position of the separated sugars in a test strip the corresponding areas of the experimental chromatogram were excised and eluted with distilled water, the eluates concentrated and sugar levels determined by an anthrone method. Lipid was determined by weighing the dried material left after evaporation of the ether from an ether extract of the hydrolysate. The protein content of the bacteriocin was determined using the method of Lowry et al. (1951). The amino-acid complement of bacteriocins may be determined, after hydrolysis, by paper chromatography and some indication of the quantitatively more important acids can be obtained from the results but use of an amino-acid analyser is advantageous in the quantitative estimation of the amino-acid residues in a hydrolysate. Colicins E2, E3 (Herschman and Helinski, 1967a), pyocin (Kageyama, 1964) and the bacteriocin of *Lactobacillus fermenti* (de Klerk and Smit, 1967) are examples of bacteriocins whose amino-acid compositions have been determined in this way.

B. Physical properties

Some sort of comparison of the molecular sizes of bacteriocins can be made by studying their diffusibility through agar. The method used by Šmarda and Obdržálek (1966) is to drop 0·1 ml of a colicin solution of known concentration on to a disc of filter paper on the surface of an agar plate. The size of the inhibition zone in the lawn of the indicator organism after various prediffusion times gives an indication of the diffusion speed. Colicin Q is second only to colicin V in speed of diffusion (Šmarda and Obdržálek, 1966) whereas colicin ML diffuses badly (Jacob et al., 1952). The permeability to bacteriocin of a semi-permeable membrane can also give an indication of its molecular size. Neither colicin Q (Šmarda and Obdržálek, 1966) nor colicin ML (Jacob et al., 1952) are dialysable whereas colicin V does pass through cellophane.

Several workers have commented on the inability of bacteriocins to pass through filters such as the porcelain Chamberland type (Jacob et al., 1952). Šmarda and Obdržálek (1966) have tested the filterability of colicin Q through a series of collodion ultrafilters of known average pore size ranging from 55–11 nm; they have also found that colicin Q will pass through an ultrafilter of average pore size 10–5 nm (Membranfiltergesell-schaft, Göttingen) but have noted that 40–85% of the total amount of colicin was adsorbed on to the ultrafilter. This is a well known problem connected with filtration of bacteriocins (see Section III) and the absence of such an antibiotic from a filtrate should not necessarily be taken to indicate that the molecule is too large to pass through the pores of the filter.

Estimates of the molecular weight of bacteriocins have been made as a result of the comparison of the elution position from a Sephadex column of the antibiotic with that of proteins of known molecular weight and Dandeu and Barbu (1967b) estimated that the molecular weight of colicin K is of the order of 75,000 using this method.

Jesaitis (1970), also working with colicin K, estimated the Stokes radius of this molecule from its elution position from a G-200 Sephadex column relative to that for the monomer of bovine serum albumin. The value obtained was used together with values for the colicin's sedimentation rate and partial specific volume to estimate the molecular weight as ca. 45,000. The frictional ratio, f/f_o, was calculated to be 1·70, which indicates a highly asymmetric molecule and probably accounts for the discrepancy between her value for the molecular weight and that of Dandeu and Barbu (1967b). Similar, high, frictional values were obtained by Konisky and Richards (1970) from a consideration of $s_{20, w}^{\circ}$ and $D_{20, w}^{\circ}$ data for colicins Ia and Ib. These authors also calculated from published data that the f/f_o value for colicins E2 and E3 is 1·41 and for colicin E1 is 1·75.

Thus caution must be exercised in accepting molecular weight estimates obtained from molecular exclusion chromatography data. However, in some instances better agreement is obtained between results from this method and from ultracentrifugal studies. For example, Timmis (1970) found the molecular weight of colicin D to be ca. 89,000 from $s_{20, w}^{\circ}$ and $D_{20, w}^{\circ}$ values and ca. 90,000–10,000 from Sephadex G-200 elution data. Examples of other bacteriocins for which molecular weight determinations have been made by using the ultracentrifuge are: pyocin (Kageyama, 1964)—8,800,000; colicin E2 (Herschman and Helinski, 1967a)—62,000; and megacin (Holland, 1961)—51,000.

The molecular weights of colicins Ia and Ib (Konisky and Richards, 1970) and D (Timmis, 1970) have also been estimated by the sodium dodecyl sulphate (SDS) polyacrylamide gel electrophoresis method of Shapiro et al. (1967).

The isoelectric point (pI) of bacteriocins can be determined by the isoelectric focusing method, mentioned earlier (p. 356). For example, Jesaitis (1970) found the pI of two components of colicin K to be 5·14 and 5·21.

C. Stability

The stability of a bacteriocin preparation is of practical importance when choosing methods of manipulation. Like many biologically active proteins the stability of several bacteriocins has been shown to decrease with increasing purity and this fact must be borne in mind when handling these substances. It must also be remembered that although factors affecting stability are treated individually below they are to a great extent interrelated. Thus, ideally, a full description of the purity of the preparation and the conditions during treatment is required with any statement regarding stability.

The factors affecting stability of greatest interest are temperature, pH and the various agents, in addition to heat, such as u.v. light and chloroform used to sterilize bacteriocin preparations.

The heat stability of bacteriocins differs considerably and in some instances this has enabled differential destruction to be carried out. The crude bacteriocin from *Sh. sonnei* P9 (O) consists of colicin E2 together with a smaller contaminating fraction which can be removed by pasteurization since colicin E2 is stable at 65°C in broth at pH 7·6 for nearly 30 min and treatment at 60°C for 30 min causes no loss of activity. Preparations of this same bacteriocin in a basal salts medium are, however, very much more sensitive to temperature and begin to lose activity at room temperature fairly quickly. Most bacteriocins can be lyophilized and recovered without great loss of activity but exceptions to this generality are known. Kageyama and Egami (1962), for example, found that pyocin activity was destroyed after lyophilization.

The effect of variation in pH on potency after 24 h at 37°C on some bacteriocins is small except at the extremes of the pH scale (Šmarda and Obdržálek, 1966). In contrast others such as some pyocins are stable at 37°C only between pH 7–9 (Kageyama and Egami, 1962).

Chloroform is routinely used in the sterilization of several bacteriocins but the potency of some of them is reduced by this agent. According to Hamon (1964) the colicins of group E are rapidly inactivated by chloroform and the activity of colicin I is reduced by this compound (Keene, 1966). However crude colicin E2 preparations in broth are sometimes sterilized with chloroform in this laboratory† and only when the antibiotic is in solutions with low protein content or is kept in contact with the chloroform for more than a few hours does this treatment cause loss of activity. Formalin is not so often used as a sterilant but Keene (1966) found that colicin I activity was completely destroyed by this compound.

† Azide and chlorhexidine have been found to be useful inhibitors of bacterial growth during chromatography (see Section V.B, 5).

Ultraviolet light is less frequently used as a sterilant but colicins in solution in broth, as would be expected, are highly resistant although inactivation will occur after prolonged exposure to high doses. Colicin Q, for example, loses activity when irradiated in broth with a 300 W lamp at a distance of 30 cm for 1 h (Šmarda and Obdržálek, 1966).

VII. SEROLOGY

Hamon (1956b) listed the use of serological methods in bacteriocin research under three headings: (i) as an aid to classification of bacteriocins; (ii) to distinguish between components of complex bacteriocins; (iii) to eliminate bacteriocin when searching for lysogenic phage. The intrinsic interest that attaches to bacteriocins as antigens and to their immune reactions might well be added to the list.

Although some bacteriocins have not yet been examined for antigenicity, most of those that have been studied are capable of stimulating the production of specific antibodies under suitable conditions.

A. Preparation of antisera

1. *Preparation of bacteriocins for immunization*

The authors with the greatest experience in the serological study of bacteriocins have grown the producer cultures in media which contained only, or largely, dialysable substances. The medium used by Goebel and Barry (1958), Amano *et al.* (1959) and by Hutton and Goebel (1962) for colicin K and colicin V was prepared by adding to 15 litres of 1% Casamino-acid containing 0·03M phosphate at pH 7·0 the sterile concentrated dialysate from 4 lb of beef-heart infusion, and the sterile dialysate of 25 g Difco yeast extract; as an energy source 300 ml of a neutralized 30% solution of sodium lactate and 450 ml of 50% glucose were used.

The colicins obtained from these cultures were further purified partly or completely (see Section V).

Hamon (1957) immunized rabbits with enormous doses of colicins or pyocins; the injections were tolerated well—a fact which he attributes to having grown the producers in 3% peptone water prepared with a peptone (Vaillant, Volume 5B), which contains a large proportion of small molecules (amino-acids, dipeptides). Bacteriocin production was improved by the addition of 10% infusion broth to the medium, without increasing the toxicity of the product. For injection, 10 ml of bacteriocin was diluted with 50 ml physiological salt solution.

To obtain single bacteriocins rather than mixtures as antigens, Hamon made use, wherever possible, of u.v.-induced or transferred colicins on the assumption that, of several bacteriocins, only one might be inducible, only one transferable.

In this laboratory, colicin E2–P9 has been studied serologically. The producer organisms are grown in the ordinary meat-infusion-peptone-broth for 48 h. They are then spun off and the supernatant is sterilized by heating for 30 min at 60°C or by filtration through a membrane filter (Smith, 1966); it is then freeze-dried and concentrated by taking it up, just before use, in distilled water to one-half or one-third of the volume of the crude preparation used for freeze-drying.

We have had few losses of animals due to toxic effects of the immunizing preparations.[†]

2. Course of immunization

Goebel and his collaborators (references as in A, 1, above) made antisera not only against the purified colicins K and V which were electrophoretically homogeneous, but also against trypsin-degraded colicins which had lost their antibacterial properties but which were still highly antigenic, and against the protein part of colicin K obtained by dissociating the purified colicin with phenol. They further prepared antisera against the producer bacteria, against a mutant which was no longer colicinogenic, and against the purified O-antigens of these organisms.

Antiserum against the sterile purified and the degraded colicin was made by wetting weighed samples of each with 0·5 ml of alcohol and dissolving them in saline. The rabbits received a preliminary intradermal injection of 0·2 ml containing 5 mg of colicin preparation per ml. One week later they were injected intravenously on alternate days with 0·1, 0·2, and 0·5 mg. After a week's interval a further course of three injections of 0·5 and 1·0 mg was given and this was repeated after yet another week. The rabbits were bled one week after the last injection.

For the antibacterial sera living organisms only were used. Here, too, the courses were introduced by an intradermal injection of 0·2 ml containing 10^{10} cells per ml. After a 5-day pause intravenous injections were given at 3- to 4-day intervals, at doses of $2·5 \times 10^7$, 5×10^7 and 5×10^7 cells. After a week's rest a second course followed of three injections, each of 10^9 cells. After another week's interval a third course was given with dosage as for the second course. The animals were bled one week after the last injection.

Antiserum against the protein component of colicin K was prepared by mixing this component with complete Freund's adjuvant and injecting it subcutaneously in three doses of 2·0 mg of antigen at roughly monthly intervals. These animals were bled two weeks after the last injection.

[†] Successful immunization has been achieved with highly purified colicin D (Timmis, 1970).

Hamon immunized rabbits by intraperitoneal injections, giving a total of nine injections over three weeks. The volume used each time was 60 ml, made up of 10 ml of the crude bacteriocin (sterilized with chloroform) and 50 ml physiological salt solution.

R. Shannon (personal communication), Smith (1966) and Mayr-Harting (unpublished experiments) immunized rabbits against colicin E2–P9 and against the producer organisms. The animals were given 5–6 intravenous injections at ca. 5-day intervals. The volumes were increased from 1 ml to 3 ml of the slightly concentrated colicin solution. Particularly high titres were obtained on one occasion when, accidentally, an interval of a fortnight had occurred half-way through an immunization course. It might be worthwhile to explore the possibilities of fewer injections at intervals rather longer than usual.

The preparation of antibacterial sera followed a similar pattern. Only killed organisms were used (30 min at 60°C) and the dosage rose from ca. 5×10^7 organisms to ca. 2×10^9 in saline. The volume injected was always 1 ml.

Holland (1961, 1962), for his preparation of antiserum against megacin A, diluted the purified megacin in sterile phosphate buffer and mixed it 1 : 1 with an adjuvant consisting of 9 vol Bayol F and 1 vol Arlasel A. Antiserum prepared with an antigen without adjuvant had no precipitating properties, and its neutralization titre was appreciably lower than that of the "adjuvant" serum. Rabbits were injected twice weekly for 9 weeks, each time with 96 μg megacin protein.

According to Nagy et al. (1959) the bacteriocin produced by B. megaterium 216, i.e. megacin A, is the only megacin having antigenic properties.

B. Serological reactions

1. Use of neutralization tests for classification of bacteriocins

This method was found particularly useful by Hamon (1957) who used it in the classification of bacteriocins to which resistant mutants are impossible to obtain (e.g. some pyocins) so that classification on the basis of cross-resistance is not possible. He noticed also that many antisera act on more than only the homologous bacteriocin and it is thus possible to classify by serological means even those which are poor antigens.

Before the neutralization test proper, Hamon determines the "Critical Test Dilution" (CTD) of the bacteriocin, i.e. the highest dilution which, when spotted on a plate inoculated with a standard number of sensitive organisms, gives complete inhibition in the area of the spot. In the neutralization test, 0·9 ml of bacteriocin at CTD is mixed with 0·1 ml of antiserum so as to give final antiserum dilutions ranging from 1 : 10 to

1 : 1000. The mixtures are kept at 37°C for 24 h and then spotted on plates carpeted with the standard inoculum.

2. *Distinction between neutralizing and precipitating antibodies*

Amano *et al.* (1959) made this distinction† and the methods dealing with these two kinds of antibodies will, therefore, be treated here separately.

(a) *Neutralizing antibodies*

(i) Neutralization tests based on the spot method.

Amano *et al.* (1959) carried these out as follows: 0·5 ml of antiserum in a series of dilutions was added to 200 μg of the purified colicin K in 0·5 ml saline. The tubes were incubated for 2 h at 37°C and then stored at 5°C overnight. A loopful of each mixture was then spotted on a colicin assay plate which had been prepared by pouring 2·5 ml of molten agar (0·5%) seeded with 5×10^7 cells of *E. coli* B on a base layer of nutrient agar. The plates were incubated for 6 h at 37°C and then read. The endpoint was the highest dilution of serum which so completely neutralized the colicin that there was no inhibition of growth.

A variation of this method was used by Hutton and Goebel (1962). Plates were prepared with soft agar seeded with *E. coli* C6 to which was added 0·3 ml of anticolicin serum, against either colicin K or V. The plates were then spotted with the appropriate colicin dilutions. The perfect specificity of neutralization, i.e. anti-K serum acting only on colicin K and anti-V serum neutralizing only colicin V, was clear-cut.

That the neutralizing action of the antiserum is an immunological reaction and not an enzymatic destruction of the colicin could be demonstrated in the following experiment: a 1 : 40 dilution of anti-K serum was allowed to react with a preparation of colicin K (200 μg/ml) for 2 h at 37°C and overnight at 5°C; the colicin was completely neutralized. The antibodies were then destroyed by heating for 15 min at 100°C. About half the original colicin activity could still be recovered.

(ii) Neutralization tests using the Diffusion Zone Method.

By this method (Smith, 1966; Mayr-Harting, unpublished experiments) it is possible to express the antiserum potency in terms of the number of Lethal Units of colicin E2 which it neutralizes. The assay plates are set up as described in Section III.B, 3. The mixtures of colicin with antiserum in various dilutions are incubated for 1 h at 37°C in a waterbath and then pipetted into the punch holes of the assay plates. The decrease in the colicin titre can be determined accurately by comparing the diameter of the inhibition zones with those of a standard curve for the colicin.

Some further experiments and the work described under (iii) suggest

† But see p. 369.

that preincubation of the antiserum–colicin mixture may be unnecessary.

(iii) Neutralization of colicin adsorbed to the cell.

Kudlay *et al.* (1966) studied the effect of antiserum in the reversal of the action of colicin already adsorbed to cells. They worked with colicin S5 produced by *Shigella alcalescens* P14, and their preparations contained between 5×10^7 and 2×10^8 Lethal Units per ml.

The colicin preparation was added to a logarithmic phase culture of *E. coli* K 12 Hfr (H) and the mixture was incubated for 20 min at 37°C. Dilutions were then made in antiserum to a final dilution of 1 : 4 of the latter and at 5-min intervals samples were taken for viable counts. Whereas in normal rabbit serum and in antibacterial serum the numbers of viable bacteria dropped as rapidly as in the colicin control without serum, the number of survivors decreased only very slowly in the mixtures with anti-colicin serum. The authors point out that antiserum, like trypsin, can cause a complete reversal of the lethal action of the colicin, even after adsorption of the colicin to the cell must be virtually complete (see Section VIII.A, 4). Similar results were reported for colicin E1 by Šmarda (1965b).

Although these investigations were not carried out with a view to assaying the potency of the antiserum, survivor counts might be a very suitable method for this purpose, provided the colicin is used in a multiplicity of not more than one Lethal Unit per cell. It might also be possible to determine a velocity constant of antiserum action, similar to the constant K which measures the potency of an antiphage serum.

(b) *Precipitating antibodies*

(i) Tube tests.

The orthodox tube precipitin test as applied to anti-colicin serum was described by Hutton and Goebel (1962). 0·5 ml of a dilution of antiserum (two parts serum, three parts saline) was mixed with 0·5 ml of appropriate dilutions of the antigen. The reactions were read after 2 h at 37°C and 18 h at 4°C.

Experiments of this pattern also permitted a quantitative determination of the precipitable antibody nitrogen in the antiserum (Amano *et al.*, 1959). Varying quantities of colicin (12·5–400 μg) were dissolved in 0·5 ml of saline containing 0·01% merthiolate, and mixed with 0·5 ml of a 1 : 3 dilution of the homologous antiserum. The tubes were incubated at 37°C for 1 h and at 5°C for 1 week and were shaken daily. The precipitates were sedimented by centrifuging, washed twice with chilled saline, and dissolved with three drops of 0·5N NaOH. The samples were then brought up to a volume of 2·5 ml with saline and analysed for tyrosine by a modification of the Folin–Ciocalteu method. The amount of precipitated antibody could be determined from a protein standard curve, obtained by using an antibody solution prepared by fractionating at 50% saturation with $(NH_4)_2SO_4$.

By testing throughout the range (from excess antibody to excess antigen) for colicin activity of the supernatants, they found that even supernatants containing an excess of antigen no longer showed any colicin activity. To precipitate 200 μg of colicin, 26 times more antiserum had to be used than would have been sufficient for its neutralization.

Colicin was precipitated not only by the homologous antiserum and by the antiserum against the producer strain, but also by the antiserum against the Col⁻ mutant which did not neutralize it. Vice versa, the anti-colicin serum agglutinated the Col⁻ mutant to the same titre as the producer strain. Agglutination reactions were set up by preparing antiserum dilutions and mixing 0·5 ml of these with 0·5 ml of a suspension of 10^9 living organisms per ml in saline. Incubation was for 2 h at 37°C and at 5°C overnight.

(ii) Agar gel precipitation tests.

In the searching experiments by Amano et al. (1959) and Hutton and Goebel (1962) agar gel diffusion was carried out as described by Ouchterlony (1962, 1953) (Oakley, this Series, Vol. 5A). One per cent agar (Baltimore Biological Laboratory) in 0·1M borate buffer was used, with 0·1 g of merthiolate per litre added as a preservative. A piece of 1-in. adhesive tape was placed across one end of a glass slide (2 by 3 in.). Five ml molten 1·5% agar was next poured on the slide and when it had set a pattern of wells was cut with a stainless steel cutter and a "Perspex" mould. The holes were 6 mm in dia. and at a distance of 8 mm from each other, centre to centre. Two drops of the test dilutions were put into the wells; the slides were incubated for 48 h at room temperature and then photographed. In the earlier experiments plates were used, and these were incubated for one week at 37°C before being photographed.

† There was clear-cut "looping" of the lines formed by colicin K with those formed by the antigen extract from the Col⁻ mutant against the colicin antiserum, showing that the precipitation was due entirely to the O-antigen component present in the colicin preparation. This was confirmed when the anti-colicin serum after absorption with the cells of the non-colicinogenic mutant no longer formed precipitation lines with the colicin although it still neutralized. The later experiments showed again the strict specificity of the antisera produced against colicins K and V.

There is a discrepancy in results between the experiments reported in 1958 and those reported in 1962 by Goebel and his colleagues. In the early experiments dealing only with colicin K, double precipitation lines between the colicin and its antibody were observed although the purified colicin

† See footnote on p. 367.

15

had appeared homogeneous when examined by electrophoresis. In the later experiments, each of the colicins examined showed only one precipitation line. The authors do not comment on this but it seems possible that the cause for this discrepancy lies in the different temperature and duration of incubation of the experimental material.

Smith (1966) used E2 colicins and their various producer organisms as antigens. Her precipitation tests were carried out in 20 ml volumes of 1% Difco Noble agar in saline poured into Petri dishes. To facilitate cutting clean wells the plates were refrigerated for 1 h beforehand. The wells were 9 mm in dia. and were cut so that four surrounded a central well at a distance of 6 mm (edge to edge) from it. The central well was filled with antiserum; the outer ones with colicin.

In one series of experiments, following up some earlier experiments by R. Shannon (personal communication), Smith used 9 mm dia. plugs of nutrient agar with 48-h colonies of the producer strain on the surface, instead of wells filled with the antigen. These plugs were placed on the agar 2 h before the antiserum was put into the central well to allow the colicin time to diffuse from the plugs into the plate.

R. Shannon (personal communication) considerably reduced the size of the experimental set-up by using microscope slides (1 by 3 in.). One ml of Difco Noble agar in saline was pipetted on to the centre third of the slide and contained there by grease-pencil marks drawn beforehand. The central well for the antiserum and the cylindrical blocks of agar cut out with the producer strains on their surface were 4 mm in dia. (No. 1 cork borer); the distance (edge to edge) from the central well to the small agar blocks was 5 mm. Incubation was at room temperature in a moist chamber for 2–3 days.

The results obtained by both these workers for colicin E2 were analogous to the results of Goebel and his colleagues for colicins K and V.

(c) *Complement-fixing antibodies.* Ivánovics *et al.* (1959b) carried out complement-fixation tests with megacin and megacin antiserum, besides describing neutralization and precipitation tests. With crude lysozyme lysates of induced producer cells and with megacin concentrate the specific antiserum, which had been absorbed with an extract of the uninduced cells, gave a positive complement-fixation test up to a titre of 1 : 250. With the lysozyme extract of non-induced cells the reaction was negative.

VIII. REACTION OF BACTERIOCIN WITH THE SENSITIVE CELL

Although most experimental work on this subject has employed various colicin indicator systems, results obtained with other bacteriocins (except, perhaps, megacin A) support similar general conclusions.

It is now generally accepted that the reaction of bacteriocin with a sensitive cell may be divided into two main phases. The first consists of a rapid, normally irreversible,† adsorption to specific receptors at the cell "surface" (Adsorption Phase). This is followed, some measurable time later, by the appearance of pathological changes leading eventually to death of the cell (Lethal Phase). Whereas the Adsorption Phase occurs in resting, or even dead cells, progression to the Lethal Phase is energy-dependent and its onset may be delayed by use of metabolic inhibitors.

The subject has been discussed and reviewed by Reeves (1965a), Nomura and Maeda (1965) and Nomura (1964, 1967a).

A. Nature and number of receptors

1. *Specificity and irreversibility of adsorption*

Information on the specificity of the adsorption of bacteriocin by sensitive cells has come from five main experimental approaches: (a) genetical; (b) quantitative adsorption; (c) inhibition of adsorption; (d) serological; (e) experiments with radioactive bacteriocin. The work with radioactive bacteriocin, which confirms and extends the conclusions obtained from the other approaches, will be separately dealt with in Section A, 4, below.

(a) *Genetical observations.* It has long been known that strains of bacteria that are normally sensitive to several types of colicin may produce mutant clones which are resistant to only one of these types. This observation was one of the earliest pointers to the possible specificity of fixation of bacteriocin by the sensitive cell (see Section IX.E).

(b) *Quantitative adsorption experiments.* The principle of this approach is as follows. A bacteriocin solution of known potency is allowed to react with an excess of the cells under examination. After sufficient time has been allowed for adsorption (see Section III.B, 2 and VIII.B, 2) the cells are removed by centrifugation, and the residual bacteriocin in the supernatant fluid is assayed. By comparison of the original and residual potencies it is possible to decide whether, and to what extent, adsorption has occurred.

The method, and its pitfalls, will be described under Section A, 3, but where it has been successfully applied the following results have been obtained:

(i) Sensitive cells remove bacteriocin from solution (Mayr-Harting, 1964; Mayr-Harting and Shimeld, 1965; Šmarda, 1965a; Šmarda and Šmarda, 1965).

† But see p. 374.

(ii) Dead "sensitive" cells may adsorb bacteriocin provided that they are killed by methods that do not damage the receptors (Mayr-Harting and Shimeld, 1965).

(iii) Cells of bacteriocin-resistant mutants adsorb either hardly at all (Hamon and Péron, 1960; Reeves, 1965b; Mayr-Harting, unpublished experiments, and see Section A, 4) or markedly less than their "sensitive" related strains (Šmarda, 1965a; Šmarda and Šmarda, 1965).

(iv) Isolated cell walls adsorb megacin C, whereas isolated cytoplasmic membranes do not (Holland, 1967b)—*but see footnote to p.* 392.

The results of the Šmardas showed that whereas a population of sensitive cells reduced the titre of a colicin E3 solution to 0.3% of its original potency, when resistant cells were used under similar conditions the residual titre was 12.5% of the original. Although these figures are probably of low precision the results strongly suggest that there may be "non-specific" adsorption in addition to the specific (and lethal) uptake of bacteriocin. The same authors pointed out that they obtained significant (44%) adsorption when the heterologous *Staphylococcus aureus* was used in place of the coliform indicator strains. The divergence between these results and those which suggest that such non-specific adsorption, if it occurs, is very small may reflect the difference encountered not only between different cell strains, but also in the same strain when grown under different conditions of cultivation (see Section A, 3).

(c) *Inhibition of adsorption.* Some of the earliest experiments, which used this approach, were executed by Bordet and Beumer (1948). Extracts of the colicin-sensitive strain *E. coli* C6 were prepared by various methods and these were tested for their ability to inhibit the adsorption of colicin by sensitive strains. The methods of extraction were:

(i) cells grown in surface culture on nutrient agar were suspended in water and sterilized by heating at 58°C;

(ii) a similar suspension was filtered through a Chamberland L3 filter;

(iii) an extraction in trichloroacetic acid was made by the method of Boivin and Mesrobeanu (1937);

(iv) the sediment from the previous extraction was macerated at pH 9.5–10.0.

The test of inhibition entailed mixing 10 drops of extract with 10 drops of a colicin solution (a filtrate of *E. coli* V). A control tube replaced the extract with physiological saline. The mixture was left to react overnight at 37°C and then four drops were put into nutrient broth inoculated with the sensitive strain (*E. coli* C6).

Extract (iv) neutralized the colicin completely whereas partial inhibition was recorded with the other extracts. Bordet and Beumer found also that an extract would inhibit not only the combination of colicin with the strain from which it was made but also with other strains sensitive to the same colicin, whereas extracts made from a colicin-resistant strain showed no inhibitory activity. These findings strongly support the notion of specific receptors.[†]

It should be mentioned that the adsorption of bacteriocins may be *non-specifically* inhibited by certain ions. The concentration of cations profoundly affects the adsorption of colicins; Šmarda (1965b) quotes evidence that the adsorption of colicin E1 may be entirely prevented in concentrations of $NaCl \geq 3\%$. (See also B, 2 (c), p. 389.)

(d) *Serological experiments.* Bordet (1948) found that antiserum made against the colicin-sensitive strain *E. coli* C6 protected not only cells of this strain against the bactericidal effect of colicin, but also those of other colicin-sensitive strains, in spite of their not showing any agglutination. Bordet placed 10 drops of anti-serum into each of two tubes of nutrient broth. Two similar tubes each received 10 drops of normal serum, whilst two further tubes served as controls. The volumes of nutrient broth were not recorded.

Mayr-Harting and Shimeld (1966) in similar experiments found that the degree of protection afforded by antiserum depended on the number of sensitive cells. In these experiments antiserum was prepared in rabbits by giving five injections, at intervals of 4–5 days, of saline suspensions of appropriately treated organisms. The dosage was increased over the course of immunization from 5–10×10^7 cells per ml to 1×10^9 cells per ml.

The protection experiments consisted of adding 0·1 ml of antiserum to 5 ml of nutrient broth containing 10^5 sensitive cells per ml. Half an hour at 36°C was allowed for combination of antibody with the cell antigens and then 0·5 ml of colicin solution was added. Survivor counts were done at intervals up to 2 h. Antisera were prepared against normal sensitive cells as well as against cells whose receptors had been destroyed (see Section A, 3). Cross-protection of organisms that were sensitive to the same colicin (i.e. possessed the same receptors) but which differed antigenically was unsuccessfully attempted by these authors.

An attempt to repeat these experiments about a year later met with no success in that it proved impossible to demonstrate any protection whatsoever. This may well have been due to yet another instance of the dependence

[†] Recent interest has centred on the possible role in bacteriocin receptors of lipopolysaccharide (LPS), and inhibition studies have been made on LPS extracted from sensitive and "resistant" strains (Marotel-Schirmann and Barbu, 1969; Chang and Hager, 1970).

of the production of receptors on the conditions of cultivation (see Section A, 3). Since the protective effect of anti-bacterial antiserum is due probably to steric hindrance of the access of bacteriocin to its receptors, failure to demonstrate protection could be due not so much to an alteration in the number of receptors per cell but rather to an effect on their distribution on the cell surface (but see footnote to p. 392). It is clear that in future experiments strict control of the conditions of cultivation will be necessary at every stage of the experiments.

Irreversibility of adsorption. Indirect evidence that the adsorption of bacteriocin to its specific receptors is usually irreversible (except in special cases, see Section A, 5) comes from many experiments, e.g. the kinetic experiments described in Section B.

Direct evidence was obtained from the failure of attempts to elute colicins (E2, E3, and K) which had been adsorbed to sensitive cells by employing eluents of various ionic strengths at 37°C (Nomura, 1964). Cavard and Barbu (1970) attempted to show reversible fixation of colicins by using a variety of eluents and conditions. They concluded that "the bond between a colicin and its receptor is very stable". Further confirmation comes from the experiments of Maeda and Nomura (1966) where it was shown that radioactive colicin E2 remains attached to the cell wall+cell membrane fraction of the sensitive cell even after mechanical disruption and differential centrifugation (see Section D, below).

The possibility that at low temperatures of incubation adsorption of some bacteriocins may be reversible has been discussed by Holland (1967b) for megacin A, and by Kageyama *et al.* (1964) for pyocin. However, more recent evidence suggests that reversal of adsorption is *not* the likely explanation of the observations on megacin A (Holland, personal communication).

In view of the weight of evidence against reversibility of the primary adsorption of bacteriocin, the recent work of Reynolds and Reeves (1969) has especial importance. Colicin (CA42–E2) was incubated with sensitive cells for 5 min at 37°C to allow adequate adsorption. The suspending fluid was then rapidly filtered off by means of a membrane filter (Millipore); the cells were washed with warm medium on the membrane, and were then resuspended in fresh, warm medium.

In one series of experiments the resuspended cells were incubated at 37°C and samples were taken at intervals for counting viable cells (Miles and Misra method). The number of surviving cells *continued to decrease* over a 30-min period until a constant survivor ratio of ca. 10% was reached. If colicin adsorption is truly irreversible the survivor ratio should be fixed by the number of cells "doomed" during the reaction (pre-filtration) period and should remain constant over the sampling period.

In a second series of experiments, to the resuspended cells was added an inoculum of sensitive cells (strain P501) that could be distinguished by their thymine independence. The mixture was incubated and sampled as before but viable cells were estimated on medium with or without thymine. It was found that ca. 40% of the cells of strain P501 were killed under these conditions.

We have confirmed and extended this work in our laboratory (R. Shannon, personal communication), and we have shown that, in the second type of experiment, death of the added inoculum does not occur when the cells are resistant to the colicin used.

These results strongly suggest that *at least some* of the adsorbed colicin is capable of desorption. They suggest also that earlier attempts to demonstrate reversibility of adsorption may have failed because the rate or the extent of desorption might be much less than that of adsorption and, therefore, the concentration of "free" colicin could have been below the sensitivity of the assay methods (see Section III).

2. *Nature of the specific receptors*

Somewhat surprisingly, very little work has been carried out on the chemical nature of receptors and in the words of Nomura (1967a), "Isolation and characterization are clearly needed". How far this is possible of achievement remains to be established.

The methods of study so far applied are as follows:

(a) *The extraction studies* of Bordet and Beumer and others described in Section A, 1, above. Similar studies were carried out by Mayr-Harting and Picken (1966) who used extraction methods (iii) and (iv) on cells of *E. coli* C6 and attempted inhibition of the colicin complex produced by *Sh. sonnei* P9. No evidence of receptors was found in the trichloroacetic acid extract (iii) but the alkaline extract (iv) appeared to dissolve 50–60% of receptors for the colicin complex. In view of the fact that it is now known that *Sh. sonnei* P9 produces both E2 and I colicins it would be necessary to repeat these experiments using separate indicators for each colicin before any firm conclusions could be drawn.

(b) *Denaturation studies* were carried out by Mayr-Harting (1964) who showed that the receptors possessed by *E. coli* C6 and by *Sh. sonnei* 2 for the colicins produced by *Sh. sonnei* P9 have the following properties: resistance to destruction by heat at 60°C and by treatment with formaldehyde or phenol; susceptibility to destruction by heat at 100°C and by ethanol. These properties are shared by the flagellar and fimbrial antigens of Enterobacteriaceae although these structures were probably absent from the sensitive organisms used.†

† Denaturation by heat has been used also by Marotel-Schirmann and Barbu (1969) in their studies on the possible role of lipopolysaccharide in colicin receptors.

Mayr-Harting (1964) used a novel approach in testing for the effects of denaturation. Large assay plates were prepared as described in Section III.B, 3 except that the inoculum comprised 10^7 indicator cells per ml *either alone or plus* 10^9 per ml cells that had received one of the denaturation treatments. The reservoirs were charged with a doubling series of colicin dilutions and, after prediffusion and incubation, the resulting inhibition zones were measured and plotted against $\log_2$ (colicin concentration). Parallel regression lines were obtained but where the denaturation treatment had not affected the receptors the mean zone sizes were much reduced compared with the control owing, presumably, to the greater absorbing capacity of the inoculum. This method affords a reliable and sensitive method for use with diffusible bacteriocins.

It is to be hoped that the methods of chemical fractionation and analysis that have already been applied to bacteriophage receptors and to cell-wall antigens will eventually be applied also to bacteriocin receptors.

3. *Number of specific receptors per cell*

The classical approach to determination of the average number of specific bacteriocin receptors per sensitive cell is an extension to that outlined in Section A, 1, above. The basis of the method is the adsorption of a bacteriocin solution of known potency by various known numbers of cells. After allowing a contact period sufficient for the completion of reaction, the cells are spun down and the supernatant fluid is assayed for residual bacteriocin. The difference between original and residual titres allows the calculation of the average amount of bacteriocin adsorbed per cell. If this amount is expressed in Lethal Units (L.U.) (see Sections III.B, 2, III.C, and VIII.B, 2) it is a measure of the number of specific receptors per cell.

The method has two interconnected pitfalls. The first is that, since the result depends on the difference between two assay results, the method of assay must be sufficiently precise to allow reliable estimates of both titres. Most early work was done with the sensitive but imprecise Survivor Count Method (Section III.B, 2) but recent determinations have used more reliable methods, e.g. the Turbidimetric Method of Reeves (Section III.B, 4) or the Diffusion Zone Method (Section III.B, 3). A consideration of the properties of the Diffusion Zone Method leads to the second pitfall, i.e. that the minimum concentration of colicin assayable by this method may be as high as ca. 10^9 L.U. per ml. Since a crude preparation of colicin E2–P9 may contain 10^{11} or 10^{12} L.U. per ml, and since the maximum number of specific colicin receptors per cell rarely exceeds 100 (as determined by this approach), it follows that high concentrations of bacterial cells must be used in order to achieve meaningful results.

These considerations explain why many authors failed to show significant adsorption when using neat bacteriocin (Hamon and Péron, 1960; Šmarda and Šmarda, 1965).

The method used by Mayr-Harting (1964, and unpublished experiments) and Mayr-Harting and Shimeld (1965) was as follows:

(i) The concentration of L.U. per ml in a sample of colicin E2–P9 was found by assaying a known dilution of a crude preparation by the Survivor Count Method (Section III.B, 2).

(ii) An undiluted sample of the same colicin solution was then mixed with various known numbers of cells of the sensitive indicator strain (*E. coli* C6). For the system it was found that a suitable number of cells was in the region 10^{10} to 10^{11} per ml. This was achieved by growing the indicator strain for 12–18 h at 37°C on the surface of 12 in. square plates of nutrient agar. The surface growth was then scraped off with a glass rod and resuspended in a small quantity of either sterile physiological saline or nutrient broth. Serial dilutions were made from this suspension and 2 ml of each dilution were mixed with an equal volume of neat colicin E2 preparation. The period allowed for completion of adsorption was 2 h at 36°C, after which time the survivors (if any) were counted, and then left overnight in the refrigerator.

(iii) The cells were then spun off and the supernatant fluid was assayed for residual colicin, in comparison with the unadsorbed control solution, by means of the Diffusion Zone Method (Section IIIB.3). By subtracting the number of residual L.U. from the number of L.U. in the original colicin solution the number of L.U. that had been absorbed was obtained. This figure divided by the number of organisms used for absorption equalled the average number of receptors per organism.

(iv) To check whether there were still any receptors unoccupied by colicin, the fluid was carefully drained from the cell sediment by inversion of the centrifuge tubes on sheets of sterile filter paper. The cells were then resuspended in a fresh colicin solution of appropriate concentration which, in turn, was assayed after time had been allowed for absorption to take place.

The value obtained for the system described was ca. 11 L.U. per cell, i.e. 11 specific receptors per cell, but this value was found to be profoundly affected by the constitution of the medium in which the sensitive cells were grown (Mayr-Harting and Shimeld, 1965) and by the age of culture. This last point has been studied by Shimeld (1966, and personal communication), who also examined the distribution of cell sizes in cultures of various ages by direct microscopical observation using an image-shearing eye-piece (Quesnel, this Series, Vol. 5A). From these results it was possible to compare the density of receptors per unit bacterial surface area under the various conditions.

Reeves (1965b) using an essentially similar method to that outlined above (apart from the use of the Turbidimetric Assay Method) obtained generally similar results with three different E2-sensitive strains. The estimated average number of receptors per cell ranged from 30 to 90.

Further information has been obtained from experiments using radioactive bacteriocins (see A, 4, below) and the significance of these results will be briefly discussed in Section VIII.B, 3.

4. Studies with radioactive bacteriocins

The recorded work using radioactive bacteriocin is due largely to Maeda and Nomura (1966) whose methods are those outlined below.

(a) *Preparation of radioactive bacteriocin.* Colicins E2 and E3 were labelled with ^{3}H-leucine as follows: cells of the producer strain were grown to a density of 5×10^8 per ml in a glucose-salts-Casamino-acids medium. They were harvested by centrifugation, washed once, resuspended in glucose-salts medium to original density, and shaken at 37°C for 15 min. One ml of this culture was mixed with 2 ml of glucose-salts medium containing 1 mc of ^{3}H-leucine. Mitomycin C ($0 \cdot 2$ μg/ml) was added as an inducer and the mixture was shaken at 37°C for 4 h. The cells were harvested by centrifugation, and colicin was extracted from the cells and purified by column chromatography.

In the case of the colicin E3 preparation an absorption with an E3-resistant strain was necessary to remove (? non-specifically) absorbable labelled material.

Maeda and Nomura prepared some ^{14}C-labelled colicin E2 by the use of $0 \cdot 1$ mc of ^{14}C-*Chlorella* protein acid hydrolysate in place of ^{3}H-leucine in the above procedure.

Radioactive pyocin labelled with ^{35}S has been used by Kageyama *et al.* (1964) and their methods of preparation were described by Ikeda *et al.* (1964). For details the original paper should be consulted but an outline of their approach is as follows: cells of the producer organism were grown in a glucose-glutamate-salts medium incorporating ^{35}S-sulphate and mitomycin C until the cell density reached $1 \cdot 5 \times 10^9$ per ml. The cells were then separated by centrifugation and washed. The labelled pyocin was extracted by lysis of the cells using egg-white lysozyme in the presence of EDTA. This extract was then treated with DNAse, clarified by centrifugation, and purified.

(b) *Measurement of radioactivity.* Maeda and Nomura measured the radioactivity of their ^{3}H-labelled colicins by precipitation on to membrane, or glass-fibre, filters with 5% trichloroacetic acid and, after drying, placing them in a liquid scintillation counter. Their ^{14}C-labelled colicin E2 was counted, after precipitation with 5% trichloroacetic acid and re-solution in 2N NH$_4$.OH, by use of a gas-flow counter.

(c) *Measurement of adsorption of radioactive colicin to cells.* Maeda and Nomura grew cells of the indicator strain in a tryptone-salts medium to a density of 5×10^8 per ml. The cells were then spun down, washed and resuspended in a Tris buffer-salts medium to a density of ca. 2×10^8 per ml. Radioactive colicin was added to the suspension and was incubated for the absorption period. Thereafter the cells were spun off (7700 g for 10 min) washed in the buffer-salts medium, and resuspended in 5% trichloro-acetic acid. The radioactivity of the resultant precipitate was measured as described above.

(d) *Confirmation of results obtained by other methods.* Maeda and Nomura (1966) found that 80–90% of their radioactive colicin was adsorbed by sensitive cells whereas less than 6% was taken up by resistant cells. It should perhaps be emphasized that these authors were directly measuring the colicin adsorbed on the cell in contrast to the indirect approach of other methods reported above. Kageyama *et al.* (1964) obtained similar results for pyocin (but their assays of radioactivity were carried out on the super-natant fluids, i.e. an indirect method). The pyocin results also indicated that although adsorption occurred to sensitive cells held at 0°C killing activity was negligible. However, whereas pyocin appeared not to be adsorbed by pyocinogenic strains, the results of Nomura (1964) and Maeda and Nomura (1966) for colicins E2 and E3 demonstrate that colicinogenic cells may adsorb colicin (Section A, 5).

Maeda and Nomura (1966) were also able to show that when increasing concentrations of radioactive colicin E2 were added to a known density of indicator cells and allowed to adsorb for 45 min at 37°C, a plateau was reached in the uptake of radioactivity corresponding to 20–30 L.U. per cell, i.e. 20–30 specific receptors per cell. The results of Mayr-Harting and Shimeld (1965) demonstrating the effect of the conditions of cultivation on the apparent number of receptors per cell were also confirmed.

Finally, various amounts of colicin E3 were mixed with fixed densities of sensitive cells at 0°C for 30 min, the cells were spun off and unadsorbed E3 was assayed in the supernatant fluid. The cells were then treated with excess radioactive colicin E2 and the amount of radioactivity adsorbed was assayed. The procedure was then repeated using "cold" E2 followed by "hot" E3. The results indicated that the two colicins shared the same specific receptors.

5. *Reversal of adsorption by trypsin*

Nomura and Nakamura (1962) first showed that sensitive cells which had already adsorbed a lethal quantity of colicin K could be "rescued" by treatment with trypsin. It has been reported by some authors (Kudlai *et al.*, 1965; Šmarda, 1965b) that specific antibacteriocin serum may, rather surprisingly, also allow "rescue" *after* adsorption of bacteriocin. The mechanism of this phenomenon has yet to be elucidated, but evidence that prevention of killing by trypsin treatment is due to destruction of the colicin *in situ* on the bacterial receptor was obtained from the following methods.

(i) Nomura (1964) working with colicin E3 showed that trypsin did not destroy a pre-existing structure that was necessary for colicin action by trypsin treatment of the sensitive cells before addition of colicin. Experiments were done in the presence of 2 : 4-dinitrophenol and chloramphenicol in order to prevent any resynthesis of the hypothetical trypsin-sensitive substance after removal of trypsin.

Washed log-phase sensitive cells were suspended in buffer solution containing 50 μg/ml chloramphenicol. Half of this suspension was treated with trypsin (250 μg/ml) for 30 min at 37°C; the other half was incubated without trypsin. After spinning down, the cells were washed twice with cold buffer solution containing 2 : 4-dinitrophenol (10^{-3}M) and chloramphenicol (50 μg/ml) and resuspended in the same solution. Colicin E3 was then added and at intervals of 30 min and 60 min thereafter viable counts were performed with and without the further addition of trypsin (250 μg/ml) to the previously untreated cells. The sensitivity of the cells was not altered by previous treatment with trypsin.

(ii) Maeda and Nomura (1966) were able to extend these observations by using their radioactive preparation of colicin E2 (Section A, 4 (a), above). It was clearly demonstrated that the action of trypsin was the removal of already adsorbed colicin from its receptors without destruction of their combining capacity for fresh colicin.

Washed cells were treated with excess radioactive colicin E2 (multiplicity = 8) and then cooled by mixing with two volumes of cold buffer. After centrifugation and washing they were resuspended to their original density in Tris-glucose-Casamino-acids medium containing chloramphenicol (50 μg/ml). The treated cells were divided into three aliquots which were incubated at 37°C. Of these, one aliquot received no further treatment; the second received trypsin (500 μg/ml) immediately; the third received trypsin (500 μg/ml) 1 h later. At various intervals of time up to 3 h, 1 ml samples were withdrawn from each tube and diluted with 2 ml of buffer solution containing trypsin inhibitor (500 μg/ml). Cells were separated by centrifugation and their radioactivity was measured (Section A, 4 (b), above). Only 40% of the radioactivity remained on the cells after 3 h treatment with trypsin.

In other experiments, cells were treated with a large excess of "cold" colicin E2 (multiplicity = 2000) and allowed to adsorb for 5 min at 37°C. After washing, the cells were resuspended in medium containing chloramphenicol. Trypsin was added either immediately or after 1 h. Samples were taken at intervals and their capacity to adsorb fresh radioactive colicin E2 was determined after treatment with trypsin inhibitor. Control cells which had not received trypsin treatment were also included and colony counts were performed. The results showed that trypsin treatment led to recovery of adsorbing capacity.†

(iii) In investigating the problem of whether colicinogenic cells which are immune to the action of their own type of colicin nevertheless adsorb it, Maeda and Nomura (1966) originally found that E2-colicinogenic cells adsorbed only ca. 1/4 of that adsorbed by sensitive cells. However if the colicinogenic cells were grown in medium containing trypsin, then they adsorbed to the same extent as did the sensitive cells. These results imply that the colicin liberated by cells of the producer strain may cover some receptors on the other intact cells; growth in the presence of trypsin uncovers these receptors.

B. Kinetics of adsorption

The kinetic aspects of bacteriocin adsorption by sensitive cells has been studied mainly by two related experimental approaches. Subsequent discussion of methods and results will be helped by definition, at this stage, of a few terms and symbols. Suppose a solution of bacteriocin, of concentration L_0, is allowed to react with a suspension of viable sensitive cells, of concentration N_0. Then let samples be withdrawn at intervals after mixing and the concentration of surviving viable cells, N_t, be determined by means of a suitable method of viable counting (Postgate, this Series, Vol. 1). The "survivor ratio" R_t ($R_t = N_t/N_0$), or, more usually, its logarithm (log R_t), may then be plotted against the time, t, at which the sample was taken. These "Survivor Plots" may be carried out for various values of N_0 and L_0 and constitute the first experimental approach.

If the adsorption process is allowed to go to completion, i.e. $t \to \infty$, then the end survivor ratio R_∞ may be examined for its dependence on N_0 and on L_0. Although this procedure (End Ratio Method) may be done as an

† Survivor count experiments by Reynolds and Reeves (1969), using "cold" colicin CA42-E2, suggested that such recovery was far from complete.

extension of the first experimental approach it is convenient to deal with it separately.

1. *Experimental methods*

(a) *Survivor Plot Method.* This approach has been used by a number of authors and for a variety of bacteriocins, e.g. for colicins (Fredericq, 1952; Jacob *et al.*, 1952; Fredericq and Delcour, 1953; Goebel *et al.*, 1956; Hamon and Péron, 1960; Nomura, 1964; Reeves, 1965b; Shannon and Hedges, 1967); for pyocins (Jacob, 1954; Hamon and Péron, 1960; Kageyama *et al.*, 1964); for megacins (Holland, 1961, 1965; Marjai and Ivánovics, 1962).

The chief precautions to be observed are as follows:

(i) The mixing of bacteriocin solution and cell suspension should be as rapid and thorough as possible. Moreover, mixing should be maintained, e.g. by stirring, throughout the reaction period in order to allow representative samples to be taken.

(ii) The original inoculum of N_0 cells should not contain bacteriocin-resistant cells, which would upset determinations of N_t.

(iii) Since this method is usually (and most profitably—see below) applied to reaction mixtures where bacteriocin is present in excess concentration, the presence of small numbers of non-viable cells in the inoculum (N_0) is normally of little importance. Where L_0 is not in excess the non-viable cells may lower the bacteriocin concentration still further by their ability to adsorb (see Section A).

(iv) In experiments where the reaction period is protracted it may be necessary to prevent the continued growth of the surviving cells in the reaction vessel, especially when the bacteriocin preparation is a nutrient culture fluid. Reeves (1965b) took the precaution of adding 2 : 4 dinitrophenol (2×10^{-3}M final concentration) to reaction mixtures that were incubated for more than 2 min (at 37°C). Nomura (1964) used chloramphenicol (20 μg/ml final concentration) for a similar purpose.†

(v) When a sample is taken, at time t, it must be immediately diluted to an extent that makes further adsorption of bacteriocin unlikely. This operation simultaneously dilutes out any growth-inhibitor that may have been added (as in (iv) above). The counting procedure must then follow at once lest growth of survivors occurs.

As remarked above, this experimental approach is most revealing when bacteriocin is present in moderately excess concentration (see Section B, 2).

† Before any such inhibitor is used it is necessary to establish that it does not influence the sensitivity of the indicator system. For example, chloramphenicol may markedly affect the sensitivity of cells to colicin D (Timmis, 1970).

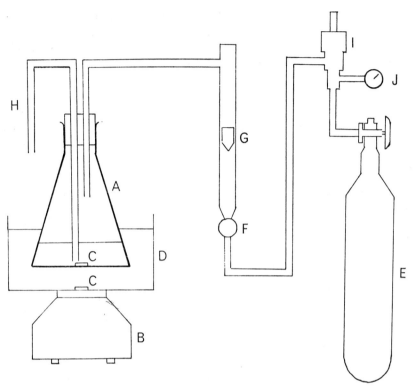

FIG. 5. Adsorption kinetics of colicin E2–P9: apparatus for rapid sampling of reaction mixture. (A) reaction flask, (B and C) magnetic stirrer, (D) constant-temperature water bath, (E) oxygen cylinder, (F) flow control valve, (G) flowmeter, (H) delivery tube, (I) Adams regulator (5 lb/in.²), (J) cylinder pressure gauge. (Reproduced with permission from Shannon and Hedges, 1967.)

Unfortunately this entails that the survivor ratio, R_t, falls very quickly during the initial stages of the reaction period (see Fig. 6, Section B, 2) and some method of rapid sampling is necessary if the early part of the survivor plot is not to be misrepresented. To this end a method was published by Shannon and Hedges (1967) of which the principal features are described below.

The apparatus shown diagramatically in Fig. 5 was constructed. Experimental runs were normally carried out at 0°C, at which temperature the water bath (Fig. 5, D) was maintained. A 6-h broth culture of the sensitive organism (*E. coli* C6) containing ca. 7.5×10^7 viable cells per ml was allowed to equilibrate in the water bath, as was a sample of the colicin preparation to be used (E2–P9). A 21-ml quantity of the sensitive culture was next transferred to the reaction flask and kept in agitation. By admission of gas to the reaction flask, 16 drops were expelled from the delivery tube. The volume of each drop (at a dropping rate of 100/min) was 0·06 ml. The 17th drop was collected in 20 ml of diluent and was further diluted for viable counting (Miles and Misra method with four-fold replication) in order to estimate N_0. A 20-ml sample of the colicin preparation was then added to the cell suspension in the reaction flask and an accurate timer was set in motion. The delivery tube was flushed out by means of a large admission of gas to the reaction vessel, and the dropping rate was adjusted to 100/min by means of the gas flowmeter (a gas flow rate of 200 ml/min corresponded to this delivery rate). Drops were collected in 20 ml of diluent at 10-sec intervals. These suspensions were immediately diluted 1 : 10 to arrest colicin adsorption. Further dilutions and colony counts were carried out, as above, in order to estimate N_t.

Consistent results were obtained by this method, some of which are shown in Fig. 6 (Section B, 2).

(b) *End Ratio Method.* Whereas the Survivor Plot Method is usually carried out with bacteriocin in moderate excess, the End Ratio Method necessarily requires that organisms are present in excess of the number of Lethal Units (L_0) of bacteriocin. The basis of this approach is the same as that for the Survivor Count Method of bacteriocin assay (Section III.B, 2), and the precautions to be observed in its execution have been mentioned above (Section III.C).

Some authors have used the general approach of this method but with estimates of the survivor ratios obtained early in the course of the reaction, i.e. by using R_t rather than R_∞. Although this may often be successful it can give misleading results, the reasons for which will be discussed in Section B, 2.

The End Ratio Method (or its variant using R_t) has been applied to various colicins (Fredericq, 1952; Jacob et al., 1952; Fredericq and Delcour, 1953; Jacob, 1954; Nomura, 1963; 1964; Mayr-Harting, 1964; Reeves, 1965b; Šmarda and Šmarda, 1965); to megacin (Holland, 1961); and to pyocins (Jacob, 1954; Kageyama et al., 1964).

(c) *Special methods*

(i) Maeda and Nomura (1966) followed the kinetics of adsorption of colicin E2 by a "direct" approach using radioactive colicin (Section A, 4). Colicin was present in excess concentrations ($L_0 : N_0 = 16$ or 24) and adsorption was carried out at 0°C and at 37°C. Samples were taken at intervals and the radioactivity adsorbed to cells was determined after centrifugation and washing, as described in Section A, 4.

(ii) Šmarda (1962) modified the Survivor Plot Method by reacting colicin-sensitive cells with colicin on the surface of an agar gel. A 24-h culture of the indicator strain was inoculated on to an area (1 cm²) of a nutrient agar plate saturated with colicin, so that ca. $7 \cdot 9 \times 10^6$ viable cells were contained in this area. The plates were quickly dried and then incubated at 34°C. At intervals from 2 min to 12 h specimens of $0 \cdot 5$ cm² area were cut from the inoculated area and the cells were washed off into 1 ml of 2% peptone water. After further dilution colony counts were carried out, and R_t was estimated and plotted against t in the usual way. The advantage of this method was that it allowed direct phase-contrast microscopy to be carried out on the sensitive cells during the reaction period (see Section B, 3).

(iii) As an extension of their Survivor Plot Method, Shannon and Hedges, (1967) studied the kinetics of adsorption of colicin E2–P9 by populations of sensitive cells in which the distribution of cell sizes (and, therefore, presumably of the average number of receptors per cell) was altered by population fractionation experiments. Samples of a 6-h broth culture of the sensitive strain were subjected to centrifugation for equal times but at various values of relative centrifugal force. Stained films were prepared from the supernatant fluids and photographed under standard conditions so as to allow subsequent measurement of the relative cell dimensions. The deposits were heated at 60°C for 20 min in order to kill the cells while leaving their receptors intact (see Section A, 2). Each supernatant fluid was mixed with its corresponding deposit and then subjected to the technique of the Survivor Plot Method. The reason for mixing the heat-killed deposits with the viable cells of the supernatant fluids was in order that the *total* colicin-adsorbing capacity should remain nearly equal while the survivor determinations were carried out on cells of different size (and, presumably, receptor number).

Two ways in which the method could be further improved are:

(1) Replacement of stained films for micrometry by the use of phase-contrast microscopy. It is likely that cells of different cell-age shrink to differing degrees during fixation for staining.

(2) Replacement of the simple centrifugation method by a more rigorous method of cell separation, e.g. centrifugation in a dense solution or filtration through graded membrane filters (Helmstetter, this Series, Vol. 1).

2. *Methods of analysis of results*

One of the principal objectives of the study of the kinetics of adsorption has been to decide whether death follows upon a "single-hit" or a "multi-hit" adsorption of bacteriocin. In order to be clear what is implied by these terms it is necessary to distinguish between three simplified basic possibilities, viz.

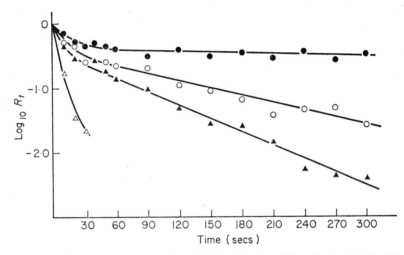

Fig. 6. Adsorption kinetics of colicin E2–P9: Survivor Plots obtained with differ-ent dilutions of colicin at 0°C. Symbols for colicin dilution: ●, 1 : 16; ○, 1 : 8; ▲, 1 : 4; △, 1 : 2. (Reproduced with permission from Shannon and Hedges, 1967.)

(i) The adsorption of a single bacteriocin molecule to a specific recep-tor leads to death of the sensitive cell. The cell may have more than one such receptor, but if any one of them is "hit" then death ensues.

(ii) Death follows only upon the adsorption of more than one molecule of bacteriocin but these may be adsorbed successively to separate, independent receptors, i.e. a co-operative effect is needed.

(iii) In order that bacteriocin is able to adsorb to its specific receptors it it necessary that n molecules arrive *simultaneously* at a receptor site, i.e. that an $(n+1)$th order reaction occurs.

Now, case (i) is clearly a single-hit event and case (ii) is equally clearly a multi-hit event. What may be less obvious is that case (iii) can follow single-hit kinetics, at least while only the Survivor Plot Method is applied, because a "receptor" is now a site which adsorbs n molecules simultaneously and the "hitting" of one such receptor could lead to death.

Moreover, if *active* bacteriocin units were found always as undissociated polymers then the word molecule could be replaced in each of the cases above by "polymer" and none of the methods described in this Section would differentiate between molecule and polymer. For this reason the words lethal *"particle"* or lethal *unit* are commonly adopted in the literature and such will be the practice here.

(a) *Survivor Plot Method.* The rationale of using this approach as a method of studying the kinetics of adsorption rests on the findings reported in

Sections A, 1 and A, 4 showing that the lethal adsorption of bacteriocin is normally irreversible. Thus, the estimate N_t represents not only those sensitive cells that have been killed in the time t but also those that are as yet viable but doomed to die because they have already adsorbed the lethal quantity of bacteriocin (see Section C, below).

Published Survivor Plots (log R_t versus t) have generally been similar to those shown in Fig. 6. Where bacteriocin is in great excess the Survivor Ratio (R_t) falls rapidly to levels where the counting method often becomes unreliable. Where the sensitive cells (N_0) are in excess the curves soon flatten into a plateau which, ideally, represents R_∞. Where bacteriocin is present in mild excess the Survivor Plot assumes a characteristic form showing a rapid initial drop in R_t which curves into a linear decrease. The presence of the final linear region is not always obvious, possibly for one of three main reasons: (i) bacteriocin is not present in sufficient excess; (ii) the presence of some form of resistant cells in the population N_0; (iii) the blurring of the distinction between the initial region and the subsequent linear plot owing to insufficiently rapid sampling of the reaction mixture.

However, all of the published Survivor Plots are apparently consistent with a single-hit mechanism; the crucial feature distinguishing single- from multi-hit mechanisms being the absence of a "shoulder" in the initial region of the graph. Reeves (1965a, 1965b) criticized much of the previously published data on the ground that the plot of the initial region was not established beyond doubt owing to the lack of estimates of precision and to insufficiently rapid sampling. For this reason Hedges (1966) undertook a theoretical study of the implications of assuming various degrees of "hit" to be necessary for killing in order to establish the likelihood of being able to distinguish between various models on the sole basis of the Survivor Plot with bacteriocin in moderate excess. It was shown that given a rapid and precise experimental method then the unequivocal distinction should be possible. To this end the method of Shannon and Hedges (1967) was designed and the results obtained were well in accord with a single-hit mechanism.

(b) *End Ratio Method.* The results of this approach form the logical basis of the Survivor Count Method of bacteriocin assay. The main assumptions made in connexion with the Survivor Count Assay have been set out in Section III.B, 2 and further discussed in Section III.C.

If these assumptions are justified then the predicted value of R_∞ is given by:

$$R_\infty = e^{-L_0/N_0} \tag{1}$$

where the symbols are as defined at the beginning of Section VIII.B. The quantity L_0/N_0, i.e. the average number of L.U. per sensitive cell in the

reaction mixture, is often referred to as the "multiplicity", as in bacteriophage studies (Billing, this Series, Vol. 3B). It follows that:

$$\left.\begin{array}{l} \log R_\infty \propto -L_0; \text{ at constant } N_0 \\ \log R_\infty \propto -1/N_0; \text{ at constant } L_0 \end{array}\right\} \quad (2)$$

Furthermore, if the right hand side of equation (1) is written as a Taylor
series then, to a first approximation:

$$R_\infty \simeq 1 - L_0/N_0 \quad (3)$$

Equation (3) may be written:

$$N_d = N_0 - N_\infty \simeq L_0 \quad (4)$$

where N_d is the number of cells rendered non-viable per ml.

It must be stressed that the relations embodied in equations (3) and (4)
hold only when the multiplicity is low, i.e. $L_0/N_0 \ll 1$. In this case they
express the "common-sense" expectation that the cells killed will rarely
have adsorbed more than one bacteriocin "particle" and, hence, the number of cells killed corresponds to the number of L.U. originally present.

Experimental results that accord with the expectations presented above
have been reported for colicins of the E group by Nomura (1964) and
Reeves (1965b). Kageyama et al. (1964) obtained a relation between R_∞
and L_0 for pyocin that was linear down to a Survivor Ratio of 1% but
flattened out at higher multiplicities. As was pointed out by the authors,
the occurrence in the original inoculum of pyocin-resistant cells could have
accounted for this terminal plateau (and see below).

In contrast, both Goebel et al. (1956) working with colicin K, and Fredericq and Delcour (1953) working with colicins E and K, obtained plots of
$\log R_t$ versus L_0 that showed evidence of plateaux in their *initial* regions
(i.e. at low multiplicities). Fredericq and Delcour took this as evidence of a
multi-hit mechanism of action but this is unlikely for two reasons. First,
the initial plateaux were obtained only when the adsorption period was
short. This was also the case in Goebel's experiment where the determinations of N_t were made directly after mixing the reactants. Under these
conditions one might expect a disproportional difference to appear between
survivors at high and low multiplicities. At high multiplicities the *early*
adsorption would approximate to first order kinetics since L_0, and therefore the probability of a "hit", would remain virtually constant. At low
multiplicities, however, L_0 would be continually diminished by adsorption
and the kinetics would tend towards second order. Therefore, a departure
from the Poisson expectations for R_∞ might easily appear when R_t is
examined at small values of t. It should, however, be pointed out that Reeves

(1965b) obtained the Poissonian expectations with a reaction period as short as 1 min. The second reason for suspecting that the results of Fredericq and Delcour do not indicate a multi-hit mechanism is that their plateaux do not pass through the origin ($R_t = 1$; $L_0 = 0$) but pass below it contrary to expectation (see Hedges, 1966).

A number of authors have reported findings which apparently do not accord with the expectations of the hypothesis embodied in equations (1) to (4), above. Thus, in studies on E-group colicins it has been reported that R_∞, at constant L_0, was entirely or almost independent of N_0 over a wide range of inocula (Mayr-Harting, 1964; Šmarda, 1965a; Šmarda and Šmarda, 1965). In other cases R_∞, or R_t has been found to vary in direct proportion to N_0 (Fredericq, 1952; van Horn, 1961). The causes of these unexpected relations have not been directly demonstrated but a clue to the answer may lie in the fact that all of these anomalous results were obtained with colicin in high concentrations so that the final values of R_∞ were very low (0·00014% in Mayr-Harting's experiments). Indeed when Mayr-Harting (1964) repeated these experiments using lower concentrations of colicin there was reasonable agreement with the Poisson expectations. The results strongly suggest that what is measured as R_∞ under conditions of high multiplicity may be entirely, or partly, made up of cells that are resistant to bacteriocin action. Both Mayr-Harting (1964) and Šmarda and Šmarda (1965) have pointed out that upon sub-cultivation such cells give rise to sensitive progeny, i.e. are genotypically sensitive, but it remains a possibility that a certain proportion of an inoculum of sensitive cells is, under certain conditions, phenotypically resistant (see Section B, 3, below).

A further anomalous result has also been reported under conditions of high multiplicity, viz. that, at constant N_0, R_∞ varied inversely as L_0 (Fredericq, 1952; Fredericq and Delcour, 1953; Šmarda and Šmarda, 1965; Shannon, personal communication). The cause of this finding remains unexplained but it seems possible that various non-specific or secondary effects may have been involved. It may be significant that Fredericq's (1952) estimates of survivors included cells which did not show colonial development until after prolonged incubation.

In summary it can be stated that under the conditions recommended for the Survivor Count Assay (Section III.B, 2), Poissonian expectations are generally obeyed but that when concentrated preparations of bacteriocin are employed anomalous results may be obtained.

(c) *Special analytical approaches*

(i) Jacob *et al.* (1952) and Jacob (1954) calculated the adsorption velocity constant, K, from the relation:

$$-dN_t/dt = K L_t N_t$$

Under conditions of excess bacteriocin the initial (1 min) rate was measured and L_t was equated with L_0 (in L.U. per ml). A value of 8×10^{10} ml/min was obtained for a colicin and 29×10^{10} ml/min for a pyocin. The precise meaning of these quantities is difficult to assess especially in view of the way in which L_0 was assayed.[†]

(ii) The number of bacteriocin molecules corresponding to a Lethal Unit (L.U.) has been estimated for a colicin E2-indicator system by Maeda and Nomura (1966) using the following approach. The amount of radioactive colicin E2 that was adsorbed to sensitive cells yielding $R_\infty = 0.37$ was measured as described in Section VIII.A, 4. From equation (1) of Section 2 (b), above, it is evident that this survivor ratio corresponds to a multiplicity of 1 : 1. By assuming a molecular weight of 60,000 for this colicin preparation and from the condition of unit multiplicity it was possible to convert the reading of radioactivity into an estimate of ca. 100 molecules adsorbed per cell (with a range of ca. 40–300 molecules per cell). Whether this result should be interpreted as 1 L.U. = 100 molecules of colicin E2 is discussed in Sections III.C and VIII.B, 3.

By using a purified preparation of megacin A of known molecular weight, Holland (1961) obtained a value of ca. 136 molecules adsorbed per cell at $R_\infty = 0.50$. Similar results were reported for colicins E, A, and K by Cavard and Barbu (1970).

(iii) Reeves (1965b) re-plotted his End Ratio Method data as "calculated multiplicity" versus L_0 where the calculated multiplicities were based on assumptions of (a) single-hit, (b) double-hit, and (c) treble-hit kinetics. The results provided the best fit with the single-hit hypothesis but Reeves pointed out that it would be difficult absolutely to discount the possibility of a 2-hit mechanism.

(iv) Shannon and Hedges (1967) compared the goodness of fit of their experimental Survivor Plots with predictions generated by computer in accordance with a model proposed by Hedges (1966). At the same time the actual distribution of cell sizes in the sensitive population was measured by photomicrometry (see Section B, 1 (c)) and compared with the various hypothetical distributions fed to the computer. A reasonable correspondence was obtained between prediction and observation.

(v) At the beginning of Section B, 2, above, it was pointed out that n molecules (or "particles") of bacteriocin might have to participate in a $(n+1)$th order simultaneous reaction in order for adsorption to occur. This

---

[†] An adsorption coefficient was calculated also by Reynolds and Reeves (1969) by using Poissonian expectations to obtain the average number of colicin molecules adsorbed after 1 min exposure. A value of ca. $6-7 \times 10^{-11}$ ml/min was obtained for adsorption in nutrient broth but adsorption was profoundly influenced by the ionic constitution of the medium, and the coefficient was found to be a useful index.

unlikely situation could be tested for by plotting the gradient (or its log-arithm) of the final linear region of Survivor Plots, determined with bacterio-cin in excess, against L_0 (or its logarithm) as described by Hedges (1966; appendix B). This approach has yet to be applied.

3. *Interpretation of results*

The interpretation of the kinetic data has been discussed by several authors and the reader is particularly referred to: Nomura (1964); Nomura and Maeda (1965); Reeves (1965a); Hedges (1966); Nomura (1967a); Holland (1967b). In this Section a model is proposed that could account for much of the data on adsorption and as justification for its inclusion is offered the hope that it may stimulate the further refinement of existing methods and the devising of new approaches.

It is suggested that the adsorption of bacteriocin molecules to sensitive cells may occur by three mechanisms:

(i) "Non-specific" adsorption to various cell substances. This could be either reversible or irreversible under normal experimental conditions and would not lead to death of a sensitive cell.

(ii) Irreversible adsorption to specific (lethal) receptors.† Death of a sensitive cell follows upon the "hit" of any one such receptor. Cells normally have more than one such receptor.

(iii) Irreversible adsorption to specific (non-lethal) receptors,† the occupation of which by a "particle" of bacteriocin does not lead to death of the cell.

It is further supposed that the absolute and relative numbers of each type of receptor varies, (a) among individual cells of an inoculum and (b) in populations grown under different conditions of cultivation, in ways yet to be determined.

A ratio of specific (lethal) receptors to non-lethal receptors equal to ca. 1 : 100 would account for the estimate of 100 colicin molecules involved in killing a single sensitive cell (Maeda and Nomura, 1966) while agreeing with the substantial evidence that the mechanism follows single-hit kinetics (also see Holland, 1967b). It would imply that, on average, 100 specific adsorptions ("hits") would have to occur in order to be reasonably certain of scoring a lethal hit.

The distinction between lethal and non-lethal types of specific receptor might be simply that the latter are situated superficially on the cell-wall, whereas the former are positioned in such a way as to allow contact of the

† But see p. 374 (*Irreversibility of adsorption*).

bacteriocin molecule with the cell membrane,[†] where it is thought to exert its effect (see Nomura, 1964, 1967a; Holland, 1967a; and Section D, below). In this case it is conceivable that occasional cells may be produced of identical genotype to the parent cell but completely lacking the lethal type of receptors, i.e. phenotypically resistant cells. This mechanism could account for many of the anomalous results obtained by the End Ratio Method reported above.

Another possibility that should be borne in mind in designing and interpreting experiments is that there may exist "inactive" species of bacteriocin molecules, i.e. molecules sufficiently similar to the active form to allow adsorption but lacking the lethal activity. Since all the assay methods (Section III) rely on measuring activity, the presence of these variant molecules would normally escape detection.

An implication of such "inactive" molecules and of the picture of receptor types presented above is that the adsorbing site of a bacteriocin "particle" could be distinct from the "active" site. This distinction should be capable of experimental testing.

C. Kinetics of the lethal phase

The possibility of studying the kinetics of the Lethal Phase of bacteriocin action, as distinct from the kinetics of adsorption, stems from a combination of three properties. First, the fact that the primary specific adsorption of bacteriocin to the sensitive cell is irreversible *under normal experimental conditions* entails that once a sensitive cell has adsorbed the lethal dose it is doomed to die.[‡] Secondly, the fact that progression from the Adsorption Phase to the Lethal Phase may be prevented by the use either of low temperatures of incubation (Holland, 1962, 1967b; Kageyama *et al.*, 1964) or of energy-uncouplers, e.g. 2,4-dinitrophenol. Lastly, the fact that the results of bacteriocin adsorption can be reversed by the use of trypsin, and perhaps anti-bacteriocin serum (see Section VIII.A, 5), allows the determination of the time at which cells actually become non-viable or at which some other pathogenic effect occurs.

1. *Time-course of bacteriocin action*

The first report of the use of trypsin to reverse bacteriocin action was

[†] Šmarda and Taubeneck (1968) have reported the application of some of the methods described in this Section to the action of certain colicins on stable L-forms of colicin-sensitive organisms. These L-forms appear completely to lack cell-wall structures but are sensitive to colicins with the same specificity as their parent rod-form cells. The results suggest that, in the organisms studied, the site of the specific (lethal) receptors may be on the cytoplasmic membrane itself.

[‡] But see p. 374 (*Irreversibility of adsorption*). In view of the recent findings of Reynolds and Reeves (1969) care is needed in interpreting the experiments reported in this Section.

that of Nomura and Nakamura (1962) in a study of colicin K. A culture of sensitive cells was treated with excess colicin for 10 min. If not otherwise treated the synthesis of β-galactosidase and of nucleic acids ceased and R_t fell to 10^{-4}. When trypsin (250 μg/ml) was added 30 min after the addition of colicin both protein and nucleic acid syntheses resumed in the culture and the killing action was reversed as determined by survivor counts and by the ability of cells to permit multiplication of bacteriophage T4.

It was further demonstrated that the recovery process was unaffected by the presence of the following metabolic inhibitors: $-$CN (10^{-3}M); 2,4-dinitrophenol (10^{-3}M); chloramphenicol (20 μg/ml); Azauracil (300 μg/ml). Later work by Maeda and Nomura (1966) using radioactive colicin E2 confirmed these findings and indicated the existence of a time factor, i.e. whereas the addition of trypsin to cells 5 min after treatment with colicin allowed up to 10% of the original inoculum to be recovered, if trypsin was not added until 30 min later the recovery rate was very low.

A method that allowed more detailed study was described for a colicin E2–CA42 system by Reynolds and Reeves (1963). A log-phase culture of the sensitive strain in nutrient broth was mixed with a mild excess of colicin at $t = 0$ and held at 37°C. At suitable intervals (the first being at $t = 2·5$ min) samples were taken and treated in one of two ways:

(i) the sample was immediately diluted in nutrient broth in order to prevent further adsorption of colicin and viable counts were made; or
(ii) the sample was taken into a solution of trypsin (5 mg/ml) containing 2,4-dinitrophenol (2×10^{-3}M) in order to prevent growth in the trypsin. These samples were left in contact with trypsin for 20 min in order to allow complete reaction.

The first type of sample allowed the construction of a Survivor Plot (Section B, above) showing the kinetics of *adsorption* of lethal particles; the second type of plot allowed the estimate of the fraction of N_0 that was actually non-viable at time t, i.e. a true *death* curve. The results obtained showed that there was a lag of between 5–10 min before any detectable death occurred—in spite of over 90% of the population having already adsorbed a lethal quantity of colicin in the same period, as determined by the adsorption curve (sample (i)).

Similar results were obtained by Šmarda (1965b) for various colicins.

One snag of the method described above is that, if the population of sensitive cells (N_0) is considered as a whole, the process of adsorption and of killing are seen to be progressing simultaneously. A more distinct separation of the two phases was achieved in a later experiment of Reynolds and Reeves (1963). Sensitive cells were treated with 2,4-dinitrophenol (2×10^{-3}M) *before* adding colicin and were then diluted into trypsin for counting. In this experiment it was found that cells which had adsorbed a lethal quantity of colicin could be "rescued" by trypsin as long as 1 h after adsorption. The practical importance of this result is that it should permit the study of lethal phase kinetics in cell populations where the Adsorption Phase has been completed.

No experiment of this type has yet been reported, but work in progress in this laboratory (Shannon and Hedges, unpublished experiments) employs a different approach towards the same end. Populations of sensitive cells are treated with a known concentration of colicin at 0°C. Colicin is sometimes used in large excess so as to saturate the specific (lethal) receptors on all cells of the population; at other times it is used at known multiplicities less than 1 : 1 in order that on average only one lethal "particle" is adsorbed per killed cell. At a temperature of 0°C progression to the Lethal Phase of action may be considerably retarded (see Kageyama *et al.*, 1964) and within the adsorption period employed (usually 5 min) the Adsorption Phase is virtually complete while cell death is negligible. In some experiments 2,4-dinitrophenol is present during the Adsorption Phase as an added precaution against the occurrence of cell death.

At the end of the adsorption period the cells are separated from the colicin solution (and from free metabolic inhibitor when present) by rapid filtration through a membrane filter (APD = 0·45 μm) using a Swinny adaptor and hypodermic syringe (Mulvany, this Series, Vol. 1). They are then quickly re-suspended to their original volume in nutrient broth (which may be pre-warmed to 37°C) and held at 37°C. Samples are taken at suitable intervals and either diluted immediately for viable counts or mixed with an equal volume of trypsin solution (Trypsin 250, Difco; 5 mg/ml in alkaline buffer). Trypsin treatment is continued for 5 min at room temperature whereupon the mixture is rapidly diluted for viable counting (the dilution serves also to arrest trypsin action).

Results obtained from preliminary experiments using this approach for a colicin E2–P9 : *E. coli* C6 system confirm that there is an initial lag before *any* detectable non-reversible lethal effect occurs, of duration depending on the conditions of experiment (10–30 min). The shape of the curve (Death Curve) obtained when plotting log R_t (in this case R_t represents the "true" survivor ratio) versus t was always a horizontal region followed by a curve very similar to that obtained in the Survivor Plot Method for the kinetics of the Adsorption Phase.

Usually the Death Curve is not absolutely parallel to the corresponding Survivor Plot but diverges from it as time increases. This observation led us to repeat the experiments using populations of sensitive cells that had been fractionated to give samples of more uniform distribution of cell sizes (see Section VIII.B, 1 (c)). The results obtained will be briefly discussed in (C, 3), below.

2. Multiplicity effect

In experiments using colicins E2 and E3, Nomura (1964) employed reaction conditions that permitted a virtually total adsorption of bacteriocin. The concentration of bacteriocin was varied so that the effect of multiplicity ($L_0 : N_0$) could be studied on protein synthesis. The multiplicities were calculated from the experimental data according to the Survivor Count Method (using R_t where $t = 15$ min). Protein synthesis was followed by measuring the incorporation of ^{35}S-sulphate into bacterial protein.

The results showed that whereas inhibition of protein synthesis always occurred, the rate of onset of inhibition was more rapid at higher multiplicities of colicin.

The effect of multiplicity was studied also by the Death Curve Method of Shannon and Hedges, described above. It was found that the initial lag in killing action was shortened and the subsequent gradients of the Death Curve increased at higher multiplicities.

3. Interpretation of results

The results of data on the Lethal Phase have been discussed in the light of proposed model systems, notably by Nomura (1964, 1967a) and Nomura and Maeda (1965). With particular regard to the kinetic data one feature seems worth emphasizing, viz. the multiplicity effect.

The methods described above (under C, 2) have yielded results that strongly suggest that whereas the adsorption of a single "particle" of bacteriocin is sufficient to kill a sensitive cell (see Section VIII.B) the adsorption of more than one "particle" may significantly increase the *rate* of death.

The experiments of Shannon and Hedges outlined at the end of C, 1 are suggestive of the idea that large cells die more quickly than small cells—possibly because the larger cells have more specific (lethal) receptors on them and so have the opportunity of adsorbing more bacteriocin.

The actual form of the Death Curves so far obtained has yet to be subjected to detailed analysis because much experimental work remains to be done. One suspects, for instance, that even if the population of sensitive cells were absolutely homogeneous with respect to the number of receptors per cell and that all of these receptors were "hit" there would still be an inherent variation between cells in the time elapsing between adsorption and death. In this connexion it would perhaps be profitable to combine some of the methods described above with those for synchronization of cell-divisions (Helmstetter, this Series, Vol. 1) in order to investigate the effect of cell-age.

D. Effect on the sensitive cell

The experiments carried out on the effect of bacteriocins can conveniently be divided into three categories: those concerned with the location of the antibiotic at the time when it exerts its effect, those dealing with the biochemical lesions, and those investigating the cytological changes.

1. *Location of active bacteriocin*

Evidence that bacteriocins exert their effect while located at the surface of the cell has been provided by Nomura and Nakamura (1962) who showed that the inhibition of β-galactosidase, RNA and DNA syntheses in growing cells of *E. coli* B and of β-galactosidase synthesis in resting cells of this organism was reversible by trypsin. The method adopted was to grow the bacteria in a Tris-glycerol-Casamino-acids medium, harvest, wash and re-suspend them in the same medium for experiments with growing cells and in the same medium—except that glycerol and Casamino-acids were omitted—for experiments with resting cells. The organisms were treated at 37°C with colicin K (10 μg/ml) purified according to Goebel and Barry (1958) and nucleic acid synthesis was measured by following incorporation of ^{14}C-adenine. In the experiments on β-galactosidase synthesis thiomethylgalactoside was added as an inducer about 5 min after the colicin, and then 25 min later trypsin was added. The level of enzyme was assayed in 1 ml toluenized aliquots of the culture.

The ability of trypsin to reverse the killing effect of colicin K, as demonstrated by an increase in the numbers of colony forming units, and also the ability of the cells to yield infective centres when infected with phage T4 is not affected by 10^{-3}M cyanide, 10^{-3}M 2,4-dinitrophenol, 20 μg/ml chloromycetin, or 300 μg/ml azauracil (Nomura and Nakamura, 1962). The results obtained by these methods are consistent with the interpretation that the effect of trypsin is a reversal rather than a repair and with the idea that the bacteriocin acts at the surface of the cell.[†]

2. *Biochemical studies*

The most widely studied effects of bacteriocins on bacterial cells are those on the synthesis of protein, DNA, and RNA; on respiration; and on the size of the population of treated cells. The effects on macromolecular syntheses are usually studied by treating a growing population with bacteriocin and estimating the levels of the polymers by a suitable method

[†] Two recent approaches are likely to be fruitful in establishing both the site and nature of bacteriocin action, viz.:
    (a) experiments with "tolerant" mutants (see Section IX.E),
    (b) the development of techniques employing isolated membrane vesicles obtained from sensitive, resistant, and tolerant bacteria (Bhattacharyya *et al.*, 1970).

after extraction of the cells in samples of the population withdrawn periodically (Arima et al., 1968; Holland, 1968). Protein synthesis may also be measured by determining the incorporation of ^{35}S into protein and by following the synthesis of β-galactosidase (Nomura and Maeda, 1965). Alterations in the respiration of colicin-treated cell may be followed manometrically (Brandis and Thofern, 1963) and effects on the population size may be determined turbidimetrically (Holland, 1963; Cavard et al., 1967b), using a Coulter counter (Holland, 1968), or by viable counts. Koninsky and Nomura (1967) have carried out more detailed investigations into the gross effects found by approaches of the type given above and have isolated ribosomes from E. coli cells treated with colicin E3. Their results demonstrated that the 30s ribosomal subunit is altered in such a way that RNA is not bound thus accounting for the observed inhibition of protein synthesis by this bacteriocin.

In a few instances studies have been carried out on aspects of intermediary metabolism. For example, Larionova (1967) has investigated the effect of colicin D-026/14 on anaerobic glycolysis by E. coli C6 by determining residual glucose and lactic acid formed by cell suspensions in a phosphate buffer–glucose mixture under nitrogen.

The absence of β-galactosidase has been used as an indication of lack of leakage from fully induced colicin K treated cells (Nomura and Nakamura, 1962), as has ^{32}P from ^{32}P-labelled cells (Nomura, 1963). However this has subsequently been shown not to indicate complete lack of leakage since radioactive potassium rapidly escapes from ^{42}K-labelled cells treated with colicin K (Nomura and Maeda, 1965). Further evidence that some bacteriocins affect the permeability characteristics of the bacterial membrane was obtained by Luria (1964) who showed that colicins E1 and K, but not E2, blocked the permeases for β-galactosides, isoleucine and potassium ions. Prompted by such results Cavard et al. (1967a) have studied the modifications of phospholipid metabolism of E. coli K12 under the influence of colicin K. The method adopted to measure the effect of colicin on existing phospholipid was to treat cells labelled with ^{32}P and at intervals centrifuge chilled samples of the cells in the cold. The supernatant and the cell pellet were then extracted with a methanol : chloroform mixture and the extracts examined after thin layer chromatographic separation on silica gel. To examine the effect of de novo synthesis of phospholipid ^{32}P was added at various intervals to cultures which 10 min later were chilled, the cells centrifuged off, and the supernatant and pellet extract were examined as described above.

3. Cytological studies

Certain workers have observed directly the effects of bacteriocins on sensitive cells. Direct observations on both *E. coli* cells and spheroplasts have been made by Šmarda and Vrba (1962) and Šmarda (1965). In the first publication it was reported that *E. coli* B1 was grown in broth for 12 h at 34°C and then penicillin G was added to a final concentration of 1000–5000 units/ml. After a further 3–4 h at 34°C spheroplasts so formed were separated by centrifugation and added in a drop to a block of agar 5 × 5 mm cut, aseptically, from a plate in which the agar had been saturated with a solution of colicin. Intact cells were isolated and added to agar in the same way. The organisms were then examined using phase contrast or electron microscopy. Later this work was extended (Šmarda 1965a) by using lyso-zyme- and glycine-produced spheroplasts.

IX. GENETICAL ASPECTS

The bulk of work published on bacteriocin genetics deals with the nature of the bacteriocinogenic factors, their transmission, their localization within the cells, and their relationship with fertility factors, prophages and other agents of heredity. Little work has been published on the genetics of resis-tance or sensitivity to bacteriocins, and the chromosomal sites of resistance or sensitivity have been established for only very few colicins.

A. Transfer of Col factors by conjugation

1. *Early methods*

These are still useful in cases where little is known about the sexual structure and, generally, the position of the Col factor in the organism in question.

Fredericq (1954) inoculated into one tube a Col⁺Strˢ strain and a Col⁻Strʳ strain which were then grown together for 24 h. Ten-fold dilutions of this culture were plated on 20 ml agar containing 500 μg streptomycin per ml by mixing 1 ml of the culture dilution with 1 ml melted agar at 50°C. After this second layer had set, a third layer of 10 ml of streptomycin agar was poured on top and the plates were incubated at 37°C for 48 h. Only streptomycin-resistant cells grew in the sandwich layer. The surface of the plate was then inoculated with a streptomycin-resistant indicator, which could be the original Col⁻ strain provided it was colicin-sensitive, or any other suitable strain that was both streptomycin-resistant and coli-cin-sensitive. The new Col⁺ clones could be recognized from their pro-duction of zones of inhibition in the indicator layer, and the streptomycin-resistant colonies to which the Col factor had been transmitted could be retrieved from the depths of the agar.

By this method Fredericq (1954) succeeded in transferring a variety of Col factors from and to *E. coli* and *Sh. sonnei*, although some could not be transferred. He was also able to show that *E. coli* K 30 produced two colicins of which only one could be transferred; the other, Col V, was not transferable.

2. Standard methods for transfer of Col factors by conjugation

(a) *Transfer of Col I.* Ozeki *et al.* (1962) and Stocker *et al.* (1963) worked out the detailed mechanism of the transfer of Col I to salmonellae. They found that, in colicinogenic colonies, only very few cells are competent donors. If, however, the original donor culture contains a fairly large proportion of non-colicinogenic organisms, these become infected with the Col factor during growth in broth and are then able to act as "intermediate" donors, i.e. competent donors to a culture of the acceptor strain. They remain competent donors for about seven generations, but usually during the eighth generation competence is abruptly lost.

Suitable proportions of original donor to intermediate donor are within a range of 1 : 200 and 1 : 1, and Ozeki *et al.* (1962) found the ratio 1 : 20 optimal. The routine method for the transmission of Col I between salmonellae, based on the findings of Stocker and his school, is as follows;

(i) 10 ml of nutrient broth is inoculated with 5×10^5 colicinogenic donors and 10^7 intermediate, i.e. non-colicinogenic, bacteria. It is immaterial whether this proportion of colicinogenic to non-colicinogenic individuals is naturally present in the subculture of the colicinogenic strain, or whether it is prepared artificially.

(ii) Incubation, without aeration, is continued for 18 h. The proportion of colicinogenic organisms in the culture should then have increased to 30–40%.

(iii) The culture is diluted 1 : 10 in broth and then incubated for a further 2 h, after which the proportion of colicinogenic organisms should be 50–90%. This culture is termed the HFCT (High Frequency Colicin Transfer) preparation.

(iv) 1 ml of the HFCT culture is mixed with 1 ml of the streptomycin-resistant recipient strain, and incubated for ca. 1 h.

(v) 0·1 ml samples, in suitable dilutions, are plated on streptomycin agar and overlayered with another layer of soft streptomycin agar. After overnight incubation, 0·1 ml of the streptomycin-resistant indicator strain, incorporated in soft streptomycin agar, is poured on top and the plate is incubated overnight. Colonies of cells to which the Col factor has been transferred are evident from the inhibition zones produced in the indicator layer.

It is recommended that a colicin-resistant organism is chosen as an intermediate donor, as sensitive donors tend to adsorb free colicin thus making the estimation of producer-clones difficult. Selection of organisms that have newly acquired the ability to produce colicin is generally and most simply done by using a streptomycin-sensitive donor and a streptomycin-resistant acceptor culture; but resistance to another colicin, or nutritional markers, may have to be used if no streptomycin-sensitive donor strain is available.

The number of competent donors in a culture was determined by Ozeki et al. (1962) in various ways. The most direct seems to be the following: constant volumes of an overnight broth culture of the streptomycin-resistant acceptor strain are mixed with graded numbers of the streptomycin-sensitive donor. After 15 min at 37°C, samples are diluted 1 : 100, plated on streptomycin agar, and overlayered in the usual way with the streptomycin-resistant indicator as the final top layer. The number of inhibition zones in this layer expresses the number of streptomycin-resistant organisms which have acquired the Col factor during the short incubation with the original donor culture, and hence measures the number of competent donors in the latter. For the donor strain, S. typhimurium cys D 36 (Col I), the ratio was found to be one competent donor for every 5000–8000 organisms.

This ratio could be confirmed by prolonging incubation in broth slightly beyond 15 min before plating. In tubes that had received less than 3000–5000 donor organisms this extended incubation did not result in the demonstration of Col factor transfer. In contrast, where the original inoculum was such that only one or two transfers would have occurred within the initial 15-min incubation, after the extension the number of transfers had markedly increased, thereby demonstrating that organisms which had been successfully infected rapidly became intermediate donors.

Clowes (1961) and Monk and Clowes (1964a, 1964b) adapted this method to study the transfer of Col I between strains of E. coli. The kinetics of Col factor transfer are somewhat different in E. coli as the donor strains contain a greater proportion of competent donors than do those of S. typhimurium, namely ca.1 : 100; furthermore, the donor state for Col I in E. coli is stable and does not depend on recent colicinogenization. But here, too, the rate of transfer is dependent on the ratio of donor to acceptor; if the ratio is 40 : 1 virtually no transfer takes place, whereas at a ratio of 1 : 20 ca. 90% of the acceptor organisms acquire the Col factor within 6 h.

The basic requirements for experiments that aim at transferring Col I are then: (i) a minimum number of bacteria of the donor culture must be present in order to contain at least a few competent donors, (ii) the concentration of organisms in the mixed culture must be sufficiently great to make collisions a frequent event, (iii) the culture must not have reached its maximum viable population, i.e. it must be possible for a few further divisions to take place.

Ozeki *et al.* (1962) found it easy to transfer Col I and Col B; but transfer of Col E1 was rare, and the transfer of Col E2 and of Col K did not take place at all. These last Col factors could, however, be transferred if the donor strain contained in addition to them one of the easily transferable Col factors in the HFCT state. They could also be transferred if the donor strain was F+ or Hfr (Moody and Clowes, 1964). In contrast, the transfer of Col I was drastically reduced when the donor strain was F+ or Hfr (Nagel de Zwaig *et al.*, 1962).

To show that the Col I factor was transmitted during pairing of donor and recipient, Stocker *et al.* (1963) labelled the acceptor culture with formazan granules. The organisms were grown in nutrient broth containing 2,3,5-triphenyl tetrazolium chloride (0·01% w/v). After incubation for 24 h the culture was diluted 10-fold into broth containing double that concentration of the tetrazolium salt and incubated for another 2 h, after which most organisms contained visible granules. The pairing between marked and unmarked organisms could then be observed by direct microscopy.

(b) *Transfer of Col factors other than Col I; and between organisms other than salmonellae and shigellae.* Col factors of different origin, even if they have the same specificity of action, behave differently with regard to the ease or difficulty of their transfer; the recipient strain is also important.

Smith (1966) succeeded in transferring Col E2 from *E. coli* K-317 to *Sh. sonnei* 56R and to *Salmonella typhimurium* LT2. She consistently failed to transfer the Col E2 factor which had originated in *Sh. sonnei* P9 to *E. coli* 317, irrespective of whether the transfer was attempted from a *Shigella* or a *Salmonella* strain, and not even after an F factor had been introduced into the intended donor strain. This difference in the characteristics of Col factors of different origin but which direct the synthesis of colicins with identical specificity has recently been demonstrated very strikingly by MacFarren and Clowes (1967). They studied three Col V factors of different provenance and found that they were not only different in many ways from Col I but differed also from each other.

It has never been found possible to transfer Col V1, the Col factor of Gratia's original colicin V producer (*E. coli* CA 7), not even when Col I which acts as a sex factor was introduced into the producer strain. On the other hand, Col V2 and Col V3 (present in *E. coli* K-94 and in *E. coli* K 30 respectively, the latter in combination with Col E1) are transferred easily and are able to act like sex factors. They cause cells which harbour them to produce F pili and, unlike Col I, provide the cell with receptors for male-specific phages, although V3 is much less efficient in this respect than V2. Like F, but unlike Col I, Col V2 and Col V3 are "cured" by Acridine orange and by thymine starvation, although to a much smaller extent than is F. The cultures cured of their Col V factors lose also the receptor for male-specific phages and become resistant to them.

Col factors have been transmitted to organisms outside the *Escherichia–Salmonella–Shigella* group of organisms. Coetzee (1964) described the transfer of Col D and Col J to strains of the Providence group, de Witt and Helinski (1965) the transfer of Col E1 to *Proteus mirabilis,* and Amati and Ozeki (1962) the transfer of Col E1 and Col E2 to *Serratia marcescens.* As Ozeki *et al.* (1962) had found for the transfer of Col E1 and Col E2 in salmonellae, the presence of Col 1, newly introduced into the donor strain, was necessary also for their transfer to *Serratia* (although Col I did not become established in *Serratia*). The presence of Col E1 increased the transfer of Col E2 100-fold, and both of these E factors became established very firmly in *Serratia* so that they could not be cured by Acridine orange. The colicins produced in *Serratia* strains to which these factors were transferred were in every respect identical with those produced in *Salmonella* or *Escherichia.*

In *Ps. aeruginosa,* where conjugation is an established fact, no transfer of pyocinogenic factors has so far been demonstrated; nor has it been found in any other group of organisms examined for this phenomenon.

Kiselev (1967) obtained transfer of colicinogenic factors *in vivo,* using mice. He first selected *in vitro* the most suitable pairs of donor and recipient strains. The mice were prepared for the experiment by dosing them, after a 24-h fast, with streptomycin and erythromycin; they were then fed with sterilized food and given another dose of antibiotics. On the third day a bacteriological examination of the faeces showed them to be free of *E. coli* and to contain very few other organisms. On the fourth day the mice were given by mouth the recipient strain and on the sixth day the donor strain. Controls were given either one, or the other, or neither. From the seventh day onward the faeces were examined for organisms that had received either Col E1 or Col V from the donor strain by plating on streptomycin agar. Transmission of Col E1 was found to have taken place. The strains used in this experiment did not survive long in the mouse intestine and the author suggests the use of *E. coli* strains isolated from normal mouse faeces in any further experiments.

B. Transfer of Col factors by transduction

Some Col factors are only rarely transmitted by conjugation. Col E2 is generally transmitted only in conjunction with Col I, though Ozeki *et al.* (1962) report having obtained cells which received only the Col E2 factor during interrupted mating; they also describe the spontaneous loss of only Col I from a strain which had received both Col I and Col E2. Such Col factors may, however, be transmitted by transduction.

The general principle is this: a phage-sensitive potential donor strain is infected with a suitable transducing phage under conditions favouring lysis. The lysate is filtered to remove donor cells and is then used to infect a recipient strain under conditions favouring lysogenization. A multiplicity of 10 : 1 is used, and 10–15 min is allowed for the adsorption of the phage. The culture is then plated out in order to detect colicinogenic transductants.

1. *Transduction of Col factors in* S. typhimurium

Fredericq (1959) and Ozeki and Stocker (1958) obtained transduction of Col E2 in *S. typhimurium* with phage P22. Similarly, Fredericq (1958) used phage P1 to transduce Col E1 and Col B in *E. coli*. Fredericq (1959) described the following method.

S. typhimurium LT2 is made colicinogenic by growth in mixed culture with an *E. coli* or *Sh. sonnei* strain that is colicinogenic for both Col I and Col E2. Phage P22 is then grown on this doubly colicinogenic culture and the filtrate is used to lysogenize a non-colicinogenic culture of *S. typhimurium* LT2. In so doing it transduces Col E2, but is not able to transduce Col I. It is thus possible to obtain organisms singly colicinogenic for a Col factor which cannot normally be transferred singly during conjugation. The organisms to which colicinogeny has been transduced are selected by plating serial 10-fold dilutions on a base layer and then proceeding in the usual way for the detection of colicin producers in layered plates (see Section II).

As the transfer of colicinogeny by phage takes place at a much lower rate than by conjugation, inhibition zones in the indicator carpet are produced only if the inoculum in the sandwich layer is rather large: it should contain 10^5–10^6 colonies. A smaller inoculum is not likely to contain transduced cells; a larger one may be non-specifically inhibitory for the indicator. From an inoculum of this size it is impossible to pick out individual colonies of transductants; therefore all the growth under an inhibition zone must be punched out (e.g. with a piece of glass tubing), suspended in broth, serially diluted, and again plated as a sandwich layer; this procedure must be repeated until individual colonies can clearly be seen to be responsible for the inhibition zones.

The ability of the phage to transduce other markers is not affected by the colicinogeny of the bacterial strain on which it is propagated, and the frequency of Col factor transduction is roughly the same as that of nutritional markers.

The Col factor which has been most successfully transduced is Col E2. Col I is barely transduced at all. So far, no strain producing colicin K has been found to be sensitive to phage P22.

2. *Transduction of Col factors in* Escherichia coli

The phage P1 has been generally used to transduce Col factors from colicinogenic to non-colicinogenic derivatives of *E. coli* K 12. Although the technique is the same as with salmonellae, the two systems show marked differences. Col E2, so easily transduced in salmonellae, could not be transduced in *E. coli*, whereas Col E1 and Col B were. Furthermore, the transduction of nutritional markers was clearly affected: a phage grown on a Col B strain was unable to transduce any nutritional markers; a phage propagated on a Col E1 strain transduced such markers but with a much reduced efficiency compared with a phage grown on a non-colicinogenic strain.

C. The nature of the Col factor

Silver and Ozeki (1962) provided direct evidence concerning the chemical nature of the Col factors and showed that they were cytoplasmically-situated pieces of DNA. The method involved measurement of the transfer of radio-actively labelled DNA from a donor to a recipient culture under conditions of High-Frequency Col-Factor Transfer. The donor was *Salmonella typhimurium* LT2 *cys D* 36. Tryptone broth containing ^{14}C-thymidine was inoculated with one part *S. typhimurium* LT2 *cys D* 36 (Col I) and 20 parts of the same strain that was either non-colicinogenic, or had Col E2, or Col E1 + Col E2. After overnight incubation the mixed culture was diluted four-fold into fresh radio-active broth and incubated for a further 2·5 h. At this stage Col I was transferred at high frequency and, as a result, preparations which could transmit Col I, or Col I with either or both of the Col E factors, were obtained.

The recipient strain was *E. coli* C 600, resistant to colicins I, E1, and E2. In preparation for the experiment an overnight culture of this strain was diluted 1 : 10 with fresh broth, incubated for 2·5 h with aeration, then centrifuged, washed, and resuspended in broth to a density of 10^9 per ml.

For the transfer experiment 3 ml of each, donor and recipient strain, were mixed in a 500-ml Erlenmeyer flask, and incubated for 75 min at 37°C. The culture was then assayed for the transfer of Col factors, centrifuged, and resuspended in 4 ml fresh broth. Chromosomal transfer was found to be so low as not to affect the measurement of Col factor transfer. The culture was then subjected to "lysis from without" with an excess of phage T 6 (to which salmonellae are resistant) in the presence of DNA'ase.

Lysis of the recipient strain was complete after 15 min at 37°C. The lysates were then filtered through Millipore filters and the radio-activity in the filtrates was measured. The controls consisted of the donor alone—to determine whether any of its DNA was released spontaneously—and of a Col⁻ culture used as a "donor".

An estimate of the amount of DNA associated with each Col factor was obtained as a percentage of the total DNA of the donor cells by:

(i) taking the difference between levels of radio-active thymidine transfer (a) from donors that transmitted Col I alone, and (b) from donors that transmitted Col I plus one or both of the other Col factors;

(ii) assuming that only one copy of each Col factor was transmitted.

In experiments done with ¹⁴C-labelled uracil or leucine no measurable transfer of radio-active material was observed.

Amati (1964) found that the uptake of ¹⁴C-labelled thymidine was much increased in u.v.-induced cells, indicating an increase in the synthesis of nucleic acid.

The method he used was briefly as follows: cells from an overnight culture of *E. coli* C 600 were transferred to fresh broth and grown with aeration to ca. 3×10^8 cells per ml. They were then centrifuged in the cold, resuspended in saline to 1/10th of the original volume, and u.v.-irradiated for 60–90 sec. A ten-fold dilution was made in fresh broth containing 0·2 μc per ml of ¹⁴C-thymidine, and the suspension shaken as a shallow layer in a flask in a 37°C water bath. Samples of 2 ml were taken at intervals and poured into 2 ml of chilled 10% trichloroacetic acid. After 1–2 h the precipitates were collected on Millipore filters and washed three times with cold 2% trichloroacetic acid. The radio-activity remaining on the filters was measured in a low background gas-flow counter.

Samples were also taken for measurement of absorption at 500 nm wavelength, viable count (Postgate, this Series, Vol. 1), and Lacuna Count (see Section III.D).

The approximate number of copies of the factors in the induced cells could be calculated on the assumption that the increased uptake of thymidine reflects multiplication of the Col factors, and that these differ in their DNA content (Silver and Ozeki, 1962).

De Witt and Helinski (1965) used a very ingenious method for the calculation of the amount of DNA transmitted in Col factor transfer, and for its characterization. This involved the transfer of Col E1 from *E. coli* K 30 to a strain of *Proteus mirabilis*; these two organisms differ in the guanine–cytosine proportion of their DNA, so that these band in the gradient centrifuge at different densities (Sykes, this Series, Vol. 5B). After fractionating on a methylated albumin–kieselguhr column the DNA of the *Proteus* which had been made colicinogenic, an additional band with the buoyant density of the *E. coli* DNA was revealed. This satellite material amounted to about 0·3% of the cell's total DNA. When the colicinogenic *Proteus* strain was labelled with ^{3}H-thymine and the non-colicinogenic *Proteus* with ^{14}C-thymine, an excess of tritium counts could be shown in the fractionated DNA of the colicinogenic culture; this, combined with a count of lacunae this strain produced (see Section IIID), permitted the conclusion that 0·02–0·05% of cells were producing colicin E1. In a culture induced with mitomycin C, 5–60% of the cells produced lacunae, and much larger amounts of DNA having the density of *E. coli* DNA were obtained. There was a direct correlation between the amount of "satellite" DNA and the level of colicin production. De Witt and Helinski calculated that, while uninduced cells contained only one copy of the Col factor, the induced cells contained 30–100 copies. This increase in Col factor material was the first immediate result of induction (see Section IV . C).

Induction with mitomycin C was carried out by adding it in a final concentration of 1 g per ml to cultures grown to 6×10^{8} organisms per ml. The cultures were then incubated for another 2 h with vigorous aeration before being harvested.

For details of the method of labelling, extracting, and fractionating the DNA, the reader is referred to the original publication.

D. "Curing" of bacteriocinogenic factors

1. *Col factors*

The methods for curing cells of Col factors follow those generally used for curing cells of F factors.

(a) *Acridine orange.* A log-phase culture of the organisms to be cured is diluted to 10^{4} cells per ml in broth containing 50 μg/ml of Acridine orange. After overnight incubation this culture is diluted so as to give single colonies on plating. These colonies are then overlayered and tested for colicinogeny in the usual way (see Section II).

(b) *Thymine starvation.* 0·1 ml of an overnight culture in M 9 medium containing 40 μg per ml thymine is diluted into 5 ml of M 9 medium with only 2 μg per ml thymine, and incubated for 24 h at 37°C. Dilutions are then plated on agar containing 40 μg per ml thymine, and tested for colicin production as usual (see Section II).

2. *Staphylocinogenic factors*

Only one of the many bacteriocinogenic factors produced by Gram-positive cocci has proved susceptible to "curing", that produced by staphylococci of phage type 71 (Taylor and Mayr-Harting, 1970; Taylor, Spires and Mayr-Harting, to be published). The methods are similar to those used by other authors to cure staphylococci of their penicillinase plasmids.

(a) *Raised growth temperature.* In nutrient broth at 42°C the loss of staphylocinogenic factor varies from 5 to 80%; on agar it is 100%.

(b) *Ethidium bromide.* Addition of 10^{-5}M of ethidium bromide to the growth medium leads to a loss of up to 80%.

(c) *Rifampicin.* Addition of 0·01 μg/ml of rifampicin to the growth medium leads to a loss of up to 60%. The concentration of rifampicin is critical and the range between massive killing of the organism and no elimination of the bacteriocinogenic factor may be narrow.

(d) *Growth in the presence of bacteriophage.* The typing phages 55 and 71 have been used; more effective than either is a polyvalent phage of serological group *d*, isolated from sewage. The phage is applied either by spotting on a lawn of the bacteriocin producer or, at a multiplicity greater than 1, in nutrient broth. One or more subcultures with phage may be necessary before maximal "curing" is obtained. The extent to which curing has taken place is determined by replica plating (Section II.B). Thus, the time course of curing may be followed. The composition of individual colonies with regard to bacteriocinogenic properties may be determined by plating out suspensions of single colonies and replicating these plates. Replica plating may be used also to determine linkage or absence of linkage between the bacteriocinogenic factor and other genetic determinants by replicating on other suitable media before making the final replica on a lawn of the indicator culture.

E. Resistance to bacteriocins

Unlike bacteriocin production and immunity, resistance or sensitivity to bacteriocins is determined by chromosomal genes. Most of what little work has so far been published on this subject has employed the customary methods of analysis and mapping of the bacterial chromosome (Hopwood, this Series, Vol. 7B). Like most mutations, the loss of bacteriocin receptors arises spontaneously, and the resistant mutants are merely selected by the presence of the appropriate bacteriocin (Fredericq, 1948b). Fredericq and Betz-Bareau (1953a, 1953b), by doing classical recombination experiments with auxotrophs, using the sensitivities to colicins B and V as unselected markers, established a linkage between the arabinose site and the site for sensitivity to colicin V, and a linkage between the sensitivities to phage T1 and to colicin B.

Fredericq also established the fact that resistance to colicin, like resistance to phage, was due to the absence of receptors; and immunity to colicin, like immunity to phage, to the presence of the corresponding pieces of DNA–prophage or Col factor respectively. However, whereas the prophage represses the multiplication of phage DNA, the Col factor must repress some reaction involved in the killing of the cell by the colicin. From this it is clear that resistance and immunity to colicin are not allelic. By crossing an organism which was producing colicin (and therefore immune to it) with one that was resistant because of the loss of its receptor, Fredericq obtained progeny which had the receptor from the immune parent and the lack of immunity from the resistant one, and were therefore sensitive.

Gratia (1964) analysed mainly the chromosomal surroundings of the site of resistance to colicin B. He selected by phage or streptomycin resistance a large series of mutants of *E. coli* K 12, marked by various nutritional deficiencies. From these he then obtained colicin-B-resistant mutants in the following way: on a base layer of agar was poured a thin layer containing ca. 1000 organisms of a fresh colicinogenic culture. After incubating for long enough to permit diffusion of the colicin into the base layer, the seeded layer was scraped off, sterilized by chloroform vapour, and another thin layer of agar was poured on top. Colicin that had diffused into the bottom layer was then allowed to diffuse upward into the new top layer and, finally, the surface was inoculated with any one of the mutants of which a colicin-B-resistant culture was desired. A series of mutants were obtained ranging from partial resistance to colicin B alone to complete resistance to colicins B, I, and V, and to phage T1. Crossing experiments showed these mutations to be closely linked and to be close to the attachment site for prophage 80 and to the tryptophan genes.

Transduction with phage P1 confirmed the results obtained by conjugation showing the order in which these sites were linked.

An interesting category of mutant has been found recently by Holland (1967c) and Hill and Holland (1967), and termed "refractory" mutants.† These still possess the receptor for all E-colicins and adsorb them but are, nevertheless, no longer susceptible to the action of certain of them. The response to colicin may be temperature-dependent, i.e. sensitive at 30°C but resistant at 40°C, or vice versa. It must be assumed that it is the transmission system from the primary receptor to the target of action which is affected by the mutation.

As a preliminary to the isolation of these mutants the frequency of mutations in various Hfr strains was increased by growth in nutrient broth with a mutagen (500 μg/ml of 2-aminopurine) at 37°C for 14 h

† These are now called *tolerant* mutants.

without shaking; the cultures were then plated on nutrient agar without mutagen, previously overlayered with agar containing 8000 Arbitrary Units of any E-colicin.† The growth was then "replicated" on pairs of plates with each of the E-colicins and with phage BF 23. One plate of each pair was incubated at 30°C, the other at 40°C; all mutants resistant to all colicins and to the phage, at both temperatures, were discarded. Those which were sensitive to E-colicins other than that from which they were isolated, were then tested for the presence or absence of receptors in the following way.

A base of nutrient agar was overlayered with agar containing 6×10^3 units of colicin E2 or E3, or 4×10^4 units of colicin E1. Small streaks of 14-h broth cultures under test were then made on the surface and the plates incubated for 14 h at either 30°C or 40°C, according to which of these temperatures was optimal for the expression of resistance. They were then sterilized by chloroform vapour, overlayered with a layer of sterile agar, and this, in turn, was overlayered with agar seeded with the indicator *E. coli* ROW.

Strains which had lost the receptor allowed the colicin to pass through to the top layer, and the indicator organisms were killed. Strains which still possessed the receptor but were refractory to the action of the colicin, prevented its diffusion to the top layer by adsorbing it, and above them a "cap" of the indicator culture developed. Quantitatively, the adsorption of colicin by the refractory strains was found to be almost as great as that of the sensitive indicator culture.

X. APPLICATIONS

A. Bacterial classification

Hamon and his collaborators (Hamon and Péron, 1962a, 1963a, 1963b) have used bacteriocins in attempting to delimit bacterial genera and species, and to classify strains whose taxonomic position was uncertain when judged by the usual criteria. Both the activity-spectra of bacteriocins produced by strains under examination and their sensitivity-patterns to other bacteriocins were used as taxonomic characters in these studies. A similar approach to the classification of Gram-positive organisms has been made by Seed (1970).

B. Bacterial typing

Numerous workers have made use of bacteriocins to obtain, for epidemiological purposes, greater resolution of similar bacterial strains. Whereas

† The Unit of these authors differs from that of most workers who have made use of the Arbitrary Unit obtained by the Critical Dilution Method (Section III.B, 1) being in this case the highest dilution giving *minimal*, not complete, inhibition.

phage-typing has been done mainly by determining the sensitivity-pattern of the strain to be typed, with only occasional use being made of the determination of lysogenicity, the tendency in bacteriocin-typing has been the opposite: bacteriocin-typing is usually done by *production* of bacteriocin and only occasionally by *sensitivity*. Ever since Abbott and Shannon (1958) published their results of typing *Sh. sonnei* by colicin production, the reason given for this preference is the lack of stability in the bacteriocin sensitivities of all kinds of organisms. It is difficult to follow this reasoning: the instability affects the sensitivity of indicator strains just as much as it affects the test strains to be typed by sensitivity.

One of the causes of this lability has been pointed out by Ikari *et al.* (1958) and by Emilyanova (1967). The former authors, working with *Sh. boydii*, found that rough and mucoid variants were frequently sensitive to more colicins than were the smooth S-forms, and also gave wider inhibition zones than did the S-forms with those colicins to which all colony forms were sensitive.† Rough forms of *Sh. boydii* were obtained by three different methods: (i) by prolonged incubation in nutrient broth; (ii) by incubation in 0·2% phenol broth; (iii) by growth in broth containing homologous antiserum (1 : 5). The method of obtaining mucoid variants was not described, but these were reverted to the S-form by growth in broth containing between 10^{-3} and 10^{-4} μg/ml of kinetin (6-furfurylaminopurine), thereby reducing their bacteriocin sensitivity. Emilyanova, when typing *Sh. sonnei* by sensitivity, also found that R-forms were enormously more sensitive to colicins B, C, D, I, and K than were S-forms. In contrast, the S-forms were a little more sensitive to colicin V than were the R-forms.

From these findings it follows that, whether typing is done by production or by sensitivity, the colony form of the organism exposed to possible colicin effect should be closely observed. Whereas the variation in surface structure is relatively small among shigellae, other organisms, e.g. *Ps. aeruginosa*, have a much greater repertoire of colony forms with corresponding variations in the receptor content of the bacterial surface. The difficulties of selecting always the same colony form when using the strain as an indicator, or when using "repeat" isolates for typing by sensitivity, are very great; to keep stock strains in a single stable growth form is even more difficult.

1. *Typing by bacteriocin production*

The methods are essentially the same as those employed for the detection of bacteriocinogeny (Section II), and the most commonly used form is as follows. The test strain is streaked across the surface of a plate of nutrient

† See also Marotel-Schirmann and Barbu (1969).

agar which is then incubated for 48 h. The culture is next exposed to chloroform vapour for ca. 30 min by placing a blotting-paper disc in the lid, applying a few drops of chloroform to the disc, and inverting the base of the plate into the lid. The growth is then scraped off with a glass slide and the agar surface is again briefly exposed to chloroform vapour, which is afterwards allowed to evaporate by opening the plate for 30–60 min. The indicator strains are next streaked at right angles across the original streak of the test organism and the plate is incubated until the results can be read.

There are a number of variations on this standard method, including suiting the culture medium to the organisms to be typed. For most organisms of the *Escherichia–Shigella–Salmonella* group ordinary "nutrient agar" has been found satisfactory. In order to suppress growth-inhibitory substances when typing *Ps. aeruginosa*, Darrell and Wahba (1964) and Wahba (1965) added to tryptone-soya agar (Oxoid): iodoacetic acid, 10^{-5}M; sodium citrate, 0.1%; K_2HPO_4, 0.1%. Gillies and Govan (1966) found, however, that 5% fresh blood added to nutrient agar made a medium suitable for typing *Ps. aeruginosa*, and such has also been the experience in this laboratory (A. Mayr-Harting and A. R. Thom, unpublished experiments). When typing *Proteus*, Cradock-Watson (1965) required a medium that inhibited "swarming" in addition to supporting colicin production: MacConkey's bile agar was found to be satisfactory.

The influence of the time and temperature of incubation on the test strains has also been investigated. Gillies and Govan (1966) emphasize that the incubation temperature for bacteriocin-typing of *Ps. aeruginosa* must be 32°C rather than 37°C, and this has also been our experience. Farrant and Tomlinson (1966) found that some colicins produced by *Sh. sonnei* were partly destroyed by incubating the producer strains for 3 days at 37°C and recommended overnight incubation at 33–35°C.

The methods of cross-streaking have also been varied. Tscheuschner (1966) puts 1 ml of a 6–8-h culture of the indicator strain on a disc of sterile blotting paper in a Petri dish. A glass slide, cut to the appropriate length, is then pressed with its long edge on to the blotting paper and thence on to the agar surface. Five cross-streaks per plate is suitable for the usual 9 cm Petri dish; if more are applied there may be, with very diffusible bacteriocins, a danger of adjacent cross-streaks interfering with each other.

To apply this method on the scale of a Public Health Laboratory routine some gadgets have been developed similar to those used in phage-typing (Parker, this Series, Vol. 7B). Barrow and Ellis (1962) designed a multiple slide inoculation apparatus; Lidwell and Carpenter (1961) described an apparatus by which multiple cross-streaking is carried out by nine loops, charged with the indicator cultures, that are guided across the plate in a moveable arm.

The results of typing strains of shigellae and escherichiae by this general approach are clear-cut, because colicins diffuse freely and the inhibition of sensitive strains is clearly visible well outside the area in which the producer strain has grown. Other bacteriocins, however, may diffuse very little or not at all, and inhibition of the cross-streak may not extend beyond the original producer streak. It is then difficult to decide whether the inhibition is due to a bacteriocin or to a phage (see Section II, C).

McGeachie and McCormick (1963) investigated and defined separately the optimal conditions for production and for diffusion, i.e. the two components which enter into the detection of a bacteriocinogenic strain. Whereas optimal *production* of colicin occurred in Hartley digest broth + 1·2% agar, and yields were depressed by addition of even small quantities of peptone (except for Neopeptone or Proteose Peptone, Difco), the widest *inhibition zones* were obtained on peptone-water agar and were reduced by addition of glucose. Based on these results, McGeachie (1965) developed a typing method in which both production of colicin and its diffusion take place under optimal conditions. A copious inoculum of the test strain is plated on Hartley broth + 1·2% agar and is incubated for 18–24 h. The plates are chloroformed in the usual way and are then placed at −15°C overnight, thawed at room temperature, and the resultant liquid is centrifuged at 2000 rpm for 15 min. Each indicator strain is next inoculated on to a peptone-water agar plate, either by surface-spreading or by seeding an agar layer (both methods give identical results), and 13 or 14 wells are punched in each plate by means of a No. 3 (dia. = 6 mm) cork borer. The wells are filled with ca. 0·1 ml of agar extract from the test cultures and the results are read after overnight incubation. McGeachie (1965) supplements the results obtained by this method by examining also the bacteriocin-sensitivity of his strains to the colicins of eight producer strains.

2. Typing by bacteriocin-sensitivity, or by a combination of sensitivity and production

A combined approach was used by Linton (1960) in order to type coliforms isolated from clinical material. The isolates were first screened for colicin production with a standard "universal" indicator, and only if this test was positive was the full set of ten indicator strains used to establish the production-pattern. Finally, the pattern of sensitivity of each strain to the colicins produced by Fredericq's standard strains was determined. Linton found sensitivity to be a stable characteristic of the strains in "repeat" isolations from patients, but perhaps his material is atypical since it was derived from urinary infections where strains would not be subjected to the effects of colicins and phages as they undoubtedly are in the intestine.

Hamon (1958, 1959) also used a combination of methods to type entero-pathogenic strains of *E. coli*, and found that the results of typing by sensitivity were entirely consistent with the epidemiological evidence.

Naito *et al.* (1966) used a combined approach with the emphasis on colicin production for typing strains of *Sh. sonnei*. Supernatant fluids from cultures of the test organisms were heated at 50°C for 30 min, and were then spotted (neat, and diluted 1 : 2 and 1 : 4) on to a top layer of agar seeded with an indicator strain. Out of 76 strains tested eight were selected as sensitive indicators. After having classified the test strains by their spectra of activity on the eight indicators, Naito and his colleagues determined the sensitivity of the test strains to colicins produced by the same eight indicator strains. In this way three of the five classes or types which had been obtained by the activity-spectra of the test strains could be further subdivided.

In an earlier Section (VIII.A, 3) we pointed out that the apparent number of bacteriocin receptors possessed by an indicator organism, and, hence its sensitivity, can be profoundly influenced by the nature of the growth medium and by other conditions of cultivation. It follows that rigid standardization of these factors is necessary if reproducible typing results are to be obtained, and media used for growth of the indicator strains should be chosen with care. Naito *et al.* (1966) used heart-infusion broth for growth of producer strains whose activity-spectra were to be determined, but recommended peptone-water for growth of strains used as indicators: a recommendation supported by the experience of Mayr-Harting and Shimeld (1966).

Both McGeachie (1965) and Naito *et al.* (1966) carried out extensive tests of the reproducibility of their typing methods, and both found typing by colicin production to be slightly more stable than typing by sensitivity.

A method of colicin-typing that relies solely on sensitivity-patterns was described by Parr *et al.* (1960). Both enteropathogenic strains and non-pathogenic strains of *E. coli* were tested for sensitivity to the colicins produced by a set of 21 organisms by placing spot-inocula of the latter on the surface of plates seeded with the test strains.

3. *Selection of sensitive indicator strains*

This seems to be generally an empirical and even haphazard procedure: very little information has been published on what must be, in many cases, a process that consumes much time and effort. A somewhat more systematic approach was used by Hamon (1959) in his work on colicin-typing of enteropathogenic strains of *E. coli*. Hamon collected mutants of the sensitive organism *E. coli* KS, each of which was resistant to a different colicin. From these strains were selected seven to be used as indicators and whose sensitivity-patterns were determined against Fredericq's 17 standard colicins.

The most thorough and systematic search for colicin indicators is due to Kudlai and her collaborators (Davidova *et al.*, 1966) whose method follows. First, the sensitivity-patterns of 763 strains of *E. coli* were determined in order to select those *sensitive* to only one or, at most, two colicins. These strains, which are not common, constitute the most important group of their battery of indicators. A second group was made up by selecting mutants specifically *resistant* to a single colicin, and a third group consisted of what were termed "colicinogenic hybrids", i.e. strains that were made immune to certain colicins by having the corresponding Col factor transmitted to them. The use of this third group allows a distinction to be made between colicinogenic strains where mutants resistant to one colicin would be *ipso facto* resistant to a group of colicins, e.g. Colicins V and I can be distinguished although mutants show cross-resistance. With the complete set of indicator strains it is thus possible to determine exactly the colicin(s) produced by any strain instead of merely recording a pattern of observed inhibition.

Davidova (1966) reported the results of typing 2000 strains by colicin production using Kudlai's set of indicator strains, and considers that the monosensitive indicators constitute the most useful group. (She intends to add more strains to this group, which would further simplify the problems of typing.)

Davidova (1966) also made use of serological analysis of the colicins produced by test strains (see Section VII), an approach which is particularly useful in the case of polycolicinogenic strains. This method, however, has severe limitations: as Likhoded (1963) has shown, colicin V (produced by certain strains) is not antigenic; colicins B and D show cross-neutralization. Davidova is therefore rather sceptical regarding the application of serological analysis of colicins as a routine method. One feature of Davidova's report is somewhat surprising and worth remarking here: no colicin was encountered in this large-scale study that did not correspond to one of the already known colicins. However, we did not have the full text of her thesis and it is possible that this point is covered elsewhere.

Girdo (1967), perhaps with some oversimplification, showed that the activity-spectrum of any colicin was constant, irrespective of the strain producing it. When, for instance, the activity-spectrum of colicin D produced by a strain isolated from a patient was found to be narrower than that of colicin D produced by Fredericq's standard strain, Girdo showed, by electrophoretic analysis (see Section V.C) that the former colicin exhibited only a single component, whereas the standard had two.

For the diagnosis of colicins produced by a test strain Girdo (1967) made use of the morphology of the inhibition zones. He observed not only their width—which is to some degree dependent on the medium, the density of the indicator inoculum, and the number of colonies growing within the zone—but also the nature of the zone edge. Girdo points out that colicins A, C, D, and G produce inhibition zones that are wider at the surface of the agar than in its depths.

4. *Quantitative aspects of typing by colicin production*

Recently, McGeachie and McCormick (1967) have emphasized the need to apply quantitative methods in order to obtain consistent patterns of colicin action and sensitivity-spectra, and have warned that the ordinary standard techniques are inadequate to ensure this. In their endeavour to put colicin typing on a sound quantitative basis, they first determined an Arbitrary Unit (A.U.) for the activity of colicins A, B, D, K, S4, and V on a single indicator strain (*E. coli* C6). Next was determined the number of A.U. required to inhibit each of 15 other indicator strains to the same endpoint. The results lay between 1·0 A.U. (i.e. the indicator was equally sensitive as *E. coli* C6) and 500 A.U. However, not only were there great differences in the number of A.U. required to inhibit different indicator strains, but the titres of the six colicins produced under identical cultural conditions varied enormously, e.g. the stock cultures which produced colicin K yielded 10^4 A.U., whereas the stock cultures for colicin D yielded only 10^3 A.U.

Where typing is done by means of agar gel diffusion methods the rate of diffusion of the colicin is a further factor to be considered. Whereas 10^3 A.U. of colicin S4 produced an inhibition zone 10 mm wide, 10^3 A.U. of colicin V produced a 24 mm zone. Marked qualitative differences of pattern were obtained when each colicin was tested at different dilutions, and it follows that solely qualitative reading of such patterns could produce very misleading results in typing methods that rely on activity-patterns. Moreover, not only were the patterns related to the titres of the colicins tested, but derivatives of the indicator strains showed considerable differences in terms of the number of A.U. required to inhibit them: such differences in titres of colicin activity may be as much as ten-fold for strains of shigellae.

McGeachie and McCormick suggest, therefore, that for routine colicin-typing two conditions are essential: (i) The titre of the colicins used must be determined and then adjusted, by concentration or dilution, to a standard titre (e.g. 100 A.U.). This makes, of course, for a good deal of preliminary work, particularly if the "universal" indicator (*E. coli* C6), which is not really "universal", must be replaced by another indicator strain. (ii) The indicator strains must be examined at frequent intervals, using colicins of known titre, to make sure that no change in sensitivity has occurred. Whereas such changes are perhaps infrequent in shigellae and escherichiae (provided that the cultural conditions for the indicator strains are strictly standardized), in strains of *Ps. aeruginosa* they are only too common and are usually irreversible (A. Mayr-Harting and A. R. Thom, unpublished experiments). Although prevention of these changes may be impossible, it is important to know whether any change has occurred so as not to mis-interpret the activity-pattern of the producer strain under test.

Bacteriocin-typing is only a special application of the study of antagonistic phenomena between micro-organisms. The complexity of the problem of investigating these phenomena in general has been outlined by Rosebury *et al.* (1954), who devised some quantitative methods of study. The special case of bacteriocin-typing is, of course, far less complex and it is the more surprising that only recently has consideration been given to its quantitative aspects.

C. Use as a biochemical tool

In spite of the classification of bacteriocins as antibiotics there are two areas in which distinct differences exist between bacteriocins and antibiotics of the conventional type. The first of these is that the spectra of activity of the former are very restricted when compared to those of the latter. The second is that the metabolism of organisms under the influence of "classical" antibiotics is affected only in relatively restricted areas and the effect is proportional to the concentration of antibiotic whereas in cells under the influence of a single bacteriocin molecule many metabolic processes appear to be affected more or less simultaneously. Holland (1967a) has suggested that the single bacteriocin molecule may achieve these effects by interacting with the "regulatory circuits" of the bacterial cell. It seems possible that, in a way analogous to the use of metabolic inhibitors in elucidating the pathways of intermediary metabolism, bacteriocins may be useful tools in the experimental approach to the study of regulatory mechanisms.

Holland (1967a) has also reiterated the need for more information about the cytoplasmic membrane, which would enable a better understanding of bacteriocin action, which in turn might throw light on the role of the membrane in cellular organization. However, it seems not impossible that bacteriocins may be useful in studies on the basic biochemical nature of the membrane.

Rampini *et al.* (1967) describe the simultaneous use of two colicins in a different way to that envisaged in the above paragraph. These authors have selected thermosensitive mutants in which it is probable that an alteration of an essential part of the bacterial membrane has occurred. The technique used to select these mutants is somewhat similar to that whose theory and background and technique have been described by Neidhardt (1964) and is as follows.

Mutants were generated from *E. coli* K_{12} by treatment with ethyl methane sulphonate (EMS) and the desired mutants obtained by selecting those resistant simultaneously to colicins E1 and K at 30°C. The mutants were then tested for their thermosensitivity at 42°C and only those inhibited at this temperature retained. Several lines of evidence indicate that these are probably membrane mutants and not organisms which are resistant to colicins E1 and K due to loss of the appropriate receptor.

REFERENCES

Abbott, J. D., and Shannon, R. (1958). *J. clin. Path.*, **11**, 71–77.
Alföldi, L. (1958). *Annls Inst. Pasteur, Paris*, **94**, 474–484.
Amano, T., Goebel, W. F., and Smidth, E. M. (1959). *J. exp. Med.* **108**, 731–752.
Amati, P. (1964). *J. molec. Biol.*, **8**, 239–246.
Amati, P., and Ozeki, H. (1962). *VIIIth International Congress of Microbiology*, p. 26.
Arima, K., Katoh, Y., and Beppu, T. (1968). *Agr biol. Chem.*, **32**, 170–177.
Barrow, G. C., and Ellis, C. (1962). *Mon. Bull. Minist. Hlth*, **21**, 141–147.
Barry, G. T., Everhart, D. L., Abbott, V., and Graham, M. G. (1965). *Zentbl. Bakt. ParasitKde (Abt. I)*, **196**, 248–263.
Ben-Gurion, R., and Hartman, I. (1958). *J. gen. Microbiol.*, **19**, 289–297.
Bhattacharyya, P., Wendt, L., Whitneym, E., and Silver, S. (1970). *Science*, **168**, 998–1000.
Boivin, A., and Mesrobeanu, L. (1937). *Revue Immunol.*, **3**, 319–335.
Bordet, P (1948). *C. r. Séanc. Soc. Biol.*, **142**, 257–259.
Bordet, P., and Beumer, J. (1948). *C. r. Séanc. Soc. Biol.*, **142**, 259–261.
Borunova, S. F., and Girdo, B. M. (1966). *Antibiotiki*, No. 6, pp. 513–518.
Bradley, D. E. (1967). *Bact. Rev.*, **31**, 230–314.
Bradley, D. E., and Dewar, C. A. (1966). *J. gen. Microbiol.*, **45**, 399–408.
Brandis, H., and Thofern, E. (1963). *Naturwissenschaften*, **50**, 482–483.
Cavard, D., and Barbu, E. (1970). *Annls. Inst. Pasteur, Paris*, **119**, 420–431.
Cavard, D., Polonovsky, J., and Barbu, E. (1967a). *C. r. hebd. Séanc. Acad. Sci., Paris.*, **265**, 1851–1854.
Cavard, D., Schirmann, J., Lux, M., Rampini, C., and Barhn, E. (1967b). *C. r. hebd. Séanc. Acad. Sci., Paris.*, **265**, 1255–1258.
Chang, Y-Y., and Hager, L. P. (1970). *J. Bact.*, **104**, 1106–1109.
Chapple, P. J. (1959). Ph.D. Thesis, University of Bristol.
Chapple, P. J. (1962a). *Nature, Lond.*, **195**, 1325–1326.
Chapple, P. J. (1962b). *J. clin. Path.*, **15**, 484–487.
Clowes, R. C. (1961). *Nature, Lond.*, **190**, 988–989.
Coetzee, J. N. (1964). *Nature, Lond.*, **203**, 897–898.

Cradock–Watson, J. E. (1965). *Zentbl. Bakt. ParasitKde* (*Abt. I*), **196**, 385–388.
Dandeu, J. P., and Barbu, E. (1967a). *C. r. hebd. Séanc. Acad. Sci.*, *Paris*, **264**, 173–176.
Dandeu, J. P., and Barbu, E. (1967b). *C. r. hebd. Séanc. Acad. Sci.*, *Paris*, **265**, 774–776.
Darrell, J. H., and Wahba, A. H. (1964). *J. clin. Path.*, **17**, 236–242.
Davidova, N. V. (1966). Candidate Thesis, University of Moscow.
Davidova, N. V., Kudlai, D. G., and Petrovskaya, V. G. (1966). *Zh. Mikrobiol. Epidem. Immunol.*, No. **7**, pp. 91–94.
Dixon, M., and Webb, E. C. (1964). "Enzymes", 2nd ed. Longmans, London.
Dulbecco, R., Vogt, M., and Strickland, A. R. G. (1956). *Virology*, **2**, 162–205.
Emilyanova, O. I. (1967). *Zh. Mikrobiol. Epidem. Immunol.*, No. **9**, pp. 40–44.
Farkas-Himsley, H., and Seyfried, P. L. (1962). *Nature, Lond.*, **193**, 1193–1194.
Farkas-Himsley, H., and Seyfried, P. L. (1963). *Can. J. Microbiol.*, **9**, 329–338.
Farrant, W. N., and Tomlinson, J. H. (1966). *J. Hyg.*, *Camb.*, **64**, 287–303.
Finney, D. J. (1952). "Statistical Method in Biological Assay". Griffin, London.
Foulds, J. D., and Shemin, D. (1969). *J. Bact.*, **99**, 661–666.
Fredericq, P. (1948a). *Rev. Belge. pathol. Med. exp.*, **19** (Suppl. 4), 1–107.
Fredericq, P. (1948b). *C. r. Séanc. Soc. Biol.*, **142**, 853–855.
Fredericq, P. (1950). *C. r. Séanc. Soc. Biol.*, **144**, 437–439.
Fredericq, P. (1952). *C. r. Séanc. Soc. Biol.*, **146**, 1295–1297.
Fredericq, P. (1954). *C. r. Séanc. Soc. Biol.*, **148**, 399–402.
Fredericq, P. (1957a). *A. Rev. Microbiol.*, **11**, 7–22.
Fredericq, P. (1957b). *In* "Drug Resistance in Micro-organisms" (Ciba Foundation Symposium, Eds S. E. W. Wolstenholme and C. M. O'Connor), pp. 323–335. Churchill, London.
Fredericq, P. (1958). *A. Rev. Carnegie Inst.*, *Washington.*, **57**, pp. 396 seq.
Fredericq, P. (1959). *C. r. Séanc. Soc. Biol.*, **153**, 357–360.
Fredericq, P. (1963). *Ergebn. Mikrobiol. ImmunForsch. exp. Ther.*, **37**, 114–161.
Fredericq, P., and Betz-Bareau, M. (1953a). *C. r. Séanc. Soc. Biol.*, **147**, 1653–1656.
Fredericq, P., and Betz-Bareau, M. (1953b). *C. r. Séanc. Soc. Biol.*, **147**, 2043–2045.
Fredericq, P., and Delcour, G. (1953). *C. r. Séanc. Soc. Biol.*, **147**, 1310–1311.
Fredericq, P., Joiris, E., Betz-Bareau, M., and Gratia, A. (1949). *C. r. Séanc. Soc. Biol.*, **143**, 556–559.
Fredericq, P., and Levine, M. (1947). *J. Bact.*, **54**, 785–792.
Gillies, R. R., and Govan, J. R. W. (1966). *J. Path. Bact.*, **91**, 339–345.
Girdo, B. M. (1967). *Antibiotiki*, No. **7**, pp. 572–578.
Goebel, W. F., and Barry, G. T. (1958). *J. exp. Med.*, **107**, 185–209.
Goebel, W. F., Barry, G. T., Jesaitis, M. A., and Miller, E. M. (1955). *Nature, Lond.*, **176**, 700–701.
Goebel, W. F., Barry, G. T., and Shedlovsky, T. (1956). *J. exp. Med.*, **103**, 577–588.
Gratia, A. (1925). *C. r. Séanc. Soc. Biol.*, **93**, 1040–1041.
Gratia, A. (1932). *Annls Inst. Pasteur*, *Paris*, **48**, 413–437.
Gratia, A. (1944). *C. r. Séanc. Soc. Biol.*, **138**, 893–894.
Gratia, A., and Fredericq, P. (1946). *C. r. Séanc. Soc. Biol.*, **140**, 1032–1033.
Gratia, A., and Weerts, E. (1946). *C. r. Séanc. Soc. Biol.*, **140**, 1246–1248.
Gratia, J.-P. (1964). *Annls Inst. Pasteur*, *Paris*, **107** (Suppl. 5), 132–151.

Gutterman, S. K., and Luria, S. E. (1969). *Science*, **164**, 1414.
Halbert, S. P., and Magnuson, H. J. (1948). *J. Immunol.*, **58**, 397–415.
Hamon, Y. (1956a). *Annls Inst. Pasteur, Paris*, **91**, 82–90.
Hamon, Y. (1956b). *C. r. hebd. Séanc. Acad. Sci., Paris*, **242**, 1240–1242.
Hamon, Y. (1957). *Annls Inst. Pasteur, Paris*, **92**, 489–500.
Hamon, Y. (1958). *Annls Inst. Pasteur, Paris*, **95**, 117–121.
Hamon, Y. (1959). *Annls Inst. Pasteur, Paris*, **96**, 614–629.
Hamon, Y. (1964). *Annls Inst. Pasteur, Paris*, **104**, 18–53.
Hamon, Y., and Péron, Y. (1960). *C. r. hebd. Séanc. Acad. Sci., Paris*, **251**, 1840–1842.
Hamon, Y., and Péron, Y. (1961). *Annls Inst. Pasteur, Paris*, **100**, 818–821.
Hamon, Y., and Péron, Y. (1962a). *C. r. hebd. Séanc. Acad. Sci., Paris*, **254**, 2868–2870.
Hamon, Y., and Péron, Y. (1962b). *C. r. hebd. Séanc. Acad. Sci., Paris*. **255**, 2210–2212.
Hamon, Y., and Péron, Y. (1962c). *Annls Inst. Pasteur, Paris*, **103**, 876–889.
Hamon, Y., and Péron, Y. (1963a). *C. r. hebd. Séanc. Acad. Sci., Paris*, **257**, 309–311.
Hamon, Y., and Péron, Y. (1963b). *Annls Inst. Pasteur, Paris*, **104**, 127–131.
Hamon, Y., Véron, M., and Péron, Y. (1961). *Annls Inst. Pasteur, Paris*, **101**, 738–753.
Hartman, I., and Ben-Gurion, R. (1958). *J. gen. Microbiol.*, **21**, 135–143.
Heatley, N. C., and Florey, H. W. (1946). *Br. J. exp. Path.* **27**, 378–390.
Hedges, A. J. (1960). *J. appl. Bact.*, **23**, 269–282.
Hedges, A. J. (1966). *J. theor. Biol.*, **1**, 383–410.
Herschman, H. R., and Helinski, D. R. (1967a). *J. biol. Chem.*, **242**, 5360–5368.
Herschman, H. R., and Helinski, D. R. (1967b). *J. Bact.*, **94**, 691–699.
Higerd, T. B., Baechler, C. A., and Berk, R. S. (1967). *J. Bact.*, **93**, 1976–1986.
Hill, C., and Holland, I. B. (1967). *J. Bact.*, **94**, 677–686.
Hinsdill, R. D., and Goebel, W. F. (1964). *Annls Inst. Pasteur, Paris*, **107** (Suppl. 5), 54–66.
Holland, I. B. (1961). *Biochem. J.*, **78**, 641–648.
Holland, I. B. (1962). *J. gen. Microbiol.*, **29**, 603–614.
Holland, I. B. (1963). *Biochem. biophys. Res. Commun.*, **13**, 246–250.
Holland, I. B. (1965). *J. molec. Biol.*, **12**, 429–438.
Holland, I. B. (1967a). *In* "Antibiotics I: Mechanism of Action" (Eds D. Gottlieb and P. D. Shaw), pp. 684–687. Springer-Verlag, New York.
Holland, I. B. (1967b). *In* "Antibiotics I: Mechanism of Action" (Eds D. Gottlieb and P. D. Shaw), pp. 688–695. Springer-Verlag, New York.
Holland, I. B. (1967c). *Molec. gen. Genetics.*, **100**, 242–251.
Holland, I. B. (1968). *J. molec. Biol.*, **31**, 267–275.
Homma, J. Y., and Suzuki, N. (1964). *J. Bact.*, **87**, 630–640.
van Horn, E. A. (1961). M.Sc. Thesis, University of Bristol.
Hutton, J. J., and Goebel, W. F. (1962). *J. gen. Microbiol.*, **45**, 125–141.
Ikari, N. S., Robbins, M. L., and Parr, L. W. (1958). *Proc. Soc. exp. Biol. Med.*, **98**, 142–144.
Ikeda, K., Kageyama, M., and Egami, F. (1964). *J. Biochem., Tokyo.* **55**, 54–58.
Ivánovics, G., and Alföldi, L. (1955). *Acta microbiol. hung.*, **2**, 257–292.
Ivánovics, G., and Alföldi, L. (1957). *J. gen. Microbiol.*, **16**, 522–530.
Ivánovics, G., and Nagy, E. (1958). *J. gen. Microbiol.*, **19**, 407–418.
Ivánovics, G., Alföldi, L., and Nagy, E. (1959a). *J. gen. Microbiol.*, **21**, 51–60.

Ivánovics, G., Nagy, E., and Alföldi, L. (1959b). *Acta microbiol. hung.*, **6**, 161–169.

Jacob, F. (1954). *Annls Inst. Pasteur, Paris.*, **86**, 149–160.

Jacob, F., Lwoff, A., Siminovitch, L., and Wollman, E. (1953). *Annls Inst. Pasteur, Paris*, **84**, 222–224.

Jacob, F., Siminovitch, L., and Wollman, E. (1951). *C. r. hebd. Séanc. Acad. Sci., Paris*, **233**, 1500–1502.

Jacob, F., Siminovitch, L., and Wollman, E. (1952). *Annls Inst. Pasteur, Paris*, **83**, 295–315.

Jesaitis, M. A. (1970). *J. exp. Med.*, **131**, 1016–1038.

Kageyama, M. (1964). *J. Biochem., Tokyo*, **55**, 49–53.

Kageyama, M., and Egami, F. (1962). *Life Sciences*, (9), 471–476.

Kageyama, M., Ikeda, K., and Egami, F. (1964). *J. Biochem., Tokyo*, **55**, 59–64.

Keene, J. H. (1966). *Can. J. Microbiol.*, **12**, 425–427.

Kekessy, D. A., and Piguet, J. D. (1970). *Appl. Microbiol.*, **20**, 282–283.

Kingsbury, D. T. (1966). *J. Bact.*, **91**, 1696–1699.

Kiselev, R. N. (1967). *Zh. Mikrobiol. Epidem. Immunol.*, No. **8**, pp. 60–64.

de Klerk, H. C., and Smit, J. A. (1967). *J. gen. Microbiol.*, **48**, 309–316.

Kohiyama, M., and Nomura, M. (1965). *Zentbl. Bakt. ParasitKde (Abt. I)*, **196**, 211–215.

Koninsky, J., and Nomura, M. (1967). *J. molec. Biol.*, **26**, 181–195.

Koninsky, J., and Richards, F. M. (1970). *J. biol. Chem.*, **245**, 2972–2978.

Kudlai, D. G., Likhoded, V. G., and Petrosov, V. V. (1966). In "Genetika mikroorganismov". Symposium at Moscow, 1965 (Ed. V. D. Timakov), pp. 210–213.

Kuttner, A. G. (1966). *J. exp. Med.*, **124**, 279–291.

Larionova, T. H. (1967). *Antibiotiki*, No. **12**, pp. 1074–1077.

Lidwell, O. M., and Carpenter, K. P. (1961). *Mon. Bull. Minist. Hlth*, **20**, 119–120.

Likhoded, V. G. (1963). *Zh. Mikrobiol. Epidem. Immunol.*, No. **11**, 89–94.

Linton, K. B. (1960). *J. clin. Path.*, **13**, 168–172.

Litkenhous, C., and Liu, P. V. (1967). *J. Bact.*, **93**, 1484–1488.

Lowry, O. H., Rosenbrough, N. J., Farr, A. L., and Randall, R. J. (1951). *J. biol. Chem.*, **193**, 265–275.

Ludford, G. C., and Lederer, M. (1953). *Aust. J. exp. Biol. med. Sci.*, **31**, 553–560.

Luria, S. E. (1964). *Annls Inst. Pasteur, Paris*, **107** (Suppl. 5), 67–73.

Luzzati, D., and Chevalier, M. R. (1964). *Annls Inst. Pasteur, Paris*, **107** (Suppl. 5), 152–162.

MacFarren, A., and Clowes, R. C. (1967). *J. Bact.*, **94**, 365–377.

McGeachie, J. (1965). *Zentbl. Bakt. ParasitKde (Abt. I)*, **196**, 377–384.

McGeachie, J., and McCormick, W. (1963). *J. clin. Path.*, **16**, 278–280.

McGeachie, J., and McCormick, W. (1967). *J. clin. Path.*, **20**, 887–891.

Maeda, A., and Nomura, M. (1966). *J. Bact.*, **91**, 685–694.

Maré, I. J., Coetzee, J. N., and de Klerk, H. C. (1964). *Nature, Lond.*, **202**, 213.

Marjai, E., and Ivánovics, G. (1962). *Acta microbiol. hung.*, **9**, 285–295.

Marjai, E., and Ivánovics, G. (1964). *Acta microbiol. hung.*, **11**, 193–198.

Marotel-Schirmann, J., and Barbu, E. (1969). *C. r. hebd. Séanc. Acad. Sci., Paris*, **269**, 866–869.

Matsushita, H., Fox, M. S., and Goebel, W. F. (1960). *J. exp. Med.*, **112**, 1055–1068.

Mayr-Harting, A. (1964). *J. Path. Bact.*, **87**, 255–266.

Mayr-Harting, A., and van Horn, E. A. (1961). *Zentbl. Bakt. ParasitKde (Abt. I)*, Ref. **179**, 319.

Mayr-Harting, A., and Picken, J. M. (1966). *Abstracts of the VIIIth International Congress of Microbiology*, p. 14.

Mayr-Harting, A., and Shimeld, C. (1965). *Zentbl. Bakt. ParasitKde (Abt. I)*, **196**, 263–270.

Mayr-Harting, A., and Shimeld, C. (1966). *In* "Antibiotics—Advances in Research, Production and Clinical Use" (Eds M. Herold and Z. Gabriel), pp. 687–691. Butterworths, London.

Mindich, L. (1966). *J. Bact.*, **92**, 1090–1098.

Mitchison, D. A., and Spicer, C. C. (1949). *J. gen. Microbiol.*, **3**, 184–203.

Monk, M., and Clowes, R. C. (1964a). *J. gen. Microbiol.*, **36**, 365–384.

Monk, M., and Clowes, R. C. (1964b). *J. gen. Microbiol.*, **36**, 385–392.

Morris, C. J. O. R., and Morris, P. (1963). "Separation Methods in Biochemistry". Pitman, London.

Moutousis, C., Papavassiliou, J., and Papavassiliou, N. (1960). *Acta microbiol. hellenica*, **5**, 139. cited by Papavassiliou (1963).

Nagel de Zwaig, R., Anton, D. N., and Puig, J. (1962). *J. gen. Microbiol.*, **29**, 473–484.

Nagy, E., Alföldi, L., and Ivánovics, G. (1959). *Acta microbiol. hung.*, **6**, 327–336.

Naito, T., Kono, M., Fujise, N., Yakushiji, Y., and Aoki, Y. (1966). *Jap. J. Microbiol.*, **10**, 13–22.

Neidhardt, F. C. (1964). *In* "Progress in Nucleic Acid Research and Molecular Biology" (Eds J. N. Davidson and W. E. Cohn). Academic Press, New York.

Nicholle, P., and Prunet, J. (1964). *Annls Inst. Pasteur, Paris*, **107** (Suppl. 5), 174–189.

Nomura, M. (1963). *Cold Spring Harb. Symp. quant. Biol.*, **28**, 315–324.

Nomura, M. (1964). *Proc. natn. Acad. Sci. U.S.A.*, **52**, 1514–1521.

Nomura, M. (1967a). *A. Rev. Microbiol.*, 257–284.

Nomura, M. (1967b). *In* "Antibiotics I: Mechanisms of Action" (Eds D. Gottlieb and P. D. Shaw), pp. 696–704. Springer-Verlag, New York.

Nomura, M., and Maeda, A. (1965). *Zentbl. Bakt. ParasitKde (Abt. I)*, **196**, 216–239.

Nomura, M., and Nakamura, M. (1962). *Biochem. biophys. Res. Commun.*, **7**, 306–309.

Nüske, R., Hösel, H., Venner, H., and Zinner, H. (1957). *Biochem. Z.*, **329**, 346–360

Ornstein, L. (1964). *Ann. N.Y. Acad. Sci.*, **121**, 321–349.

Ouchterlony, Ö. (1953). *Acta path. microbiol. scand.*, **32**, 231–240.

Ouchterlony, Ö, (1962). *In* "Progress in Allergy" (Eds P. Kallos and B. H. Waksman), Vol. 4, pp. 30–154. Karger, Basel.

Ozaki, M., Higashi, Y., Saito, H., An, T., and Amano, T. (1966). *Biken J.*, **9**, 201–213.

Ozeki, H., Smith, S. M., and Stocker, B. A. D. (1962). *J. gen. Microbiol.*, **28**, 671–687.

Ozeki, H., and Stocker, B. A. D. (1958). *Heredity*, **12**, 525–526.

Ozeki, H., Stocker, B. A. D., and de Margerie, H. (1959). *Nature, Lond.*, **184**, 337–339.

Papavassiliou, J. (1961). *Arch. Inst. Pasteur, Tunis*, **38**, 57–63.

Papavassiliou, J. (1963). *Path. Microbiol.*, **26**, 74–83.

Parr, L. W., el Shawi, N. N., and Robbins, M. L. (1960). *J. Bact.*, **80**, 417–418.

Rampini, C., Schirmann, J., and Barbu, E. (1967). *C. r. hebd. Séanc. Acad. Sci.*, *Paris*, 264, 1660–1663.

Reeves, P. R. (1963). *Aust. J. exp. Biol. med. Sci.*, 41, 163–170.

Reeves, P. R. (1965a). *Bact. Rev.*, 29, 24–45.

Reeves, P. R. (1965b). *Aust. J. exp. Biol. med. Sci.*, 43, 191–200.

Reynolds, B. L., and Reeves, P. R. (1963). *Biochem. biophys. Res. Commun.*, 11, 140–145.

Reynolds, B. L., and Reeves, P. R. (1969). *J. Bact.*, 100, 301–309.

Richardson, H., Emslie-Smith, A. H., and Senior, B. W. (1968) *Appl. Microbiol.*, 16, 1468–1474.

Rosebury, T., Gale, D., and Taylor, D. F. (1954). *J. Bact.*, 67, 135–152.

Rüde, E., and Goebel, W. F. (1962). *J. exp. Med.*, 116, 73–99.

Sandoval, H. K., Reilly, H. C., and Tandler, B. (1965). *Nature, Lond.*, 205, 522–523.

Seed, H. D. (1970). Ph.D. Thesis, University of Bristol.

Shannon, R., and Hedges, A. J. (1967). *J. Bact.*, 93, 1353–1359.

Shannon, R., and Hedges, A. J. (1970). *J. appl. Bact.*, 33, 555–565.

Shapiro, A. L., Vinuela, E., and Maizel, J. Jr. (1967). *Biochem. biophys. Res. Commun.*, 28, 815–820.

Shimeld, C. (1966). *J. gen. Microbiol.*, 45, vii–viii.

Sicard, N., and Devoret, R. (1962). *C. r. hebd. Séanc. Acad. Sci.*, *Paris*, 255, 1417–1419.

Silver, S., and Ozeki, H. (1962). *Nature, Lond.*, 195, 873–874.

Šmarda, J. (1960). *Folia biologica.*, *Praha*, 6, 225–232.

Šmarda, J. (1961). *Folia microbiol.*, *Praha*, 6, 44–48.

Šmarda, J. (1965a). *Zentbl. Bakt. ParasitKde (Abt. I)*, 196, 240–248.

Šmarda, J. (1965b). *Antimicrob. Ag. Chemother.*, pp. 345–348.

Šmarda, J., and Čermák, V. (1964). *Z. allg. Mikrobiol.*, 4, 358–366.

Šmarda, J., Kondelka, J., and Kleinwächter, V. (1964). *Experientia*, 20, 500–501.

Šmarda, J., and Obdržálek, V. (1966). *Zentbl. Bakt. ParasitKde (Abt. I)*, 200, 493–497.

Šmarda, J., and Šmarda, B. (1965). *Folia microbiol.*, *Praha*, 10, 368–374.

Šmarda, J., and Taubeneck, U. (1968). *J. gen. Microbiol.*, 52, 161–172.

Šmarda, J., and Vrba, M. (1962). *Folia microbiol.*, *Praha*, 7, 104–108.

Smith, C. E. (1965). *Zentbl. Bakt. ParasitKde (Abt. I)*, 196, 270–275.

Smith, C. E. (1966). Ph.D. Thesis, University of Bristol.

Smithies, O. (1959). *Biochem. J.*, 71, 585–587.

Stocker, B. A. D., Smith, S. M., and Ozeki, H. (1963). *J. gen. Microbiol.*, 30, 201–224.

Taylor, R. L., and Mayr-Harting, A. (1970). *J. gen. Microbiol.*, 61, Proceedings, vi.

Taylor, R. L., Spires, V. J., and Mayr-Harting, A. (In preparation).

Timmis, K. N. (1970). Ph.D. Thesis, University of Bristol.

Tscheuschner, I. (1966). M.D. Thesis, University of Göttingen.

Turba, F., and Enenkel, H. J. (1950). *Naturwissenschaften*, 37, 93.

Vesterberg, O., and Svensson, H. (1966). *Acta chem. scand.*, 20, 820–834.

Wahba, A. H. (1965). *Zentbl. Bakt. ParasitKde (Abt. I)*, 196, 389–394.

de Witt, W., and Helinski, D. R. (1965). *J. molec. Biol.*, 13, 692–703.

CHAPTER VIII

Specific Procedures and Requirements for the Isolation, Growth and Maintenance of the L-Phase of some Microbial Groups

W. R. Maxted

Central Public Health Laboratory, London, England

I. INTRODUCTION

It has long been recognized that bacteria may remain viable and multiply even though they lack a cell-wall. The ability to do so usually demands special media, and the growth shows extraordinary distortion and pleo-morphism, similar to that seen among the Mycoplasmatales. The aberrant mode of growth is conditioned by the lack of cell-wall and failure of the normal division mechanism. Organisms growing in this way are termed L-phase variants. They metabolize normally in every way except that they lack the ability to synthesize a cell-wall.

First identified by Klieneberger in 1935, L-phase variants have been studied intensively during the last 15 years. The extensive bibliography testifies to the wide interest in the L-phase both as a microbiological entity and as a potential pathogen.

The techniques employed for the study of L-phase variants vary as widely as the parental bacteria from which they are derived. It is imprac-ticable to describe all the variations in techniques and materials employed in L-phase work. Personal experience with streptococcal and staphylo-coccal L-phase will be used to illustrate the study of the L-phase in general, and a selection of references to the others, especially the Gram-negative bacteria, will be used to illustrate methods in current use.

Several excellent reviews of the L-phase have appeared in recent years which provide an adequate source of references to both the familiar and to the more obscure observations and specialized methods of study (Hayflick 1969, Guze, 1968).

A. Terms and definitions

A difficulty common to most of these studies is the variety of terms and definitions employed. The name *L-form* was given to the pleomorphic forms of *Streptobacillus moniliformis*, seen by Klieneberger (1935), which are known to be derived from that organism and cannot be considered as symbiotic mycoplasmas. The term L-form is still used, but Edward (1960) proposed that the terms *L-phase* or *L-phase variant* should replace it; and this proposal was accepted at the First Conference on the Biology of Pleuropneumonia-like Organisms. The terms L-phase and L-phase variant will be used here. *L-phase growth* can be described as a morpholo-gical variant of bacteria, which grows and multiplies in special media as minute particles and pleomorphic globules which do not take the Gram stain. L-phase variants are generally devoid of cell-wall material although some traces of mucopeptide elements may still be present. They survive and propagate under conditions in which protoplasts would be disrupted. The smaller granular form penetrates the agar and grows below the sur-face; this and the extreme plasticity of the individual units is their most consistent characteristic. The L-phase is potentially reversible to the bacterial parental form.

There is no doubt that L-phase growth can arise from laboratory-made protoplasts or spheroplasts, two terms which need some definition. The criteria used for protoplasts are those suggested by Brenner *et al.* (1958). *Protoplasts* are bounded by cytoplasmic membrane only, and are therefore spheres irrespective of the shape of the parent bacterium. Phage receptor sites, cell-wall antigens and all material which occurs specifically in the cell-wall are absent. The protoplast is thus extremely osmotically fragile and will not grow in normal laboratory media.

Spheroplasts are bacterial cells whose cell-wall has been modified or damaged. They often recover the complete cell-wall and then grow as bacterial forms on laboratory media without osmotic stabilizers.

II. INDUCTION AND PROPAGATION

A. General media requirements

For the cultivation of L-phase organisms, as for that of the parent bacteria, a variety of broth bases can be used in either liquid or solid media. Table I shows a selection of media that have been recommended for a number of organisms in the L-phase. Because of the lack of cell-wall the L-phase require some additional osmotic stabilization. This can be attained by the addition of a variety of substances. The degree of stabilization required may depend on whether the parent organism is Gram-positive with a high internal cell pressure (20–30 atmospheres), or Gram-negative with an internal pressure of 6–10 atmospheres (Mitchell and Moyle, 1956). Gram-negative L-phase variants are therefore much more stable than those from Gram-positive organisms and need less additional support.

For most purposes the required osmolarity can be supplied by sodium chloride or sucrose. For the Gram-negative bacterial species, media with 0·2 to 0·5M sodium chloride (Landman and Ginoza, 1961) or 0·3M sucrose are required. An osmotic environment for induction and growth of Gram-positive L-phase is obtained with 0·43 to 0·51M sodium chloride (Sharp, 1954; Crawford *et al.*, 1958) or 0·5 to 1·0M sucrose (Maxted, 1968). The selection of the appropriate osmotic stabilizer may be of prime importance in some cases. Attempts to induce L-phase of *Streptococcus pneumonia* and *Neisseria gonorrhoea* on sucrose agar were successful but failed completely if sodium chloride was incorporated (Madoff and Dienes, 1958; Roberts, 1966), while *Bacillus megaterium* behaved in the reverse way (Kusaka, 1967). *Streptococcus viridans* gave a much higher yield with a phosphate than with sodium chloride, but *Escherichia coli* showed no induction on phosphate agar but gave excellent yields with sucrose (Hijmans and Dienes, 1955; Landman *et al.*, 1958).

TABLE I

The constitution of media used for the growth of L-phase variants of a variety of bacteria

Basic medium	% agar additives	Osmotic stabilizer	Protein added	Organism	Reference
Brain heart infusion 1·2	Glucose 0·2%	3% NaCl 20–25% sucrose	10% horse serum	Streptococcus pyogenes	Freimer et al., 1959 Maxted, 1968
Brain heart infusion 1·0	MgSO$_4$ 0·2%	5% NaCl	10% human or horse serum	Staphylococcus aureus	Hamburger & Carleton, 1966
Difco PPLO agar	Yeast extract 10% MgSO$_4$ 0·2%	0·3M sucrose	10% horse serum	Mycobacterium tuberculosis	Willet & Thacore, 1966
Casein digest 1·0	Meat extract 10% Glucose 1·6% MgSO$_4$ 0·2%	3·5% NaCl	Nil	Escherichia coli	Lederberg & St Clair, 1958
Tryptic digest or 1·3 brain heart infusion		0·2M phosphate	10% horse serum	Alpha haemolytic streptococci Enterococci	Hijmans & Dienes, 1955 Hijmans & Kastelein, 1960
Tryptic digest 0·8			20% ascetic fluid	Salmonella typhimurium Haemophilus influenzae	Dienes & Zamecnik, 1952
Albimi 1·0 Brucella broth		3% salt	Nil	St. pyogenes	van Boven et al., 1967
Chemically defined	Complex see ref.	0·1M phosphate	Nil	St. pyogenes	
Semi-synthetic 0·8 (see ref.)		0·5M succinate	Nil	Bacillus subtilis	Landman et al., 1968

Most of the media used also contain 10% horse serum, or an equivalent amount of a serum fraction or ascitic fluid; this is believed to act not as a growth factor, but by neutralizing inhibiting substances in the medium. Solid media containing rather less agar than usual (0·8%) are said to favour L-phase growth while stiffer agar gels (2–3%) encourage the process of reversion. Because of the difficulty of obtaining cultures of L-phase in liquid medium, diphasic cultures are often used. These consist of an agar slant immersed in L-phase broth medium, and because of the long incubation time required diphasic medium is prepared in screw-capped bottles.

It is usual to store media without antibiotics or serum. These are added just before use, and melted agar should be held at 45°C before pouring.

B. Propagation

Once the L-phase has grown on the surface of solid medium it may be propagated by the agar block method which is also used extensively for mycoplasmas (Fallon and Whittlestone, this Series, Vol. 3B).

An agar block showing typical surface colonies is cut out from the plate with a sterile scalpel and inverted on to the surface of a fresh agar plate. After overnight incubation the block is pushed further along the surface on to a fresh area of medium and the plate reincubated. If this procedure is continued, eventually a continuous sheet of growth is obtained on the agar, and from this further plate cultures can be made as well as attempts to propagate the growth in liquid media. Blocks of agar containing well grown surface colonies are put into bottles of diaphasic broth/agar and incubated. Sometimes growth free from the agar appears within 2–3 days of the inoculation, but in most instances prolonged incubation is necessary.

III. METHODS OF INDUCING L-PHASE VARIANTS

Induction may be brought about by interference in the synthesis of cell-wall or by the removal of preformed cell-wall in a medium which gives sufficient osmotic support to prevent lysis of the protoplast. The selection of the inducing system depends therefore on the sensitivity of the species, and often of a specific strain, to the inducing agent. There are numerous inducing agents and a variety sufficient to cover most practical purposes are listed in Table I. The processes involved are described in Hijmans' excellent review "The Mycoplasmatales and the L-phase of Bacteria" (Ed. Hayflick, 1969) which also mentions additional inducing agents and lists the bacterial species reported to grow in the L-phase. It is usually only possible to initiate L-phase growth on solid medium, and this fact tends to govern the technique of induction. With the antibiotic inducing agents and glycine it is customary to include them in appropriate concentration in the medium and inoculate a suitable number of bacteria

TABLE II

Agents which have been used to obtain L-phase variants of bacteria

Inducing agent	Organism	Reference
Penicillin	*Staphylococcus aureus* *Streptococcus* group A, B & G *Proteus vulgaris*	⎫ ⎬ Dienes & Sharp, 1956 ⎭
Bacitracin	*Streptococcus pyogenes* *Neisseria meningitidis*	Gooder & Maxted, 1961 Roberts, 1966
Cephalothin	*N. meningitidis*	⎫
Vancomycin	*N. meningitidis*	⎬ Roberts, 1967
Ristocetin	*N. meningitidis*	⎭
D-cycloserine	*St. pyogenes*	Michel & Hijmans, 1960
Glycine	*Salmonella typhosa*	Dienes *et al.*, 1950
Phage-associated		
lysin (group C)	*St. pyogenes*	Freimer *et al.*, 1959
lysin (group D)	*Streptococcus faecalis*	Bleiweis & Zimmerman, 1961
Lysozyme	*Bacillus subtilis* *Mycobacterium tuberculosis*	Landman & Halle, 1963 Willett & Thacore, 1966
Lysostaphin	*S. aureus*	Watanakunakorn *et al.*, 1969
Antibody and	*Salm. typhosa*	Dienes *et al.*, 1950
complement	*Vibrio cholerae*	Ianetta & Wedgwood, 1967

on to the surface of an agar plate, or to use a pour plate technique. With enzyme induction, protoplasts are first prepared in suspension in a mixture of enzyme and osmotic stabilizer and inoculated on to or into the appropriate agar medium containing sufficient penicillin to suppress bacterial growth.

A detailed example of each of these methods is given together with techniques which have been used for both "natural" and antibiotic induction in the animal body.

A. Penicillin induction of staphylococcal L-phase variants

The basal medium used by Dienes and Sharp (1956) has given satisfactory results and consists of 3·7% Difco brain heart infusion, 1·3% agar and 3% salt. To this 10% inactivated horse serum (i.e. serum which has been heated to inactivate complement) is added and 100 μg/ml of penicillin. Young cultures of staphylococci are preferable, but 15 h cultures also give good results. Approximately 0·04 ml of culture is spread on the surface of each plate, which is then sealed or placed in a plastic bag to prevent drying by evaporation during incubation. The L-phase colonies develop after three or four days at 37°C and may be propagated in broth or on agar by the usual agar block technique. The induction occurs equally readily if the staphylococci are inoculated into molten agar and pour plates made.

The use of a penicillin gradient is seldom necessary. In general staphylococci seem to lend themselves very readily to L-phase induction; Hamburger and Carleton (1966) have described the direct induction and growth of L-phase in broth using methicillin. Using brain heart infusion broth with 5% NaCl, 10% horse serum and 100 μg/ml methicillin, and a heavy inoculum of staphylococci, L-phase organisms appeared at the end of the first week, increased in numbers and 10^7 cells remained viable for 42 days in broth. Subcultures to salt-serum agar gave typical colonies of L-phase growth but the addition of Mg^{2+} ions to the agar appeared to be essential for growth on solid medium.

The plate induction technique serves equally well for streptococci but here some strains may require the use of a ditch or well containing the antibiotic. A few drops of a young culture are spread over the surface of L-phase agar and allowed to dry. A central well approximately 8 mm in dia. can be cut out of the plate with a cork borer, or a ditch cut out of the agar with a scalpel, and filled with penicillin solution (1000 μg/ml). After 3–4 days incubation L-phase colonies appear in the zone of inhibition, and can be propagated by the agar block technique. The same technique is used for induction by other antibiotics.

B. Enzymic induction of streptococcal L-phase variants

The enzymes which have been used for this type of induction are all muramidases, which in osmotically stable media remove preformed cell-wall and form protoplasts from which L-phase growth is obtained on appropriate media.

Three of the enzymes are obtained from a bacterial source. Two from the propagation of specific phages on their host bacteria and the third, lysostaphin, is a bacteriolysin found in the supernatant of broth cultures of *Staphylococcus* K-6-W1. The three enzymes are limited in their range of attack.

Source of muralytic enzymes obtained from bacteria

	Found in phage lysates after propagation of phage active on:	Enzymes active on cell-walls of:	Reference
Streptococcal phage associated lysins	1. Group C streptococci	Groups A, C & E streptococci	Maxted, 1957
	2. Group D streptococci	Group D streptococci	Bleiwers & Zimmerman, 1961
Lysostaphin	Found in culture supernatant of *Staphylococcus* K-6-W1	Coagulase positive staphylococci	Schindler & Schuhardt, 1964

All these have been used for the mass induction of L-phase growth. The fourth muramidase, lysozyme, is found in most animal tissues and body fluids. The lytic spectrum of this enzyme is wider than that of the phage-associated lysins or lysostaphin.

The group C phage lysin and lysostaphin have also both been used for the experimental induction of the L-phase in mice (see Section IV). The presence of lysozyme in the animal body emphasizes the importance of this enzyme as a factor in any "natural" cycle of L-phase induction.

The technique for induction by means of lysostaphin and the two phage associated lysins is very similar. The lysin active on group A streptococci is used here as a model for all three lysins, lysozyme induction is also given in detail.

1. *Phage-associated lysin induction of group A streptococcal L-phase*

The enzyme used in this procedure is a muralysin obtained when propagating bacteriophage on a group C streptococcus (Maxted, 1957) and can be used in its crude state for the purpose of L-phase induction. The group C streptococcus phage lysate contains a muralysin which attacks the cell-wall of group A organisms.

The enzyme (phage lysate) is diluted with an equal volume of 4M NaCl. To 5 ml of the enzyme-salt mixture 0·1 ml of a 5 h broth culture of group A streptococci is added and 0·1 ml of 2% sodium thioglycollate to activate the enzyme. After 5–10 min incubation samples are spread on the surface of L-phase medium or inoculated into molten agar and plates poured. The plates are incubated for 3–4 days at 37°C. Although L-forms induced by this method will grow readily without penicillin the inclusion of a small concentration (10 μg/ml) is helpful in suppressing any surviving bacterial cells. During the early stages of any subsequent subculturing reversion to the bacterial form occurs fairly readily in the absence of penicillin. The basal media can be brain heart infusion broth or tryptone soya broth. When converted into agar 10% horse serum is added. The osmotic stabilizer may be 0·5M NaCl or 1·0M sucrose.

It has been shown that the different serological types of *St. pyogenes* show a great diversity in their preference for one or the other of these stabilizing agents (Sharp, 1954; Hryniewicz and Maxted, unpublished data). As the yield of L-phase growth is reflected in this parental preference, a preliminary test in order to establish the best system for a given strain is recommended.

2. *Lysozyme*

Not all bacteria have cell-walls that are susceptible to the enzyme lysozyme, but from those which are it is possible to make protoplasts in the appropriate osmotic condition and thus often possible to obtain L-phase growth from such suspensions (Weibull, 1953).

In the presence of EDTA the range of bacteria susceptible to the action of lysozyme is considerably extended (Repaske, 1958). The inclusion of EDTA in the inducing system is therefore recommended.

Two examples of lysozyme L-phase induction *in vitro* are considered here; one a very simple system for group D streptococci (King and Gooder, 1965) and the other a much more complex system for *Mycobacterium tuberculosis*, a very much more demanding organism (Willett and Thacore, 1966).

3. *Lysozyme induction of group D streptococci*

A washed suspension of streptococcal cells, containing 10^9 colony forming units/ml was exposed at 37°C for 2 h to 200 μg/ml of lysozyme (pH 7·1). The osmotic stabilizer used by King and Gooder was 8% polyethylene-glycol. There is no reason to suppose that this is essential.

Rhamnose loss, used as an index of loss of cell-wall, varied with the streptococcal strain studied. Whether this was almost complete (90%) or only partial (50%) approximately half the lysozyme-treated cells gave rise to L-phase growth when plated on L-phase agar containing less than 2% agar.

4. *Lysozyme induction of* Mycobacterium tuberculosis *L-phase variants*

The persistent and often recurring disease resulting from infection with this organism suggests that L-phase or some such transient form might sometimes be involved. The slow growth of the bacterial form and its more demanding nature present additional difficulty and make a specific description of the method worthwhile.

The lysozyme induction of the L-phase of *M. tuberculosis* reported by Willett and Thacore was carried out on a complex growth medium (Tween 80 medium), details of which can be found in the report, and also on a comparatively simple medium which is given here.

Cells for induction are grown in Tween 80 medium and also washed with this medium.

Inducing system:

100 μg/ml lysozyme	⎫ In 10 ml volumes
2000 μg/ml EDTA	⎬ of Tween 80 albumin
1·1 μg/ml hydrated magnesium sulphate	⎭ medium, pH 7·1

Sucrose (0·34M) was necessary for osmotic stabilization of the spheroplasts. Washed cells were added to give an absorbance of 0·03 and 450 nm and the suspension incubated at 37°C and shaken daily.

L-phase growth medium consisted of PPLO agar (Difco) enriched with:

10% horse serum

0·3M sucrose

0·2% hydrated magnesium sulphate

10% fresh yeast extract.

The inoculum was 1 ml of lysozyme-treated spheroplasts for each 20 ml of agar medium. Pour plates were made and incubated in an atmosphere containing 10% CO_2

PPLO broth with the supplements as for PPLO agar was also used with an inoculum of 1 ml spheroplast suspension per 5 ml broth. Broth cultures were also incubated in CO_2.

On the agar medium, L-phase colonies appeared after 17 days incubation and increased in size and numbers over the next 4–6 weeks. The PPLO broth however showed visible growth within 3–4 days and "large bodies" appeared.

It should be noted that EDTA and magnesium sulphate are included in the inducing system and the authors state that the tubercle spheroplast is still surrounded with large amounts of lipoprotein and lipopolysaccharide and may therefore not appear spherical.

Because lysozyme is present in most animal tissue and body fluids, the opportunity exists for *in vivo* L-phase induction by this enzyme. Such a mechanism must obviously be considered in studies concerning the mechanism involved in "natural" induction.

C. Induction by antibody and complement

The reports of successful induction by means of antibody concern Gram-negative organisms only.

Salmonella typhi, Vibrio cholerae and *E. coli* (Dienes *et al.*, 1950, Ianetta and Wedgwood, 1967).

The system is a simple one. Dilutions of rabbit antiserum are mixed with an equal volume of guinea-pig serum diluted 1 : 6 as a source of complement and the organisms (10^8/ml) are suspended in the mixture. After a short incubation (15–30 min at 37°C) samples are plated on soft agar medium containing 10% horse serum.

Among bacteria which are apparently resistant to the enzyme, the presence of lysozyme in the serum may well make for the more efficient conversion of antibody and complement-damaged cells to protoplasts (Crombie and Muschel, 1967).

It is of considerable interest that Wittler's (1952) report of the presence of L-phase of *Bordetella pertusis* in the lungs of infected mice states that the organisms were more frequently found in profusion in the lungs of mice known to have antibody to that organism.

D. Induction of L-phase variants by glycine

The use of glycine as an inducing agent for L-phase of *Haemophilus influenzae* was reported by Dienes and Zamecnik (1952) and more recently by Lapinski and Flakas (1967). Dienes used a simple medium without the addition of any osmotic stabilizing agent but with 20% ascetic fluid added. The more recent report by Lapinski and Flakas is the source of the technique described here.

The inducing system was as follows. Trypticase soya agar (BBL), 2 parts; Levinthal broth, 1 part; this gives a soft agar suitable for the L-phase development of *H. influenzae* in the presence of glycine (1·5% w/v) or penicillin.

The plates are inoculated with samples of a 6 h culture of *H. influenzae* in Levinthal broth and the plates are incubated at 37°C, in a CO_2 atmosphere, for 7 to 30 days.

With glycine, typical L-phase colonies appeared within 5–7 days but the yield was less than when penicillin was used as an inducing agent. The L-phase could be propagated on the same basal medium with 10% sucrose added or on Levinthal broth agar with 20% sucrose in the presence of penicillin but not with glycine. Reversion took place in the absence of inducing agent on chocolate (heated blood) agar, or on broth agar with staphylococci streaked across the L-phase inoculum.

E. Induction of L-phase variants with D-cycloserine

Ward and Martin (1962) succeeded in inducing the L-phase from a variety of bacteria with this antibiotic. The inducing system was as follows:

>Oxoid sensitivity test medium
>3% sodium chloride
>20% inactivated ascetic fluid.

A solution of D-cycloserine 1000 μg/ml was put into wells or troughs after the plates had been streaked with the test strain. Ninety-six strains belonging to ten different genera were tested and of these 16 gave L-phase colonies. The strains that could be induced by cycloserine could also be induced by penicillin, but penicillin induction was much more prolific.

Michel and Hijmans (1960) attempted to induce L-phase growth from seven different strains of streptococci by means of D-cycloserine and succeeded in obtaining L-phase colonies in very small numbers from one strain only. The medium was a tryptic digest beef heart infusion containing 1·3% agar, 10% inactivated horse serum and 0·6M sucrose. A strong solution of cycloserine was deposited in troughs cut in plates already inoculated with streptococci.

Glycine failed completely to induce L-phase from any of the same seven strains of streptococci. In spite of the poor result obtained with group A streptococci and D-cycloserine and the complete failure with glycine, if 1·5% glycine was incorporated in the basal medium when D-cycloserine induction was attempted, the yield of L-phase colonies obtained was greatly increased. This additive effect of glycine could also be shown when inducing the L-phase by means of penicillin. Similar results have also been reported by Madoff et al. (1967).

Michel and Hijmans demonstrated that another amino-acid, DL-serine, also showed a similar synergism when used in conjunction with the same two antibiotics.

IV. INDUCTION OF L-PHASE *IN VIVO*

A. "Natural" induction in laboratory animals

In the animal body numerous cellular enzymes exist which are capable of attacking the cell-wall of bacteria and forming protoplasts. The support necessary for their survival could be given by mucine, or by spermine which occurs in many tissues and is reported to have a stabilizing effect on protoplasts. The requirements in respect of osmotic stabilization may thus have less importance *in vivo* but at many sites the osmotic value is higher than that of serum (Opie, 1949; Ullrich et al., 1961).

Reports of the isolation of streptococcal L-phase from the peritoneum of mice experimentally infected with streptococci (Mortimer, 1964; Rotta et al., 1965) have been adequately supported by our own observations (Maxted, 1968; Hryniewicz and Maxted, unpublished data). However, this only occurred regularly if certain strains of streptococci were used. Mortimer originally used a strain of type 14 and we have also used this strain and strains of type 1 and type 50 successfully. In our hands the type 50 strain (B514) was by far the most successful. Streptococci were inoculated into the peritoneum of a number of mice, which were killed at intervals during the succeeding 8 h. The peritoneum was washed out with L-phase broth, and 0·1 ml amounts plated on the surface of L-phase agar. Colonies growing in the L-phase could not be identified with certainty on solid media without penicillin because of the presence of very large numbers of bacterial colonies. On the penicillin agar only the L-phase grew, usually more than 100–500 colonies per 0·1 ml of inoculum. Similar numbers of streptococci from broth cultures of the type 50 strain plated directly on to L-phase agar with penicillin never grew more than 5–10 colonies. The type 14 and type 1 strains gave small numbers of L-phase colonies from the mouse, and none when plated directly from broth.

There was thus some suggestion that the L-phase was indeed present in the mouse and not induced on the surface of penicillin agar. Repeated subculturing of many different strains of streptococci grown in broth on to the surface of L-phase agar incorporating 50 μg/ml of penicillin has shown this to be a very poor method of inducing L-phase. Success with mouse peritoneal washings plated in a similar manner seemed reasonable evidence that L-phase or protoplasts were induced in the mouse. Also, Mortimer provided additional evidence for this when he filtered similar mouse peritoneal washings and obtained L-phase colonies from the filtrate spread on to the surface of L-phase agar. The point at issue is the real state of these viable units in the mouse. Are they present as L-phase as we recognize it in the laboratory, or as protoplasts or spheroplasts? It may even be that streptococci cultured in the mouse are simply more suscept-ible to penicillin induction on agar. If that were so the successful filtration experiments would then require further explanation.

It has been shown that laboratory-made protoplasts of group A strepto-cocci do not give rise to L-phase colonies when inoculated on to L-phase agar containing vancomycin while stabilized L-phase variants grow well. As infected mouse peritoneal material also failed to grow in the L-phase on vancomycin agar, but did so on penicillin agar, it seems possible that the viable units in the peritoneal washings, which multiplied on the penicillin medium, were present as spheroplast or protoplast and not in an estab-lished L-form state (Maxted, 1968).

B. *In vivo* induction by means of enzymes and antibiotics

The L-phase of group A streptococci has also been successfully isolated from mice infected with the organism and subsequently treated with the muralytic enzyme (cell-wall lysin) when the infection had become well established (Hryniewicz and Maxted, unpublished). Enzyme was injected into the peritoneal cavity and samples of washings plated at intervals. A rapid fall in the number of bacteria coincided with the appearance of large numbers of L-phase colonies grown on osmotically stabilized medium.

The L-phase of staphylococci has also been induced enzymically *in vivo* by means of lysostaphin (Schaffner *et al.*, 1967). Mice infected intraven-ously with staphylococci were treated 6 h later with lysostaphin. L-phase was grown from homogenized tissue $\frac{1}{2}$ to 2 h after treatment. L-phase was also grown successfully from mice infected in a similar manner but treated with oxacillin instead of lysostaphin. Cultures from infected but untreated mice failed to yield L-phase colonies.

Staphylococcal L-phase was also isolated successfully from experimental rabbits with pyelonephritis which had been treated with penicillin (Young and Dahlquist, 1967). The L-phase could be cultured both from the urine

and from homogenized kidney tissue on L-phase medium without penicillin. Guze and Kalmanson (1964a, b) and Kalmanson and Guze (1964)
inoculated rats intravenously with *Streptococcus faecalis* and established
undoubted streptococcal pyelonephritis. They were then treated with
penicillin and at intervals animals were sacrificed and their kidneys homogenized and cultured on both routine media and L-phase media without
penicillin. Even 13 weeks after penicillin treatment ceased it was possible
to culture the streptococcus from kidney but only on L-phase medium. The
organism had apparently persisted in the rat in the protoplast form without
reverting. *In vivo* induction with penicillin in mice has also been accomplished with *Salmonella typhimurium, Proteus mirabilis, E. coli, St. faecalis*
and *Staphylococcus aureus* (Godzeski *et al.*, 1967). It is evident that it is
possible to obtain natural enzymic or antibiotic induction of the L-phase
in vivo, and that the animal body supplies adequate osmotic stabilization.

V. THE L-PHASE *IN VIVO*

A. The L-phase in human disease

The hypothesis that the L-phase survives *in vivo* and plays a part in
human disease is obviously an attractive one. It would explain some of the
instances of therapeutic failure with cell-wall inhibiting antibiotics, and
offers an avenue for exploration of the origin of non-suppurative complications of certain bacterial diseases.

There is considerable evidence that the L-phase has been isolated from
a variety of clinical conditions and the reader is referred to Guze (1968)
and Hayflick (1969) for details. However, in spite of the evidence, contro-
versy still exists as to the consistency with which this can be done and the
significance of the findings.

Although a viable unit needing osmotic support may be grown as L-phase,
in what state did it exist in the body? We return again to the vexing possibility that the L-phase as we recognize it in the laboratory, is in fact purely
a laboratory artefact although perhaps made only from a certain type of
cell-wall damaged material. As Hijmans *et al.* in Hayflick (1969) have
pointed out the great problem is that the L-phase is only a phase in the
complete growth cycle and both *before* and *after* this phase the growth is
bacterial. The isolation of bacteria from clinical material cannot indicate
whether or not the L-phase has aided survival at some intermediate stage.
However, the laboratory induction and handling of L-phase growth is now
comparatively simple but it was 20 years after the initial report of their
existence (Klieneberger, 1935) before any real progress in the methods of
induction was made. It is now obvious that such induction is simply a

laboratory trick and it may be that the key to convincing and consistent isolation of L-phase from human disease will also prove to be a matter of the greater understanding of techniques and manipulative methods necessary for success.

Doubts surrounding the ability of the L-phase to survive *in vivo* and the possibility that the known techniques are inadequate are underlined by the laboratory work done on *in vivo* induction and survival in experimental animals.

B. Survival and pathogenicity of L-phase in laboratory animals

In spite of a small number of reports to the contrary, it may be said that in general the L-phase is not pathogenic for mice. This is certainly so in our own experience of the L-phase of group A streptococci, where the L-phase derived from highly virulent mouse strains of streptococci failed to initiate disease and could not be isolated either from the site of injection or from any organ after a lapse of only 8 h. The earlier work of Freundt (1958), and of Schmitt-Slomska *et al.* (1967) supports our finding. Infection of mice with the L-phase of *Streptobacillus moniliformis* (Heilman, 1941), *Vibrio cholerae* (Minck and Minck, 1951) and *Salm. typhimurium* (Mooser and Joos, 1952) also failed to give evidence of pathogenicity.

On the other hand some instances of pathogenicity have been reported for L-phase of *Salm. typhimurium* and cholera vibrios. It may well be that the retention of some cell-wall substances by Gram-negative L-phase organisms does on occasion result in some pathogenicity. There are few reports of the L-phase of Gram-positive organisms showing pathogenicity for laboratory animals. Kagan (1967) reported the occurrence of angina and heart lesions in monkeys which had received intratonsillar and intravenous injections of L-phase variants. Schmitt-Slomska *et al.* (1967) showed the persistence of the L-phase in the tissue of mice 25 days after peritoneal inoculation of group A streptococcal L-phase. The typical colonial morphology of L-phase organisms was recovered only after a series of subcultures. Such difficulties and some of the failures may serve to underline the earlier observation that greater experience of the laboratory manipulation of L-phase in a less unnatural environment than a test-tube is required. It must be borne in mind that the L-phase may revert *in vivo* to the bacterial form and then give rise to infection. There have been reports of such reversion and this may well be the true function of the L-phase in disease (Schnauder, 1955; Silberstein, 1953 and Freundt, 1956). It is interesting that L-phase of *E. coli* and *Klebsiella* which failed to give reversion in the laboratory, reverted to the bacterial form only after injection into rat kidney (Winterbauer *et al.*, 1967).

VI. REVERSION TO THE BACTERIAL FORM

There is no doubt that L-phase growth can revert to the original bacterial form. However, the main concern is the way this can be brought about at will and whether well established stabilized L-phase variants ever revert.

It is comparatively easy to obtain reversion from L-phase organisms that have only been passaged 5 to 10 times on L-phase medium containing penicillin or other inducing antibiotic. Subcultures are made on to and into similar medium without antibiotic and bacterial colonies will appear in time, often apparently arising from a well grown L-phase colony. Various procedures have been claimed to assist the change although with most recently induced L-phase these are unnecessary. With established stable L-phase growth it is said that reversion never takes place, and this of course is one of the chief subjects of discussion in the numerous debates concerning the similarities or differences between the mycoplasmas and the L-phase of bacteria, since part of the definition of L-phase refers to its ability to revert.

However, reversion has been accomplished among L-phase organisms considered to be stable, and in some instances this may have been initiated by some laboratory procedure but most of the evidence suggests that it occurs by chance.

Just as soft agar and high concentrations of serum favour L-phase growth, so hard agar combined with a reduction in the amount of serum favours reversion to the bacterial form. Penicillin must of course be omitted from the medium or penicillinase added to it. Some of the more interesting instances are those described by Landman et al. (1968) who obtained reversion from the L-phase of *Bacillus subtilis* quite regularly both in young L-phase and a 9-month-old stable line by reducing the serum concentration and replacing the agar completely by 25–30% gelatin. Gelatin has also been used successfully by King and Gooder (1965) for bringing about the reversion of group D streptococcal L-phase.

Yeast extract (Marston, 1961) and egg yolk (Schmitt-Slomska et al., 1967) have both been reported as being an aid to reversion, indeed the number of factors said to help in this process almost equal the number of media variations used in the study of the L-phase. Details and references to many of these procedures may be found in Guze (1968) and Hayflick (1969).

The L-phase of many Gram-negative species revert very easily to their bacterial form. The fact that they are often stable in normal growth media with no added osmotic stabilizer, still retain phage absorption sites, and agglutinate with the bacterial antisera suggest that some cell-wall material is still present and this may aid in reversion.

VII. ISOLATION OF L-PHASE VARIANTS FROM CLINICAL MATERIAL

The methods and materials which have been used in attempts to isolate the L-phase from clinical material are again many and various, but in general the procedure is as follows.

The L-phase medium selected for use should be one that will be likely to grow most common pathogens. The osmotic stabilizers should be those which have given good results in experimental work and are easy to handle, sodium chloride and sucrose are the most common. Both solid and liquid media should be used, the liquid medium in the form of diphasic preparation, that is an agar slant covered with L-phase broth. All media should contain 10% horse serum or a serum fraction.

Liquid specimens (blood, urine, ascitic fluid, etc.)

Ideally, if there is sufficient material, several cultures of each kind should be put up, but the specimen should at least be divided into four parts and two cultures in liquid and two on solid medium prepared. Penicillin should be added to one culture of each pair. The plate cultures are in the form of pour plates, since it is the general experience that pour plates are somewhat more successful than surface plating, presumably because of the additional support given to the colony by the surrounding agar.

Solid specimens

Tissue is macerated by any of the usual laboratory methods, suspended in L-form broth and distributed in the same way as the liquid specimens. Swabs may also be shaken up in broth medium for distribution in a similar way. Pour plates are sealed or put into plastic bags and incubated for 4 days and the broth culture incubated for a similar time. Plates are then examined at 2-day intervals and colonies appearing subcultured by the agar block technique on to L-phase and ordinary medium. The broth cultures are subcultured into fresh broth medium at weekly intervals even if no growth is apparent and samples also inoculated on to plates at regular intervals. The broth cultures should not be discarded as sterile until they have been incubated for at least 4 weeks.

It is apparent that even one specimen soon provides a large number of subcultures and the receipt of several specimens for processing at one time provides quite a large scale investigation. Control cultures of uninoculated media must always be put up and preferably not less than two samples of each medium. These provide a check on extraneous bacterial contamination and also on the introduction into the cultural system of mycoplasmas, which might well be confused with L-phase growth. It is obvious that such a scheme of culturing may give a variety of results, but the conclusions which may be drawn are as follows:

(a) No growth in any medium—culture sterile.
(b) Growth in normal medium and in L-phase medium without penicillin—straightforward bacterial infection.
(c) Growth of bacteria only in L-phase medium without penicillin—viable units (protoplasts) are present which need osmotic support in order to resume reproduction.
(d) L-phase growth in L-phase medium with and without penicillin—protoplasts or L-phase units present.

VIII. IDENTIFICATION OF THE ORIGIN OF L-PHASE GROWTH

The inhibition of the growth of mycoplasmas by means of specific antiserum applied on paper discs to the surface of agar plates has become a recognized diagnostic procedure.

There are reports that this technique applied to the L-phase has also been successful (Kagan, 1967) but there is insufficient evidence as to the specificity of the test when applied to a large range of L-phase variants. If antiserum to the parent bacterium should prove to be active this way, it would be invaluable not only for the identification of the L-phase but also its bacterial origin.

The identification of the bacterial parentage of L-phase growth is of undoubted importance. Stable non-reverting L-phase may well be difficult to differentiate from the mycoplasmas and although it is claimed that this can be done by studies of the deoxyribonucleic acid base composition and nucleic acid hybridization, these techniques are time consuming and complex, and in some cases involving Gram-positive organisms, inconclusive.

When L-phase growth continues to synthesize type specific antigen as in the case of group A streptococci, the use of fluorescent type-specific conjugates provide a means of identification (Karakawa et al., 1965). This is a useful method for identifying precisely L-phase known to be streptococcal in origin, but is obviously too restricted a method when faced with material of completely unknown origin.

A recent paper by Theodore et al. (1969) suggests that differentiation might be possible by means of polyacrylamide-gel electrophoresis of crude L-phase cell membranes extracted with phenol-acetic acid-water. The bands appearing in the gel when run at a pH 4·3 showed distinctly different patterns for L-phase of *Streptobacillus*, *Staphylococcus*, *Streptococcus* and *Proteus* (see Cooksey, this Series, Vol. 5B).

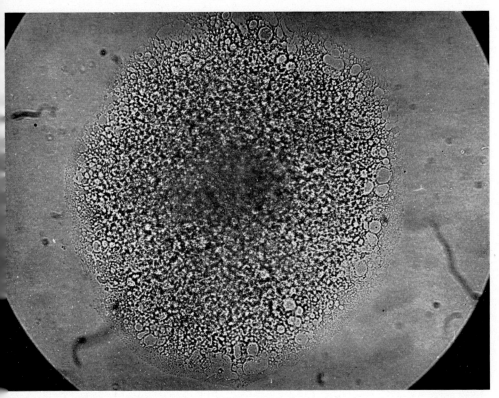

Fig. 1. Colony of L-phase variant of *Streptococcus pyogenes* showing dense centre and globular "foam-like" periphery (× 20 approx.).

Although the electrophoresis pattern for different genera was quite distinct, the pattern for two different species of *Streptococcus* were very similar. If such differentiation between the genera should prove to be consistent and cover a sufficiently good range of organisms it would be of inestimable value in the identification of L-phase isolated from clinical material, in order to establish the probable bacterial origin. The differentiation of L-phase and mycoplasmas is discussed in the Chapter on *Mycoplasmas* (Fallon and Whittlestone, this Series, Vol. 3B).

IX. MORPHOLOGY

A. Colonial appearance on solid media

The characteristic of all L-phase growth on solid media is its penetration below the agar surface. This is so, irrespective of the parent bacterium or the inducing system. This characteristic is also a feature among *Mycoplasma*

FIG. 2. Mucoid colonies of L-phase variant of *Streptococcus pyogenes*. These do not show the typical "foam-like" periphery (× 8 approx.).

species. The similarity macroscopically and microscopically between all L-phase and the mycoplasmas is due to the lack of a rigid cell envelope. It is claimed, however, that differences in colony size and staining reaction make it possible for those with considerable experience in this field to distinguish between L-phase growth and *Mycoplasma* (Madoff, 1960).

The dark central zone of the colony, consisting of densely packed granules penetrates the agar and also gives a raised centre to the colony. Surrounding this is a periphery of clear and flat foam-like growth lying on the surface. This gives the "fried egg" appearance to some colonies which has been consistently described for L-phase and *Mycoplasma* (Fig. 1). It must be emphasized that L-phase growth, although always penetrating the agar, varies considerably in colonial appearance and size and depends closely on the medium used, e.g. amounts of serum present, the strength of agar, and dryness of plates, etc. (Fig. 2).

B. Liquid cultures of L-phase variants

With the L-phase of many bacteria successful broth culture has been difficult to obtain. When successful the appearance varies widely. Nearly

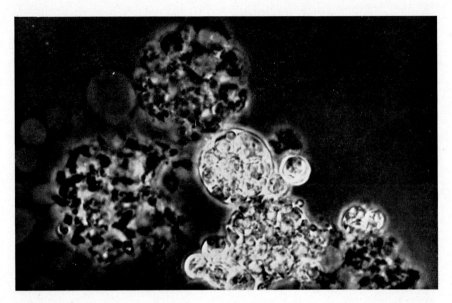

Fig. 3. Microscopical appearance of unit seen in a liquid culture of the L-phase of *Streptococcus pyogenes* (× 350 approx.).

all begin as individual granular aggregates which may continue to grow in this form. Some species following subculture become glutinous and form an amorphous mass at the base of the tube. An unusual form of growth is shown by *P. vulgaris* L-phase whis has been found to grow on the surface of the broth (Dienes, 1953). By the use of a continuous growth apparatus it has been possible to keep a culture of the L-phase of *St. pyogenes* growing in very fine granules suspended in the medium, showing none of the usual extraordinary pleomorphism (Maxted, 1968).

C. Microscopic appearance of the L-phase

Phase contrast microscopy gives an excellent general picture of L-phase growth. Again, this parallels most of the mycoplasmas in showing a very high degree of pleomorphism. This is so pronounced and varies so much with media, numbers of subcultures and the age of the cultures that it is difficult to say that any form is representative. Cultures often consist of a mixture of minute granules and enormous globules (Fig. 3). Each investigator adds something to the general description but all agree that there are three basic elements each of which can vary in size. These are the huge swollen forms or large bodies, varying from 1 μm to 50 μm in dia.; the granular forms which may be round or elongated, especially when grown on agar, and vary in size from 0·1 μm to 1·0 μm; and finally the "elementary corpuscles", the smallest of which is beyond the resolving power of the light microscope but which may reach 0·5 μm in dia. Both the latter forms may occur within a large body where they show Brownian movement or lie together in a mass.

Electron microscope studies parallel those made with the light microscope and descriptions of round protoplast-like bodies, small granular elements and vesicular structures are common. The reader is referred to the work of Dienes and Madoff (1968), Weibull (1965) and Coussons and Cole (1968), for very detailed descriptions of L-phase microscopic morphology and an explanation of the structures seen.

X. THE SEPARATION OF VIABLE L-PHASE MATERIAL FROM BACTERIAL GROWTH

The size of viable L-phase units is a matter for debate but in general L-phase growth passes through filters of a smaller pore size than will allow the passage of the bacterial parent. Therefore, in circumstances where it is desirable to separate the L-phase from bacterial growth, filtration may do this successfully. The pore size selected will of course vary with the bacteria concerned but in general filters of 0·65 μm pore size are suitable. However, the loss of viable L-phase material is often very great indeed during the process. Although the smallest viable unit for most species is thought to be 0·3–0·5 μm it is advisable to select the largest possible pore size which will hold back the parent organism, i.e. 0·65 μm for streptococci and staphylococci and 1·0–1·2 μm for the spore-bearing bacilli. L-phase units much larger than the pore size selected will sometimes pass through the filters. This is thought to be due to their extreme plasticity, which enables them to elongate and be squeezed through pores of very small dimensions. This feature is also demonstrated by growing L-phase on filter discs of small pore size lying on the surface of L-phase agar. It has been found that L-phase colonies appear directly on the agar surface as a result of growth through the filter pores.

Filtration methods have proved useful in the isolation of L-phase from body fluids and also in experimental work on the ability of L-phase to revert to the parent form of growth. Millipore filter membranes are excellent for this purpose.

Experimental work to determine the smallest viable particle which is capable of reproduction is quite a different problem from the separation of L-phase from bacterial phase. The literature abounds with reports on this, and it is difficult to find much agreement. It is evident that the extreme plasticity of these elements influences the results to a very marked degree. The loss of viable material when the smaller pore size membranes are used is always enormous, but it may be safe to say that most L-phase growth appears to have viable material which passes through filters of 0·3–0·6 μm pore size.

XI. STAINING METHODS

The method selected for the staining of L-forms for microscopical study will vary with the type of culture. Most experience has been gained with cultures grown on solid medium. A simple technique is used by Dienes for staining colonies to be studied microscopically *in vitro*. A small agar block containing a number of surface colonies is removed and the agar beneath the colonies trimmed off with a razor blade so that the remaining block is only 1 mm thick. This thin block is then placed on a microscope slide and the colonies covered by a coverslip or fragment of coverslip, upon which a film of Dienes' stain has previously been dried. The preparation is then sealed all round with wax or vaseline, to prevent drying and can be viewed microscopically with a low power objective.

A. Dienes' stain

Methylene blue	2·5 g
Azure II	1·25 g
Sodium carbonate	0·25 g
Benzoic acid	0·2 g
Maltose	10·0 g
Water	100 ml

An excellent whole-colony staining method, a modification of the method described by Klieneberger-Nobel (1962), is used by Gourlay and Leach (1970). The smears are fixed in Bouin's fixative followed by 45 min staining with 1/50 Giemsa at 50°C. Any of the staining methods advocated for *Mycoplasma* will give equally good results when used to stain L-phase variants (Fallon and Whittlestone, this Series, Vol. 3B).

B. Acridine orange

This dye, in conjunction with a good optical system for fluorescent work, has given some very elegant preparations (Pratt, 1965). The dye differentiates between RNA (red) and DNA (green) and has been used to follow the development and distribution of these two polynucleotides during the growth of the L-phase both in colonial forms and the particulate growth in broth culture. In the latter case treatment of the fixed smears with nuclease before staining produced extremely clean preparations showing the variation in size extremely well. Impression smears of colonies stained with Acridine orange have proved satisfactory. The technique given here is that described by Pratt (1965). Impression preparations of colonies on agar are made by inverting a block of agar containing suitable colonies on to a coverslip and immersing it in the fixative, Bouin's fluid. After fixation the agar block is peeled off, leaving the colonies fixed to the glass surface. The fixative is washed from the preparations with 50% (v/v) ethanol and acetate buffer. The fixed preparation is immersed for 10 min in 0·2M acetate buffer of the same pH as used for the staining solution. They are then stained for 10 min with Acridine orange, washed in buffer for 10 min and mounted in buffer. The edges of the preparation are sealed with wax.

Fixed preparations of growth in broth are stained in a similar way. Acetate buffer pH 3 is recommended.

Stain

0·05% (w/v) of Acridine orange is dissolved in 0·2M acetate buffer pH 3.

Bouin's fluid (fixative)

Saturated aqueous solution of picric acid 75 parts.

Formalin	25 parts
Glacial acetic acid	5 parts v/v

C. Fluorescent antibody

This technique can be used very successfully providing the conjugate contains antibody to intracellular material or antigen not located on the cell-wall (Karakawa et al., 1965; Kagan, 1967). No special modification of the techniques in general use is necessary and both direct and indirect staining methods are usable (Walker et al., this Series, Vol. 5A). Adequate knowledge of the specificity and performance of the conjugate is always important in fluorescent antibody studies and this is of particular importance when working with the L-phase, a field in which precise information and experience are lacking.

XII. PRESERVATION OF L-PHASE GROWTH

There have been very few reports on methods for the preservation of L-phase growth, but those that are available do not suggest that this is a very difficult matter. Panos and Barkulis (1959), and Hijmans et al. (1969) were successful in resuscitating lyophilized cultures of the L-phase of streptococci after 2 and 4 months interval respectively. Our own experience with lyophilization has been excellent, our streptococcal L-phase cultures have remained viable over a period of 6 years. Our method is to grow the strains in either sucrose or salt BHI broth containing 10% horse serum as usual, and dry 0·5 ml samples of well-grown 2–3 day broth cultures. A simple method which has given good results over a short term (approx. 6 months) is to invert an agar block of well-grown L-phase surface growth on to an agar slant of L-phase agar prepared in a screw capped bottle with a small amount of condensation water present. If the cap is screwed tightly such cultures remain viable for many months.

Hijmans *et al.* (1969) have reported that cultures with 10% serum stored at −70°C were still viable after three years. Roberts (1966) froze heavy growth of the L-phase of *Neisseria meningitidis* on agar blocks with acetone and dry ice and stored them at −20°C but has since recommended storage at −60 to −160°C for adequate preservation (Guze, 1968).

REFERENCES

Bleiweis, A. S., and Zimmerman, L. N. (1961). *Canad. J. Microbiol.*, **7**, 363.
Brenner, S., Dark, F. A., Gerhardt, P., Jeynes, M. H., Kandler, O., Kellenberger, E., Klieneberger-Nobel, E., McQuillen, K., Rubio-Huertos, M., Salton, M. R. J., Strange, R. E., Tomcsik, J., and Weibull, C. (1958). *Nature, Lond.*, **181**, 1713–1715.
Caravano, R. (1968). "Current Research on Group A Streptococus" (Ed. R. Caravano). Excerpta Medica Foundation, Amsterdam.
Coussons, R. T., and Cole, R. M., (1968). *In* Caravano, R. (1968). p. 327.
Crawford, Y. E., Frank, P. F., and Sullivan, B. (1958). *J. infect. Dis.*, **102**, 44–52.
Crombie, L. B., and Muschel, L. H. (1967). *Proc. Soc. exp. Biol. Med.*, **124**, 1029–1033.
Dienes, L. (1953). *Proc. Soc. exp. Biol. Med.*, **83**, 579–583.
Dienes, L., and Sharp, J. T. (1956). *J. Bact.*, **71**, 208–213.
Dienes, L., Weinberger, H. J., and Madoff, S. (1950). *J. Bact.*, **59**, 755–764.
Dienes, L., and Zamecnik, P. C. (1952). *J. Bact.*, **64**, 770–771.
Dienes, L., and Madoff, S. (1968). *In* Caravano, R. (1968). pp. 332–334.
Edward, D. F. (1960). *Ann. N.Y. Acad. Sci.*, **79**, 492.
Freimer, E. H., Krause, R. M., and McCarty, M. (1959). *J. exp. Med.*, **110**, 853–874.
Freundt, E. A. (1956). *Acta path. microbiol. scand.*, **38**, 246–258.
Freundt, E. A. (1958). "The Mycoplasmataceae", p. 103. Munksgaard, Copenhagen.
Godzeski, C. W., Brier, G., and Farran, J. D. (1967). *Ann. N.Y. Acad. Sci.*, **143**, 760–777.
Gooder, H., and Maxted, W. R. (1961). *Soc. gen. Microbiol. Symp.*, **11**, 151–173.
Gourlay, R. N., and Leach, R. H. (1970) *J. Med. Microbiol.*, **3**, 111–123.
Guze, L. B. (1968). *In* "Microbial Protoplasts, Spheroplasts and L-forms" (Ed. L. B. Guze). The Williams & Wilkins Co., Baltimore.
Guze, L. B., and Kalmanson, G. M. (1964a). *Science, N.Y.*, **143**, 1340–1341.
Guze, L. B., and Kalmanson, G. M. (1964b). *Science, N.Y.*, **146**, 1299–1300.
Hamburger, M., and Carleton, J. (1966). *J. infect. Dis.*, **116**, 221–230.
Hayflick, L. (1969). *In* "The Mycoplasmatales and the L-phase of Bacteria" (Ed. L. Hayflick). Appleton-Century-Crofts, New York, N.Y.
Heilman, F. R. (1941). *J. infect. Dis.*, **69**, 32–44 and 45–51.

Hijmans, W., van Boven, C. P. A., and Clasener, H. A. L. (1969). *In* Hayflick, L. (1969).

Hijmans, W., and Kastelein, M. J. W. (1960). *Ann. N.Y. Acad. Sci.*, **79**, 371–373.

Hijmans, W., and Dienes, L. (1955). *Proc. Soc. exp. Biol. Med.*, **90**, 672–675.

Hryniewicz, W., and Maxted, W. R. unpublished data.

Ianetta, A., and Wedgwood, R. J. (1967). *J. Bact.*, **93**, 1688–1692.

Kagan, G. Ya. (1967). *Ann. N.Y. Acad. Sci.*, **143**, 734–748.

Kalmanson, G. M., and Guze, L. B. (1964). *J. Am. med. Ass.*, **190**, 1107–1109.

Karakawa, W. W., Rotta, J., and Krause, R. M. (1965). *Proc. Soc. exp. Biol. Med.*, **118**, 198–201.

King, J. R., and Gooder, H. (1965). *Bact. Proc.*, p. 58.

Klieneberger, E. (1935). *J. Path. Bact.*, **40**, 93–105.

Klienenberger-Nobel, E. (1962). *In* "Pleuropneumonia-like-organisms (PPLO) Mycoplasmalaceae". Academic Press, London and New York.

Kusaka, I. (1967). *J. Bact.*, **94**, 884–888.

Landman, O. E., and Ginoza, H. S. (1961). *J. Bact.*, **81**, 875–886.

Landman, O. E., Altenbern, R. A., and Ginoza, H. S. (1958). *J. Bact.*, **75**, 567–576.

Landman, O. E., and Halle, S. (1963). *J. molec. Biol.*, **7**, 721–738.

Landman, O. E., Ryter, A., and Fréhel, C. (1968). *J. Bact.*, **96**, 2154–2170.

Lapinski, E., and Flakas, E. D. (1967). *J. Bact.*, **93**, 1438–1445.

Lederberg, J., and St Clair, J. (1958). *J. Bact.*, **75**, 143–160.

Madoff, S. (1960). *Ann. N.Y. Acad. Sci.*, **79**, 383–392.

Madoff, S., and Dienes, L. (1958). *J. Bact.*, **76**, 245–250.

Madoff, S., Burke, M. E., and Dienes, L. (1967). *Ann. N.Y. Acad. Sci.*, **143**, 755–759.

Marston, J. (1961). *J. infect. Dis.*, **10**, 75–84.

Maxted, W. R. (1957). *J. gen. Microbiol.*, **16**, 584–595.

Maxted, W. R. (1968). *In* Caravano, R. (1968). p. 320.

Michel, M. F., and Hijmans, W. (1960). *J. gen. Microbiol.*, **23**, 35–46.

Minck, R., and Minck, A. (1951). *C. r. Séanc. Soc. Biol.*, **145**, 927–929.

Mitchell, P., and Moyle, J. (1956). *Symp. Soc. gen. Microbiol.*, **6**, 150–180.

Mooser, H., and Joos, H. (1952). *Schweiz. Z. allg. Path. Bakt.*, **15**, 735–739.

Mortimer, E. A. (1964). *J. Lab. clin. Med.*, **64**, 887.

Opie, E. L. (1949). *J. exp. Med.*, **89**, 185–208.

Panos, C., and Barkulis, S. S. (1959). *J. Bact.*, **78**, 247–252.

Pratt, B. C. (1965). Ph.D. Thesis, London.

Repaske, R. (1958). *Biochim. biophys. Acta*, **30**, 225–232.

Roberts, R. B. (1966). *J. Bact.*, **92**, 1609–1614.

Roberts, R. B. (1967). *Proc. Soc. exp. Biol. Med.*, **124**, 611.

Rotta, J., Karakawa, W. W., and Krause, R. M. (1965). *J. Bact.*, **89**, 1581–1585.

Schaffner, W., Melly, A. M., Koenig, G. M. (1967). *Yale J. Biol. Med.*, **39**, 230–244.

Schindler, C. A., and Schuhardt, V. T. (1964). *Proc. nat. Acad. Sci. U.S.A.*, **51**, 414–421.

Schmitt-Slomska, J., Sacquet, E., and Caravano, R. (1967). *J. Bact.*, **93**, 451–455.

Schnauder, G. (1955). *Z. Hyg. InfektKrankh.*, **141**, 404–410.

Sharp, J. T. (1954). *Proc. Soc. exp. Biol. Med.*, **87**, 94–97.

Silberstein, J. K. (1953). *Schweiz. Z. allg. Path. Bakt.*, **16**, 739–755.

Theodore, S. T., King, J. R., and Cole, R. M. (1969). *J. Bact.*, **97**, 495–499.

Ullrich, K. J., Kramer, K., and Boylan, J. W. (1961). *Progress in Cardiovascular Diseases*, **3**, 395–431.

van Boven, C. P. A., Kastelein, M. J. W., and Hijmans, W. (1967). *Ann. N.Y. Acad. Sci.*, **143**, 749.

Ward, J. R., and Martin, C. H. (1962). *Proc. Soc. exp. Biol. Med.*, **111**, 156–160.

Watanakunakorn, L., Golberg, L. M., Carleton, J., and Hamburger, M. (1969). *J. infect. Dis.*, **119**, 67–74.

Weibull, C. (1953). *J. Bact.*, **66**, 688–702.

Weibull, C. (1965). *J. Bact.*, **90**, 1467–1480.

Willett, H. P., and Thacore, H. (1966). *Can. J. Microbiol.*, **12**, 11–16.

Winterbauer, R. H., Gutman, L. T., Turck, M., Wedgwood, R. J., and Petersdorf, R. G. (1967). *J. exp. Med.*, **125**, 607–618.

Wittler, R. G. (1952). *J. gen. Microbiol.*, **6**, 311–317.

Young, R. M., and Dahlquist, E. H. (1967). *Am. J. clin. Path.*, **48**, 466–473.

Author Index

Numbers in *italics* refer to the pages on which references are listed at the end of each chapter.

A

Abbott, J. D., 410, *417*
Abbott, V., 326, 351, 352, *417*
Abbott, W. S., 176, *190*
Abkoude, E. R., van, 300, *310*
Adams, J. M., 284, *310*
Adams, M. H., 193, 194, 195, 200, 211, 212, 224, *258*
Adams, W. S., 281, *311*
Adderson, R. R., 125, *137*
Ainsworth, G. C., 30, 35, 87, 92, 93, *94*
Alexander, D. C., 104, *135*
Alfoldi, L., 327, 328, 342, 343, 350, 366, 370, *417*, *419*, *420*, *421*
Algranati, I. D., 304, *313*
Almond, M., 22, *26*
Alten, J. B. T., 206, *261*
Altenbern, R. A., 425, *448*
A. M. A., 112, *135*
Amano, T., 317, 328, 364, 367, 368, 369, *417*, *421*
Amati, P., 346, 347, 402, 405, *417*
Ambler, R. P., 45, *94*
Ames, B. N., 286, *310*
An, T., 317, 328, *421*
Anderegg, J. W., 305, *311*
Anderson, T. F., 202, 211, 212, 228, 233, 234, 235, 236, 238, 239, 241, 252, *258*, *259*, *261*
Andreev, V. M., 309, *311*
Andrewes, C. H., Sir, 93, *94*
Anonymous, 91, *94*
Anton, D. N., 401, *421*
Aoki, Y., 413, *421*
Arber, W., 233, 238, *260*, 278, *310*
Arima, K., 397, *417*
Armitage, Janet E., 123, *135*
Aron, J. D., 106, *135*
Asand, K., 211, 217, 242, *260*
Asbeck, F., 269, 285, 302, *310*
Astrachan, L., 246, *261*

B

Babb, R., 73, 77, *97*
Backus, J. W., 8, *26*
Baechler, C. A., 327, 346, *419*
Bail, O., 22, *26*
Balis, M. E., 283, *312*
Baillie, A., 39, *94*
Baker, E. E., 232, *258*
Ball, G. H., 64, *94*
Barber, D. L. A., 106, *135*
Barbu, E., 42, *94*, 354, 356, 359, 362, 373, 374, 375, 390, 397, 410, *417*, *417*, *418*, *420*, *422*
Barhn, E., 397, *417*
Barkulis, S. S., 446, *448*
Barlow, G. E., 104, *135*
Barlow, J. L., 268, *311*
Barner, H. D., 247, *258*
Barnet, L., 193, 202, 228, *258*, 273, 296, 297, *310*
Barraclough, Elizabeth D., 126, *135*
Barrett, M. J., 13, *26*
Barrow, G. C., 411, *417*
Barry, G. T., 326, 327, 328, 329, 342, 351, 352, 355, 364, 382, 388, 396, *417*, *418*
Bascomb, S., 63, 73, 77, 78, *96*
Bauer, F. L., 8, *26*
Bayreuther, K., 269, 285, 302, *310*
Beavan, G. H., 283, *310*
Behrens, B., 175, *190*
Belavtseva, E. M., 298, *312*
Belskma, M., 108, *137*
Bendet, I., 228, 236, *260*, 273, 276, 288, *310*, *311*
Ben-Gurion, R., 343, *417*, *419*
Benzer, S., 273, 296, 297, *310*
Beppu, T., 397, *417*
Berenblum, J., 280, *310*
Berk, R. S., 324, 327, 346, *419*
Berry, G., 103, 118, *135*

Subject Index

A

ACD, *see* Analogue/digital conversion.
Acridine orange,
  col factor transfer, and, 402, 406
  colicin induction by, 347
  L-phase variant stain, 445–446
Adansonian taxonomic groups, nature
    of, 32
Adsorption, of bacteriophage, *see also
    under* Bacteriophage, 223–234
Adsorption medium, for phage culture,
    211, 212
AGDOC, 150
Algae,
  culture collections of, 92
  monographs on, 93
Algal virus LPP-1, purification, 276–277
ALGOL, computer language,
  assignment statements in, 9–10
  basic features of, 7–8
  conditional clauses in, 10
  numerical taxonomy, computer pro-
      grammes for, 82
  procedures in, 11–12
  programmed jumps in, 10–11
  programming in, 8–9
  simulation and, 15–16, 19
Alphanumeric data, computer process-
    ing of, 102–104
Alumina, phage-infected cell disinte-
    gration with, 242
American Petroleum Institute (API),
    information retrieval system,
    150
Amino-acid analyser, computer pro-
    cessing of data from, 106–108,
    109, 110, 111, 112
Analogue computers,
  glossary description of, 138
  microbiological uses of, 1–3, 5
Analogue/digital conversion (ACD), 137
Analogue processing, glossary defini-
    tion of, 138
Analysis of variance, statistical tech-
    nique, 47

Antibiotics, *see also under specific names*,
  L-phase induction by, 427, 428–429
Antibodies, to bacteriocins, 367–370
Antibody blocking power, of bacterio-
    phages, 226
Antiphage serum, 224, 225–226
Antisera,
  bacteriocins, to, 364–370, 373
  preparation of, 364–366
  testing of, 367–370
Arcton, bacteriophage purification with,
    269
ASCA, *see* Automatic Subject Citation
    Alert.
Assay, *see* Bioassay.
Automated process, *see under name of
    process.*
Automatic Subject Citation Alert
    (ASCA) service, 125, 149
Automation, for generating taxonomic
    data, 46

B

Bacillus coli Migula, 89
B. megaterium,
  bacteriocin assay with, 329
  bacteriocin induction in, 346
  L-phase induction, 425
  lysogeny in, 255–256
  lysozyme disruption of, 350
  megacin production by, 321–322, 343,
      347, 350
  U.V. irradiation of, 321, 346
B. pyocyaneus Gessard, 89
B. subtilis,
  bacteriophage, 264
  L-phase variants, 426, 428, 438
B. thuringiensis, bioassays for exotoxin,
    164, 178, 188
Bacitracin, inducer of L-phase variants,
    428
Bacteriocins,
  adsorption of, 328–329, 371–396
  agar-gel diffusion of, 330, 369
  antisera to, 324, 364–366, 367–370, 373